# MAGILL'S
# SURVEY
# OF
# SCIENCE

# MAGILL'S SURVEY OF SCIENCE

## EARTH SCIENCE SERIES

Volume 1
1-524
A—Earth's Crust

*Edited by*

# FRANK N. MAGILL

*Consulting Editor*
DR. JAMES A. WOODHEAD

## SALEM PRESS

Pasadena, California    Englewood Cliffs, New Jersey

∞ The paper used in these volumes conforms to the
American National Standard for Permanence of Paper
for Printed Library Materials, Z39.48-1984.

**Library of Congress Cataloging-in-Publication Data**
Magill's survey of science. Earth science series/edited
by Frank N. Magill.
   p. cm.
   Includes bibliographical references.
   1. Earth sciences. I. Magill, Frank Northen,
1907-  .
QE28.M33  1990            89-10923
550—dc20                 CIP
ISBN 0-89356-606-3 (set)
ISBN 0-89356-607-1 (volume 1)

PRINTED IN THE UNITED STATES OF AMERICA

# PUBLISHER'S NOTE

The *Earth Science Series* is the second set in the ongoing *Magill's Survey of Science*, joining the *Space Exploration Series*, published in 1989. The five volumes on the Earth Sciences and the five on history of Space Exploration will be augmented by three more five-volume sets covering the Life Sciences (scheduled to appear in 1991), the Applied Sciences, and the Physical Sciences. Together, these volumes will provide the general reader with insights into a broad spectrum of sciences and technologies—topics that are normally accessible only to academicians and experts in these fields. Following in the Magill tradition of supplying information in an easy-to-comprehend and quickly retrievable format, *Magill's Survey of Science* offers the nonspecialist an essential overview of areas and issues increasingly critical to experts and laypersons alike.

In the 377 articles of *Earth Science*, the earth and solar system serve as the setting for living organisms and human applications of scientific principles. The scope is both broad and comprehensive: 141 articles cover the major subfields of physical geology, including geomorphology, glacial geology, mineralogy and crystallography, petroleum geology and engineering, sedimentology, stratigraphy, structural geology, tectonics, volcanology, and igneous, metamorphic, and sedimentary petrology; twenty-six articles treat areas of economic geology, from essential minerals (coal, gold, fertilizers, building stone) and other earth resources to the variety of ways man harnesses geothermal, wind, ocean, solar, and nuclear power to meet his energy needs; thirty articles examine a range of issues in geochemistry, from radioactive dating techniques, used to determine the ages of fossils, to geochemical reactions and interactions that determine rock chemistry, to the powerful array of investigative tools that chemists have used to reveal the earth's secrets: electron microscopes, infrared spectra, X-ray fluorescence. Geophysics, another major subdivision of the earth sciences, is given full coverage in thirty-five articles on geodesy, gravity, geomagnetism and paleomagnetism, heat flow within the earth, and earthquakes.

The planet's history, as well as its impact on the development of life and various early life forms, is explored in twenty-two articles on fossils, ice ages, dinosaurs, mass extinctions, and evolution. Water, a major force in the shaping not only of life but also of the earth even before the emergence of life, is examined in all its forms and sources in twenty-seven articles, sixteen of which consider aspects of oceanography. There are thirty-six articles on the solar system—from planets to smaller bodies such as meteorites—that cast further light on our own planet and its history. The earth's major mountain ranges are treated in eight separate articles; soils, the understanding of which is crucial to agriculture, are discussed in another eight articles; and the atmosphere, from meteorological phenomena (hurricanes, tornadoes, lightning, winds) to the greenhouse effect and ozone depletion, accounts for eighteen articles. Readers requiring fundamental descriptions of the major methodologies of the earth sciences will find these covered throughout the set in special articles devoted to the tools of the physical geologist, geochemist, and remote-sensing engineer. Finally, a core of ongoing environmental issues must be addressed in any overview of the earth sciences: Hazardous wastes, land-use planning and management, earthquake prediction, acid rain, and the aforementioned greenhouse effect are among those areas of concern that require full understanding and continuing attention.

"Earth science," then, encompasses the origin, evolution, composition, and processes of the earth, across time and as it affects—and is influenced by—human beings. Much more than geology, the earth sciences incorporate not only the basic subdisciplines of that traditional field but also oceanography, meteorology, astronomy, geophysics, and geochemistry, as well as the subdisciplines of paleontology, hydrology, seismology, and soil science. It extends as well to those technologies and techniques—from Landsat to the electron microprobe—that have enabled researchers to discover more about the world in which we live.

Each article retains the familiar Magill format: Averaging seven pages in length, all articles begin with ready-reference top matter, including an indication of the discipline or field of study and a summary statement in which the writer explains why the essay is significant to the study of earth and its processes. A list of principal terms defines key terms to orient the reader to each essay. A summary section forms the major part of each article, providing a description of the definitive features of the topic. Two types of essay are provided. In the first type, "Summary of the Phenomenon" describes the characteristics of the particular earth science phenomenon under discussion: the nature of the geology process, the composition and origin of the geologic feature, the development of the geologic age, or the background of a public policy or health issue such as oil spills, atmospheric ozone, and hazardous wastes. In the other type of essay, "Summary of the Methodology" makes accessible to the reader the methodologies used in earth science research and analysis, as well as resource development, including tools, technologies, and problem-solving strategies—for example, geologic and topographic maps, mass spectrometry, and nuclear waste disposal. Following "Summary of the Phenomenon" is a description of how the topic is studied in the field and laboratory; following "Summary of the Methodology" is an overview of its application by researchers, engineers, or technicians for academic, commercial, or social purposes. "Context," the concluding section of both types of essay, presents the conclusions, applications, and implications derived from investigation of the topic. The writer discusses how and in what social, political, and cultural climate the information was gained and changed. Finally, an annotated, selected "Bibliography" will direct the reader to external sources that are accessible to the nonspecialist or student, which may be consulted for further study. "Cross-References" lists those articles appearing in the set that will offer additional information on the same or a related topic.

At the end of each volume, an alphabetical listing of the contents of the entire set appears, followed by a category listing of the contents, which groups the essays by general area of interest: engineering geology, mineralogy, volcanology, urban geology, and so on. Two more tools, appearing at the end of volume 5, assist the reader: A glossary of more than five hundred entries defines key terms that appear throughout the essays; and the comprehensive index, which contains names of principal topics and terms, including cross-references, to aid the reader in locating information.

Throughout, units of measurement adhere to the *Système International d'Unités*: Distances are measured in kilometers rather than miles, temperature in Kelvins or degrees Celsius rather than degrees Fahrenheit. As the topic of the set is scientific and its scope is international, the internationally accepted system of scientific measurement was chosen as most appropriate.

Finally, acknowledgment is extended to the contributors, academicians, and professionals who worked to communicate their expert understanding of the earth sciences to the lay reader. A list of these dedicated individuals, and their affiliations, can be found in the front matter to volume 1.

# CONTRIBUTORS

Stephen R. Addison
*University of Central Arkansas*

Mary D. Albanese
*American Institute of Professional Geologists*

Arthur L. Alt
*College of Great Falls*

Michael S. Ameigh
*St. Bonaventure University*

Valentine J. Ansfield
*University of South Dakota*

Richard W. Arnseth
*Science Applications International Corporation*

George K. Attwood
*Maharishi International University*

N. B. Aughenbaugh
*University of Mississippi*

Victor R. Baker
*University of Arizona*

John M. Bartley
*University of Utah*

Thomas W. Becker
*Webster University*

John L. Berkley
*State University of New York College at Fredonia*

Elizabeth K. Berner
*Yale University*

David M. Best
*Northern Arizona University*

Richard J. Boon
*Environmental Resource Specialist*

Scott Brande
*University of Alabama in Birmingham*

Danita Brandt
*Eastern Michigan University*

Alan Brown
*Livingston University*

Michael Broyles
*Collin County Community College*

David S. Brumbaugh
*Northern Arizona University*

James A. Burbank, Jr.
*Western Oklahoma State College*

Scott F. Burns
*Louisiana Tech University*

Byron D. Cannon
*University of Utah*

Robert E. Carver
*University of Georgia*

Dennis Chamberland
*Science Writer*

D. K. Chowdhury
*Indiana University and Purdue University at Fort Wayne*

Habte Giorgis Churnet
*University of Tennessee at Chattanooga*

Mark Cloos
*University of Texas at Austin*

Raymond A. Coish
*Middlebury College*

John H. Corbet
*Memphis State University*

William C. Cornell
*University of Texas at El Paso*

James R. Craig
*Virginia Polytechnic Institute and State University*

William W. Craig
*University of New Orleans*

Ralph D. Cross
*University of Southern Mississippi*

Robert L. Cullers
*Kansas State University*

E. Julius Dasch
*NASA Headquarters*

Larry E. Davis
*Washington State University*

Ronald W. Davis
*Western Michigan University*

Dennis R. Dean
*University of Wisconsin—Parkside*

Albert B. Dickas
*University of Wisconsin—Superior*

ix

James A. Dockal
*University of North Carolina at Wilmington*

Bruce D. Dod
*Mercer University*

Dave Dooling
*D2 Associates*

Walter C. Dudley, Jr.
*University of Hawaii at Hilo*

Dean A. Dunn
*University of Southern Mississippi*

Steven I. Dutch
*University of Wisconsin—Green Bay*

David K. Elliott
*Northern Arizona University*

John J. Ernissee
*Clarion University of Pennsylvania*

David G. Fisher
*Lycoming College*

Dennis R. Flentge
*Cedarville College*

Richard H. Fluegeman, Jr.
*Ball State University*

George J. Flynn
*State University of New York College
at Plattsburgh*

Robert G. Font
*Strategic Petroleum, Inc.*

Annabelle M. Foos
*University of Akron*

John W. Foster
*Illinois State University*

Dell R. Foutz
*Mesa State College*

Robert C. Frey
*Independent Geologist*

A. Kem Fronabarger
*College of Charleston*

Charles I. Frye
*Northwest Missouri State University*

Roberto Garza
*San Antonio College*

Joyce Gawell
*Science Teacher*

Karl Giberson
*Eastern Nazarene College*

Gail G. Gibson
*University of North Carolina at Charlotte*

Billy P. Glass
*University of Delaware*

Douglas Gomery
*University of Maryland*

Gregory A. Good
*West Virginia University*

Pamela J. W. Gore
*De Kalb Community College*

Hans G. Graetzer
*South Dakota State University*

Martha M. Griffin
*Columbia College*

William R. Hackett
*Idaho State University*

William J. Hagan, Jr.
*St. Anselm College*

Edward C. Hansen
*Hope College*

Jasper L. Harris
*North Carolina Central University*

Sara A. Heller
*College of Charleston*

Charles E. Herdendorf
*Ohio State University*

David F. Hess
*Western Illinois University*

Earl G. Hoover
*American Institute of Professional Geologists*

Robert A. Horton, Jr.
*California State University at Bakersfield*

Ruth H. Howes
*Ball State University*

Samuel F. Huffman
*University of Wisconsin—River Falls*

Pamela Jansma
*Jet Propulsion Laboratory, National Research
Council*

Albert C. Jensen
*Central Florida Community College*

# CONTRIBUTORS

Brian Jones
*Science Writer*

James O. Jones
*University of Texas at San Antonio*

Richard C. Jones
*Texas A&M University*

Pamela R. Justice
*Collin County Community College*

Kyle L. Kayler
*Richard H. Gorr and Associates*

John P. Kenny
*Bradley University*

Diann S. Kiesel
*University of Wisconsin Center—Baraboo/Sauk County*

Michael M. Kimberley
*North Carolina State University*

Richard S. Knapp
*Belhaven College*

David R. Lageson
*Montana State University*

Ralph L. Langenheim, Jr.
*University of Illinois at Urbana-Champaign*

Gary G. Lash
*State University of New York College at Fredonia*

Joel S. Levine
*NASA Langley Research Center*

Leon Lewis
*Appalachian State University*

W. David Liddell
*Utah State University*

J. Lipman-Boon
*Independent Scholar*

James Charles LoPresto
*Edinboro University of Pennsylvania*

Donald W. Lovejoy
*Palm Beach Atlantic College*

Gary R. Lowell
*Southeast Missouri State University*

Spencer G. Lucas
*New Mexico Museum of Natural History*

David N. Lumsden
*Memphis State University*

Michael L. McKinney
*University of Tennessee, Knoxville*

Paul Madden
*Hardin-Simmons University*

David W. Maguire
*C. S. Mott Community College*

Mehrdad Mahdyiar
*Leighton and Associates*

Glen S. Mattioli
*University of California, Berkeley*
*California Institute of Technology*

Michael W. Mayfield
*Appalachian State University*

Paul S. Maywood
*Bridger Coal Company*

Lance P. Meade
*American Institute of Mining Engineers*

Nathan H. Meleen
*American Geophysical Union*

Randall L. Milstein
*Michigan Geological Survey*

Joseph M. Moran
*University of Wisconsin—Green Bay*

Otto H. Muller
*Alfred University*

Phillip A. Murry
*Tarleton State University*

John E. Mylroie
*Mississippi State University*

Brian J. Nichelson
*U.S. Air Force Academy*

Bruce W. Nocita
*University of South Florida*

Edward B. Nuhfer
*University of Wisconsin—Platteville*

Divonna Ogier
*Oregon Museum of Science and Industry*

Steven C. Okulewicz
*City University of New York, Hunter College*

# CONTRIBUTORS

James L. Whitford-Stark
*Sul Ross State University*

Ian Williams
*University of Wisconsin—River Falls*

Shawn V. Wilson
*Science Writer*

Dermot M. Winters
*American Institute of Mining Engineers*

James A. Woodhead
*Occidental College*

Grant R. Woodwell
*Mary Washington College*

Jay R. Yett
*Orange Coast College*

David N. Zurick
*Eastern Kentucky University*

# CONTENTS

# EARTH SCIENCE

# MAGILL'S
# SURVEY
# OF
# SCIENCE

# THE ABYSSAL SEA FLOOR

*Type of earth science:* Oceanography

*The abyssal plains lie beyond the continental margins at depths greater than 2,000 meters. They are thought to be the flattest areas on earth and are carpeted with thick layers of sediment. Their greatest economic value lies in the metallic minerals that form part of these sediments.*

### Principal terms

MANGANESE NODULES: lumps of minerals consisting mostly of iron, manganese, nickel, and copper, which form on deeper parts of continental shelves

SEDIMENT: solid matter, either organic or inorganic in origin, that settles on a surface; it may be transported by wind, water, or glaciers

SUBMARINE CANYON: a channel cut deep in the sea-floor sediments by rivers or submarine currents

SUBMERSIBLES: miniature submarines capable of carrying two or three persons and descending to oceanic depths as great as 11,000 meters

TERRIGENOUS: originating from the weathering and erosion of mountains and other land formations

TRENCH: a long, narrow, and very deep depression in the ocean floor

TURBIDITY CURRENT: a current resulting from a density increase brought about by increased water turbidity; the turbid mass continues under the force of gravity down a submarine slope

## Summary of the Phenomenon

The abyssal plains of the deep ocean floor represent the flattest surface areas on the earth. They are far flatter than any plain on land. Geologists define an abyssal plain as having a slope ratio of less than 1:1,000. Abyssal plains occupy about 40 percent of the ocean basin floor and are widespread in the major ocean basins, the Gulf of Mexico, and the Mediterranean Sea. The peculiar topography of the abyssal plains is the result of deep sediments deposited by turbidity currents. Additional sediments are derived from the rain of biological material from the surface. At one time, mariners and researchers believed that the entire ocean basin beyond the continental margin was a flat, featureless plain. Subsequent studies using sonic devices, deep-sea cameras, submersibles, and other instruments revealed a rugged, varied topography over most of the ocean floor. The research also supported the conclusion that abyssal plains represent less than half the area of all the ocean basins.

It was, however, not always thus. As the continents drifted apart and the ocean basins were formed following the breakup of Pangaea about 150 million years ago, the ocean floor was well contoured. The dominant feature of what are now the abyssal plains was broad areas of low hills. Weathering of the continental landmasses produced an abundance of sedimentary material that eroded into the oceans. The coarse material settled on the continental shelves and partly on the continental slopes. The fine material drifted farther offshore and settled on the continental rise and the adjacent abyssal hills. In the course of time, the hills were covered by the sediment to become the abyssal plains. Remnants of the ancient terrain exist beyond the abyssal plains in the form of abyssal hills less than 1,000 meters high, steep-sided seamounts, and flat-topped seamounts. Seamounts frequently jut above the ocean surface as islands. The guyots are seamounts that have been eroded by ocean waves. Also called table mounts, the guyots may be 1,000-1,500 meters below the sea surface. In some areas of the ocean, the abyssal plains are cut by deep, narrow trenches whose bottoms may lie many kilometers below the surface of the sea. The deepest is the Marianas trench in the Southwest Pacific. It is 11,000 meters deep, the deepest place on earth.

Abyssal plains are most abundant in the Atlantic Ocean and Indian Ocean basins. They usually form next to the edges of the continental margins rather than near the centers of the basins. The Pacific Ocean basin features a few abyssal plains, but for the most part the Pacific basin exhibits the relict, rough topography. There, the abyssal hills, thinly covered with sediment, rise 200 to 400 meters above the basin floor. Deep-sea drilling in the Northeast Pacific has revealed basalt as the major rock type of the abyssal hills.

There are several explanations offered for the thin sedimentation of the Pacific abyssal plains. One suggests that since there are relatively few large rivers that drain into the Pacific Ocean, transport of sediments is reduced; therefore, the sediments deposited since the Pacific was formed were too sparse to bury the hilly topography. Another explanation points to the submarine trenches as possible traps for the sediments where the trenches lie between the continental margins and the abyssal plains. Sediment-laden turbidity currents, flowing down the steep sides of the continental slopes, plunge into the trenches and dump the sediment load. With much of the sediment going into the trenches, little of it flows out over the plains. A third possibility is the powerful "storms" that sweep across the ocean floor in places, scouring it in some regions and reforming the sediments in others. Oceanographic instruments moored on the ocean floor at depths of 4,800 meters have detected massive bottom currents flowing at a rate of more than 0.5 meter per second. Labeled as storms by researchers, the turbulent conditions can rage for about a week, lifting loads of sediment and moving them elsewhere.

Each year, nearly 15 billion tons of weathered rock are eroded from the land and carried by rivers and streams to the sea. Some of this material is deposited in vast deltas, such as are found at the mouths of the Mississippi and Amazon rivers. A large proportion is trapped on the continental shelves. A few billion tons are transported over the great depths to settle on the abyssal plains. They are joined by a rain of calcareous or siliceous skeletons of microscopic drifting organisms, plankton, that are abundant in the upper, sunlit portion of the water. These biological remains add about 3 billion tons of sediment annually. In addition, the sediment includes particles swept up by strong winds blowing over the deserts of the world, such as the Sahara. These particles travel great distances through the atmosphere and settle over the vast expanse of the oceans. They settle slowly to the bottom to form part of the carpet of sediment. Sediments may also be transported from the continental shelf onto the abyssal plain. This process has been detected in the Gulf of Mexico, where underwater landslides break off masses of sediment deposited by the Mississippi River. During times of low sea level, ocean waves breaking at the shelf edge cause the sediments to collapse and slide down the steep continental slope. From there, the sediments fan out in the deep ocean over the abyssal plain.

The thin carpet on the ocean floor includes mineral matter derived from a variety of sources. It includes the ash erupted by volcanoes thousands of kilometers away and extraterrestrial material in the form of meteorites. Some minerals precipitate directly out of the seawater and accumulate as crystals or nodules. The sediments over large tracts of the abyssal plain include manganese nodules. These valuable, mineral-rich nodules in places obscure the sediments beneath them. Because of the biological skeletons in them, these sediments have a very fine texture and are classified as oozes. The oozes are named after the dominant organism represented: globigerina ooze, radiolarian ooze, and so on. The oozes are calcareous if the dominant organisms were foraminifera and pteropods, animals with chalky skeletons; they are siliceous if the remains were derived from radiolarians or diatoms.

Red clay is a very common sediment on the abyssal plains. It consists of the finest-grained particles eroded into the sea. It is the most durable of the sediment types on the ocean floor. Calcareous skeletons dissolve rapidly as they sink toward the floor and are scarce in the sediments. Siliceous skeletons are limited in their distribution. They are found mainly under the productive surface waters of the polar and equatorial zones.

Sediments accumulate very slowly on the abyssal plains. The amount and time involved ranges from a few centimeters to only a fraction of a millimeter per one thousand years. Clay particles accumulate at a rate of less than 2 millimeters every one thousand years; shells may accumulate at a rate of 20 millimeters every one thousand years.

Abyssal plain sediments are classified by geologists as terrigenous, biogenous, hydrogenous (or authigenic), and cosmogenic. The latter include meteorites and tektites, small rounded objects composed almost entirely of glass. Although their origin is unknown, tektites are believed to be meteoric. Terrigenous sediments are the clays, sands, and gravels derived from the land. Most of them are lacustrine sediments; that is, they were transported by water as material eroded by rivers and streams. Some, however, were transported by glaciers during the Pleistocene epoch. Many sites of such sediments, including Georges Bank, off New England, and the Grand Bank, off Newfoundland, are the terminal moraines of such glaciers. During the thousands of years since they were deposited, these sandy moraines have been worked and reworked by ocean currents and waves and deposited farther out onto the abyssal plains. Some glacial deposits have been moved thousands of kilometers by floating icebergs. As the continental glaciers, such as on Greenland and Antarctica, travel toward the sea, they erode and transport sand, silt, and gravel. These are incorporated in the ice and, as the glacial ice breaks off into the sea as icebergs, the sediments are carried off by ocean currents. Ultimately, when the icebergs melt, they drop their mineral burdens into the sea to become part of the sea-floor sediments. Many of the fine components of the terrigenous sediments, including the silts and clays, are aeolian, or windblown, sediments.

The biogenous sediments owe their origin entirely to materials derived from organisms in the water column. They include the tests, or shells and external skeletons, of phytoplankton and zooplankton. As the organisms die in the sunlit, or photic, zone, their remains fall to the ocean floor as "snow." Many biogenous sediments are highly fossiliferous. These fossil-rich deposits enable scientists to date the sediments and to interpret ocean temperatures in the geologic past. Carbon 14 dating has also been used to establish the relative age of biogenous sediments where carbonaceous minerals are present.

Hydrogenous, or authigenic, sediments are those that have precipitated out of the seawater solution. These sediments are particularly common on abyssal plains in the Pacific. They include phosphorite nodules and manganese nodules. Some hydrogenous sediments are found in the vicinity of hot springs near mid-ocean ridges. The minerals in the metal-rich water spewing from the springs are carried by deep ocean currents across the sea floor. The metals precipitate out and add to the layering on the plain. The nodules grow by accretion around some hard nucleus, usually a pebble or a fossilized shark's tooth. The temperature of the water from the hot springs generally is about 10-15 degrees Celsius (compared to the ambient deep-water temperature of 2 degrees Celsius). Several extremely hot springs, however, have been found with vent waters about 300 degrees Celsius. Hot springs on the ocean floor in the vicinity of the Galápagos Islands are believed to be above a massive magma chamber. Here the molten mantle of the earth is estimated to be between 1,200 and 1,400 degrees Celsius. Some springs, really more like seeps, have been found oozing water at ambient temperature. These so-called cold seeps also release metal-rich water. Seamounts on the abyssal plain in the southwest Pacific Ocean basin feature cold springs spewing out mineral-laden water.

For decades, scientists considered the abyssal plains to be among the most unchanging environments on the earth. The water temperature is a near-constant 2 or 3 degrees Celsius year-round. The salinity is unvarying and the darkness is constant and total. The plains are generally tectonically stable, as well. They were therefore frequently looked on as a safe repository for a variety of wastes. Nations dumped quantities of obsolete chemical and biological weapons and some nuclear materials on the abyssal plains, certain that they would remain there forever and do no harm to the human race. As land dumps became unavailable, the abyss was even considered as a place to dump industrial and domestic wastes and high-level nuclear wastes. Research has demonstrated, however, that the abyss is not as unchanging as it was once believed to be.

## Methods of Study

The abyssal plain, of all the ocean's benthic features, is the only one that has borne out the theory that the ocean floor was a flat, featureless expanse. The few scattered soundings made toward the end of the nineteenth century for transoceanic telegraphic cables yielded small amounts of data. Later, the British oceanographic vessel *Challenger* made many soundings in areas not previously probed. During a global voyage, the *Challenger*'s crew laboriously lowered long hemp ropes and, later, single-strand wire to great depths. The ropes and wires were retrieved slowly with capstans turned by the crew. Individual soundings of a few thousand meters often required several hours to complete. Sometimes the hemp rope broke under its own weight and the entire effort was wasted. Despite the obstacles, however, data about the sea floor accumulated. As the nineteenth century ended, some ten thousand soundings had been made in water deeper than 2,000 meters and about five hundred in water deeper than 5,500 meters.

Information about the creatures of the abyssal plain was being gathered as well, although slowly. Retrieval of damaged submarine cables brought back a host of organisms attached to the cable sheathing. This evidence dismissed forever the belief in an "azooic zone," a depth limit in the ocean below which no life existed. The *Challenger* also had deployed dredges and trawls that dragged over the ocean floor. Bizarre-looking fishes, worms, and clamlike animals came up in the collecting gear, as did intriguing samples of the rocks and minerals that carpeted the abyssal plain. These collections, however, were made at great expense of time and equipment. The dredges and trawls, like the sounding lines, took hours to drop and retrieve. Frequently the gear turned upside down and never collected anything. Sometimes the lines and cables were twisted by swift currents and left in a hopeless tangle that, again, collected nothing. Modern oceanographic geologists continue to use dredges, although the hazards are much the same; the gear is still one of the mainstays of research on the ocean floor.

Several different kinds of "grab" are used to scoop large samples of the surficial sediments, but more intensive sampling is done with "corers." These long pipes are dropped or pushed into the sediment to collect a cylinder of the material. Stretched out in the laboratory and cut lengthwise, the core samples expose the millennia-long history of the sediment. The texture, particle size, color, and chemistry of the sample can be measured and correlated with specific dates. Drills operated from surface ships have penetrated the rock under the abyssal plains to depths of more than two thousand meters.

The depth of the sediments on the floor of the abyssal plains has been measured with a variety of techniques. The oldest technique involved tossing sticks of dynamite into the ocean behind a moving vessel. Special instruments measured the time it took for the vibrations set off by the explosion to reach the ocean floor and bounce back. Since rock and sediment of differing material reflected the vibrations differently, careful analysis of the echoes could reveal the nature of the sediments and their depth. The dangerous practice of using dynamite was replaced by the bouncing of harmless subsonic signals off the ocean floor. This same technique had long been used to measure the depth of water over the ocean floor. Remarkably detailed soundings of the ocean floor, with printouts of the surface features, are made with multiple scanning devices towed by research vessels. These devices include a multibeam system called Sea Beam and a special side-scanning device called Gloria.

Cameras—still, motion-picture, and video—loaded with black-and-white or color film, have captured the features of the abyssal plains. They show ripple marks from submarine currents and the remains of ancient volcanic eruptions. This pictorial record is a valuable adjunct to the physical specimens collected.

Rock and sediment samples and photographs offer dramatic evidence of the nature of the abyss, but no technique surpasses sending humans to the bottom to make on-the-spot assessments of what is being collected or photographed. Several manned submersibles, such as the U.S. minisub *Alvin* and its French counterpart, *Cyana*, have carried researchers many kilometers into the depths of the sea. These craft have enabled their human passengers to view the ocean floor at first hand and to collect and photograph materials systematically.

## Context

The abyssal plains were first a scientific mystery and then a scientific curiosity, but the potential value of the manganese nodules that carpet the plains in places has made them an international arena. Other than the nodules and perhaps some valuable sulfide minerals from hot springs, there is little of value in the great depths of the world ocean. The plains do not support valuable fisheries, and the immense depths involved preclude routine collection of any sort of material. They still serve as locations for transocean communication cables, but the discovery of abyssal "storms" has caused concern. Underwater photographs show that such storms have washed sediments from under the cables, leaving them to hang suspended between undamaged parts of the sea floor. As with their terrestrial counterparts, the suspended cables will "strum" violently in the storm currents and eventually break. The storms also are causing petroleum geologists to reconsider their ideas about where to search for unexploited deposits of oil.

The knowledge of the existence of abyssal storms is also causing a reevaluation of the abyssal plains as repositories for toxic or other wastes. If the wastes are to be containerized, a site with little or no storm-generated submarine currents—a calm area—is desirable. In contrast, if the scheme is to disburse and dilute the wastes, then a storm-prone area is desirable.

These plans are still conjectural. What is certain is that the manganese nodules are present on the abyssal plain in great volume. Their traces of cobalt and nickel make them particularly desirable to the United States, which lacks these resources. The technology to mine the minerals is available, despite the great depths and great costs. What is needed to encourage mining is a significant increase in the demand for the minerals.

## Bibliography
Borgese, E. M. *The Mines of Neptune: Minerals and Metals from the Sea*. New York: Harry N. Abrams, 1985. The recovery of mineral resources of the sea floor is described in a lively, interesting style. The wealth of excellent illustrations— color and black-and-white photographs and drawings—show samples of minerals and the equipment used to gather them. Recommended for anyone with an interest in seabed mineral resources.

Champ, Michael A., William P. Dillon, and David G. Howell. "Non-living EEZ Resources: Minerals, Oil, and Gas." *Oceanus* 27 (Winter, 1984/1985): 28-34. This article describes the mineral resources on the seabed from the coast out several hundred kilometers. It discusses the exclusive economic zone (EEZ) and how the sand and gravel, phosphorite, ferromanganese nodules, and oil and gas on the continental shelf and abyssal plains are held by the United States. Suitable for high school readers.

Charlier, R. H., and B. L. Gordon. *Ocean Resources: An Introduction to Economic Oceanography*. Washington, D.C.: University Press of America, 1978. Examines the metallic and nonmetallic resources of the ocean floor and the economics of recovering them. Covers hard minerals, polymetallic nodules, tin, and sand and gravel. The possible use of the deep sea bed as a dumping ground is considered as well. Readable by upper-level high school students.

Gross, M. Grant. "Deep-Sea Hot Springs and Cold Seeps." *Oceanus* 27 (Fall, 1984): 2-6. This issue presents a number of papers that describe the ocean-floor vents that spew metallic minerals in the great depths. Many of the observations of the abyssal zone around the vents were made and reported by scientists aboard submersibles.

Heezen, B. C., and C. D. Hollister. *The Face of the Deep*. New York: Oxford University Press, 1971. A well-illustrated volume that explains clearly what the ocean basins look like, how they were formed, the nature of the minerals and sediments that carpet the sea floor, and the dynamics of the processes that shape the basins. Describes the process of taking deep-sea soundings and translating them into detailed drawings that allow one to see what the basins would look like if the water were removed. A good book for the general reader.

Leet, L. D., Sheldon Judson, and M. E. Kaufman. *Physical Geology*. 7th ed. Englewood Cliffs, N.J.: Prentice-Hall, 1987. A well-balanced textbook with topics of particular relevance to marine geology. Includes chapters on sea-floor topography, plate tectonics, seamounts, and the effects of waves and currents on ocean-floor sediments. Useful as a reference text for the general reader interested in earth science.

Maury, M. F. *The Physical Geography of the Sea, and Its Meteorology*. Cambridge, Mass.: Harvard University Press, 1963. A reprint of the classic oceanographic textbook first published in 1855. Maury is considered the American father of the science of oceanography, and the volume is considered the first real textbook on the subject. It discusses the depths of the ocean, the basin and bed of the Atlantic

Ocean, sediments, and how samples and data are collected. The style is sometimes archaic, but the reader will gain a perspective on the history of ocean-floor science that is well worth the effort.

Rabinowitz, Phillip, Sylvia Herrig, and Karen Riedel. "Ocean Drilling Program Altering Our Perception of Earth." *Oceanus* 29 (Fall, 1986): 36-40. Deep-sea drilling has provided earth scientists with a better understanding of the nature of the sediments of the ocean basins. The studies described in the article made use of ocean-floor drilling and a deep-water camera able to photograph a volcano almost 3 kilometers below the sea surface. A good article for those interested in the methodology of research in the ocean basins. Suitable for high school students.

Wertenbecker, W. "Land Below, Sea Above." In *Mysteries of the Deep*, edited by Joseph J. Thorndike. New York: American Heritage, 1980. An easy-to-read, informative discussion of the nature of sea-floor processes. Discusses the history of ocean-floor research, the impact of volcanism and deep-sea currents in shaping the benthic zone, seamounts and other submarine topography, and how the ocean floor is mapped. Excellent photographs and drawings. Of value to anyone interested in the nature of the ocean floor.

*Albert C. Jensen*

## Cross-References

# ACID RAIN

*Field of study:* Atmospheric sciences and meteorology

*Acid rain is rain that is more acid than natural rain as a result of reactions with pollutive acidic gases, such as sulfur dioxide and nitric oxides. Lakes, forests, soils, and human structures in the eastern part of the United States and southeastern Canada have been damaged by acid rain.*

*Principal terms*

ACIDITY: the concentration of hydrogen ions in a solution

ALKALINE: having a pH greater than 7

BICARBONATE: an ion formed of one hydrogen atom, one carbon atom, and three oxygen atoms which is very effective in natural waters at neutralizing hydrogen ions and reducing acidity

LIMESTONE: a rock containing calcium carbonate which reacts easily with acid rain and tends to neutralize it

NEUTRALIZATION: the removal of hydrogen ions from solution by their reaction with other ions, which lowers the acidity of the solution

NITRIC ACID: an acid formed in rain from nitric oxide gases in the air; it often contributes to acid rain

NITRIC OXIDE GASES: gases formed by a combination of nitrogen and oxygen, particularly nitrogen dioxide and nitric oxide

pH: a measure of the acidity of a solution; the lower the pH, the greater the concentration of hydrogen ions and the more acid the solution

SULFUR DIOXIDE: a gas formed by the combination of sulfur and two oxygen atoms

SULFURIC ACID: an acid formed in rain from sulfur dioxide gas in the air; it is the primary acid in acid rain

## Summary of the Phenomenon

Acid rain is rain that is more acid than it would naturally be, usually because it has reacted with acidic pollutive gases. The acidity of rain is measured in pH units. Pure water, which is neutral, has a pH of 7 (the concentration of hydrogen ions is $10^{-7}$) and any solution with a pH greater than 7 is basic. Any solution with a pH less than 7 is acidic; the lower the pH, the more hydrogen ions, and the more acid the solution. The natural acidity of rain is determined by its reaction with carbon dioxide gas in the atmosphere, a reaction which produces carbonic acid. Carbonic acid partly dissociates to produce hydrogen ions and bicarbonate ions. As a result of this reaction, pure rain should be moderately acidic, with a pH of 5.7. Any rain with a pH less than 5.7 is called "acid rain" and has reacted with acidic atmospheric gases other than carbon dioxide, such as sulfur dioxide, which produces sulfuric acid in rain, and nitrogen dioxide, which produces nitric acid in rain. In some extreme cases, acid rain has been analyzed with a pH as low as 2.4, which is as acidic as vinegar. In addition to acid rain, there is "dry deposition" from the atmosphere of acidic sulfate particles and sulfur and nitrogen gases, which occurs without rain. The acidic particles are trapped by vegetation or settle out, and the gases are taken up by vegetation. "Acid deposition" refers to acid rain plus dry deposition of acids.

Acid rain was first recognized in Scandinavia in the early 1950's. It was dis-covered that acid rain (with a pH from 4 to 5) came from winter air masses which were carrying pollution from industrial areas in central and western Europe into Scandinavia. Rain became more acid over the next twenty years, and the area of Europe receiving acid rains increased. By the mid-1970's, most of northwestern Europe was receiving acid rain with a pH of less than 4.6. As a result of the discovery of acid rain in Europe, scientists began measuring the acidity of North American rain. Initially, around 1960, acid rain was concentrated in a bull's-eye-shaped area over New York, Pennsylvania, and new England. By 1980, however, most of the United States east of the Mississippi River and southeastern Canada was receiving acid rain (pH less than 5.0) and the central bull's-eye was receiving very acid rain (pH less than 4.2). The greatest increase in acidity of U.S. rain was in the southeastern United States.

The primary cause of acidity in U.S. and European rains is sulfuric acid, which comes from pollutive sulfur dioxide gas produced by the burning of sulfur-containing fossil fuels—particularly coal, but also oil and gas—by power plants and industry. In the United States, much of the sulfur dioxide gas is produced in the industrial area of the Midwest; however, sulfur dioxide gas, and the resulting sul-furic acid, can be transported for a distance of 800 kilometers to the northeast by the prevailing winds in the atmosphere before being rained out as acid rain in the northeastern United States and southeastern Canada. To reduce the acidity of rain in the East, then, the emissions of sulfur dioxide gas in the Midwest would have to be reduced. Another source of sulfur dioxide gas is smelters which process ores, such as the Sudbury, Ontario, smelter, located north of Lake Huron in Canada, which is the single largest sulfur source in the world. This smelter, which has a very high smokestack, spreads sulfuric acid over a large area hundreds of kilometers down-wind from it. The original intent of building high smokestacks was to reduce local air pollution, but the net effect has been to spread the pollution over large areas. Acid rains are even found in Alaska, where sulfuric acid particles have been trans-ported from the coterminous United States.

Nitric acid is a secondary cause of acid rain (contributing about 30 percent of the acidity), but one which is increasing. Nitric acid comes from the nitrogen oxide gases, nitrogen dioxide and nitric oxide, which are produced by fossil fuel burning. In contrast to sulfur dioxide, 40 percent of the pollutive nitrogen oxide gas comes from vehicles and most of the rest from power and heating. The production of nitrogen oxide therefore tends to be concentrated in urban areas. Nitric acid is an important component of acid rain in Los Angeles, for example, because air pollution from vehicles tends to be trapped in this area.

Some acid rain results from natural causes. Reduced sulfur gases, such as hydrogen sulfide and dimethyl sulfide, are produced by organic matter decay and converted to sulfur dioxide and sulfuric acid in the atmosphere. This process results in naturally acid rain. Volcanoes are another natural source of sulfur dioxide gas. Nevertheless, about 75 percent of the sulfur dioxide gas produced in the United States comes from the burning of fossil fuels. Naturally acid rain (with a pH less than 5.5) is uncommon, being chiefly known in remote areas such as the Amazon basin and some oceanic areas.

There are natural factors that work to reduce or neutralize the acidity of rain in certain areas. Windblown dust (particularly that containing limestone) tends to make rains in arid areas of the western United States less acid, with a pH of 6 or more. Also, the presence of ammonia gas, which is produced in agricultural areas by animal wastes, organic matter decomposition, and fertilizers, will reduce the acidity of rain.

The detrimental effects from the deposition of acid rain include the corrosion of man-made structures and buildings, changes in soils, increases in the acidity of lakes, and biological effects, particularly in high-altitude forests. The corrosive effects of acid rain are particularly obvious on limestone, a rock composed of calcium carbonate, which reacts easily with acid rain. In many New England cemeteries, tombstones made of marble (metamorphosed or heated limestone) have been badly corroded, although older tombstones made of slate, which is less affected by acid rain, are intact. Limestone buildings are similarly corroded.

The effect of acid rain on soils depends on their composition. Alkaline soils, which contain limestone, easily neutralize acid rain. Even in soils which do not contain limestone, several processes operate to neutralize acid rain. Cation exchange occurs, whereby the hydrogen ions from the rain are exchanged for metal ions, such as calcium or magnesium, on the surface of clays and other minerals. This exchange removes hydrogen ions from soil solutions and makes the solutions less acid. Another neutralization process involves the release of soil aluminum into solution and the accompanying uptake of hydrogen ions. This process occurs by dissolution of aluminum bound to clays and organic compounds. Frozen soils and sandy soils containing mostly quartz, which does not react with acid rain, have little ability to neutralize acid rain.

Lakes in certain areas have become acidic (with a pH less than 5) from the deposition of acid rain. Areas with many acid lakes include the Adirondack Mountains in New York, the Pocono Mountains in Pennsylvania, the Upper Peninsula of Michigan, Ontario, Nova Scotia, and Scandinavia. Generally, the deposition of very acid rain (with a pH less than 4.6) over a long period is required. Lake waters which have a tendency to become acidified initially have little ability to neutralize acid rain, because they are low in bicarbonate ions, which come dominantly from limestone. Such lakes are described as being poorly buffered. (Buffering is the resistance to change in pH upon the addition of acid.) The soil in the drainage area surrounding acid lakes does not neutralize acid rain adequately before it reaches the lake because of a lack of limestone and clay minerals or because the soil cover is thin or lacking altogether. In addition, some lakes, although not usually acid, may have periods of acidity during the runoff of snowmelt, which collects acid precipitation stored in the snow. This runoff gives a sudden large pulse of very acid water to the lake. In certain areas, such as Florida, acid lakes result at least partly from causes other than acid rain, such as organic acids from the decay of vegetation in poorly drained areas and nitric acid from fertilizer runoff. The gradual acidification of lakes results in the death of their fish populations because of reproductive failure, as well as other changes in the organisms living in the lake. A reduction in the number of species occurs at all levels of the food chain. In some cases, snowmelt acidity can cause a massive, instantaneous fish kill in lakes.

Rivers are also known to become acid. Eastern U.S. rivers show high concentrations of sulfate and a low pH in cases where the soil cannot neutralize the acid rain that it receives. Certain acid rivers are caused by acid drainage from mine dumps rather than by acid rain. Organic-rich acid rivers, which are naturally acid, are found in the eastern United States coastal plain and in the Amazon basin. These rivers have naturally high concentrations of dissolved organic acids and are very dilute.

Acid rain is implicated in the decline and death of certain forests, particularly evergreen forests at high elevations. These forests receive very acid precipitation from the base of clouds at the mountaintops. It is thought that acid rain does not actually kill forests but rather provides a stress, causing them to become less resistant and die of other causes. The actual stress provided by acid rain is still being studied. Possible stresses include loss of soil nutrients and leaching of nutrients from the leaves, destruction of soil microorganisms, and increased susceptibility to cold winters.

Efforts have been made to reduce the acidity of rain, particularly by controlling sulfur emissions. Power plants have been required to reduce the sulfur content of coal that they burn; lower-sulfur coal produces less sulfur dioxide. The sulfate concentrations in rain in the northeastern United States have been reduced by this method. The nitrogen oxide emissions from cars have also been reduced. In some cases, acid lakes have been treated with limestone to neutralize their acidity temporarily, but the only permanent solution is a reduction in the acidity of the rain that they receive.

## Methods of Study

The acidity of rain can be measured directly by a pH meter. A pair of electrodes is inserted into a solution, and the electrical potential, or voltage, is measured between them. This voltage is a measure of the concentration of hydrogen ions in the solution—the acidity. Networks have been constructed to collect rain samples over large geographical areas. The acidity of rain over the whole year must be measured, because pH varies between rainfalls, both seasonally and depending on whether the air masses that produce the rain have passed over significant sources of pollution. The pH of rain is also measured over a period of years. In addition to the concentration of hydrogen ions, the concentration of other ions, such as sulfate (from sulfuric acid) and nitrate (from nitric acid), is measured in the rain samples. That gives evidence of the source of the acidity—that is, which proportion is attributable to sulfuric acid and which to nitric acid. The pH of samples collected over a large geographical area are plotted on a map, and contours are drawn through equal values of the pH. Such maps show which areas are receiving the most acid rain. The amount of sulfate and nitrate being deposited by rain is also plotted separately. Meteorologists also have information about the path followed by a storm system as it moves across the country. Such atmospheric systems transport pollutive gases from one area to another. Combining depositional patterns on maps with information about the path followed by a storm shows where the gases in rain may be coming from and suggests sources of the acidity.

Computers have been used to predict where acid rain will fall and how acid it will be given the sources and sizes of sulfur and nitrogen emissions, particularly from power plants and smelters, and the weather patterns. Predictions of this type require a detailed knowledge of the atmospheric chemistry by which sulfur dioxide is converted to sulfuric acid and the oxides of nitrogen are converted to nitric acid. This type of modeling is necessary to predict how much reduction in the acidity of rain in a distant area will result from a given reduction in a power plant sulfur source, for example.

Studies of the effects of acidity on soils have been conducted. Laboratory experiments can be done to see how soil clays and other minerals react to the addition of acid rain, including which chemical species are taken up and released. In addition, soil solutions and minerals are collected and analyzed from actual field areas affected by acid rain. Ideally, this analysis should be done over a period of time to determine whether any changes in the soil solution chemistry are occurring. From a knowledge of the soil chemistry, it is possible to predict how long a soil can receive acid rain before it loses the ability to neutralize the acidity.

The acidity and chemical composition of lakes in various areas have been measured over long periods, and their fish and other biota have been sampled. That enables scientists to see increases in lake acidity and to correlate the increases with changes in the populations of fish and biota. In some areas, lakes have been artificially acidified so that the changes in their chemistry and biological populations can be observed. Apparently, acid lake water inhibits the reproduction of fish and other creatures in addition to destroying organisms that they use for food. Computer models of acid rain falling on susceptible drainage areas of lakes have been made in order to predict how the drainage area reacts to acid rain and how much reduction in acid rain would be necessary to lower the acidity of the lake to the point where it would support fish. In badly affected areas such as the Adirondacks, it may be necessary to reduce the acidity by one half.

To study forest decline, surveys of present forest conditions are compared with historical records for the same areas. For example, in high-elevation areas in New England and the Adirondacks, more than half of the red spruce died between 1965 and 1990. Tree rings, which record annual growth, show reduced growth in certain forests. It is known that acid rain causes changes in the soil, such as the release of aluminum, which is toxic to root tissues and so prevents the uptake of essential nutrients. In addition, acid rain causes the loss from the soil of certain nutrients, such as sodium, calcium, and magnesium. Another effect of acid rain is the reduction of soil microorganisms. Yet, since acid rain from nitric acid contains nitrogen, a plant nutrient, it may fertilize the soil if there is a deficiency of soil nitrogen. One problem in studying forests receiving acid rain is determining which of the many changes occurring are contributing most to forest damage. It is often difficult to distinguish between the stresses of acid rain and other stresses, such as drought, cold, and insects. Field studies are being made that involve artificially acidifying forests to determine which mechanisms are important.

## Context

Acid rain has been a subject of considerable discussion and controversy. It has even affected U.S.-Canadian relations, because the Canadian government claims that the United States has not done enough to control the gaseous emissions that cause acid rain in Canada. It is well established that the eastern part of the United States and southeastern Canada are receiving very acid rain. There are a large number of acid lakes in certain susceptible areas which receive acid rain, such as the Adirondack Mountains in New York, the Pocono Mountains in Pennsylvania, the Upper Peninsula of Michigan, and southeastern Canada. These lakes have a reduced fish population and have undergone other changes in their aquatic life. In addition, high-elevation conifer forests in areas receiving very acid rain have been damaged, although the exact mechanism is not well known. Changes in soils in areas receiving acid rain can also be expected.

To make rain less acid, emissions of sulfur dioxide and nitrogen oxide gases must be reduced. The major approach is to reduce the sulfur dioxide emissions from power plants burning fossil fuels, particularly coal. That can be done by burning low-sulfur coal and by treating the emissions from these plants to reduce their sulfur content. Considerable efforts have been made to regulate the sulfur content of coal burned by power plants, but to make further reductions in sulfur emissions, other steps are required. Treating sulfur emissions from existing power plants is the fastest method to reduce sulfuric acid rain, but it is expensive, results in a loss of efficiency, and does not remove nitrogen oxides. Another approach involves the repowering of old coal-burning power plants with newer technologies which produce less sulfur dioxide and nitrogen oxide emissions. This method takes longer but is more economical. Vehicle emissions of nitrogen oxides can be reduced by air pollution controls on cars.

Much of the controversy surrounding acid rain is tied to the debate over how to reduce sulfur and nitrogen gas emissions, where and by how much they need to be reduced, and how fast it should be done. These decisions mean large expenses for the utility industry. Scientists' ability to predict the results of emission changes and the long-term effects of acid rain on lakes, forests, and soils is improving, but there is considerable work still to be done.

## Bibliography

Berner, Elizabeth K., and Robert A. Berner. *The Global Water Cycle: Geochemistry and Environment.* Englewood Cliffs, N.J.: Prentice-Hall, 1986. This book includes a number of sections on acid rain and its effects. Chapter 3 describes the formation and global distribution of sulfur and nitrogen gases, from both natural and man-made causes. Acid rain is also extensively discussed. Chapter 5 describes acid rivers, including those that result from sulfate pollution and those that result from natural organic acidity. Chapter 6 discusses acid lakes and how they form. Designed for college freshmen.

Cowling, E. B. "Acid Precipitation in Historical Perspective." *Environmental Science and Technology* 16 (February, 1982): A110-A123. This article traces the historical development of the study of acid rain. It has a chronological listing of the various important discoveries in the study of acid rain and excellent references to original articles. It also describes research programs designed to study the deposition of acid precipitation and its effects on forests, soils, and lakes. Suitable for the general reader.

Glass, N. R., et al. "Effects of Acid Precipitation." *Environmental Science and Technology* 16, no. 3 (1982): A162-A169. This article summarizes research on the effects of acid precipitation on lakes, soils, and crops. For example, efforts have been made to predict which areas in the eastern United States are sensitive to acid precipitation. Includes a number of references and is written on a college level.

Johnson, Arthur H., and T. G. Siccama. "Acid Deposition and Forest Decline." *Environmental Science and Technology* 17, no. 7 (1983): A294-A305. A summary of the evidence concerning the relationship between acid deposition and forest decline. It points out that a clear cause-and-effect relationship does not exist but that acid precipitation may provide a stress to forests. Readable by college students.

Likens, Gene E., R. F. Wright, J. F. Galloway, and T. F. Butler. "Acid Rain." *Scientific American* 241 (October, 1979): 43-51. This article is intended for the general reader. It has an excellent discussion of what acid rain is and how it was recognized. It discusses the areas receiving acid rain in the United States and Europe, changes in the acidity of rain over time, and how they correlate with changes in sulfur and nitrogen emissions. The chemistry of acid lakes is also described.

Mohnen, Volker A. "The Challenge of Acid Rain." *Scientific American* 259 (August, 1988): 30-38. A discussion of the formation of acid rain and how it is possible to predict where acid deposition will occur from known sulfur emissions. The effects of acid rain on soils, forests, and lakes are covered. Ways of changing power-plant technology to reduce sulfur emissions are also evaluated. For a general audience.

National Research Council. *Acid Deposition: Atmospheric Processes in Eastern North America*. Washington, D.C.: National Academy Press, 1983. This text covers the relationships between emissions of acid-forming gases and their deposition as acid rain. Current and past research of the subject is summarized. The area covered in this article is particularly important in discussions of the United States-Canadian acid rain problem.

*Elizabeth K. Berner*

## Cross-References

Air Pollution, 24; The Atmosphere's Global Circulation, 121; Carbonates, 190; Freshwater Chemistry, 795; The Hydrologic Cycle, 1102; Precipitation, 2108; Soil Chemistry, 2382; Surface Water, 2504; Weathering and Erosion, 2723.

# AERIAL PHOTOGRAPHY

*Field of study:* Remote sensing

*Aerial photographs have been taken from balloons, aircraft, and spacecraft and at visible and invisible wavelengths. They have many applications, including map-making, archaeology, the analysis of earth resources, weather forecasting, and environmental monitoring.*

### Principal terms

ARCHAEOLOGY: the earth science that investigates the human past

CLOUD-FREE: having less than 30 percent cloud cover, allowing clear imaging of a surface area

COMPUTER-GENERATED IMAGES: images received by instruments and digitally transformed into transmittable signals that can be reprocessed into a visible format

FALSE-COLOR IMAGES: images blended from diverse segments of the invisible spectrum, indicating such properties as temperature or moisture

GEOSTATIONARY: traveling above the equator and at the same speed as the earth rotates; a geostationary satellite appears to remain in the same place

OBLIQUE: shot from a low level looking outward, so as to avoid the maplike quality of an overhead shot

REAL TIME: the term used for images that are transmitted immediately, not stored for subsequent processing or viewing

STEREOSCOPIC: capable of viewing two adjacent and paired images such that a three-dimensional effect is perceived, revealing relief characteristics

VERTICAL: shot from directly above, so as to capture the essential characteristics of a planar surface

## Summary of the Methodology

In the autumn of 1885, Gaston Tissandier and Jacques Ducom experimented with cameras borne aloft beneath an electrically powered balloon and positioned to photograph the ground below. Aerial photography was born. On December 17, 1903, a heavier-than-air craft was produced. As air travel became common, pilots familiar with the landscape observed the ease of detecting from the air not merely present details but also traces of previous human modifications of the terrain. Surface ruins were apparent to everyone, but it became obvious to airborne viewers that impressive traces of formations beneath the surface, even in rural areas subsequent to extensive farming, could be enhanced photographically. Archaeology was one of the first beneficiaries of aerial photography. Aerofilms Library, a London company, was founded in 1919 and by 1984 held a collection of more than 800,000 aerial photographs.

Aerial photography's applications to cartography were enhanced by wartime operations. Immediately after World War II, the University of Cambridge, through its Committee for Aerial Photography, initiated a series of aerial surveys of Great Britain, intent upon publishing results for successive volumes of historically focused studies. By 1983, the University Collection had its own library, a curator in aerial photography, and more than half a million items. World War II ended with the development of rocket propulsion, which could lift craft beyond the limitations of aerodynamic flight into the relative void of interplanetary space. The Soviet satellite Sputnik 1 was launched in 1957, and the space race followed. In January of 1972, the American Defense Mapping Agency was established as a separate entity within the military establishment, although 1962 had already witnessed the first civilian, unclassified symposium on remote sensing of the environment. France entered the commercial field of space imaging with its SPOT 1 satellite in 1986.

The most important development facilitating the use of the camera was the shift from glass plates to the lighter and much more flexible roll film system developed by George Eastman and W. H. Walker in 1884. Thomas Edison adapted flexible film rolls to the possibility of motion pictures in 1889. By 1923, a 16-millimeter width was in use, and in 1932 an 8-millimeter width. The hand-held camera used by the astronauts from Gemini 9 onward (1966) took 70-millimeter film specially designed for the requirements of photography from space.

The first commercial process for making color rather than black-and-white photographs was introduced in France in 1907, but it involved only glass plate technology. It was not until 1936 that Eastman Kodak developed its Kodachrome process, which involved 35-millimeter film with high-speed sensitivities. Other modes of color photography were soon displaced. The spectrum of different wavelengths, however, is by no means restricted to visible light. In the infrared range, for example, there is heat energy. Film sensitive to heat can be used to detect warm bodies or temperature gradation at night or through cloud cover. It can even penetrate the surface of the earth itself. Radioactive materials also display characteristic wavelengths.

An ionized layer of particles lies at the upper boundary of the earth's atmosphere. Electromagnetic waves transmitted from the earth were bounced off this "mirror in the sky" in 1924 by Sir Edward Victor Appleton and Miles A. F. Barnett. The principle was extended to the "radio location" of moving aircraft, and "radar" was available by 1935. While the receivers involved are not exactly cameras, the extension of the term "photography" to imply the recording of wavelengths of energy meant that side-looking airborne radar surveys could produce additional information analogous to that offered by aerial photographs. Electronic processing of camera imagery for long-distance transmission and reception yielded, between 1911 and 1936, the series of patents that produced television.

The development of advanced computers and digital processing technologies in the 1970's permitted spacecraft to carrry increasingly sophisticated instruments which could augment or replace human efforts. Although the three manned Skylab flights produced spectacular views of the earth, the less well known but more durable examples from the five Landsat satellites made available information for a complete reevaluation of the planet. Without the careful photographic inspection performed by the Lunar Orbiters, the Apollo landings would have been impossible. Equipment comparable to that used on the Lunar Orbiters and the Landsats has been sent on missions to Mars, to the Sun and the inner planets, to the outer planets, and beyond.

## Applications of the Method

The applications of aerial photography are interrelated. The method, which began with visual observation, has expanded into ranges of investigation beyond the limits of human sight. The permanent recording of images permits historical contrasts between the way things were and the way things have become.

A satellite less than 1,000 kilometers above the earth's surface circles the globe in an hour and a half. Sequential passes provide detailed observations, with direct transmission, or storage and delayed transmission, of the entire earth and its atmosphere twice a day. That allows the generation of a complete composite map of a whole landmass, or block studies from individual photographs in slightly skewed squares (because of flight paths inclined at 81 degrees to the plane of the equator). These near-squares, typically printed at 23 centimeters to the side, cover about 185 kilometers per side, or about 34,225 square kilometers of space.

Comparison of blocks taken on successive passes over the same space permits a time-lapse indication of change and is useful for identification of detail under divergent sunlit conditions. A built-in overlap factor permits observation with stereoscopic equipment, which yields three-dimensional images of the topography. Thus, not only can features be located for two-dimensional cartography, but their heights above or below sea level can be more exactly determined as well.

Satellite imaging is also capable of providing oceanographic information related to depths of water, relative temperatures, the direction and flow of currents, the interrelationship of fresh and salt waters, and a variety of fluid-flow problems related to sediments and other pollutants being naturally or humanly discharged into the seas. Polar ice, its thickness, and its movements, including those of breakaway icebergs, can be identified. The first accurate mapping of Antarctica was achieved in this way.

Specific earth features, such as the great desert regions and the peculiar movements of their surface dunes, caught the attention of space scientists. Volcanic activity, including the force and direction of smoky plumes and lava flows, was followed. Most important, satellite photography provided immediate access to meteorological events. The first Television Infrared Observation Satellite (TIROS), intended particularly for weather coverage, was placed in space on April 1, 1960, and transmitted 22,592 photographs during its 1,302 revolutions of active space life. Various successors demonstrated even greater accomplishments: TIROS 9 circled the earth twelve times on February 13, 1965, and its 480 images were assembled to form one mosaic of the complete cloud and weather system over the entire earth.

The higher-altitude satellites—those in a geostationary orbit, 38,000 kilometers above the surface—can make one photograph of nearly half the earth and, by uninterrupted communication with stations on the land beneath, transmit a continuing sequence of images illustrating moment-by-moment changes in weather patterns. The data are more clearly perceived in black-and-white photographs or in computer-generated false-color mosaics, which include infrared portions of the spectrum.

Although geography and meteorology are the most obvious fields for the application of aerial reconnaissance technology, archaeology and related historical disciplines were already being served when aerial photography had just begun. By virtue of intensive aerial investigation, more ancient Roman military encampments have been found in Great Britain than anywhere else in what was once the empire. While excavation may be necessary for the uncovering of specific details, the character of the past remains permanently displayed in the features of the earth altered by Roman engineers. Industrial technologies have also left their marks on the earth: quarries and mines, manufacturing plants and industrial estates, canal and railway systems, ports and docks, airports and their runways, and urban sprawl. No segment of human history has been overlooked by archaeological inquiry, and aerial photography is a guide even to traces of prehistoric field patterns, which reveal ancient farming techniques.

A false-color composite photograph of the U.S.-Canadian border exhibits not merely divergence of crops but also differences in farm layout and tillage patterns. Environmental monitoring reveals erosion effects of poor agricultural practices. Aerial views of water management, whether in the Great Plains, the Colorado Basin, or the Florida Everglades, help to determine patterns of surface-water storage, the impact of irrigation systems, conditions of drought, or polluting effects of fertilizers. Floods can be monitored, even if not prevented. The extent of forest-fire areas, immediate damage, and subsequent regrowth can be watched to help avoid immediate disaster and to see long-term effects. Conservation interests are served by the monitoring of breeding habitats of migratory waterfowl.

Over a two-and-a-half-year interval, from April, 1978, until September, 1980, among the many earth-orbiting satellites was the Heat Capacity Mapping Mission (HCMM), a program designed to sense thermal emissions from surfaces reflecting solar radiation. Placed in a near-polar orbit at 620 kilometers, the satellite measured temperature differences at specific sites at twelve-hour or longer intervals. It observed the special heating effects of urban "islands" and added to scientists' understanding of soil and crop types, moisture constituencies, thermal pollution, and large-scale sea-surface conditions. HCMM was capable of distinguishing varieties of rock, especially hard crustal materials from various low-density alluvial fills. It could also distinguish rocks of the same type that had different textures. Even though these data required correlation with photographs, they provided, particularly in Nevada, indications of varieties of intrusion at a level comparable to that of geologic maps. A complete map of the entire United States was produced by this technique. Several significant impact crater structures in northeastern Canada were identified, and other features, including Hurricane David (September, 1979), were examined.

## Context

One of the important results of aerial photography, especially from space, has been the detailed mapping of storm systems throughout their formation, development, and movement. This tracking can permit accurate forecasting and the construction of warning systems to alert persons in the paths of those storm systems.

Mapping, including its geographically precise form, cartography, had a long and distinguished history before the advent of aerial photography. Its possibilities, however, have been enlarged by views from space. Landsat 1 was able to photograph 100 percent of the United States and 78 percent of the world's landmasses under cloud-free conditions. A map of the United States could be constructed from a composite of five hundred pictures, whereas even high-altitude airplanes would require 500,000 photographs to accomplish the same task.

Diverse forms of imaging also permit an examination of geologic detail with significance for petroleum or mineral discovery. In addition to the configuration of the earth and its crustal contents, attention can be paid to those eruptive forces and faulting movements which are threatening to human life and property. Skylab 1 closely scrutinized volanic activity and the resulting spew of debris into the atmosphere, whose implications for climatic modification cannot be ignored. Aerial photographs have also enhanced the study of plate tectonics and the crustal movements that trigger earthquakes.

No view of the earth from the air can avoid perceiving the works of human hands. Some of these images provide the archaeologist and the urban planner with information about the historical progress of urban life. They also reveal the destructive forces unleashed by humans, such as the removal of the great rain forests, with ecological consequences for the future that cannot be ascertained.

## Bibliography

Beresford, M. W., and J. K. S. St. Joseph. *Medieval England: An Aerial Survey.* 2d ed. Cambridge, England: Cambridge University Press, 1979. Carefully selected black-and-white illustrations, accompanied by explanations and arranged within eleven sections, attempt to provide a view of the medieval English world.

Frere, S. S., and J. K. S. St. Joseph. *Roman Britain from the Air.* Cambridge, England: Cambridge University Press, 1983. With 142 aerial photographs of great clarity taken from low-flying aircraft, surviving examples of Roman ruins and landscape features are eloquently described. The volume demonstrates how well human impacts on the earth are preserved. Includes supplementary references.

Hudson, Kenneth. *Industrial History from the Air.* Cambridge, England: Cambridge

University Press, 1984. Superb photographs illustrate features of industrial technological development during the nineteenth and twentieth centuries in Great Britain. The photographs are accompanied by self-contained narratives and integrated into ten thematically arranged sections. Readable by all.

National Aeronautics and Space Administration, Johnson Space Center. *Skylab Explores the Earth*. NASA SP-380. Washington, D.C.: Government Printing Office, 1977. Skylab 4 spent eighty-four days in space and was particularly designed as a mission to photograph earth features. Seventeen thematic essays, involving 206 Skylab photographs and 49 comparative examples from other spacecraft, give an impressive indication of what could be seen. The text is readable, though occasionally technical. The illustrations and captions will be enjoyed by all.

National Geographic Society. *Atlas of North America: Space Age Portrait of a Continent*. Washington, D.C.: Author, 1985. Although the volume was intended to provide general cartographic information, the extensive use of photographs of earth from space, derived from thirteen different spacecraft—three manned missions, all five Landsats, plus defense and other meteorological satellites—makes it a useful introduction to aerial photography for all readers.

Short, Nicholas M., Paul D. Lowman, Jr., Stanley C. Freden, and William A. Finch, Jr. *Mission to Earth: Landsat Views the World*. NASA SP-360. Washington, D.C.: Government Printing Office, 1976. A large-format collection of four hundred plates, mostly in color, with a detailed caption for each. Forty percent illustrate features of the United States; the remainder show diverse portions of the earth. An introductory essay explains the Landsat satellites and the data-gathering system in readable language. This volume is a companion to the book by Williams listed below.

Short, Nicholas M., and Locke M. Stuart, Jr. *The Heat Capacity Mapping Mission (HCMM) Anthology*. NASA SP-465. Washington, D.C.: Government Printing Office, 1982. A review of the Heat Capacity Mapping Mission, which was launched on April 26, 1978, and remained in operation until September, 1980. Thermal remote sensing was able to produce chiefly black-and-white composite illustrations, the significance of which is described herein. The book is designed to inform the nonspecialist about the data collected and how they are used. Includes a gallery of one hundred plates with interpretative comments.

Williams, Richard S., Jr., and William D. Carter, eds. *ERTS-1: A New Window on Our Planet*. U.S. Geological Survey Professional Paper 929. Washington, D.C.: Government Printing Office, 1976. The first Earth Resources Technology Satellite (which later became Landsat 1) produced a flood of data, at a rate of 1,316 pictures per day, which were made available to scientists in thirty-seven countries. Eighty-six distinctive technical reports illustrated by 256 figures demonstrate the range and capacities of machine-generated aerial photography applied to the earth sciences.

Wilson, David R. *Air Photo Interpretation for Archaeologists*. London: B. T.

Batsford, 1982. This source explains the nature of evidence, methods of identification of features observed from the air, and principles of photograph interpretation. A basic work accessible to all readers. Extensive bibliography.

*Clyde Curry Smith*

## Cross-References

Archaeological Geology, 86; The Atmosphere's Global Circulation, 121; Desertification, 346; Floods, 719; Infrared Spectra, 1232; Land Management, 1327; Landsat, 1358; The Structure of the Oceans, 1871; Plate Tectonics, 2079; Remote Sensing and the Electromagnetic Spectrum, 2166; Earth Resources, 2175; Side-Looking Airborne Radar, 2349; Skylab, 2375; Soil Erosion, 2387; Weather Forecasting, 2717.

# AIR POLLUTION

*Field of study:* Atmospheric sciences and meteorology

*Air pollution is generated from both natural and man-made sources. Natural sources include pollen from plants, gases and particulate matter from volcanoes, and windblown dust. Man-made sources include industrial and automobile emissions and airborne particles associated with human-induced abrasion.*

### Principal terms
ACID RAIN: precipitation having relatively high levels of acidity
ATMOSPHERE: a mixture of gases surrounding the earth
CARBON DIOXIDE: a natural component of the atmosphere; it is a good absorber of sensible heat energy
GREENHOUSE EFFECT: the environmental situation that results from the trapping of sensible heat energy in the atmosphere by atmospheric gases
INVERSION: an unusual atmospheric condition in which temperature in the troposphere increases with altitude
OXIDES OF NITROGEN: gases formed when fuels containing nitrogen are burned
OXIDES OF SULFUR: gases formed when fuels containing sulfur are burned
OZONE: a gas containing three atoms of oxygen; there is a zone in the stratosphere where ozone is highly concentrated
PHOTOCHEMICAL OXIDANTS: pollutants developed from primary pollutants through a complex series of reactions
PHOTOCHEMICAL REACTION: a chemical reaction occurring in polluted air through the action of sunlight on pollutant gases to synthesize new gases

## Summary of the Phenomenon
Air pollution results from the addition of gases, solids, and liquids to the atmosphere. The concentration of pollutants depends on prevailing atmospheric conditions as well as emission rates. Once pollutants are put into the atmosphere, it is impossible to control them to any significant degree. Thus, emissions at the local level contribute to regional and global air pollution problems, such as smog and photochemical oxidants, acid precipitation, the depletion of the ozone layer, and global warming associated with the greenhouse effect. Although there are many air pollutants, the major ones are usually associated with burning, particularly the burning of coal and oil products. They are hydrocarbons, oxides of sulfur, oxides of nitrogen, carbon monoxide, photochemical oxidants, and particulate matter.

The atmosphere is a mixture of gases (and particulate matter) surrounding the earth. The concentration of some of the gases in clean air is fairly constant both spatially and temporally. Consequently, these gases are referred to as stable or permanent gases. Nitrogen and oxygen, the two most abundant of the permanent gases, account for nearly 99 percent of the total atmosphere by volume: nitrogen 78 percent, and oxygen 21 percent. The gases that experience noticeable temporal and spatial variations are termed variable gases. The two most abundant of these are water vapor and carbon dioxide. The average concentration of carbon dioxide is about 0.033 percent. It varies seasonally in response to the growth cycle of pollens, daily in response to plant photosynthesis, and spatially in response to the burning of fossil fuels. Water vapor is also highly variable. The other variable gases have natural origins and tend to have relatively high concentrations in urban areas. They are methane, carbon monoxide, sulfur dioxide, nitrogen dioxide, ozone, ammonia, and hydrogen sulfide.

The atmosphere is stratified based on its vertical temperature gradient. From the surface up, the major layers are the troposphere, the stratosphere, the mesosphere, and the thermosphere. The troposphere contains the bulk of the atmospheric gases and, under normal conditions, is characterized by a fairly uniform temperature decline from the surface upward. The uppermost limit of the troposphere is called the tropopause, a transition zone between the troposphere and stratosphere where temperatures stabilize with increasing altitude. The troposphere extends up to about 10 kilometers. The next layer encountered is the stratosphere, which extends from about 12.5 kilometers up to about 45 kilometers above the surface. In its lower layer, the temperature gradient is somewhat stable. At an elevation of about 30 kilometers, however, the temperature starts to increase. Located within the stratosphere about 24 to 32 kilometers above the earth's surface is a zone with a relatively high concentration of ozone, a form of oxygen developed from three atoms of oxygen. This is called the ozone layer. It is important because ozone is a good absorber of ultraviolet rays emitted by the sun.

The two uppermost layers, the mesosphere and the thermosphere, have a distinctive temperature gradient. In the mesosphere, temperatures decline steadily with altitude, a condition that continues until its transition zone with the thermosphere, called the mesopause, is reached. The last layer, the thermosphere, slowly gives way to outer space and has no defined upper limit. No known effects of air pollution have been identified in these two strata.

The vertical and horizontal mixing of air is necessary to dilute pollutants in the atmosphere. Under normal conditions, temperatures decline with altitude in the troposphere. This decline in temperature with altitude is referred to as the thermal or environmental lapse rate. The warmer air near the surface rises, mixes with the air above it, and is dispersed upward by winds. This dilution process is important in reducing the concentration of pollution near the surface. Conversely, the vertical mixing of air is inhibited when the temperature profile in the troposphere inverts, developing a temperature or thermal inversion. When an inversion exists, cooler air near the surface, which is heavier than the warmer air above it, does not rise.

Pollutants then accumulate below the warmer air, increasing their concentration.

Conditions for temperature inversions develop when the earth readily radiates heat energy from its surface on clear nights or when air subsides and warms adiabatically from compression. On cool, clear nights, the earth readily radiates heat energy to space, causing the surface to cool. Air near the surface is in turn cooled by conduction, while the air above it is still fairly warm. This is referred to as a radiation inversion. Radiation inversions are common during the fall of the year and are usually short-lived, since the sun heats the air near the surface, when it rises, causing the inversion to dissipate as the day advances. The less frequent but more persistent subsidence-type inversions occur when air subsides in high-pressure systems or in valleys, where air descends along adjacent mountain slopes. These episodes may last for days, allowing pollutants to concentrate to excessive levels, causing eye irritation, respiratory distress, reduced visibility, corrosion of materials, and soiling of clothes.

The atmosphere has inherent self-cleaning mechanisms. Pollutants are removed from the atmosphere through fallout from gravitational settling, through rainout in condensation processes, through washout as waterdrops and snowflakes fall to earth, and through chemical conversion. Solar radiation, winds, and atmospheric moisture are important meteorological factors in these removal processes.

Chemical reactions between two or more substances in the atmosphere produce secondary pollutants, pollutants created from other pollutants that are released directly from identifiable sources. Smog and acid precipitation are products of such reactions. Stability in the atmosphere that accompanies inversions provides favorable conditions for smog to develop. Smog is caused by chemical reactions between sulfur oxides, hydrocarbons, and oxides of nitrogen. Smog that is characterized by sulfur oxides is called sulfurous smog and is associated with burning fuels high in sulfur content. This type of smog is common in Europe and the eastern United States. Photochemical smog, on the other hand, develops when oxides of nitrogen and hydrocarbons undergo photochemical reactions and produce ozone and other chemical oxidizers. Sunlight catalyzes the reactions, and automobile exhaust is a primary source. This is the type of smog for which Los Angeles is noted.

While smog is a relatively localized phenomenon, closely associated with urban areas, acid precipitation is more widespread. Its effects are found in national parks, agricultural regions, and forested areas as well as urban centers. Acid rain develops when oxides of sulfur and oxides of nitrogen combine with water vapor in the atmosphere to form sulfuric and nitric acids that fall back to earth during the precipitation processes. Once released into the atmosphere, these compounds can travel hundreds of kilometers before returning to earth in precipitation or as dry particulates. They can travel from 1,000 to 2,000 kilometers over three to five days. This long-range transport allows time for chemical reactions to convert pollutant gases into components of acid precipitation. Evidence suggests that the pH values in precipitation have been dropping, becoming more acidic, for some years. Wet precipitation is not the only way pollutants find their way to the surface. Diffusion and settling enable acidic gases and particles to find their way to the ground even under dry conditions. It is now widely accepted that both wet and dry deposition can be traced to human activity.

Much evidence has been gathered indicating the damaging effects of acid precipitation. Some of the effects are damage to wildlife in lakes and rivers, reduction of forest productivity, damage to agricultural crops, and deterioration of man-made materials. Acid precipitation is also suspected of helping release heavy metals from soils and pipelines into drinking water supplies. It has different impacts on different ecological systems and is most damaging to aquatic ecosystems. Acidity in precipitation at a given time depends not only on the quality of pollutants being produced but also on the prevailing and immediate atmospheric conditions. Stagnant air, resulting from upper-level inversions, tends to cause higher levels of acidity. Furthermore, prevailing and local atmospheric systems are associated with the spread of acid precipitation over broader areas. Higher smokestacks simply disperse the pollutants over larger areas, increasing their residence time in the atmosphere.

It is now realized that the impact of air pollution may be more far-reaching than the troposphere. Evidence suggests that some pollutants are making their way up to the stratosphere and are causing the ozone layer to break down. Even though ozone constitutes a very small portion of the atmosphere (about one part per million), it absorbs most of the ultraviolet rays from the sun, preventing them from reaching the earth. Recent findings suggest that there has been a breakdown of the ozone shield in the Antarctic, where a hole has been identified in the ozone layer; the ozone layer also appears to be getting thinner over the Arctic. Attempts to explain this phenomenon center on two conflicting explanations. One assumes pollutants to be the cause, and the other emphasizes natural shifts in air movements. While earlier laboratory studies showed that oxides of nitrogen could attack ozone, more recent attention has focused on chlorofluorocarbons (CFCs) as responsible for the decline in ozone. These compounds are used as coolants for refrigerators and air conditioners, propellants for aerosol sprays, agents for producing foam, and cleansers for electronic products. Being inert gases, they do not degrade readily in the troposphere. These substances eventually make their way into the stratosphere. Laboratory studies have shown that when the CFC molecules come in contact with ozone that has absorbed intense ultraviolet light, they break down into more reactive gases, such as chlorine. Since these gases tend to linger in the atmosphere for many years, it is believed that even if people were to discontinue using CFCs, the ozone layer would continue to disintegrate for years to come.

Recent evidence suggests that CFCs not only destroy the ozone but also trap heat energy radiated from the ground and contribute to heating the atmosphere. The trapping of sensible heat energy in the atmosphere by gases is called the greenhouse effect. The most important gas contributing to the greenhouse effect, however, is not chlorofluorocarbon but carbon dioxide. Carbon dioxide moves in a continuous cycle throughout the environment. It provides a link between the organic and inorganic components of the environment. Reacting with water and solar energy in plants, it forms chemical energy that is passed through the food chain.

Carbon dioxide is given off by plants and animals to the atmosphere during respiration. When plant and animal remains decay, carbon dioxide is passed to the atmosphere and hydrosphere through the weathering of rocks, volcanic activity, and the burning of fossil fuels. When fossil fuels are burned, the natural processes are short-circuited, releasing large amounts of carbon dioxide directly into the atmosphere.

About 0.03 percent of the total atmosphere is carbon dioxide. Molecules of carbon dioxide in the atmosphere absorb infrared radiation, acting like a greenhouse. While it is transparent to shortwave radiation from the sun, carbon dioxide absorbs strongly in the sensible heat or longwave radiation band. It is hypothesized that an increase in atmospheric carbon dioxide causes a decrease in outgoing longwave radiation, and thus an increase in the atmospheric temperature, causing less condensation of water molecules and thereby allowing for more incoming shortwave radiation because of a decrease in the albedo rate. The albedo is the rate that solar radiation is reflected to outer space and scattered by atmospheric gases and particles.

The global rise in air temperature between 1870 and 1940 has been attributed to the addition of anthropogenic carbon dioxide to the atmosphere. Since the 1940's, however, temperatures have shown a decrease, despite the fact that carbon dioxide is still being added to the atmosphere. It may be argued that this decrease in temperature during the latter period does not disprove the hypothesis that temperatures will increase with the addition of carbon dioxide, since there is a period in which rising temperatures lag behind increased insolation: energy from the sun. On the basis of this premise, some scientists believe that there will be a general warming of the earth's mean atmospheric temperature. The consequences of rising global temperatures will greatly alter the earth's surface. As the atmosphere warms, polar ice and glaciers will begin to melt, and the rising oceans could drown many of the world's coastal regions, devastating low-lying countries. As shorelines rise, saltwater intrusion will contaminate drinking-water supplies of many cities worldwide. Agricultural regions of the middle-latitude countries will migrate farther northward, increasing the length of the growing seasons in Canada and the Soviet Union.

## Methods of Study

Methods of studying air pollution include controlled laboratory experiments, simulations in fluid-modeling facilities, computer simulations, and mathematical modeling. Controlled laboratory experiments are conducted in laboratories where gases are mixed to determine how they react. Laboratory experiments usually do not provide the definitive answer to what is actually occurring in the ambient environment because of the many variables that cannot be replicated. These studies, however, do suggest what should be further studied and monitored in the natural environment. Some laboratory studies have simulated atmospheric conditions in a controlled environment, such as a biosphere where the impact of pollution on plants can be determined by introducing the pollutants at various levels. Simulation studies may also include gathering data from fluid-modeling facilities, where the environment is replicated using miniature models and atmospheric conditions are controlled. These studies often contribute to an understanding of the dispersion and deposition of air pollutants.

Monitoring the atmosphere is an essential component of air pollution studies involving computer simulations and mathematical modeling. These types of studies rely largely on data sources or values from the ambient environment and are constrained by difficulties of measuring ambient levels. Sometimes, vessels containing samples of air are collected and returned to the laboratory for analysis, but continuous monitoring devices which are placed in the ambient environment are more common.

Many of the monitoring devices involve a colorimetric or photometric technique. Air to be analyzed is pumped through a chamber and allowed to react with chemicals. The reaction product is then pumped through a chamber and allowed to react with chemicals. This reaction product is then pumped into a photometer, where the concentration of light-absorbing substance is indicated by the light intensity that reaches the photometer. Particulate matter is measured by fairly simple collectors that may involve adhesive coated paper or pumping air through filters and measuring the increase in weight resulting from the trapped particles. Another method involves passing a known volume of air through filter paper and measuring the intensity of light passing through it. The intensity of light indicates the scattering and absorptive properties of aerosols; it is expressed as a coefficient. Instruments may be located at the surface, mounted on airplanes, or allowed to ascend in balloons. Acidity in precipitation is determined by standard measures of acidity using a pH indicator.

## Context

Industry continues to downplay the threat of pollution to the atmosphere and disputes the extent of damage caused by pollution. Yet, as greater amounts of pollutants are released into the atmosphere, it becomes increasingly difficult to control their levels and reverse any resulting damage. The depletion of the ozone layer, the global warming trend resulting from the greenhouse effect, acid rain, and increasing levels of smog are all very real and threatening manifestations of air pollution. Efforts to protect the atmosphere must be made on a worldwide basis, since gases cannot be confined to political boundaries. Air pollution may be lowered by reducing emissions or by extracting pollutants from the atmosphere through natural means. Thus, any plans to reduce air pollution should center on one or both of these approaches. In some cases, the cost will be high, but any responsible generation of people must make the necessary sacrifices to ensure that succeeding generations will inherit a safe, clean, and inhabitable environment.

## Bibliography

Brodine, Virginia, ed. *Air Pollution*. New York: Harcourt Brace Jovanovich, 1972. A review of the social issues relevant to air pollution. It also addresses the ways in which air pollution affects the atmosphere and human health. An excellent reference for the general reader.

Commission on College Geographers. *Air Pollution*. Washington, D.C.: Association of American Geographers, 1968. A resource document designed to assist in teaching the fundamental concepts of air pollution.

Ostmann, Robert. *Acid Rain: A Plague upon the Waters*. Minneapolis, Minn.: Dillon Press, 1982. This book provides insight into the political history and development of the acid rain problem. The effects of acid rain on society are addressed from the perspective of a concerned citizen.

Shaw, Robert W. "Air Pollution by Particles." *Scientific American* 257 (August, 1978): 96-103. An excellent article on tracing and measuring air pollution sources. A good source for those interested in air pollution monitoring processes. Applications of spectroscopy as a research tool in air pollution are addressed.

Stolarski, Richard S. "The Antarctic Ozone Hole." *Scientific American* 258 (January, 1988): 30-36. An excellent review of research efforts pertaining to ozone depletion in the Antarctic. A very understandable explanation of the chemical reactions associated with CFCs and ozone depletion. An argument is also presented for natural processes as a major contributor to the ozone hole.

Williamson, Samuel J. *Fundamentals of Air Pollution*. Reading, Mass.: Addison-Wesley, 1973. A good explanation of the physical aspects of air pollution. The approach is interdisciplinary, drawing from meteorology, chemistry, physics, engineering, medicine, and the social sciences. Some attention is given to the political aspects of air pollution problems.

*Jasper L. Harris*

## Cross-References

Acid Rain, 9; The Atmosphere's Structure and Composition, 128; Atmospheric Inversion Layers, 137; Atmospheric Ozone, 144; Climate, 217; The Greenhouse Effect, 1004.

# ALLUVIAL SYSTEMS

*Type of earth science:* Geology
*Field of study:* Sedimentology

*Alluvial systems include a variety of different depositional systems, excluding deltas, that form from the activity of rivers and streams. Much alluvial sediment is deposited when rivers top their banks and flood the surrounding countryside. Buried alluvial sediments may be important water-bearing reservoirs or may contain petroleum.*

### Principal terms

BRAIDED RIVER: a relatively shallow river with many intertwined channels; its sediment is moved primarily as riverbed material
EPHEMERAL STREAM: a river or stream which flows briefly in response to nearby rainfall; such streams are common in arid and semiarid regions
FLOODPLAIN: the relatively flat valley floor on either side of a river which may be partly or wholly occupied by water during a flood
LONGITUDINAL BAR: a midchannel accumulation of sand and gravel with its long axis oriented roughly parallel to the river flow
MEANDERING RIVER: a river confined essentially to a single channel which transports much of its sediment load as fine-grained material in suspension
OXBOW LAKE: a lake formed from an abandoned meander bend when a river cuts through the meander at its narrowest point during a flood
POINT BAR: an accumulation of sand and gravel which develops on the inside of a meander bend
TRANSVERSE BAR: a flat-topped body of sand or gravel oriented transverse to the river flow

## Summary of the Phenomenon

Deposits of silt, sand, and gravel produced by the activity of rivers and streams are called alluvial sediments. Sediment in rivers is moved primarily as either "suspended load" or "bedload." The suspended load is the finest portion of sediment—that is, silt and clay—and is carried within the flow itself by fluid turbulence. Material moved along the bottom of the river by rolling, sliding, and bouncing is called the bedload, and it makes up the coarse fraction of a river's sediment. Rivers can be divided into four categories based on their morphology: braided, meandering, anastomosing, and straight. Straight rivers are rare, usually appearing only as portions of one of the other river types, and anastomosing rivers can be considered a special type of meandering river.

Several criteria are used to characterize alluvial systems. They include grain size, dominant mode of sediment transport (suspended load versus bedload), and migrational pattern of the river channel. Alluvial sediments can be broadly divided into three interrelated depositional settings: braided river, alluvial fan, and meandering river.

Braided rivers have low sinuosity, which is defined as the ratio of the length of the river channel to the down-valley distance. They are characterized by relatively coarse-grained sediment transported as bedload. Fine-grained sediments make up a minor portion of the deposits. The main channel is internally divided into many subchannels and bars, which give the river a braided pattern. River bars are ridgelike accumulations of sand and gravel formed in the channel or along the banks, where deposition is induced by a decrease in velocity. Transverse bars are flat-topped ridges, oriented transverse to the flow, that grow by down-current additions and migration of sediment. Longitudinal bars are midchannel sand and gravel accumulations oriented with their long axes roughly parallel to current flow. During low water stages, this braided pattern is very apparent, and water occupies only one or several of the subchannels. It is only during high water stages that the entire braided channel has water in it. The bars that occur in these rivers form as a result of high sediment loads and fluctuations in river discharge.

Braided rivers form in regions where sediment is abundant, water discharge fluctuates (but may be high), and, usually, vegetation is sparse. Some braided rivers and streams have flowing water in them sporadically, with long periods of dryness in between. These streams are called ephemeral, or intermittent. Braided rivers tend to have relatively high gradients. As such, they commonly occur as the upper reach of a river that may become a meandering river downstream as the sediment's grain size and the gradient both decrease.

Alluvial fans are deposits which accumulate at the base of a mountain slope. There, mountain streams encounter relatively flat terrain and lose much of their energy, therefore depositing the sediment they were moving. This stream shifts its channel through time, as sediment continues to be deposited, and builds a fan-shaped accumulation of debris that is coarse-grained near the mountain front and becomes progressively finer-grained away from the highland. Alluvial fans are best developed and observed in arid or semiarid climates, where vegetation is sparse and water flow is intermittent. Large quantities of sediment may be moved during short-term flash-flood events. There are also humid-climate fans, such as the enormous Kosi fan in Nepal, which measures 150 kilometers in its longest dimension.

Both arid and humid fans are built at least in part by deposition in a braided stream environment. Stream discharge, and therefore sediment deposition, is discontinuous on arid fans. Braided streams may operate over the fan's entire surface or predominantly on the outer regions, away from the region where the stream leaves the confines of the mountain valley. Arid fans are also built by deposition from mudflows and debris flows. These flows differ from braided stream flows in that they contain less water and much more debris. Humid fans have braided stream systems operating continuously on their surface. Their overall deposits are similar to braided stream deposits formed in other sedimentary environments.

Meandering rivers have a greater sinuosity than braided rivers and are usually confined to a single channel. They have a lower gradient and therefore are typically located downstream from braided rivers. Sediment in meandering rivers is moved mostly as fine-grained suspended load. Several different types of sedimentary deposit result from the activity of meandering rivers. The coarsest material available to the river is moved and deposited within the deepest part of the channel. These gravelly deposits are thin and discontinuous. Point bars develop on the inside curve of a meander bend and are a major site of sand deposition, although silt and gravel may also be components of point-bar deposits. Deposition takes place on point bars because of flow conditions in the river as water travels around the bend. Erosion takes place on the bank opposite the point bar, and in this way, meanders migrate. When a river floods and tops its banks, water and finer-grained sediment spill out of the channel and onto the surrounding valley floor, which is called the floodplain. On the bank directly adjacent to the river channel, large amounts of sediment are deposited to form natural levees, elongate narrow ridges parallel to the channel; levees help to confine the river but are still topped during major floods. As the river spreads out across the floodplain, silt and clay are deposited.

Meandering rivers are constantly shifting their location within the river valley. In this way, very thick alluvial deposits may accumulate through time. New channels may be created between meanders such that old meander bends are cut off and isolated. These isolated meander bends are termed "oxbow lakes" and tend to fill quickly with sediment.

A special type of meandering river is an anastomosing river. It is characterized by a system of channels which do not migrate as much as meandering river channels and which are separated by large, permanent islands.

Alluvial sediments require running water for transport and deposition. This water may be available year-round, such that rivers and streams are constantly active. Sporadic stream discharge produces alluvial sediments in arid and semiarid environments. Alluvial sediments are also associated with glaciers. Large amounts of sediment with a wide range in grain size are deposited directly by glaciers. Streams fed by glacial meltwaters are important and effective agents of transport and deposition of this sediment. Most streams associated with glaciers are bedload streams and therefore have a braided pattern. Their sediment is usually quite coarse-grained.

Alluvial systems form broad, interconnected networks of drainage that feed water and sediment from highlands or mountainous regions to lowlands and eventually to the sea. These drainages form recognizable patterns that are controlled by the type of rock; the type of deformation, if any, that the earth's crust in the region has undergone; and the region's climate. As river systems age, the landscape changes and evolves. In this way, the surface of the land is sculpted by rivers, in concert with other surface processes.

## Methods of Study

The study of alluvial systems can be divided roughly into two categories: the study of modern river systems and the study of sedimentary rocks interpreted to have formed in some type of alluvial system. The study of modern alluvial processes and the sedimentary deposits that they generate is crucial to the understanding of such deposits in the rock record. By understanding modern rivers—the ways in which sediment is moved and deposited, the changes through time in channel shape and location, and the characteristics of the deposits in relation to specific physical conditions—geologists can begin to interpret ancient alluvial sediments.

Modern alluvial systems are studied in a number of ways. It is important to know as much as possible about the flow of water itself, so measurements are made of flow velocity, depth, and width. The channel shape and configuration are also measured. Samples of river sediment, both suspended load and bedload, are collected, and estimates are made of how much sediment is moved by a river. It is also important to look at recent alluvial sediments not now directly associated with the river system. That may be done by digging trenches or collecting samples from floodplains or other alluvial sediments. This type of study looks at the last few hundred or few thousand years of river activity and is critically important to the understanding of these systems. The geologist must study not only what is happening today but also how the system has evolved. In this way, knowledge becomes a predictive tool which greatly enhances the overall understanding of the phenomenon.

It was not until the 1960's that geologists began to realize how large has been the contribution of alluvial systems to sedimentary rocks. This realization came about as a direct result of studies of modern alluvial systems which provided the necessary information to allow the correct identification of ancient alluvial deposits. The study of ancient alluvial deposits takes many forms and provides some information that cannot be gathered from modern deposits. For example, modern deposits, for the most part, have only their uppermost surface exposed, except along the bank and in erosion gullies. Ancient accumulations, in contrast, have been transformed into rock such as shale, sandstone, and conglomerate and commonly are parts of uplifted and dissected terrains, including mountain ranges. These exposures of alluvial deposits allow the three-dimensional architecture of alluvial systems to be studied. Geologists look carefully at vertical changes and associations in the types and abundances of sediment which form as a result of alluvial processes.

It has been found that both meandering and braided rivers commonly form cycles of sedimentation that begin with relatively coarse-grained debris and progress to fine-grained debris. These cycles result mainly from the shifting and migration of the channel system. The coarser-grained base represents the channel and bar deposits, and the finer-grained top represents the overbank floodplain deposits.

The study of ancient alluvial deposits also provides clues to the geologic evolution of a region. The specific mineral composition of sedimentary rocks can indicate the nature of the terrain from which the sediment was derived. That, in turn, contributes to an understanding of the history that led to the generation of the ancient river system that produced the alluvial deposit.

## Context

Alluvial systems operate over much of the earth's surface. They move and deposit enormous quantities of sediment each year and are both a boon and a hindrance to humankind. River valleys and floodplains are desirable regions for agricultural development because of the fertile soil often found there. Rivers, however, naturally flood about every 1.5 years. This flooding causes huge losses in property, crops, and sometimes even lives. Flooding associated with alluvial fans can be highly energetic and can occur almost without warning, usually in response to heavy precipitation over a short period. Water levels can build very quickly in narrow valleys with little vegetation and produce a rushing wall of water. Such a flood occurred in 1976 in Big Thompson Canyon, near Rocky Mountain National Park, Colorado.

Many different economically valuable materials are found in alluvial deposits. Because many of these deposits are relatively coarse-grained, they have spaces between the grains which may contain usable fluids, such as water, oil, and natural gas. Many important aquifers are found in alluvial deposits. Petroleum typically originates in marine deposits, but it commonly migrates and may form reservoirs in alluvial deposits. Most sandy alluvial deposits are composed predominantly of quartz grains; however, concentrations of a number of different minerals and ores, including gold and diamonds, occur in alluvial deposits. Another very important economic resource in alluvial deposits is the sand and gravel itself. This material is used for road construction and in the manufacture of cement and concrete.

The deposition of sediment from river systems represents the wearing-away of the land. Much alluvial sediment eventually makes its way to the ocean, where it undergoes reworking by marine processes and deposition on continental shelves or perhaps in the deep sea. Through time, as continents move relative to one another, these sediments may be compressed, folded, and uplifted to become parts of major mountain chains. The Appalachian Mountains in the eastern United States and the Himalaya in northern India and China are only two examples of mountains composed in part of sedimentary rocks, some of which are alluvial in origin.

## Bibliography

Davis, Richard A., Jr. *Depositional Systems: A Genetic Approach to Sedimentary Geology.* Englewood Cliffs, N.J.: Prentice-Hall, 1983. This college-level textbook has good introductory chapters on alluvial systems and on related subjects, such as sediment transport.

Reading, H. G., ed. *Sedimentary Environments and Facies.* 2d ed. London: Blackwell, 1986. Probably the most comprehensive text available on sedimentary environments. Much of the material is technical, but the text has excellent figures and photographs and will not overwhelm the careful reader.

Schumm, Stanley A. *The Fluvial System*. New York: John Wiley & Sons, 1977.
Suitable for college-level readers, this source is packed with information on river
systems.

Smith, David G., ed. *The Cambridge Encyclopedia of Earth Sciences*. Cambridge,
England: Cambridge University Press, 1981. This easy-to-read and thorough
source contains a chapter on sedimentation. It covers fluvial, desert, and glacial
sediments and includes diagrams and photographs of braided and meandering
rivers and an alluvial fan. The production and transportation of sediments is also
discussed. For general readers.

Tarbuck, Edward J., and Frederick K. Lutgens. *The Earth: An Introduction to
Physical Geology*. 2d ed. Columbus, Ohio: Merrill, 1987. An introductory textbook suitable for high school students. Chapter 9, "Running Water," contains
sections on channel deposits (bars), floodplain deposits, alluvial fans, and various types of river. Includes many diagrams and photographs. Review questions
and a list of key terms conclude the chapter.

Walker, R. G., ed. *Facies Models*. 2d ed. Toronto: Geological Association of Canada, 1984. An excellent compilation of nineteen chapters on sedimentary systems.
Two chapters are devoted to alluvial systems. Suitable for college students.

*Bruce W. Nocita*

## Cross-References

Dams and Flood Control, 309; Deltas, 332; Drainage Basins, 384; Floodplains,
712; Floods, 719; Fossilization and Taphonomy, 768; Glacial Deposits, 937; Oil and
Gas: Petroleum Reservoirs, 1909; River Bed Forms, 2196; River Flow, 2203; River
Valleys, 2210; Sand, 2253; Sediment Transport and Deposition, 2290; Stratigraphic
Correlation, 2485; Surface Water, 2504; Weathering and Erosion, 2723.

# THE ALPS

*Field of study:* Mountain ranges

*The Alps are a mountain range that forms an arc across south-central Europe. Originally, this area was under a sea that lay between Europe and Africa. When Africa began moving in a northerly direction more than 65 million years ago, the rocks were highly folded and finally uplifted to form these mountains, which continue to rise at a rate of 0.5 millimeter per year. Glaciers, streams, and slope processes have eroded them to their present striking appearance.*

### Principal terms

CONGLOMERATE: sedimentary rock composed of gravel in a sandy matrix

DEBRIS AVALANCHE: a large mass of soil and rock that falls and then slides on a cushion of air downhill very rapidly as a unit

DEBRIS FLOW: a mass movement of high fluidity in which more than half the solid material is greater than sand size

GLACIER: a mass of ice showing motion and originating from the compaction of snow

GNEISS: metamorphic rock formed under high pressure and temperature

GRANITE: igneous rock originating from the cooling of magma slowly under the ground

LANDSLIDE: a relatively rapid movement of soil and rock downslope

LIMESTONE: sedimentary rock made of calcium carbonate

MORAINE: deposit of glacial till

NAPPE: a complex, large-scale rock fold on its side where some beds are overturned

ROCKFALL: a relatively free-falling movement of rock material from a cliff or steep slope

SANDSTONE: sedimentary rock composed of primarily sand grains

SCHIST: metamorphic rock with subparallel orientation of micaceous minerals that dominate its composition

SHALE: sedimentary rock composed of silt and clay particles

SNOW AVALANCHE: a relatively rapid movement of snow downslope

THRUST FAULT: a break in a rock body at a low angle of inclination where the hanging wall has moved up in relation to the footwall

TILL: material deposited directly by glacier ice

## Summary of the Phenomenon

The Alps are the famous mountain range of south-central Europe that makes a huge arc extending from southern France through Switzerland into Austria, Germany, Yugoslavia, and Italy. This range is approximately 800 kilometers long and covers more than 207,000 square kilometers. It lies about halfway between the

North Pole and the equator (from 44 to 48 degrees north latitude). The Alps are essentially part of a large mountain chain that extends from Europe through Greece to the higher ranges of Iran and Central Asia. All these mountains were formed about the same time.

The Alps are subdivided into the western, central, and eastern sections, and each contains a number of prominent subranges. The western Alps lie primarily in France and rise from the shores of the Riviera and the plains of Italy to form subranges of the Maritime, Cottian, Dauphiné, Savoy, and Graian Alps. The central Alps lie mainly in Switzerland with the primary subranges being the Pennine, Bernese Oberland, Lepontine, Glarus, and Rhaetian Alps. The Pennine Alps are the highest and most spectacular of the subranges and lie along the French-Swiss-Italian borders. They extend 95 kilometers from Mont Blanc (4,807 meters), the highest mountain in the Alps, to Monte Rosa (4,634 meters). Also located in this range is the famous glacially carved Matterhorn (4,478 meters), which lies on the border between Switzerland and Italy. Just north of the Pennine Alps, separated by the Rhone Valley, lies the Bernese Oberland, the second highest subrange of the Alps. The Jungfrau (4,158 meters) is one of the highest and most beautiful mountains in this range. The eastern Alps have less lofty peaks but are still noted for their spectacular scenery. The subranges are found in four countries with the Bavarian Alps in West Germany, the Dolomite and Carnic Alps in northern Italy, the Julian Alps in Yugoslavia, and the Hohe Tauern, Noric, and Stubai Alps in Austria.

For many, it is hard to conceive of the idea that the rocks that make up the Alps were once under the sea. During the Mesozoic era (about 225-65 million years ago), the continental shorelines were different. A large sea, called the Tethys Sea, lay between the continents of Africa, which formed the south shore, and Europe, which formed the north shore. Spain, Italy, Greece, and Turkey were actually small microplates at the western end of this sea and were not attached to Europe.

A large trough of sediment, or geosyncline, developed during the Mesozoic era in the Tethys Sea between the continents and extended all the way to Indonesia. Sediments eroded from the uplands of the continents collected in this geosyncline and formed sedimentary rocks on top of the basement rock of basalt and intrusions of granite. During the Triassic period (about 225-190 million years ago), some limestones were formed in the geosyncline, but most of the rocks were formed in the Jurassic (about 190-135 million years ago) and Cretaceous (about 135-65 million years ago) periods. Other limestones, marls, shales, and localized deposits of sandstones and conglomerates were formed during this time. Some metamorphic, green, lustrous schists, called Bundner Schiefer, were also created during the Cretaceous period as mafic magma intruded into the sediments.

The Cenozoic era (the last 65 million years) marked the major episode of mountain building of the Alps. The African plate began moving in a northerly direction at the beginning of the Cenozoic. By this time, the Italian microplate, called the Carnic plate, had moved to the center of the Tethys Sea. The intense compressional forces of Africa pushed the Carnic plate northward into the geosyncline sediments. The European continent acted as an immovable object. First of all, the compression produced complicated folding and faulting of the sedimentary rocks in the geosyncline. The Alps are noted for the highly complicated anticlines (upfolds), synclines (downfolds), recumbent folds (folds on sides), and thrust faults (rock breaks at low angles) created during this time. Most of the intense compression occurred from the Eocene through the Miocene epochs (about 55-5 million years ago). Second, these rocks of the geosyncline between the Carnic microplate and the European continent were uplifted by the compression to form the Alps as the crust was reduced in width by as much as 250-400 kilometers. The rate of closing was approximately 5 centimeters per year. It is believed that this uplifting process is continuing at a rate of 0.5 millimeter per year. The mountain building was not a single episode but was episodic and interrupted by prolonged periods of relative calm. Most of the uplift has occurred in the last 30 million years.

A nappe is a large recumbent fold that may be kilometers across and that is generally bounded by a thrust fault. The largest and most studied nappes in the world are in the Alps. The Alps were the first mountain range in which nappe structures were found to play a predominant role in development. The nappe concept was developed in the late 1800's in the Swiss Alps when geologists recognized thick sequences of older rocks over younger rocks over thrust faults, a sequence typical of nappes. To explain these structures, Hans Konrad Escher von der Linth and his student Albert Heim described the Glarus overthrust in terms of a nappe, and the concept was born.

The incredible crustal shortening and the uplift formed these large overlapping nappe structures. For example, the Pennine Alps are made of seven major nappes that came from the central portion of the geosyncline. They form the metamorphic core of the Alps and were formed from very old sedimentary rocks with the help of the intense temperatures and pressures of regional metamorphism during the mountain-building process. The most common metamorphic rocks are gneisses, mica schists, the green Bundner Schiefer schists, phyllites, and slates. The Bernese Oberland Alps are also called the High Calcareous Alps because they are composed mainly of six nappes that originated close to the European side of the geosyncline and are made mainly of limestone. Also in this range are the Ultrahelvetic nappes made of flysch, a sandstone formed during the mountain-building process from sediment formed from the erosion of other nappes. The Pre-Alps are just north of the Bernese Oberland and also are mainly limestone. According to some theories, they originated far to the east of the nappes of the High Calcareous Alps in the geosyncline but slid over them via gravity sliding during the uplift. The nappes that make up the eastern Alps and the western Alps came mainly from the part of the geosyncline closest to Africa. The Jura Mountains, which lie to the northwest of the Alps on the Swiss-French border, also came from the same geosyncline, and they came from the portion closest to the European continent.

The Alps were continually being eroded during their uplift. Based on the sediment deposits at the edges of the Alps, it has been estimated that the mass of the

Alps has been reduced during the last 30 million years into about a quarter of its original volume. Erosion of the Alps created fine-grained sediment that became a rock called flysch and a coarse-grained sediment that became a rock called molasse. The Swiss Plateau, just north of the Alps, is composed of abundant flysch and molasse formed from 60 to 10 million years ago. Overall, the Alps are made primarily of sedimentary rocks formed in the Tethys Sea between 225 and 30 million years ago. Limestone is the most abundant of the sedimentary rocks. The central core of the Alps is mainly metamorphic rock. Large intrusions of granite are found near Mont Blanc and the Aar and St. Gotthard massifs and are older than the sedimentary rocks formed in the geosyncline. Other small outcrops of older Paleozoic rocks (rocks older than 225 million years) from the base of the geosyncline have been found in the Alps. Fossils of ammonites and brachiopods formed during the Mesozoic and Cenozoic are common in the rocks.

Since being uplifted, the Alps have been carved to their present shapes and forms through the processes of erosion. Ice erosion during the ice age of the last 2.5 million years has been the major action of change. Water erosion in the form of streams has also provided extensive transformation. In this steep terrain, gravity also has played a major role in erosion through landslide and avalanche production.

The Great Ice Age began about 2.5 million years ago as the climate of the world cooled. Glaciers grew and filled the stream-carved valleys of the Alps, some to a thickness of more then 2,000 meters. Only the peaks of the mountains protruded from this large ice field. These large moving masses of ice advanced and retreated numerous times as the climate cooled and warmed, each time eroding the mountains, transporting the rock debris, and eventually depositing it as till. Glaciers carved out the landforms seen everywhere in the Alps. Circular basins on the sides of mountains called cirques, knife-edged ridges between valleys named arêtes, and pointed mountain peaks called horns were carved by the ice. Many of the peaks listed on a map of the Alps end in "horn" because they have been carved by glaciers. Most of the V-shaped valleys that had been formed by streams before the ice age were broadened to a more U-shaped form by the ice. The glacial debris that was carried by the ice was eventually deposited when the ice melted as moraine. Ridges of moraine on the edges of valleys and arcuate ridges at the ends of valleys are lateral and terminal moraines produced by the glaciers at their maximum extent. Lakes also formed behind some of these terminal moraines in the valleys. The city of Geneva in Switzerland is located on one of these terminal moraine dams formed by the Rhone glacier. Massive deposits of glacial till lie at the edges of the Alps where the glaciers ended.

More than 1,200 glaciers still exist in the Alps today, with most of them in the Pennine and Bernese Oberland Alps. They continue to wear down the sides of mountains and transport glacial debris. Most are found at high elevations, but some, such as the Grindelwald glacier in Switzerland, can descend to an elevation of 1,000 meters. The Aletsch glacier of the Bernese Oberland is considered to be the largest glacier of the Alps; it is 25 kilometers long and has a surface area of

170 square kilometers. Many of the streams in the Alps have a milky green color that is produced by abundant silt from glacial abrasion and shows the glacial origin of the water. From 1925 to 1960, most of the glaciers were observed to be in recession, suggesting a warming of the climate. From 1960 to 1980, the data hint at a reversal of this trend for the majority of the glaciers that are advancing.

Water for great rivers and lakes is abundant in the Alps and comes from snow-melt and rainfall. This water feeds the many powerful streams that erode the valleys, forming V-shapes. Some deep, stream-caved gorges have been formed in the past 10,000 years since the last glaciers melted, with some, such as the Aar and Trient gorges in Switzerland, more than 150 meters deep. Water has also carved smaller landforms, such as the Swiss Pyramids, near Sion, which are pedestals of glacial moraine with boulders on the top. The four most important rivers in Europe, the Rhone, the Rhine, the Po, and the Danube, all contain abundant water from the melting of snow in the Alps. The St. Gotthard massif at the end of the Pennine Alps has been called the water tower of Europe because it is the headwaters of so many of these great rivers. Abundant large lakes are relics of the ice age and add to the scenic beauty of the Alps. Many of the lakes are deep, as they fill valleys deepened and dammed by glacial action. Lake Geneva is the largest, with a surface area of 580 square kilometers and a depth of 310 meters.

Gravity also helps erode the Alps through landslides and snow avalanches. Small landslides and rotational slumps are common on these steep slopes, especially after heavy rainfalls. The world's second-largest dam disaster occurred in 1963, when a landslide fell into the lake in back of the Vaiont Dam in the Italian Alps. A wall of water more than 100 meters high proceeded downvalley and killed 2,600 people in the village of Longarone and the surrounding towns. Debris flows are formed in steep mountain stream valleys when they flood and erode the valley bottom. It is common to find large man-made levees, or embankments, at the bottoms of these steep valleys to contain the debris flows from hitting villages at the valley bottoms. Debris avalanches are rare but devastating when they occur. In 1881, a total of 115 people were killed when a debris avalanche moved at a velocity of more than 300 kilometers per hour through the village of Elm. Rockfall is common at the edges of these steep, U-shaped valleys, and no one ever knows when a boulder may break away and head for the valley bottom. Soil creep, where the soil is moving at 1-2 centimeters per year down the slope, is also a problem on most slopes.

Each year, snow avalanches kill between twenty and thirty people in the Alps. The worst avalanches happen when there is a large snowfall on steep slopes that cannot hold the snow. The year of 1951 was called the winter of terror because there were 265 deaths in the Alps and abundant damage. It was a year of plentiful snowfall, with falls of 3-5 meters in a three-hour period occurring on numerous occasions. In 1916 during World War I, more than ten thousand soldiers were killed in the eastern Alps by snow avalanches.

With the abundant water seeping into the ground of the numerous areas with limestone bedrock, many caves have been formed in the Alps. The world's deepest cave, the Gouffre Jean Bernard, is found in the French Alps and is 1,535 meters deep. The 140-kilometer-long cave at Holloch, Switzerland, is the second longest in the world. The Elizabeth Casteret Cave in the French Alps is one of the largest single caverns in the world. The largest underground lake in Europe, a flooded cave formed in gypsum between layers of marble and schist, is located at St. Leonard in the Bernese Oberland of Switzerland.

## Methods of Study

Compared to most other high mountain ranges of the world, the Alps are highly populated and have been for many years. Scientists have been studying the Alps since the early 1800's, making them the most studied mountain range in the world. Through sheer determination, skill, and thoroughness, several generations of geologists have spent hours putting together an incredible story of the origin of these mountains. Many books have been written on the general geography, geology, structure, glaciers, past glaciations, landforms, and snow avalanches of the Alps. The Swiss have always been world leaders in the production of maps. Guillaume-Henri Dufour took thirty-two years to collect data and produce the first topographic map of Switzerland in 1864, and this twenty-five-page document was a masterpiece. At a scale of 1:100,000, it was extremely accurate. By 1920, excellent topographic and geologic maps were available for all parts of the Alps.

Because of the excellent exposures of rocks in the valley walls, the Alps became a favorite field area for geologists from around the world. The Alps provide some of the most exciting places in the world for the study of rocks (petrology) and the study of the folding and breaking of rocks (structural geology). All parts of the mountains have been intensively studied as to the rock types and the folding and faulting. Thousands of geologic maps and cross sections have been produced. These local maps have then been interpreted in relation to the rest of the Alps and their relationship to the original geosyncline deduced. Classic works of the early 1900's by Albert Heim and Leon Collet are still treated with respect. When most of the rocks had been studied, geologists began to reinterpret sites, and this comprehensive reevaluation analysis continues.

The early work of the structural geologists explained how each part of the Alps came from a particular part of the geosyncline, but it could not provide a mechanism for the movements of these vast zones of rocks. With the acceptance and development of the plate tectonics theory in the 1960's and 1970's, the geologists could then supply a process for the development of the parts of the Alps. The 1970's and 1980's were fruitful for alpine geologists, who combined the very accurate mapping and cross sections of the "classical view of the geology of the Alps" with the modern ideas of plate tectonics.

Many railroad and automobile tunnels have been cored through the Alps during the twentieth century to help travelers avoid high mountain passes. The Simplon, Mont Blanc, Great St. Bernard, Lötschberg, and St. Gotthard tunnels have given geologists a very important chance to see inside the mountains to confirm their ideas of the origins of different sections of the Alps.

The study of glaciers and the development of the idea of an ice age both had their roots in the Alps. After many hikes in the mountains and studies on glaciers, Swiss naturalist Louis Agassiz wrote *Études sur les glaciers* in 1840. He introduced two radical ideas: Glaciers are actually moving and are eroding as they proceed down-valley; the Alps had been covered by a vast ice sheet in the past similar to Greenland, and this ice had produced much of the glacial till found in and around the Alps. Agassiz's work laid the foundation for the whole study of glaciology.

## Context

The Alps are the most populated major mountain range in the world. Other mountain areas look to the Alps for major innovations, whether for environmental, engineering, touristic, or planning purposes. Because of the population pressures on the Alps, any needed idea surely has been applied or developed already in the Alps. Scientifically, the basic concepts on the evolution of folded mountains has come from work done in the Alps. The ideas have been applied to the Himalaya and the Appalachian Mountains, both of which had similar origins. Mountains are becoming more important to humankind economically because more leisure time is being spent in these beautiful environments. The Alps are close to the large population centers of Europe and so are used extensively for tourism, skiing, mountain climbing, and hot spring resorts. Hydroelectric power generation and, to a lesser extent, mining also are of economic importance.

A healthful climate and beautiful scenery attract many tourists each year to the Alps. High mountain resorts have become major centers for winter sports such as skiing, skating, and tobogganing. Chamonix at the base of Mont Blanc in France, Zermatt at the base of the Matterhorn, Grindelwald below the Jungfrau and Eiger, St.-Moritz in the Engadin, Cortina d'Ampezzo in the Italian Dolomites, Garmisch-Partenkirchen in the Bavarian Alps, and Gastein in the Austrian Alps are such examples. These same resorts, along with others on the many alpine lakes, have also become popular summer resorts for tourists.

Mountain climbing also attracts many visitors to the Alps each year to challenge the peaks. Climbing in the Alps can be traced back to the fourteenth century, when six monks ascended Pilatus, near Lucerne. A few major peaks were climbed in the late 1700's, but mountain climbing as a thrill-seeking sport really gained popularity in the first sixty-five years of the 1800's, culminating with the conquering of the Matterhorn by a party led by an Englishman, Edward Whymper. After many attempts to climb this obelisk, previously thought to be unclimbable, the group of seven climbers reached the top on July 14, 1865, only to have four of the men fall to their death during the descent when a rope broke. In spite of the hazards, the thrills of attempting to climb steep mountains such as the Matterhorn and the Eiger yearly attract climbers from all over the world to the Alps.

Deep faults associated with differing nappes allow water to seep deep into the earth, where it is heated and then rises to the surface as mineral hot springs. Health spas have been built near these sites to take advantage of the healthful hot waters flowing from the earth. Resorts such as Leukerbad, Bad Ragaz, and Lavey-les-Bains are three successful resorts in Switzerland.

Because most of the rocks have originated under the ocean and are mainly sedimentary, few valuable minerals are found in the Alps. A few very small copper, lead, zinc, gold, and silver mines have been noted in history near the large granite bedrock areas, but none is important economically. The Alps have few mineral resources from the point of view of profitable mining. The major mineral mined in the Alps is salt, with major deposits in Austria near Salzburg and in Switzerland near Bex. Limestone is also crushed and is the major ingredient for portland cement.

"White coal," or hydroelectric power, from the rushing mountain streams is far more abundant than any mineral. Great elevational differences coupled with heavy precipitation throughout the year, augmented during the summer by the melting of snow, present superb conditions for hydroelectric power development. Many dams have been built to take advantage of this valuable natural resource. One of the highest concrete dams in the world, the Grand Dixence at 285 meters, was completed in 1961 in Switzerland for this power generation purpose. The power is used by homes in the Alps and large businesses in the cities at the edge of the Alps. Most of the trains in the Alps run on hydroelectric power. In these lands that are basically devoid of fossil fuels, this "white coal" has been a blessing.

In order to meet the needs of a growing tourism industry, people have attained some incredible engineering accomplishments in this rugged terrain. Long train tunnels have been cut through the Pennine Alps below the Simplon and Gotthard passes and through the Bernese Oberland at the Lötschberg tunnel. Automobile tunnels have also been constructed through the Pennine Alps below Mont Blanc, the Great St. Bernard Pass, and St. Gotthard Pass. At 16.32 kilometers in length, the latter is the world's longest automobile road tunnel and was completed in 1980. Construction of these tunnels took years but resulted in year-round travel and reduced travel times.

These beautiful mountains are not without environmental problems. Persistent temperature inversion layers form in the valleys and entrap air pollution, especially in the winter. Water pollution of the lakes has been a large problem in the past, with raw sewage being the major cause. With the massive building program in the 1960's and 1970's of sewage treatment plants, the quality of the water in the lakes has greatly improved. Local communities have run out of places to dump and burn their garbage, so many villages and cities have stepped up their recycling programs. Some communities burn their garbage and create electricity.

## Bibliography

Ager, D. V., and M. Brooks, eds. *Europe from Core to Crust*. London: John Wiley & Sons, 1977. The section on alpine tectonics and their relationships to plate tectonics by Jean Aubouin is very good.

Anderson, J. G. C. *The Structure of Western Europe*. Oxford, England: Pergamon Press, 1978. The chapter on alpine fold belts is superb and puts the geology of the Alps in perspective of plate tectonics. Excellent coverage of geological structures.

Cowie, Donald. *Switzerland: The Land and the People*. New York: A. S. Barnes, 1971. This book describes the physical environment of the Alps as well as the culture, history, and the people of the region.

Huxley, A. J. *Standard Encyclopedia of the World's Mountains*. New York: G. P. Putnam's Sons, 1962. This excellent reference book lists the main mountains of the world and tells stories about each one.

Koenig, Hermann. *The Alps in Colour*. Innsbruck: Penguin, 1964. This book contains many beautiful color photographs of the Alps. Good sections on geology, glaciers, and snow avalanches of the Alps.

Maeder, Herbert. *The Mountains of Switzerland*. London: Allen & Unwin, 1968. This excellent book includes many black and white photographs of the Alps. A fine section on geology, with additional sections on plants, animals, and mountain climbing.

National Geographic Society. *The Alps*. Washington, D.C.: Author, 1973. This beautiful book on the Alps stresses mainly culture but in the beginning chapters covers basic geology of the Alps.

_____. *Traveler's Map of the Alps*. Washington, D.C.: Author, 1985. This map was an insert in the *National Geographic* magazine and is one of the best maps of all of the Alps showing all the subranges.

Rutten, M. G. *Geology of Western Europe*. New York: Elsevier, 1969. The five chapters on alpine Europe constitute the best summary in English of the geology of the Alps. The view is mainly classical.

Trumpy, Rudolph. *Geology of Switzerland*. Basel: Wepf, 1980. This guidebook was put out by the Swiss Geological Commission and is the best English summary of the geology of the Swiss Alps, which is the most complex portion of the Alps. The author is the leading authority on the subject. The classical view of the geology is considered in relation to modern plate tectonics.

*Scott F. Burns*

## Cross-References

The Appalachians, 62; Dams and Flood Control, 309; Thrust Faults, 683; Folds, 739; Geosynclines, 898; Glacial Deposits, 937; Glacial Landforms, 946; Alpine Glaciers, 960; The Himalaya, 1073; Ice Ages, 1115; Landslides and Slope Stability, 1365; Regional Metamorphism, 1606; Mountain Belts, 1725; Plate Tectonics, 2079.

# ALUMINUM DEPOSITS

*Type of earth science:* Economic geology

*Aluminum deposits provide humans with a lightweight, electrically conductive metal for which there are such diverse uses as food wrap, engine blocks, and wire. The first major study of aluminum deposits attributed them to precipitation from warm acidic fluids, but most subsequent researchers have preferred ordinary soil-forming processes as the mechanism for aluminum concentration to ore grade.*

### Principal terms

BAUXITE: a deposit which is rich in aluminum and oxygen but poor in most of the other elements that are abundant in the earth's crust, such as silicon, sodium, potassium, magnesium, and calcium

BAUXITE ORE: bauxite that can be mined for a profit; generally, it must contain at least 25 percent aluminum and not more than 15 percent iron or more than 3 percent silicon

CHEMICAL SEDIMENTARY ROCK: rock that accumulated as sediment that chemically precipitated onto the bottom of a water body, typically onto the ocean floor

HYDROXIDE: a mineral that contains hydroxyl (oxygen plus hydrogen), for example, gibbsite (aluminum plus hydroxyl); an oxyhydroxide mineral contains oxygen in addition to hydroxide, for example, boehmite (aluminum-oxygen-hydroxide)

IGNEOUS ROCK: rock (for example, granite) that forms by cooling of molten matter

KARST: a type of topography developed above beds of limestone as a result of partial dissolution of the limestone by through-flowing water

REGOLITH: the surface of the earth that has been subjected to weathering

SHALE: sedimentary rock with sediment grains less than one-sixteenth of a millimeter in diameter; it exhibits thin layers like pages in a book and usually is dark in color

SILICATE MINERAL: a mineral that contains both silicon and oxygen, for example, quartz

SYENITE: a coarse-grained igneous rock that resembles granite and is rich in aluminum, sodium, and potassium

## Summary of the Phenomenon

Aluminum is the third most abundant element in the crust of the earth, constituting about 8 percent. The two more abundant elements are oxygen (48 percent) and silicon (27 percent). More than 95 percent of the aluminum in the crust occurs within silicate minerals, that is, minerals that contain both silicon and oxygen. In contrast, minable aluminum deposits (bauxite ores) are composed mostly of oxides and hydroxides of aluminum that lack silicon. Typical minerals in bauxite include gibbsite (an aluminum hydroxide) and boehmite and diaspore (both aluminum oxyhydroxides). Often, these minerals are collectively called aluminum hydroxides.

Bauxite generally is either white or red, depending on the iron content. Bauxite may contain up to 15 percent iron, whereas even the most iron-rich modern soil rarely contains more than 5 percent iron. The only covering on exposed land other than bauxite that commonly contains as much as 20 percent iron is soil that has been formed by the weathering of underlying iron-rich chemical sedimentary rocks (iron deposits). These deposits commonly contain more than 30 percent iron, but even the most aluminum-rich rocks that underlie bauxite rarely contain more than 10 percent aluminum.

The first comprehensive study of aluminum deposits was conducted in southern France and published in 1871. Aluminum concentration was attributed to precipitation from fluids that had dissolved aluminum because they had acquired corrosive volatiles such as carbon dioxide. Hot volatiles were envisioned to have risen from deep in the earth. The mixing of hot volatiles with water produced a hydrothermal solution that dissolved aluminum from ordinary rocks. The solution then precipitated the aluminum upon removal (neutralization) of the acidity, which could have occurred by reaction of the solution with limestone.

Most twentieth century researchers have rejected the original hydrothermal model for aluminum deposits. As an alternative, aluminum deposits have been attributed to intensive weathering of aluminum-rich sediment or rock, generally in the humid tropics. If this mechanism were viable, aluminum ore deposits would be forming today in the humid tropics, but no such ore deposits have been found.

The popularity of the weathering hypothesis for aluminum-rich rock has been based on the observation that silicon is slightly more soluble than aluminum when silicate minerals are attacked by the organic acids that drain from decaying plant matter. This difference could become accentuated under conditions of intensive weathering. Such intensive weathering, however, would require particularly abundant plant life; the plant life, in turn, would require abundant nutrients, including potassium. Potassium is one of the three ingredients listed on any fertilizer bag. (For example, a common "garden-variety" fertilizer is labeled 8-8-8 because it contains 8 percent each of nitrogen, phosphorus, and potassium.) Given the high solubility of potassium, this element tends to be completely removed during intensive weathering. Potassium may be retained within leaf litter on flat land, but several bauxite deposits have accumulated on hillsides.

Although modern soil-forming processes are not producing a voluminous bauxite deposit, they do concentrate aluminum. The concentration of aluminum in tropical soils mostly results in the crystallization of kaolinite. Kaolinite is a clay mineral that consists of silicon, aluminum, oxygen, and hydrogen. Globally, kaolinite is one of the most abundant soil minerals within forty latitudinal degrees of the earth's equator. In tropical soils, kaolinite is commonly accompanied by minor amounts of aluminum hydroxides; there is no significant portion of the earth's present regolith (weathered surface) in which aluminum hydroxides predominate over silicates. In contrast, aluminum hydroxides always predominate over silicates in bauxite ore. Kaolinite predominates only where bauxite ore grades vertically or laterally to other rock types.

The youngest major aluminum deposit overlies aluminum-poor sand above a major fault that forms the northern boundary of the Amazon river basin. There is no obvious aluminum-rich material that could have weathered to form this deposit, but the underlying fault could have channeled rising acidic fluids. The lack of an obvious aluminum-rich parent similarly plagues the attempted application of the tropical-weathering model to most other aluminum deposits. Ancient aluminum deposits commonly overlie aluminum-poor limestone.

The original hydrothermal model is preferred herein for the origin of aluminum deposits (bauxite ore deposits). Geologists generally agree that most ores of other metals similarly have precipitated from warm acidic (hydrothermal) solutions. Aluminum-rich hydrothermal fluids presumably have reached the earth's surface where they locally have coated the land with aluminum minerals in a blanket resembling soil. The resulting deposits, however, do not display the horizons that characterize soil: the A, B, and C soil horizons. Moreover, blanket-type aluminum deposits either have a thin reaction zone at the bottom or are separated from underlying rock by aluminum-poor sediments. Layering does take place in some blanket-type deposits, but successively deeper layers are not consistently richer in aluminum, as would be expected if the layers represent soil horizons. Layers in aluminum deposits are interpreted to record episodes of outpouring of aluminum-rich fluids.

The hydrothermal hypothesis does not exclude the influence of weathering on blanket-type aluminum deposits. Even if originally deposited by the outpouring groundwater, blanket-type deposits would become subjected to weathering like everything else at the earth's surface. This weathering, moreover, could enhance ore grade, given the insolubility of aluminum during weathering. The hypothetical hydrothermal fluid would have contained many soluble elements, including uranium, that would be removed by the infiltration of rainwater.

Aluminum deposits that have not accumulated as blankets on the land mostly have accumulated within caverns in limestone. An area with abundant limestone caverns is called karst. Karst bauxite is attributable to the same genetic process as advocated for blanket-type bauxite: precipitation from acidic fluids. Acidic fluids rapidly dissolve any limestone. Detailed studies have shown that the cavern-dissolution process in karst limestone commonly accompanied precipitation of aluminum minerals in bauxite. Any acidic solution may become neutralized (non-acidic) by dissolution of limestone. Neutralization would induce precipitation of aluminum because aluminum cannot remain in solution once an acidic solution becomes neutralized.

The nature and origin of the hypothetical aluminum-rich fluids are speculative because no such fluid is known to be precipitating an aluminum deposit currently. The following concept is based on the study of aluminum that has been concentrating for the past several thousand years in northeastern Venezuela: Metamorphism and/or melting deep in the earth's crust beneath this area is generating substantial methane (natural gas) and some hydrogen sulfide (a hydrogen-sulfur compound). This low-density volatile mixture rises several kilometers toward the earth's surface without carrying any aluminum. Outgassing of the volatiles through the ocean during earthquakes results in spectacular burning in the atmosphere. Some pillars of fire burn for several days in a row. Similar pillars of fire are observed along the northern coast of the Black Sea.

Outgassing through a continent allows the gases to oxidize before reaching the atmosphere. Methane oxidizes to carbon dioxide; hydrogen sulfide oxidizes to sulfur dioxide. The mixing of water with carbon dioxide and/or sulfur dioxide produces a strong acid; thus, groundwater becomes highly acidic. The acidified groundwater is a hydrothermal solution because the rising volatiles also contribute heat. Upward flow is enhanced by this heating and occurs preferentially along fractures in fault zones. The acidity induces the leaching of aluminum from rocks and sediments as the water rises toward the earth's surface.

Chemical reactions in this hydrothermal model are the opposite of those in the tropical-weathering model in that aluminum is preferentially soluble in the hydrothermal model but preferentially insoluble in the weathering model. Although soluble in organic acids, silicon is not very soluble in the inorganic acids that characterize hydrothermal solutions. Some hydrothermal solutions do carry abundant dissolved silicon, only because they are much warmer than the solutions that hypothetically form aluminum deposits.

Despite the disagreement about hydrothermal versus weathering processes, all bauxite researchers agree that the aluminum occurred within aluminous silicate minerals prior to separation of the aluminum from silicon. Both silicon and aluminum are ubiquitously distributed throughout the earth's crust. Among the abundant chemical elements in the crust, aluminum is one of the most evenly distributed in all types of igneous rock, averaging about 8.5 percent aluminum (15.6 percent aluminum-oxygen component). In contrast, iron in igneous rocks may range from negligible amounts to more than 15 percent. One of the most aluminum-rich igneous rock types is syenite, but even in syenite the aluminum content rarely exceeds 10 percent.

Among ordinary sedimentary rocks, aluminum is most concentrated in shale. Shale constitutes about half of all sedimentary rocks. The percentage of aluminum in the two other common types of sedimentary rock, sandstone and limestone, generally is less than half as much as that of typical shale. Average shale contains a slightly higher percentage of aluminum than does average igneous rock, which contains an average of 8.5 percent aluminum. Unfractured shale generally is impermeable to groundwater, however, so it is an unlikely source of aluminum for the hypothesized acidic groundwater. Sandstone is much more permeable and contains scattered grains of the most common of all minerals in the earth's crust, the aluminum-bearing mineral feldspar.

Of all the common rock types within the crust, limestone is one of the poorest in aluminum. Nevertheless, bauxite is as closely associated with limestone as with any other rock type. Limestone-hosted bauxite is abundant in Yugoslavia, where the name "karst" originated, and elsewhere around the Mediterranean Sea. Limestone-hosted bauxite also is abundant in such diverse areas as Jamaica, the Soviet Union, and western Pacific islands. These karst-bauxite deposits do share one attribute: They generally formed at times when there was enough subsidence or melting of the adjacent crust to account for production of volatiles at depth.

Unlike most types of ore deposits, aluminum deposits accumulate on exposed land or within open caverns that are close to the earth's surface. Most other types of ore accumulate on the sea floor or deep within the continental crust. As a result, aluminum deposits become eroded more readily than other types of ore. The average age of aluminum deposits, therefore, is less than that of most other ore deposits. Nevertheless, some of the largest aluminum deposits are tens of millions of years old, having formed in the first half of the Cenozoic era. Other ore types are typically even older. The average age of iron deposits is about 2 billion years old. By comparison, the age of planet Earth is about 4.6 billion years. Being younger than most other metallic ore deposits, aluminum ores characteristically are more porous and crumbly than other types of ore. This quality facilitates mining because less effort is required to loosen the rock. In many deposits, bulldozers or huge shovels may extract the bauxite ore without any loosening by explosives.

There appears to be a continuum among ore deposits of aluminum, phosphorus, and iron. Portions of some bauxite deposits contain more than 10 percent iron; portions of some phosphorus deposits (phosphorites) contain more aluminum than phosphorus. Aluminum concentrations in phosphorites commonly have been attributed to postdepositional weathering of the phosphorite. The alternative hypothesis is the initial precipitation of aluminum and phosphorus from a common warm fluid. The vast majority of iron deposits that have formed during the past 600 million years contain a significant percentage of chemically precipitated aluminum. Collectively, iron deposits younger than 600 million years probably contain more chemically precipitated aluminum than do bauxite ore deposits. None of this iron-bound aluminum, however, ever has been extracted commercially.

## Methods of Study

Aluminum deposits are studied mostly by companies that assess the potential profit from mining. The prime factors regarding profitability are the chemical composition of the bauxite, nature of the aluminum minerals, volume of ore, depth of cover (if any) by aluminum-poor material, distance from the nearest port, labor cost, and political stability of the host country. Aluminum must exceed about 25 percent by weight and other impurities must be limited, particularly silicon. The minimum aluminum content for mining depends upon the dominant type of aluminum mineral because the amount of energy required to separate pure aluminum varies among the aluminum minerals. Mining of aluminum deposits generally occurs by digging downward with enormous shovels that can move several cubic meters in each shovelful. An aluminum ore deposit, therefore, must be at or near the earth's surface. Although aluminum deposits generally are formed at or near the earth's surface, some have become deeply buried under other sediment.

The volume of an aluminum ore deposit is determined by drilling small holes on a fixed grid over the deposit. At least several million tons of bauxite ore are needed to justify mining because each enormous shovel costs several million dollars. The distance of the ore deposit to the nearest port is crucial because a large volume of bauxite ore must be shipped, and the cost of transportation may exceed the cost of mining if the distance is greater than a few tens of kilometers.

The cost of living generally is low in humid tropical areas; mining, therefore, is particularly concentrated in these areas. The average cost of labor in aluminum mining is as low as the average cost of labor for any other type of mining. Unfortunately, political stability commonly is inversely proportional to the cost of labor. Thus, the political stability of the host country may be a major concern to potential investors.

## Context

Aluminum is the most widely used metal among those metals that essentially were unused prior to the twentieth century. Aluminum could not be processed readily into pure metal by melting, so refining of aluminum was delayed until electric energy became available.

Modern industrial society takes for granted that aluminum will be supplied continuously. A smaller proportion of aluminum, however, is mined in industrial countries than any other metal that is widely used by industry. This leaves the industrial countries potentially vulnerable to price-fixing by a cartel of Third World producers. Price-fixing of aluminum is unlikely in the foreseeable future because Third World producers are scattered around the globe, and there has been little movement toward collective action. Another factor that would counteract any sharp increase in price is that special plastics have been found to exhibit many of the desirable properties of aluminum. As long as petroleum is available for the plastics industry, substitution for aluminum potentially regulates prices.

Aluminum prices partly depend on the cost of electric power. Immediately following World War II, aluminum companies established hydroelectric power plants in isolated parts of the globe because aluminum refining requires substantial electric power, and these remote localities were too far from major cities to use their hydroelectric power. This situation has changed with the expansion of cities in previously sparsely populated areas and with the development of techniques for long-distance transmission of electric power. Hydroelectric power plants in remote areas now have the option of selling electricity to distant cities; thus, the aluminum-refining companies are facing competition that previously did not exist.

## Bibliography

Aleva, G. J. J. "Essential Differences Between the Bauxite Deposits Along the Southern and Northern Edges of the Guiana Shield, South America." *Economic Geology* 76 (1981): 1142-1152. The world's youngest major aluminum deposit, along the Amazon River, is described and compared to older deposits in northeastern South America.

Augustithis, S. S., ed. *Leaching and Diffusion in Rocks and Their Weathering Products.* Athens: Theophrastus Publications, 1983. This volume was produced with the cooperation of the International Committee for the Study of Bauxites, Alumina, Aluminium. Many of the twenty-six papers therefore pertain to the concentration of aluminum by weathering. Aluminum deposits are described from Europe, India, China, and Africa.

Brown, Martin, and Bruce McKern. *Aluminum, Copper, and Steel in Developing Countries.* Washington, D.C.: OECD Publications and Information Center, 1987. The profitability of the mining of aluminum deposits changes with the world economy. This book describes the economics of aluminum and recommends how aluminum producers (mostly Third World countries) should interact with aluminum refiners in industrial countries.

Frakes, L. A. *Climates Throughout Geologic Time.* New York: Elsevier, 1979. This book assumes that aluminum deposits form by intensive weathering under humid tropical conditions. The distribution of aluminum deposits is correspondingly interpreted (along with other indicators) to record the history of climatic change on the earth.

LeLong, F., Y. Tardy, G. Grandin, J. J. Trescases, and B. Boulange. "Pedogenesis: Chemical Weathering and Processes of Formation of Some Supergene Ore Deposits." In *Handbook of Strata-Bound and Stratiform Ore Deposits*, edited by Karl H. Wolf. New York: Elsevier, 1976. This paper provides a thorough comparison of aluminum deposits to other earth-surface ore deposits. The chemical reactions involved in the weathering of aluminum-rich silicate minerals are reviewed and aluminum deposits are compared to earth-surface (residual weathering) deposits of nickel and manganese.

Ogura, Y., ed. "Proceedings of an International Seminar on Laterite." *Chemical Geology* 60 (1987): 1-396. This collection of forty papers provides an up-to-date overview of the weathering processes that affect aluminum-bearing silicate minerals. A paper by M. P. Tole (pp. 95-100) describes the "Thermodynamic and Kinetic Aspects of Formation of Bauxites." This paper lists chemical reactions which characterize the weathering of aluminum-bearing silicate minerals.

Stuckey, John A. *Vertical Integration and Joint Ventures in the Aluminum Industry.* Cambridge, Mass.: Harvard University Press, 1983. This book reveals that the aluminum industry in the non-Communist world is dominated by only a few companies. Prior to World War II, a virtual monopoly was maintained by the Aluminum Company of America (Alcoa). Two "more or less new firms" were created after the war: Reynolds Metals Company and Kaiser Aluminum and

Chemical Corporation. Joint ventures among these three and smaller companies have helped to stabilize the cost of aluminum production, hence consumer prices.

Valeton, Ida. *Bauxites*. New York: Elsevier, 1972. This book remains a prime reference for the geology of aluminum deposits. Few other books subsequently have been published on the topic, so it remains the most widely quoted reference.

Wilson, R. C., ed. *Residual Deposits: Surface Related Weathering Processes and Materials*. London: Blackwell Scientific Publications, 1983. This volume describes various types of residual deposits; that is, deposits of insoluble elements that remain when soluble elements are preferentially removed by weathering. The debate about the origin of aluminum deposits hinges on the issue of a residual versus hydrothermal origin. A paper by Ida Valeton in this book (pp. 77-90) describes the "Paleoenvironment of Lateritic Bauxites with Vertical and Lateral Differentiation," in which some blanket-type aluminum deposits grade downward and sideways into other rock types.

*Michael M. Kimberley*

## Cross-References

Groundwater Movement, 1020; Hydroelectric Power, 1095; Hydrothermal Mineralization, 1108; Industrial Metals, 1216; Iron Deposits, 1254; Karst Topography, 1310; Surface Mining Techniques, 1703; Oxides, 1976; Earth Resources, 2175; Sedimentary Mineral Deposits, 2296; Sedimentary Rocks: Chemical Precipitates, 2318; Soil Chemistry, 2382; Weathering and Erosion, 2723.

# THE ANDES

*Field of study:* Mountain ranges

*The Andes are the classic example of mountains formed by subduction beneath a continent and are the modern analogue for many ancient mountain belts. Earthquakes and volcanic eruptions indicate that the Andes are still rising. Because of their geologic setting, the Andes contain abundant minerals, oil, and natural gas.*

Principal terms

CONTINENTAL MARGIN: the edge of a continent that is the transition to the ocean basin; continental margins are said to be active if subduction occurs along them

CRUST: the outermost layer of the earth; continental crust is 30-35 kilometers thick; oceanic crust is 5-10 kilometers thick; the greater density of oceanic crust relative to continental crust forces it to subduct

FAULTING: the process of fracturing the earth such that rocks on opposite sides of the fracture move relative to each other; faults are the structures produced during the process

FOLDING: the process of bending initially horizontal layers of rock so that they dip; folds are the features produced by folding and can be as small as millimeters and as big as kilometers long

MESOZOIC: the era of the geologic time scale that preceded the Cenozoic era; represents the time between about 245 million and 65 million years ago

SEDIMENTARY ROCK: rock that was deposited by the settling of grains through either air or water

TERTIARY: a period in the Cenozoic era of the geologic time scale; encompasses the time span between about 65 million and 2 million years ago

THRUST BELT: a linear belt of rocks that have been deformed by thrust faults; thrust faults emplace older rocks above younger and generally move mass uphill

## Summary of the Phenomenon

The Andes are some of the most impressive mountains on earth, not only for their grandeur but also for their geologic importance. Their evolution over the past 200 million years can be explained by the subduction, or descent, of an oceanic plate below a continent. Subduction is basic to the theory of plate tectonics, which is the fundamental paradigm of the earth sciences. The ease with which plate tectonics explained the Andes convinced numerous scientists of the validity of the theory and established the mountains as the classic example of the active, or Pacific, type of continental margin. Furthermore, many researchers consider the Andes a modern analogue for the Sierra Nevada Range of California and for the Appalachian Mountains of the eastern United States; these areas are said to have formed along Andean-type margins more than 100 million and 450 million years ago, respectively.

The Andes rise 7,000 meters and stretch 7,500 kilometers along the western edge of South America from Venezuela to southern Chile. The rugged terrain and the topographic relief attest the youth of the mountains. Elevation drops rapidly from the high peaks of the Andes to the floor of the Pacific Ocean, a few hundred kilometers west, where a trough 7,000 meters deep, the Peru-Chile trench, lies parallel to the continental margin. The mountains and trench together are known as the Andean arc and are active today. Indeed, the periodic volcanic eruptions are consequences of subduction at the Peru-Chile trench and are reminders that the Andes are still forming.

The Andes can be divided into three morphological provinces that parallel the South American continental margin. From west to east these are the western cordillera ("cordillera" means "mountain system"), the altiplano, and the eastern cordillera. Each is distinct physiographically and geologically. The provinces are easily delineated in the Andes of southern Peru, Bolivia, and northern Chile where the features are related exclusively to subduction. North and south of this region, the Andes are more complex and their geologic evolution is not as straightforward. The descriptions of the provinces, therefore, are for the central Andes.

The western cordillera begins 100 kilometers inland from the coast. It rises 6,000 meters in 50 kilometers and contains Mesozoic and Tertiary volcanic rocks, whose compositions are so distinct that the rocks are called andesites after the mountains in which they lie. The eastern flank of the western cordillera descends 1,000 meters in 15 kilometers to the altiplano, a high plateau (3,800-4,500 meters) greater than 150 kilometers wide. Beneath the altiplano is a basin filled with 10 kilometers of Tertiary sedimentary and volcanic rocks. Superimposed on the Mesozoic and Tertiary rocks of the western cordillera and the altiplano is a chain of huge volcanoes (7,000 meters) that began forming less than 15 million years ago and that presently erupt. The eastern boundary of the altiplano rises abruptly to altitudes near 6,000 meters and marks the transition to the thrust belt of the eastern cordillera. Rocks of the eastern cordillera were deposited along the South American continental margin between 450 million and 250 million years ago prior to the onset of subduction. During that time, the west coast of South America looked like the present east coast of North America. These ancient continental margin rocks now lie more than 250 kilometers inland from the present continental margin. East of the eastern cordillera is the Brazilian Shield, a piece of old continental crust, or craton, next to which the Andes have grown.

Before describing the evolution of the Andes, the theory of plate tectonics must be summarized. The theory states that about twelve rigid plates define the surface of the earth. The plates, which are either continental or oceanic, ride on a partially molten layer and move relative to each other at speeds between 2 and 10 centimeters per year. Plates form at mid-ocean ridges where magma (molten rock) from deep in the earth ascends to the surface and solidifies into new sea floor. To make room for the new material, old pieces of sea floor on opposite sides of the ridge move away from each other. Thus, the mid-ocean ridge is a divergent plate boundary. Across the oceanic plate from the mid-ocean ridge is a trench that marks the convergent boundary where the oceanic plate moves toward another plate, either oceanic or continental, and subducts, or descends, below it. (Because oceanic crust is denser than is continental crust, it always subducts.) If the overriding plate is oceanic, a trench develops in the ocean basin, and a chain of volcanic islands (island arc) grows on the overriding plate. If the overriding plate is continental, the trench sits along the continental margin, and the string of volcanoes forms on the continental plate (continental arc).

The Andes are above a subduction zone, the Peru-Chile trench, which is adjacent to the continental margin of South America between the latitudes of 4 degrees north and 40 degrees south. There, the Nazca plate, one of several plates in the Pacific Ocean, subducts below the South American continental plate at a rate of 6 centimeters per year. Subduction along the South American margin has been active for 200 million years and, during this interval, has produced the three Andean provinces. Three parameters govern the physiography and geology of the provinces: the amount of sediments that descend with the subducting plate in the trench, the angle at which the subducting plate dives below the continent, and the quantity of magma generated by melting of the subducting and overriding plates that is added to the continental crust at shallow depths.

As an oceanic plate subducts, it bends below the overriding plate. This bend forms a huge depression, or trench, in the ocean floor. Sediments on the descending plate either remain attached to it and subduct or scrape against and accrete to the overriding plate. When the descending plate reaches a depth of 100 kilometers, the temperature of the earth is hot enough to melt small areas of either the subducting or the overriding plate. Because the magma generated during melting is less dense than is the surrounding solid rock, it rises through the earth, where it either crystallizes at shallow depths or erupts on the surface.

In the Andes, the overriding plate is continental. Sediments remain attached to the subducting plate and travel to great depths in the earth. These two factors explain the voluminous andesite in the western cordillera. If magma produced at a depth of 100 kilometers is contaminated either by sediments that were subducted with the oceanic plate or by continental crust, it yields volcanic rocks of andesitic composition.

The locus of volcanism on the surface is controlled by the angle at which the subducting plate descends below the overriding plate. If the angle is steep, the plate reaches a depth of 100 kilometers closer to the trench than if the angle is shallow. Changes in the angle, therefore, cause the volcanoes to migrate. In the modern Andes, the angle of subduction varies between 10 and 30 degrees. In the past, the angle was steeper. Thus the recent volcanoes are at the boundary between the western cordillera and the altiplano, whereas the older ones were in the western cordillera closer to the trench.

The addition of magma at shallow depths in the crust pushes adjacent rocks out of the way. This process causes the surface to extend and rift (fracture) immediately adjacent to the volcanic arc and to shorten farther inland. The shortening is accommodated in a thrust belt that develops approximately 200 kilometers continentward of the volcanic arc. In the thrust belt, rocks that accumulated prior to subduction are deformed by faults and folds into mountains hundreds of kilometers long, tens of kilometers wide, and thousands of meters high. The thrust belt in the Andes is the eastern cordillera. The rifting, in turn, forms a trough, or basin, between the volcanic arc and the thrust belt. The basin fills quickly with debris eroded from the adjacent highlands. Lava flows and ash eruptions from the volcanic arc occasionally are large enough to cover the basin, resulting in the interleaving of volcanic and sedimentary rocks. This is precisely the setting of the altiplano, which is a trough between two highlands: the volcanic chain of the western cordillera and the thrust belt of the eastern cordillera.

Prior to subduction, the eastern cordillera was the west coast of South America. The rise of the Andes implies that the width of South America has increased 250 kilometers in 200 million years by the formation of new continental crust. The new crust below the western cordillera has a thickness greater than 70 kilometers, compared with a thickness of continental crust of 30 kilometers below the Brazilian Shield. The large thickness of continental crust, called a root, is required by the principle of isostasy, which states that a mass excess on the surface must be compensated for by a mass deficiency at depth. Because continental crust is lighter than the mantle (layer of the earth below the crust), the space taken up by the continental root (which should be taken up by the mantle) is less dense than it should be. Geophysical data indicate that the crust beneath the Andes is homogeneous and is composed of andesite. Subduction below continental margins, therefore, may be a fundamental mechanism by which continents grow.

## Methods of Study

Techniques from a variety of disciplines in the earth sciences, including geophysics, geology, and geochemistry, are used to study the Andes. Those from geophysics document subduction and a thick continental root below South America presently, whereas those from geology reveal subduction in the past. Geochemical methods provide evidence for relationships between subduction, andesitic volcanism, and formation of continental crust.

The important geophysical tools are seismic reflection profiling and earthquake analysis. Seismic reflection profiling uses sound waves to allow scientists to determine the physical properties of the earth, the most critical of which is density, several tens of kilometers below the surface. Conceptually, seismic profiling is very simple. Sound waves travel downward from a source and reflect back to sensors on the surface when they encounter a change in the physical properties at depth. Because the velocity of the waves depends on the density of the material in which they are traveling, the time the reflected waves take to reach the sensor contains information about the depth of the change and the composition of the rock above it. From this technique, geophysicists learned that the thickness of the crust below the western cordillera and the altiplano in the central Andes was larger than that below the Pacific Ocean and the Brazilian Shield. They also discovered that the compositions of the crust at the surface and of the crust tens of kilometers below were similar.

The analysis of earthquakes involves finding their location, or epicenter. An earthquake occurs when the earth's crust breaks along a fault and the two pieces on either side of the rupture move past each other. The energy released by the faulting travels as waves through the earth. The geophysicist finds the epicenter of the earthquake by measuring the different times at which the waves arrive at various places around the world. Epicenters of earthquakes in the Andes define a zone that extends at an angle from the Peru-Chile trench to depths hundreds of kilometers below South America. This zone outlines the subducting Nazca plate and provides strong evidence that the west coast of South America is a convergent plate boundary. (These zones, called Benioff zones after the scientist who discovered them, occur along all convergent plate boundaries.)

To determine the evolution of the Andes in the past, geologic fieldwork is necessary. In the field, the geologist establishes the different types of rocks that exist and their relationships to each other. He carefully describes the rocks and documents the faults that may indicate that two adjacent sequences of rocks have had greatly different histories. In the Andes, such faults are absent, suggesting that all the rocks formed near one another. Volcanic rocks, most of which were andesites, were the most abundant and were discovered to have erupted throughout the evolution of the Andes. Thus, scientists believe that the tectonic setting of the Andes has remained the same for the last 200 million years.

In addition to geophysics and geology, geochemistry has contributed to an understanding of the Andes. Geochemists in the laboratory melted pieces of basalt and granite, the primary constituents of oceanic and continental crust, respectively. From this experiment, the scientists determined that andesites solidify from magmas that contain significant amounts of continental crust. This led to the conclusion that large areas of the overriding continent melt where the temperature is high, at great depths in the earth above subduction zones. The andesitic composition of the root below the central Andes indicated that substantial melting of the continental crust has occurred beneath the volcanic chain.

## Context

Adventurers have long sought the Andes not only for their beauty but for their riches, both of which are direct consequences of subduction. The mountains tower above the landscape and host spectacularly large ore, oil, and natural gas deposits.

The earliest geological expeditions, in the first half of the nineteenth century, were hampered by the rugged and remote terrain. The technological advances of the twentieth century, however, have solved this problem and have allowed the exploitation of the natural resources. Chile is known for copper and Bolivia for tin.

The ore deposits of the Andes are hydrothemal: They form where hot, mineral-rich fluids associated with magmas derived from deep in the earth interact with cold rock at the surface. These fluids can contain dissolved iron, silver, tin, lead, manganese, molybdenum, zinc, tungsten, and copper. The drop in temperature at the surface forces the minerals to precipitate in the surrounding rock where, given enough fluid, economically significant ore deposits will form. Large amounts of fluid require abundant magmatism. Because most magmatism on earth occurs in subduction zones, and the Andes formed by subduction, the mineral wealth of the Andes is no surprise. Predictably, most mines are in the western cordillera and in the altiplano, where magmatism was and is most active.

The vast oil and natural gas fields of the Andes lie east of the mineral deposits in the thrust belt of the eastern cordillera where the rocks have not been heated by hot fluids or magmas. The location of the fields reflects the low temperatures and thick sedimentary sequences necessary for the transformation of organic matter into oil and natural gas. Faulting in the thrust belt created traps that collected the oil and gas in economically viable deposits.

The plethora of natural resources makes the Andes one of the world's greatest mountain systems. The Andes, however, are important for still another reason: They yield insight into the potential for destruction that exists above subduction zones. Subduction zones are the locus of most of the large earthquakes and violent volcanic eruptions that presently occur. Investigations of the Andes may prevent loss of life and property that accompanies these natural events. First, geophysical instruments can monitor a volcano to determine when an eruption is imminent. (The number of small earthquakes increase when magma is moving toward the surface.) This technique successfully predicted an eruption at Mount St. Helens, an andesitic volcano in the western United States. Second, detailed examinations of volcanoes and the surrounding area may reveal the preferred slope for the descent of mudslides that are often triggered by eruptions and earthquakes. Through the centuries, mudslides have killed many hundreds of people and destroyed countless villages. Towns in the paths of slides can be moved or evacuated. Finally, analysis of the ground motion during a major earthquake may help civil engineers to design buildings that can withstand the shaking. Clearly, the ultimate goal is to predict earthquakes and volcanic eruptions far enough in advance such that adequate precautions can be taken to minimize the loss of life and property. If prediction is successful in the Andes, disasters along other convergent boundaries may be avoided.

## Bibliography

Compton, R. R. *Interpreting the Earth*. New York: Harcourt Brace Jovanovich, 1977. This book was designed to accompany a first course in geology at the college level. The Andes are not discussed specifically, but a good summary of andesitic volcanism, with emphasis on Mount St. Helens, is presented in one of the chapters. The text is useful for people interested in descriptions of areas where certain geological processes occur. Recommended for the senior high school or college student.

James, D. E. "The Evolution of the Andes." *Scientific American* 229 (August, 1973): 61-69. The article discusses the geology of the Andes and the geophysical tools that were used to document subduction below the western margin of South America. The illustrations are good, particularly a set of diagrams that show the continental margin of South America from 400 million years ago to the present. Not technical but does contain a lot of jargon. Recommended for the senior high school or college student.

Parker, S. P., ed. *McGraw-Hill Encyclopedia of Geological Sciences.* 2d ed. New York: McGraw-Hill, 1988. The encyclopedia contains short articles on a variety of topics. The Andes are not included as a separate entry but are discussed briefly in the sections on mountains and geosynclines. Not particularly useful for specific information on the Andes but is suitable for learning more about general processes such as subduction or volcanism. Illustrations are good. Recommended for college-level students.

Press, Frank, and Raymond Siever. *The Earth.* 4th ed. New York: W. H. Freeman, 1986. This text is excellently illustrated and well written. Contains several chapters that may be of interest, although the Andes are not specifically discussed. Topics include faulting and folding, plate tectonics and subduction, mountain building, volcanism and the formation of andesites, and earthquakes and seismic hazards. The inside back cover is a map of the major plates. For someone struggling with terminology, the glossary is helpful. Suitable for senior high school and college students.

Seyfert, Carl K., ed. *The Encyclopedia of Structural Geology and Plate Tectonics.* New York: Van Nostrand Reinhold, 1987. As its title suggests, this reference is a good source for learning more about plate tectonics. Not technical. Recommended for anyone interested in the subject.

Short, Nicholas M., and R. W. Blair. *Geomorphology from Space: A Global Overview of Regional Landforms.* Washington, D.C.: Government Printing Office, 1986. A compilation of pictures taken by satellites that circle the earth. The images are beautiful, and the geological features in them are spectacular. The text accompanying each picture and explaining the geologic setting can be quite technical. Understanding the text, however, is not necessary to grasp the general geology shown in each image. Several pictures of the Andes are included. Suitable for college-level students.

Uyeda, Seiya. *The New View of the Earth: Moving Continents and Moving Oceans.* Translated by Masako Ohnuki. San Francisco: W. H. Freeman, 1978. This book is included in the bibliography as a reference for someone who would like to learn about the "revolution" in earth sciences, as some have called the discovery of plate tectonics. Anecdotes of scientists who pioneered the theory are presented. The theory also is explained very well. Nontechnical. For the nonspecialist.

Windley, B. F. *The Evolving Continents.* 2d ed. New York: John Wiley & Sons, 1984. Written for the beginning geology student at the college level, this book contains a lot of terminology. Nevertheless, it is a good text for anyone interested in the evolution of continents in general and the evolution of the Andes in particular. Discusses the evolution of the surface of the earth through time, beginning approximately 3.5 billion years ago. Illustrations are excellent and are useful to examine without reading the text. Bibliography of scientific articles is superb.

*Pamela Jansma*

## Cross-References

Continental Crust, 261; Continental Growth, 268; Earthquake Distribution, 421; Earthquake Hazards, 437; Earthquake Prediction, 461; Thrust Faults, 683; Isotasy, 1269; Mountain Belts, 1725; The Oceanic Crust, 1846; Plate Margins, 2063; Plate Tectonics, 2079; Seismic Reflection Profiling, 2333; Subduction and Orogeny, 2497; Volcanic Hazards, 2601.

# THE APPALACHIANS

*Field of study:* Mountain ranges

*The Appalachian Mountains form one of the most prominent features of the North American continent, dominating the topography of the Atlantic Coast. They mark the eastern continental divide, influence the climate of the region, and provide a record of the transformation of the earth through a vast range of geological epochs.*

*Principal terms*

CATASTROPHISM: the theory that major geological events (cataclysms) shaped the earth

CORDILLERA: a long, elevated mountain chain marked by a valley-and-ridge structure

CRATON: a part of a continent that has been free of significant structural rupture for a long time; often a region with a thin covering of newer rocks

EROSION: the process by which the surface of the earth's crust is gradually broken down and worn away

FAULT: a fracture in the earth's crust along which there has been some displacement or deformation

FOLD: the deformation of rocks under external pressure; piles or layers of rock

GEOSYNCLINE: a downward warp in the earth's crust; a term in vogue prior to the development of tectonic theory

GLACIATION: the effect of a glacier on the terrain it transverses as it advances and recedes

LITHOSPHERE: the outer, rigid shell of the earth's crust; it includes the continental plates and the oceans

METAMORPHIC ROCK: rock altered by means of intense heat

OROGENY: a major event in which tectonic processes combine to radically alter the earth's crust; mountain building

TECTONICS: the process by which the broken shell of the earth's crust (the lithospheric plates) moves in varying directions to create geological features

TERMINAL MORAINE: the farthest edge or advance of a glacier

## Summary of the Phenomenon

The Appalachian Mountains in their present form are a chain of relatively low but steeply inclined ridges that follow the east coast of North America for roughly 3,000 kilometers; ranging from Newfoundland in easternmost Canada to Alabama in the southeastern United States, they extend across nearly 20 degrees of latitude and more than 30 of longitude. They were named for an Indian tribe known as the

Apalachees (or Apalachis) by the Spaniards who followed Hernando de Soto in 1540 across the southern part of the chain, as de Soto had stayed with the tribe in southern Georgia before his expedition into the mountains. The term "Appalachian Mountains" gradually was applied to the entire range, superseding local designations such as "Allegheny," even though the mountains are not a single continuous range but are rather a complex of separate mountain groups whose boundaries tend to overlap. They range from 25 to 125 kilometers in width and are described by geologist and author John McPhee as a "long continuous welt . . . long ropy ridges of the eastern sinuous welt."

Running roughly parallel to the mountain ridges, valleys of varying width divide the highland ranges. Some of them are narrow and deeply wooded, some broad and gently contoured. They all are essentially a part of the Great Valley of the Appalachians, known locally as the Shenandoah or Tennessee Valley, or some even more specific local designation. In most places, the valley is several hundred meters above sea level, while the highest points of the range rise to 2,037 meters (Mount Mitchell) in the Black Mountains in northwest North Carolina, to 2,024 meters (Clingman's Dome) in the Great Smoky Mountains near the Tennessee border, and to 1,917 meters (Mount Washington) in the White Mountains of New Hampshire. There is no continuous crest to the chain; the highest peaks are found either at the center of the mountain range or on its northwest side. This geologically interconnected series of valleys and ridges has been subdivided into geologic provinces with common general features but distinct local characteristics.

In the southern segment, four belts (or provinces) have been described which run the length of the chain. The farthest northwest is the Appalachian Plateau province, including the Poconos in Pennsylvania, the Cumberlands in Kentucky, and the Alleghenies in West Virginia. In spite of the term "plateau," the land frequently is cut by deep valleys and rugged hills. The area supports some small-scale farming but is primarily valuable as a source of coal, oil, and gas, which has led to the growth of rust-belt industry around its rim.

The second belt is designated the Valley and Ridge province because it is most characteristic of the pattern that typifies the entire chain. The most prominent mountain groups in this province are the Clinch Mountains in Virginia, the Shawangunks in New York, and the Kittatinny Mountains in Pennsylvania. The mountains are arranged along stretches of fertile valleys that are among the most productive farming regions in the eastern United States, valleys fed by the rivers that have formed them in the rivers' courses from the higher peaks. The Delaware Water Gap is typical, with fields and woodlots sculpted by the rush of water over land and, above the flatland, with huge rock deposits such as the Martinsburg formation, a very large aggregate of slate used in blackboards and pool tables.

The third province is called the Blue Ridge, running from the low Highlands of New Jersey to a single, massive ridge through the central Appalachians. There, it rises abruptly from the west and drops off just as sharply in the east. From 10 to 20 kilometers across, it diverges into two ridges south of Roanoke, where it runs in two roughly parallel chains through the southern Highlands. Between these two ridges, additional connecting ridges (including the Black Mountains) occur before the two border ridges end fairly abruptly in northern Georgia. The well-known Blue Ridge Parkway, built as a Works Progress Administration project in the 1930's, follows the crest of the eastern ridge from Virginia to the Great Smoky Mountain National Park. This section is the least populated of the Appalachians; not especially suitable for agriculture or industry but scenically exceptional, the Blue Ridge province has many summer resorts scattered amid the previously isolated communities of mountain pioneer families.

The fourth belt is the Piedmont Plateau, which slopes gradually from the Blue Ridge toward the Atlantic coastal plain. The availability of timber and water resources in this belt has led to the development of an extensive furniture industry as well as textile mills in many of its small cities, especially along the fringes toward the coastal flatlands.

The Northern Appalachians correspond primarily to the Blue Ridge and Piedmont Plateau provinces but are not as clearly demarcated. The Blue Ridge, while not actually connected, is replicated by the Hudson River highlands through the Berkshire Hills in Massachusetts and the Green Mountains of Vermont. The remainder of New England and the Canadian Maritime Provinces resemble the Piedmont Plateau. Toward the ocean, the land is generally regular, with minor topographic features, while linear ridges and hilly belts predominate closer to the line of the mountains, where the effect of glaciation is more pronounced. During the early days of the United States, this was a thriving agricultural region, but the immense growth of urban centers has transformed it into a manufacturing and communications complex, and extensive efforts are under way to preserve the unique features of the Appalachian wilderness.

The present form of the Appalachians is very different from that maintained during earlier geological eras. The mountains have risen and then been worn down several times within the scope of historical observation—what McPhee calls "the result of a series of pulses of mountain-building, the last three of which have been spaced across two hundred and fifty million years." Before that, the North American continent formed part of a larger, supercontinental entity. During the latter part of the Proterozoic eon (approximately 600 million years ago), the cratonic cores of North America, Europe, and an immense entity known as Gondwanaland separated and then began to drift apart. During that time, the evidence of marine deposits in sedimentary rock indicates that the North American continent was a low-lying, relatively flat landmass. The effects of weathering and erosion over a long period produced this level surface, and glaciation contributed to a worn, scarred appearance. Because of what is known as epeirogenic movement (the rise and fall of landmasses), the craton was sometimes covered to a large extent by water; during the Cambrian period (from 570 to 500 million years ago), much of the North American landmass was submerged, and a tropic or subtropic climate existed.

At that time, the first stirrings of the Taconic orogeny began. This surge of energy, an upheaval in which sheets of oceanic lithosphere were thrust toward the continental interior, produced the first "modern" Appalachian chain. In the Ordovician period (from 500 to 435 million years ago), the sedimentary and volcanic rock that had been built up were fractured and crumpled. The deformation (or deconstruction) of the original mountains was so great that slices of the range were transported considerable distances, folding the mountains upon themselves. The general direction of plate motion was westward, and as the high-density material of the upward-thrusting oceanic plate depressed the low-density material of the craton, forcing it downward into what is called a subduction zone, the low-density material eventually rebounded to produce orogenic waves, which further crumpled and folded the mountain chain.

In the Early Paleozoic era, the continents converged, producing the Acadian orogeny (about 350 million years ago). As the North American and African landmasses moved toward a collision, the violence of the Acadian orogeny folded and faulted the sedimentary rock that remained from the erosion of the Taconic orogeny. The intense temperatures and pressures generated by the mountain-forming process also metamorphosed some of the rock, changing the shales into slates, the sandstones into quartzites, and the limestones and dolomites into marble. The final episode of mountain building took place between 280 and 240 million years ago and is known as the Alleghenian orogeny. Occurring quite some time after the initial contact between North America and Africa, it may have been the consequence of an additional impact, possibly with a microplate (wandering island formation) such as New Guinea, Madagascar, Fiji, or the Solomon island system. These smaller masses, known also as exotic terrains because of their separation from the main continental blocks, may have collided with the North American continent to trigger the most recent orogenic episode. The proto-Atlantic Ocean was probably in the process of closing when the first collision between North America and Africa occurred, but by the Alleghenian orogeny, the continents were closer to relative fixture (or stability), thereby suggesting that another island arc may have been responsible for the orogeny. In any event, this last orogenic episode was a time of tremendous upheaval, and one of its products was the creation of the extensive anthracite deposits of eastern Pennsylvania. These coal fields were formed when severe pressure folded carbonaceous rock at least one kilometer beneath the surface. Erosion and an eventual balancing of forces that ended the upheavals brought coal seams closer to the surface, which would lead to the mining industry of the Appalachian region. Similarly, petroleum deposits—the transmuted fossils of ocean algae—were formed when rocks were heated to about 50 degrees Celsius and remained between 50 and 150 degrees Celsius for at least 1 million years. The rocks that were once part of the western Atlantic Ocean were driven by orogenic waves onto the North American continent, and, in the process of mountain building, in some areas and under the proper conditions of temperature and pressure, they formed oil deposits. The richest deposits in the Appalachians were in Pennsylvania and Ohio, where oil seeped out of the ground in such purity that it could be used prior to refining and was once sold as a health tonic. Much of this oil has been extracted, but geologists speculate that there may still be deposits of oil and natural gas off the south Atlantic coast—the product of the process which formed the Appalachian Mountains.

Although the Appalachians in their present form are not as spectacular as they once must have appeared when their highest peaks stood from 8 to 10 kilometers above the earth's surface, the terrain is continuously varied and visually engaging. In the deformed, sedimentary Appalachians—the present topographical form of the chain—the rock "not only has been compressed like a carpet shoved across a floor," as John McPhee observes, "but in places had been squeezed and shoved until the folds tumbled foward into recumbent positions." An overview reveals a consistent sinuosity: The mountains bend right into Georgia, left into Tennessee, right into North Carolina, and so on toward Newfoundland. Some geologists speculate that this pattern represents the coastline of North America in Precambrian times.

## Methods of Study

In the early days of the United States, geologists began to examine the Appalachians, but their first observations were more mineralogical than geological. William Maclure (1763-1840) published a geologic synthesis of the region east of the Mississippi in 1809, accompanied by a colored map, and while his descriptions were accurate, he believed that the rocks had been deposited just as they then appeared, thus overlooking the entire geological history of the Appalachians. Later, James Hall (1811-1898), one of the pioneers of American paleontology and stratigraphy (the study of fossils and stratified, or layered, rocks), concluded that, unlike those of the interior region, the sediments of the Appalachian region are thick, thus leading to a theory of mountain formation based on slow surficial processes such as erosion and sedimentation. A contemporary of Hall, James Dana (1813-1895), suggested that the earth's crust was being compressed as a result of a general contraction of the interior, which led to the formation of a depression where sediments could accumulate. At the same time, Henry Rogers (1808-1866) and William Rogers (1804-1882) described and illustrated the folds of the Valley and Ridge province of the Appalachians with considerable exactitude in a study in 1843. They believed that the singular formation they charted had been produced by forces acting tangentially across the fold belt and that these forces resulted from catastrophic volcanic explosions in the southeast. William Rogers went on to describe the thrust faults that were associated with the folds, and, following Rogers' approach southwestward across Tennessee, what was described as reversed asymmetry (that is, folds in a direction opposite to the main pattern) was found, which led in 1893 to the proposal that an additional underthrust had contributed to the process of rock formation. Near the end of the century, the U.S. Geological Survey sent a group of men to map the southern Appalachians on topographic base maps. These researchers added information about thrust faults, indicating that lateral thrust was greater than upward thrust.

While by the close of the nineteenth century the appearance of the region had been described and some very incisive guesses about its origins made, the essential geologic history of the Appalachians remained a mystery. Characteristics such as the sedimentary nature of rocks, their chemical composition, their magnetic components, their hardness, their fossil traces, and their igneous (hardening of magma, or volcanic material) arrangement could be determined independently by the first part of the twentieth century, but integrating the data was still largely a matter of conjecture. The methods of the geologists who explored and examined the Appalachians during the first century of fieldwork were summarized by geologist Ernst Cloos (1898-1974) as follows: Accurate topographic maps are the basis for geologic work; geologic maps are the basis for all other geological work (all rock exposures must be accurately described); besides rock mapping, it is essential to map the distribution of rock structures; and microscopic investigations must be made of the composition of the rocks, their mineral content, and the orientation of minerals. Cloos's principles, which are an exposition of the basic methods of field geology, enabled the early geologists to produce a composite picture of an entire region. Yet, their work was essentially two-dimensional, and the sequential narratives they proposed to describe the formation of the mountains through geologic eras were largely speculative.

By the middle of the twentieth century, oil company geologists had learned to use the colors of fossil pollen and fossil spores to identify the age of rock formations, and the study of conodonts (hard fragments of the bodies of ancient marine creatures embedded in rocks) as a fossil time-index enabled geologists to subdivide the Paleozoic era from 560 to 195 million years ago, thus establishing the age of many different rocks in the Appalachians where conodonts were found. Yet, as John McPhee has observed, "identifying what is there scarcely describes what happened to put it there." Although theories of continental drift had been proposed as far back as 1620 when Francis Bacon roughly had pointed out that the continents could be fitted together roughly like a jigsaw puzzle, the modern concept of drifting continents was not posed until 1912—by Alfred Wegener (1880-1930). His ideas originally were not taken seriously, but worldwide seismic data gathered by the 1960's forced a reevaluation of Wegener's work. Seismographs had been placed around the globe to record the tremors of nuclear tests and, as a result, a more accurate record of earthquakes was also compiled. This record showed that the earth is divided into twenty-odd pieces of crust and mantle (lithospheric plates) that move in a number of directions, their eventual collisions causing major geologic episodes. By 1968, the various lithospheric plates had been identified, and while plate tectonics does not explain all the mysteries of the Appalachian region, its basic principles have helped considerably in reconstructing the history of the mountain formations, particularly in conjunction with paleoecologic findings.

During the 1970's, the Consortium for Continental Reflection Profiling employed devices that severely shake the earth's crust while vibration sensors record wave patterns reflected off the rock deep below; the resulting patterns reveal structural arrangements, including faults, folds, laminations (rock in thin sheets), magnetic bodies both active and cooled, density, and the type of rock struck by the Vibroseis machinery. These determinations were then coordinated into subterranean profiles known as seismic lines, and their study led to the relocation of the hypothesized suture formed by the collision of North America and Africa 50 miles to the east to accommodate tectonic theory. Further study of these patterns revealed that the Valley and Ridge province of the Appalachians, formerly considered solidly rooted, had actually been moved westward from the coast, suggesting further collisions with microplates. All interpretations of the Appalachians until 1979 had been based on the idea of a rooted system, but the addition of subsurface data has suggested that the thrust faults in the region must be examined further. Similarly, the Great Valley of the Appalachians, the most prominent axial feature of the chain (that is, its central line of direction), is too much of "an integral, elongate, and geo-metrically formal valley," as McPhee puts it, to be the product of random collisions with different landmasses.

## Context

Beyond the intriguing problems and challenges they present for the professional geologist, the Appalachian Mountains can prove fascinating for the casual or un-trained observer or explorer. Their location places them within the relatively easy reach of more than half the population of the United States, and they offer the visitor a wonderful variety of topographical features. The famous Appalachian Trail follows their course, permitting the hiker to cover their entire length if time and energy permit, while the Blue Ridge Parkway runs nearly 300 kilometers from middle Virginia to Alabama along the crest of the highest ridge, climbing as high as 2 kilometers above sea level, close to Mount Mitchell, the highest peak east of the Rockies. The drive from Boone to Asheville, North Carolina, a distance of approx-imately 60 kilometers, offers a variety of terrain that is stunning. In the southern reaches of the chain, the high peaks near the North Carolina-Virginia border support a ski industry that has begun to rival that developed along the mountains near Vermont and New York. Some of the most extreme weather in the Eastern United States occurs along the Appalachians, including (on Mount Washington) the highest wind gust recorded on earth, the second highest being on Grandfather Mountain in North Carolina. The elevation of the Blue Ridge permits the growth of a mixed hardwood forest, normally associated with the Canadian border, as far south as Georgia.

The second oldest river on earth, the New River, has its origins near Blowing Rock, North Carolina, while the hollows (or "hollers") cut by rushing water have been the homes of Scots-Irish immigrants from pre-Revolutionary times whose isolation in the mountains has enabled them to preserve an indigenous culture (including songs, stories, and styles of speech) strikingly separate from the main flow of American society. The term "Appalachia" has come to represent an exploited region, and while the common picture of Appalachian, or "hillbilly," life is rife with stereotypes, the lack of much real knowledge about the people who inhabit the mountains has made them and their land a source of curiosity and even some concern. The still-pristine quality of much of the topography of the region has sparked much debate about land use and preservation.

## Bibliography

Cattermole, Peter, and Patrick Moore. *The Story of the Earth*. New York: Cambridge University Press, 1985. A clear, very well illustrated and graphically elegant presentation of basic geological facts about the earth. The material is presented on a level that is accessible for the layperson, and the many full-color illustrations are appealing and informative. Contains a good glossary of basic terms and a useful bibliography.

Dietrich, Richard V. *Geology and Virginia*. Charlottesville: University Press of Virginia, 1970. A good introduction to the specific issues of geological conditions in one region of the Appalachians, with some features for the intermediate-level student of geology. Includes an extensive glossary and a good list of supplementary readings. The black-and-white drawings and photographs are straightforward and historically interesting.

Fisher, George W., ed. *Studies of Appalachian Geology: Central and Southern*. New York: John Wiley & Sons, 1970. Primarily designed for the serious student of geology or the professional in the field, some specific chapters would be of use to the reader interested in examining a particular facet of Appalachian geology. The epilogue by Philip King is a good historical study of geological exploration in the region, and there is a detailed but comprehensible map of the rock distribution and tectonics of the region.

Jannsen, Raymond E. *Earth Science: A Handbook of the Geology of West Virginia*. Clarksburg, W.Va.: Educational Marketers, 1973. Essentially a textbook for an introductory course in the geology of the state of West Virginia, this book is well organized and written with the interested nonprofessional in mind. Comprehensive and thorough, it includes many maps and charts, an excellent geologic timetable, and a selective glossary. Somewhat dated.

King, Philip. *The Evolution of North America*. Princeton, N.J.: Princeton University Press, 1959. A solid, basic account of the geologic history of North America by an experienced professional who has been a lifelong employee of the U.S. Geological Survey. Subsequent discoveries have made some of the assertions less convincing, but the essential geological history of the continent and important complementary factual information are presented with authority and clarity. The section on the growth of the Appalachians is helpful for the beginning student.

Lessing, Peter, ed. *Appalachian Structures: Origin, Evolution and Possible Potential for New Exploration Frontiers*. Morgantown: West Virginia University, 1972. A series of papers by professionals who have studied the Appalachian region in great detail. Primarily for the serious professional, but the concluding remarks offer insights for the layperson as well.

Lowry, W. D., ed. *Tectonics of the Southern Appalachians*. Roanoke: Virginia Polytechnic Department of Geological Sciences, 1964. Another series of essays by professionals, the introduction and some of the abstracts illustrate the approaches that were being explored in the 1960's.

McPhee, John. *In Suspect Terrain*. New York: Farrar, Straus & Giroux, 1983. The author's work is well known; his *Basin and Range* (1981) interested many people in geology. Like that earlier book, this one explores ancient terrains in juxtaposition to travels in the modern world. While based on McPhee's observations around the Delaware Water Gap, it presents much information about the structure and geological history of the Appalachian chain. An indispensable book for anyone interested in the Appalachian range.

Rogers, John. *The Tectonics of the Appalachians*. New York: John Wiley & Sons, 1970. A specific, detailed presentation of the rock structures of all of the provinces of the Appalachian region. The introduction is informative and accessible to the nonprofessional, and the bibliography is extensive.

Zen, E-an, ed. *Studies of Appalachian Geology: Northern and Maritime*. New York: John Wiley & Sons, 1968. A companion volume to one covering the southern and central region, this book is primarily for the professional, but has some informative maps and an interesting introduction. Extensive references.

*Leon Lewis*

## Cross-References

Coal, 232; Continental Rift Zones, 275; Normal Faults, 676; Thrust Faults, 683; Transform Faults, 690; Fold Belts, 734; Folds, 739; Geosynclines, 898; Continental Glaciers, 967; Mountain Belts, 1725; The Worldwide Distribution of Oil and Gas, 1923; Plate Tectonics, 2079; Subduction and Orogeny, 2497.

# AQUIFERS

*Type of earth science:* Hydrology

*Aquifers are the source of water for approximately 40 percent of the U.S. population. The identification and protection of aquifers are important to the future of drinking water supplies in the United States.*

Principal terms
AQUIFER: any saturated geologic material that yields significant quantities of water to a well
CONE OF DEPRESSION: the depression, in the shape of an inverted cone, of the groundwater surface that forms near a pumping well
CONFINED AQUIFER: an aquifer which is completely filled with water and whose upper boundary is a confining bed; it is also called an artesian aquifer
CONFINING BED: an impermeable layer in the earth that inhibits vertical water movement
GROUNDWATER: water found in the zone of saturation
PERMEABILITY: the ability of rock, soil, or sediment to transmit a fluid
POROSITY: the ratio of the volume of void space in a given geologic material to the total volume of that material
UNCONFINED AQUIFER: an aquifer whose upper boundary is the water table; it is also called a water table aquifer
WATER TABLE: the upper surface of the zone of saturation
ZONE OF SATURATION: a subsurface zone in which all void spaces are filled with water

## Summary of the Phenomenon

To understand aquifers, one must understand how water occurs beneath the earth's surface. The world's water supply is constantly circulating through the environment in a never-ending process known as the hydrologic cycle. Natural reservoirs within this cycle include the oceans, the polar ice caps, underground water, surface water, and the atmosphere. Water on the land surface which is able to infiltrate the ground becomes underground water. "Groundwater recharge" occurs when the infiltration reaches the water table.

Underground water exists in three different subsurface zones: the soil moisture zone, the intermediate vadose zone, and the zone of saturation. The soil moisture zone is found directly beneath the land surface and contains water that is available to plant roots. This zone is generally not saturated unless a prolonged period of rainfall or snowmelt has occurred. Water in this zone is held under tension by the attractive forces between soil particles and water molecules, or surface tension forces. The depth of this zone corresponds to the depth to which plant roots can grow.

Water able to infiltrate through the soil moisture zone may pass into the inter-mediate vadose zone before reaching the water table. This zone is always unsatu-rated, and the water it contains is held under tension. The thickness of a vadose zone depends on how close the water table is to the surface.

The water table forms the uppermost surface of the zone of saturation and is characterized by a water pressure equal to atmospheric pressure. It may be only a few meters below the land surface in humid regions and hundreds of meters below the surface in desert environments. In general, the water table mimics the land surface topography. If the water table intersects the land surface, the result is a lake, swamp, river, or spring. Below the water table, in the zone of saturation, geologic materials are completely saturated, and the water pressure increases with depth. Water contained within the zone of saturation is known as groundwater. When groundwater occurs in a particular type of geologic formation known as an aquifer, it can feed a well.

An aquifer can be defined as any earth material—rock, soil, or sediment—which yields a significant quantity of groundwater to a well or spring. The definition of "a significant quantity" varies according to the intended use; what constitutes an aquifer for an individual homeowner may be quite different from what constitutes an aquifer for a municipal supply. For a geologic formation to be useful as an aquifer, it must be able both to hold and to transmit water.

The ability of geologic materials to hold, or store, water is known as porosity. Simply stated, porosity is the volume of void space present divided by the total volume of a given rock or sediment. This proportion is usually expressed as a percentage. The higher this ratio is, the more void space there is to hold water. There are various types of porosity. Unconsolidated materials (soil and sediment) have pore spaces between adjacent grains, referred to as intergranular porosity. The ratio of pore space to total volume depends on several factors, including particle shape, sorting, and packing. Loosely packed sediments composed of well-sorted, spherical grains are the most porous. Porosity decreases as the angularity of the grains increases, because such particles are able to pack more closely together. Similarly, as the degree of sorting decreases, the pore spaces between larger grains become filled with smaller grains, and porosity decreases. Values of porosity for unconsolidated materials range from 10 percent for unsorted mixtures of sand, silt, and gravel to about 60 percent for some clay deposits. Typical porosity values for uniform sands are between 30 and 40 percent.

Rocks have two main types of porosity: pore spaces between adjacent mineral grains and voids caused by fractures. Rocks formed from sedimentary deposits, such as shale and sandstone, may have significant intergranular porosity, but it is usually less than the porosity of the sediments from which they were derived because of the compaction and cementation that takes place during the process of transforming sediments into rock. Therefore, although sandstone porosities may be as high as 40 percent, they are commonly closer to 20 percent because of the presence of natural cements which partially fill available pore spaces. Igneous and metamorphic rocks are composed of tightly interlocked mineral grains and therefore have little intergranular porosity. Virtually all void space in such rocks is a result of fractures (joints and faults). For example, granite, a dense igneous rock, usually has a porosity of less than 1 percent, but it may reach 10 percent if the rock is fractured.

There are additional types of porosity which occur only in certain kinds of rocks. Limestone, a rock which is soluble in water, can develop solution conduits along fractures and bedding planes. In the extreme case, solution weathering may lead to the development of a cave, which has 100 percent porosity. The overall porosity of solution-weathered limestone sometimes reaches 50 percent. Rocks created by volcanic eruptions may contain void space in the form of trapped air bubbles (called vesicles), shrinkage cracks developed during cooling (called columnar joints), and tunnels created by flowing lava (called lava tubes). In extreme cases, the porosity of volcanic rocks may exceed 80 percent.

The presence of void space alone does not constitute a good aquifer. It is also necessary for groundwater to be able to move through the geologic material in question. The ability of porous formations to transmit fluids, a property known as permeability, depends on the degree to which the void spaces are interconnected. Some high-porosity materials, such as clay and pumice, do not make good aquifers, because the void spaces are largely isolated from one another. Materials which have high permeability include sand, gravel, sandstone, and solution-weathered limestone. Rocks with low porosities, such as shale, quartzite, granite, and other dense, crystalline rocks have low permeabilities, unless they are significantly fractured.

Groundwater moves along tortuous paths through the available void space in a given porous formation. Regardless of the material's permeability, groundwater flows much more slowly than surface water in a river. The velocity of stream flow may be measured in meters per second, whereas groundwater velocities commonly range between 1 meter a day and less than 1 meter per year, averaging about 17 meters per year in rocks. Underground rivers are uncommon, occurring only in cavernous limestone or lava tubes in volcanic terrane.

The geologic materials that make good aquifers are those that have both high porosity and high permeability. The response of any given aquifer to a pumping well will also depend, however, on its position beneath the surface and its relationship to the water table. Aquifers near the earth's surface usually have the water table as their upper boundary. The thickness of these aquifers therefore changes as the water table rises or falls. An aquifer under these conditions is an unconfined aquifer, or water table aquifer. These types of aquifer are the easiest to exploit for a water supply, but they are also the easiest to contaminate. It is therefore important to delineate the extent of unconfined aquifers and to take measures to protect them from various forms of pollution.

Because the water table is free to fluctuate in unconfined aquifers, the amount of water supplied to a well reflects the gravity drainage of water from void spaces. The volume of water available from aquifer storage, or the "specific yield," therefore approaches the upper limit set by porosity. Some groundwater is unable to drain from void spaces under the influence of gravity, because it is tightly held by surface tension forces; this retained water, known as "specific retention," forms a thin film around individual grains. The highest values of specific yield occur in coarse-grained, permeable aquifers, such as sand, gravel, and sandstone.

Some aquifers, usually found at depth, are completely filled with groundwater and bounded at the top by an impermeable layer called a confining bed. The water in these confined, or artesian, aquifers is under pressure because of the weight of overlying formations and the fact that the confining bed does not allow groundwater to escape. If a well is placed in such an aquifer, the water level will usually rise above the base of the confining bed, creating an artesian well. In some cases, water may rise above the land surface at the point where the well is placed. This condition is known as a flowing artesian well. Water will flow freely out of such wells as long as the aquifer remains under pressure. Many of the Great Plains states (Kansas, Nebraska, and the Dakotas) are underlain by important shale layers. The original pressure in these aquifers was quite high because the sandstone beds are upwarped along the eastern front of the Rocky Mountains and Black Hills, where they receive groundwater recharge.

Confined aquifers supply water to a well not through the gravity drainage of void spaces but through compression of the aquifer as water pressure is reduced during pumping. The volume of water available from storage in a confined aquifer, or the "specific storage," is only a small fraction of the total volume and is therefore always much less than porosity. When confined aquifers are pumped to the extent that they become dewatered, the accompanying pressure reduction can lead to extensive aquifer compression and land surface subsidence. This problem is most serious in cases where the confining bed is composed of clay, because the loss of fluid pressure beneath the clay causes water to be squeezed out of the clay layer by the weight of overlying formations. Once a clay layer is compressed in this way, it will not be able to reabsorb water, even if the surrounding materials become saturated again.

## Methods of Study

The first step in studying aquifers is to utilize data that have already been collected, such as geologic maps. These maps show the distribution of various geologic formations on the land surface and are therefore valuable tools for delineating the outcrop patterns of potential aquifers. If cross sections are also available, they can aid in the estimation of potential aquifer thicknesses and the identification of possible confined aquifers. Geologic maps, however, serve only as a preliminary tool in aquifer study. Any interpretations made from maps need to be verified by field descriptions and, if possible, pumping tests.

Topographic maps can be used to make generalizations about the groundwater flow system. Springs, lakes, streams, and swamps may indicate areas of ground-water discharge. Because the water table is usually a subdued version of the land surface, it may be possible to infer groundwater flow directions from the local topography. That can provide a clue as to where recharge areas occur. Other indications of recharge areas are topographic high points and a general lack of surface-water features. For groundwater recharge to occur, however, permeable materials must be exposed at the land surface.

Reliable estimates of aquifer properties require fieldwork. Often, samples are taken from the field for the purpose of determining aquifer properties, such as grain-size distribution or permeability, in the laboratory. Such tests, however, are performed only in small samples and may not be representative of the overall aquifer unit. That is particularly true in fractured rocks, where the movement of groundwater may be very difficult to predict. In such situations, the injection and monitoring of tracer dyes has proved helpful in understanding groundwater flow.

The most direct way to study aquifers is by boring holes and installing wells. By drilling, geologists are able to discover the exact nature of the subsurface materials. Detailed drilling logs are kept of the different layers and the depths at which they were encountered. Using their knowledge of geologic materials, properly trained geologists can predict which formations will constitute the best aquifers.

Once wells have been installed, additional information about the aquifer can be learned by conducting pumping tests (pumping the wells at known rates for extended periods). Because water moves relatively slowly through an aquifer, the pumping of a well removes groundwater faster than it can be replaced. The resulting water-level drawdown is called a cone of depression; it is a zone of dewatering near the pumping well which resembles an inverted cone. The exact shape of this cone is a function of the pumping rate and the aquifer properties. Therefore, certain aquifer characteristics, such as permeability, are discovered by studying the cone of depression created by a known pumping rate. To identify the shape of the cone, monitoring wells must be placed near the pumped well to detect drawdown at various distances.

The prediction of long-term well yields requires not only an understanding of aquifer properties but also a knowledge of the groundwater recharge rates. To determine the amount of water in a particular drainage basin that is available for groundwater recharge, it is necessary to develop a hydrologic budget for that basin. Hydrologic budgets attempt to account for all water inputs and losses from the basin in question. Inputs include precipitation, surface-water inflow, groundwater inflow, and water imported by humans (as for irrigation). Losses include surface-water runoff, groundwater outflow, evaporation, transpiration by plants, and water exported from the basin by humans. The difference between these inputs and losses equals the amount of water gained or lost by the groundwater reservoir.

## Context

The term "aquifer" is not precise, because its definition depends somewhat on the intended use. For an individual homeowner who requires only 7 to 20 liters per minute from a well, fractured bedrock may serve as a suitable source of water. On the other hand, only a few geologic materials are capable of delivering the larger water supply demanded by a municipality or industrial plant—often more than 1,500 liters per minute. In the case of high-capacity well requirements, the term "aquifer" is restricted to highly permeable geologic materials, such as unconsolidated sands and gravels, sandstone, and solution-weathered limestone.

Most private wells draw water from unconfined aquifers, which have the water table as an upper boundary. The saturated thicknesses of these aquifers can fluctuate as the water table rises or falls. Therefore, shallow wells completed in unconfined aquifers can be pumped dry as the water table declines during periods of prolonged drought. Because of their proximity to the land surface, these aquifers are also susceptible to groundwater contamination. Confined aquifers do not have a water table, because they are fully saturated and capped with an impermeable confining bed. The natural groundwater quality in confined aquifers is not necessarily superior to that found in unconfined aquifers, but the presence of a low-permeability confining bed may help to protect these aquifers from surface contamination.

An understanding of aquifer characteristics is important to the proper use of groundwater. The determination of maximum sustainable well yields requires a knowledge of how the aquifer stores and transmits water. Such information is also needed to estimate how close adjacent wells can be to one another without causing interference (overlapping cones of depression). Pumping water out of an aquifer at rates exceeding the rate of groundwater recharge will eventually cause the depletion of a valuable water supply. Many arid regions in the western United States are facing this problem because of years of groundwater mismanagement. The over-pumping of confined aquifers is especially troublesome, because if these aquifers become dewatered, they compress, which may lead to subsidence of the land surface.

Delineating the extent of aquifers and particularly of their recharge zones is critical to the development of policies which protect groundwater supplies from pollution. In the case of confined aquifers, recharge zones may be restricted to areas where the confining bed is absent, so contaminants entering the ground through a relatively small zone could affect a large number of downgradient wells. Moreover, because groundwater moves very slowly through the subsurface, it takes a long time to be renovated once contaminated.

## Bibliography

Davis, S. N., and R. J. M. De Wiest. *Hydrogeology.* New York: John Wiley & Sons, 1966. A well-illustrated introduction to the geologic aspects of groundwater occurrence. The hydrologic cycle and its relationship to groundwater are discussed in chapter 2. Four chapters are dedicated to a discussion of the occurrence of groundwater in different aquifer materials and geologic settings. Suitable for both high school and college-level readers.

Fetter, Charles W. *Applied Hydrogeology.* 2d ed. Columbus, Ohio: Merrill, 1988. This textbook emphasizes the practical aspects of understanding groundwater occurrence and movement. Chapter 8 contains a detailed discussion of the influence that geologic conditions have on groundwater occurrence, with special emphasis on groundwater regions in the United States. Chapter 7 addresses regional groundwater movement within aquifers and contains helpful illustrations of the principles discussed. A glossary of important terms is included. Suitable for college-level readers.

Freeze, R. Allan, and John A. Cherry. *Groundwater.* Englewood Cliffs, N.J.: Prentice-Hall, 1979. A more advanced book stressing the mathematical derivations of groundwater flow equations and their applications. Chapter 4 presents a discussion of the geologic controls on groundwater occurrence. Chapter 6 contains a number of figures illustrating the principles of regional groundwater flow.

Hamblin, W. Kenneth. *The Earth's Dynamic Systems.* 4th ed. Minneapolis: Burgess, 1985. Although not limited to the topic of groundwater, this widely used introductory textbook has a good discussion of groundwater occurrence and movement in chapter 13. The color figures are especially helpful to one unfamiliar with subsurface geology. Suitable for both high school and college-level readers.

Montgomery, Carla W. *Physical Geology.* Dubuque, Iowa: Wm. C. Brown, 1987. An introductory geology textbook which contains a good discussion of groundwater and aquifers. The full-color figures are helpful, as is the author's emphasis on the environmental aspects of water supply and pollution.

Todd, David K. *Ground Water Hydrology.* 2d ed. New York: John Wiley & Sons, 1982. A textbook emphasizing the practical aspects of groundwater occurrence and movement. Chapter 1 introduces the reader to groundwater utilization and its relationship to the hydrologic cycle. Chapter 2 discusses aquifer types and the occurrence of groundwater within the United States. Suitable for college-level readers.

Walton, W. C. *Groundwater Resource Evaluation.* New York: McGraw-Hill, 1970. Although much of this book deals with advanced techniques for analyzing aquifer properties from well pump tests, chapter 2 contains a valuable discussion of the terms pertinent to aquifers and an analysis of groundwater regions in the United States. Chapter 1 provides background on the role of groundwater within the hydrologic cycle.

*David L. Ozsvath*

## Cross-References

Groundwater: Artificial Recharge, 1012; Groundwater Movement, 1020; Groundwater Pollution, 1028; Groundwater Pollution Remediation, 1035; Groundwater: Saltwater Intrusion, 1042; Hazardous Wastes, 1059; The Hydrologic Cycle, 1102; Landfills, 1351; Nuclear Waste Disposal, 1758; Surface Water, 2504; Water Wells, 2708.

# ARCHAEBACTERIA

*Type of earth science:* Paleontology and earth history

*Archaebacteria are primitive, one-celled life forms without a distinct nucleus, different from bacteria in their genetic components. They have been found to be genetically unique and are probably one of the earth's earliest life forms.*

> *Principal terms*
>
> EUBACTERIA: minute, prokaryotic organisms that inhabit a range of habitats considerably greater in diversity than those occupied by other organisms; exclusive of archaebacteria, they constitute the majority of monerans
>
> EUKARYOTIC CELL: the cell type present in all animals, plants, fungi, and protists; they have a distinct nucleus and mitochondria, chloroplasts, and other subcellular structures absent in prokaryotic cells
>
> MICROBIALITE: a biogenic sedimentary structure that is found fossilized in sedimentary rock strata of various ages and that is attributed to the life activities of monerans
>
> MONERANS: generally, single-celled organisms that often grow in colonies and that have a prokaryotic cell
>
> PROKARYOTIC CELL: the cell type found in the kingdom Monera, characterized by a number of criteria, including the absence of a cell nucleus, mitochondria, and chloroplasts
>
> RIBOSOME: a large multienzyme complex made up of protein and ribonucleic acid (RNA) molecules that carry and process information stored in deoxyribonucleic acid (DNA); this information is also carried by RNA to synthesize proteins
>
> STROMATOLITE: a biogenic sedimentary layered structure produced by sediment trapping, binding, or precipitation as a result of the photosynthesis of microorganisms, principally cyanobacteria (blue-green algae)

## Summary of the Phenomenon

What the earth's earliest life forms were like has always been an intriguing question for both the earth sciences (paleontology) and biology. The fossil record shows that one-celled organisms are very ancient, their oldest-known fossils being almost 3.5 billion years old. The long fossil record of prokaryotes consists of both preserved fossil cells and distinctive layered mineral structures called stromatolites and microbialites; these structures were produced from the cell metabolisms of colonies of prokaryotes. From at least 3.5 billion years ago to around 1 billion years ago, microscopic prokaryotes were the earth's only organisms. They included, as they do today, a diversity of forms commensurate with their long evolutionary history. The appearance of the eukaryotic cell (more than 1 billion years ago) ushered in the age of multicelled organisms (metazoans and metaphytes) some 700 million years ago, and these have become the dominant life forms on earth. What the much earlier prokaryotic organisms were like and what type of one-celled organisms produced the microbialites is unclear. Usually these oldest of fossils are attributed to the life activities of photosynthetic organisms, particularly the cyanobacteria, referred to in many works as the blue-green algae. A number of other types of one-celled life forms could have been responsible for some of them, particularly the photosynthetic bacteria and possibly the archaebacteria.

Molecular biologists, utilizing RNA nucleotide sequencing and other biochemical methods, believe that the nature of early life forms can be discovered. Ribonucleic acid (RNA) nucleotide sequences of amino acids can be regarded as a sort of chemical "historical document" which is capable of being "read." The closer two RNA nucleotide sequences are to each other, the smaller is the evolutionary distance between them and the more recent in geologic time did they separate from each other; the further a nucleotide RNA sequence is from another, the greater is the evolutionary distance which separates the two organisms. Utilization of nucleotide sequencing can thus produce an evolutionary tree, or phylogeny, for even the most primitive of organisms, and therefore it becomes possible to determine which organisms out of the great variety of primitive life forms currently living were some of the first to appear. Through information obtained by such sequencing, archaebacteria have been recognized by molecular biologists as some of the most primitive and biochemically unique of organisms. Archaebacteria RNA sequences turn out to be distinctly different from those of other bacteria, even though the various organisms that comprise archaebacteria look like and were previously placed with the bacteria.

Archaebacteria represent a phylum within the kingdom Monera, a category which includes all those one-celled life forms that lack a cell nucleus. On the basis of their distinctive biochemistry, the archaebacteria are considered by some life scientists to represent a distinct kingdom, equal in rank to animals, plants, fungi, and protists. In both their tolerence of extreme ecological conditions and their metabolism, the archaebacteria differ from all other monerans: a condition which has led biologists to consider these organisms as particularly well suited to the adverse conditions of the early earth. The very earliest eras of geologic time may well have been the age of archaebacteria.

On a fundamental molecular level, archaebacteria are different in their biochemistry from the other prokaryotes. Nucleotide RNA sequences and other biochemical differences that exist between the various types of eubacteria (bacteria exclusive of the archaebacteria) are minor when compared to the differences between eubacteria and the archaebacteria. Nongenetic differences include such features as cell walls, those of all eubacteria being composed of a complex polymer called peptidoglycan, which is a sugar derivative. In contrast, cell walls of the various types of archaebacteria are composed of a variety of other materials, none

of which is peptidoglycan. The lipids (fats) in archaebacteria cells are also fundamentally distinct from the lipids in the cells of both eubacteria and eukaryotes.
Ribosomal RNA is what ultimately distinguishes the archaebacteria, for it is markedly different in its sequences of bases from any eubacteria. In higher eukaryotic
organisms, where the fossil record is good, greater RNA ribosomal differences exist
between those organisms that are separated by long periods of geologic time than
between those separated by shorter periods of time. Ribosomal RNA differences
and the biochemical differences that exist between the eubacteria and the archaebacteria suggest that an evolutionary distance of great magnitude separates them.

The eukaryotic cell has long been observed to be a sort of combination between
prokaryotic-type cells, functioning within the cell as chloroplasts and mitochondria,
and another cell-type that "ingested" the prokaryotes and incorporated them to
become a more complex entity in symbiotic collaboration. Archaebacteria have
some genetic characteristics that suggest a link with the eukaryotes, which has led
some scientists to propose a predecessor to them both: the "other" cell-type that
linked up with prokaryotes underwent substantial further evolution and eventually
became the eukaryotic cell. The pre-eukaryotic other cell type is known as a
urkaryote. All three of these cell types—the prokaryote, the urkaryote, and the
eukaryote—are hypothesized to have arisen from a common cell ancestor, the
progenote. The progenote may have been biochemically simpler than any of the
three fundamental life forms which arose from it, an event which might have taken
place during the the first billion years of "earth history."

Archaebacteria are represented by three classes: the extreme halophiles, the
thermoacidophiles, and the methanogens. The extreme halophiles, or halobacteria,
live only in extremely salty environments. The thermoacidophiles occupy hot, acid
environments, often rich both in metallic ions and in sulfur compounds, such as hot
springs and fumaroles. These organisms are viable under the acidic hot conditions
intolerable to other life forms, with temperatures as high as 75 degrees Celsius. The
methanogens are anaerobes that metabolize organic material to form methane; they
were the first of the archaebacteria to be discovered.

Igneous activity of various sorts appears from the geologic record to have been
much more intensive and widespread in the early earth (between 2 and 4 billion
years ago) than during more recent geologic times or at present. A terrestrial
geologic record for the first billion years of earth's history is unknown, as the
widespread igneous and tectonic activity during this time seems to have destroyed
the evidence; an actual record begins at nearly 4 billion years ago. During the next
1.5 billion years (the Archean eon), igneous phenomena and massive tectonism was
still dominant. Hot-spring and fumarolic activity would have been more commonplace during these early times than during later geologic time, and these environments are favored by the thermoacidophiles. Although the fossil and sedimenta-
tional record of the Archean eon does not negate the possibility that archaebacteria
were some of the most widespread and dominant life forms of that time, determination that a particular organic—or presumed organic—structure of the early earth

was produced by archaebacteria or by some other moneran is quite difficult and may well be impossible. A number of puzzling structures, seemingly of biogenic origin, have been reported from Archean strata. Some of these stromatolite-like or microbialite-like structures are associated with what appear to be hot-spring deposits. These structures may well represent minerals deposited as a consequence of life activities of thermoacidophiles associated with geothermal activity. Like so many stromatolite-like and microbialite-like structures, unequivocal proof as to their biogenic origin is difficult to obtain. Structures similar to them, however, are produced today in hot springs, in the hottest waters of which live communities of thermoacidophile archaebacteria.

Sometimes hot-spring deposits and structures have associated with them carbon-rich sediments or graphite. In addition, some hydrothermal veins of various ages have associated carbonaceous or graphitic material. It is possible that such material might have originated from thermophyllic archaebacteria. Stratified metallic element deposits are known from Archean strata, some of which have been thought to be of biogenic (possibly archaebacterial) origin. Some of these deposits yield microbialites exhibiting distinctive dome, finger, or layered structures containing metallic oxides or carbonates. During later geologic time as well as today, such structures are produced by the cyanobacteria and by the photosynthetic bacteria, but these younger stromatolites lack components like the oxidized metals. Other Archean stromatolites or microbialites and stromatolite-like structures associated with geothermally active environments have a distinctive "signature" different from later forms, and their origin by thermoacidophile archaebacteria cannot be ruled out.

The second group of archaebacteria, the extreme halophiles, requires an intensely saline environment. Shallow, marginal marine areas, evaporite basins, and salt flats are the niches in which these organisms generally flourish. Physiologically, the extreme halophiles are photosynthetic; however, the photosynthetic pigment is not chlorophyll, but is rather a light-sensitive red pigment, bacterial rhodopsin. The cell walls of the extreme halophiles differ from those of other bacteria in the presence of compounds that prevent destruction of the walls in the high salt concentrations under which they live. The chemical similarities of ribosomes and lipids of both the extreme halophiles and the methanogens suggest a common origin.

Again, the fossil record of these organisms is difficult to interpret; some biologists suggest that the halophiles were more prevalent early in the earth's history than they are today. Fossil rod-shaped bacterial cells have been found as far back as the mid-Archean (3.2 billion years ago); however, as the gross morphology of archaebacteria differs little from that of eubacteria, evidence remains inconclusive.

Peculiar and distinct microbialites of Archean age that are associated with radial sprays of gypsum crystals were described from western Ontario in the 1910's by Charles Doolittle Walcott. Walcott, a pioneer North American paleontologist who concentrated on the early (Precambrian and Cambrian) fossil record, made many finds of peculiar structures resembling fossils in Precambrian strata, many of which remain a mystery. Walcott thought that the radiating gypsum crystals were the rays, or spicules, of a type of spongelike organism he called atikokania. Associated with Walcott's atikokania are distinctive microbialites that contain "lenses" of gypsum that almost certainly originated in a very saline environment. These microbialites could possibly represent the product of physiological activity of the extreme halophiles when, during the process of photosynthesis, they locally removed carbonic acid from the saline water. The white lenses that characterize these distinctive microbialites are gypsum fillings between the black calcium carbonate bands, possibly precipitated by photosynthesis of halophilic archaebacteria.

Methanogens produce their metabolic energy either from the breaking down of organic compounds incorporated into sediments or from the reduction of carbon dioxide in the presence of elemental hydrogen, with the consequent release of methane. Were it not for the methanogens, organic carbon would eventually become incorporated into the sediments of the earth's crust, where it would accumulate and could not be recycled back into the biosphere; the methanogens facilitate this recycling of carbon. Methanogens, like the other archaebacteria, have biochemical features distinct from all other bacteria, suggesting that they evolved separately from them; like the other archaebacteria, methanogens differ from other prokaryotes in the sequences of nucleotides that make up the RNA in their ribosomes and protein. Fossil methanogens are more difficult to distinguish from the geologic record than other archaebacteria, however, as they leave no distinctive chemical "footprint," as the others can. The abundance of black, carbon-rich sediments in strata of the Archean eon suggests that the oxygen-free, anaerobic environment in which the methanogens flourish was commonplace during that time. The methanogens' biochemical uniqueness, and thus presumed great geologic age, along with the anaerobic Archean earth environment, suggests that they may have been a dominant part of the Archean biosphere and not restricted as they are today.

## Methods of Study

Archaebacteria were not recognized as distinct from the eubacteria until the biochemical techniques of protein and RNA sequencing became possible. Sequencing involves determination of the order or sequence of the various bases which compose the molecules of protein and RNA present in the cell. Although deoxyribonucleic acid (DNA) can be utilized in this sequencing, ribosomal RNA is more abundant and more easily used in prokaryotes. Sequencing of the RNA starts with extraction techniques that first concentrate the ribosomal RNA. The concentrate is then purified and placed into an ultracentrifuge, a device used to separate compounds of different molecular weight. Three fractions or groups of RNA molecules occur in both the cells of prokaryotes and the eukaryotes. These fractions are designated in terms of svedberg units, which relate to the rate of sedimentation of the molecules in an ultracentrifuge. The three groups of RNA molecules in prokaryotes are designated in svedberg units: 23S RNA, 16S RNA, and 5S RNA. The largest molecule, 23S RNA, is difficult to work with, and the smallest, 5S RNA, has a number of "gaps" that would probably translate out as gaps in the comparable evolutionary phylogeny; the 16S RNA molecule is that which is favored. The 16S RNA molecule is broken or reduced to smaller molecules through utilization of the enzyme T-ribonuclease. Separation of these smaller fragments is again done with an ultracentrifuge, and the various fractions are analyzed through a combination of techniques including paper chromatography, X-ray diffraction, and automated wet chemical techniques. The wet chemical techniques utilize computer-driven, automated procedures that, if done manually, would be extraordinarily laborious and time-consuming.

The huge molecules of 16S RNA might be compared with the information contained in a book, and the fragments "cleaved" by the enzymes might thus be compared with individual words or sentences or with sentence fragments of that book. As in sentences, some words repeat themselves and recur frequently; other sentences, sentence fragments, or even words can be more or less unique to a particular book and are not likely to occur in another. If these same sentences or sentence fragments do occur in another book, the two books are probably "related" in some way, such as being different editions.

Base sequences, once determined for a particular organism, are compiled into a "dictionary." The compiled sequences may occupy almost the same amount of informational space as a standard word dictionary. Once dictionaries of two organisms have been compiled, they can then be statistically compared; the closer the two dictionaries are to each other, the more closely related are the organisms. Statistical comparisions of the two dictionaries can be made utilizing correlation coefficients so that a quantitative determination of evolutionary distance between the organisms can be obtained. The evolutionary distance thus obtained through sequencing for two eukaryotic organisms with a good fossil record agrees well with that deduced from the fossil record of the organisms. The geologic time that has elapsed since the two organisms had a common ancestor can be used to calibrate or express the genetic correlation coefficients in terms of geologic time. Genetic differences between archaebacteria and eubacteria give some of the largest measures of evolutionary distances, strongly suggesting separation of these two life forms by long periods of geologic time.

## Context

Archaebacteria are primitive life forms recognized as distinctly different in a number of ways from all other bacteria (the eubacteria). From the distinctiveness of the genetic material when sequenced or "read," it is clear that archaebacteria are in fact quite different from all other life forms. This uniqueness suggests that the archaebacteria may represent a third fundamental form of life as distinct from bacteria as bacteria are distinct from eukaryotes. Archaebacteria are believed to represent some of the most primitive and ancient of earth's organisms; archaebacteria living today occupy some of the most hostile and extreme environmental niches, environments which probably early in the history of life were more commonplace than they are at present.

Archaebacteria, being one of the earliest of life forms, are thus believed to have played a significant part in the modification of the early earth and in its adaptation to the higher life forms, such as the eukaryotes, that appeared later. They may even have played a direct part in the development of the eukaryotic cell, which gave rise to most of the nonmicroscopic life forms that now inhabit the earth, including humans. Some mineral deposits of great antiquity also may have resulted from the life activities of archaebacteria.

## Bibliography

Broadhead, Thomas W., ed. *Molecular Evolution and the Fossil Record.* Short Courses in Paleontology 1. Washington, D.C.: U.S. Geological Survey, 1988. A group of papers made to accompany a short course on molecular evolution. Topics concentrate on how biochemical similarities and dissimilarities, particularly nucleotide sequences, can be utilized in the measurement of evolutionary distance. A considerable amount of molecular biology applicable to evolution and paleobiology is present in the work.

Day, William. *Genesis on Planet Earth: The Search for Life's Beginning.* New Haven, Conn.: Yale University Press, 1984. A thorough discussion of the early history of life, combining geological evidence with molecular biology and microbiology. That which is currently known about the earliest and most primitive organisms is outlined in a relatively nontechnical manner. Chemical pathways that might have led toward the complex chemistry of the prokaryote cell are presented, as well as data on RNA and protein sequencing and their part in revealing evolutionary pathways. The archaebacteria are covered in one chapter, and their molecular uniqueness as determined from RNA sequencing is discussed.

Doetsch, R. N., and T. M. Cook. *Introduction to Bacteria and Their Ecobiology.* Baltimore: University Park Press, 1973. A nontechnical work that emphasizes the natural history of the bacteria rather than the more frequent emphasis on their behavior in laboratory culture. Archaebacteria are not specifically discussed, as molecular biology, RNA, and protein sequencing which distinguish them are discussed; rather, emphasis is placed on the wide range of environments that bacteria inhabit. The role of bacteria in such geological processes as sulfide metabolism and deposition, hydrocarbon production, and iron deposition is discussed in some detail.

Kandler, Otto, and Wolfram Zillig, eds. *Archaebacteria Eighty-five: Proceedings of the EMBO Workshop on Molecular Genetics of Archaebacteria.* Forestburgh, N.Y.: Lubrecht and Cramer, 1987. A proceedings volume on molecular genetics, biology, and biochemistry of archaebacteria. Two papers are concerned with the geologic and paleontologic record of archaebacteria: "Traces of Archaebacteria in Ancient Sediments," by J. Hahn and Pat Haug, and "Morphological and Chemical Record of the Organic Particles in Precambrian Sediments," by H. D. Pflug. This latter paper illustrates a wide variety of microstructures from Precambrian sediments and discusses possible pathways by which archaebacteria and other prokaryotes could have been responsible for the concentration of many metallic ore deposits throughout various part of the Precambrian. Other papers such as "Archaebacterial Phylogeny: Perspectives on the Urkingdoms," by C. R. Woese and G. J. Olsen, present biochemical reasons substantiating the uniqueness of archaebacteria from both the eubacteria and the eukaryotes. Other papers probe the biochemical similarities with eukaryote cytoplasm and peculiar substrate requirements.

Woese, Carl R. "Archaebacteria." *Scientific American* 244 (June, 1981): 98. One of the most comprehensive articles available on the archaebacteria. Distinctive attributes characteristic of the archaebacteria as determined through molecular biology are enumerated. The author was one of the workers originally involved in the discovery of the biochemical uniqueness of archaebacteria.

*Bruce L. Stinchcomb*

## Cross-References

# ARCHAEOLOGICAL GEOLOGY

*Type of earth science:* Geology

*Archaeology is rapidly becoming a markedly more scientifically based field, a trend started with the "New Archaeology" of the 1970's. Archaeological geology covers the wide range of geological sciences that are applied to archaeology during excavation and postseason, or postexcavation, sorting, classifying, and analyzing.*

Principal terms

ABSOLUTE DATE: a date that gives an actual age, though it may be approximate, of an artifact

CURIE POINT, or TEMPERATURE: the temperature at which materials containing iron oxides lose their magnetic pattern and align with the earth's magnetic field

RELATIVE DATE: a date that places an artifact as older or younger than another object, without specifically giving an age for it

REMOTE SENSING: any of a wide variety of techniques, such as aerial photography, for collecting data about the earth's surface from a distance

STRATIGRAPHY: the deposition of artifacts in layers, or strata

## Summary of the Methodology

Archaeological geology is the application of geological methods and techniques to archaeology. The two disciplines have become so closely intertwined at times that some have spoken for a new term to describe their partnership: "geoarchaeology." A term aimed more specifically at the contributions of the physical and chemical sciences associated with archaeology (such as potassium-argon dating) is "archaeometry." Without such scientific methods, archaeology becomes guesswork at best; dating of finds, for example, should be derived from empirical data, or information that can be proven through experiment and observation, rather than deduced from theory without corroboration. Archaeology is, basically, deductions made about an artifact from the context in which it is found; geology helps to define and date that context, thereby providing the empirical information from which speculation about the artifact can be derived.

The principle of superposition was probably one of the first geological methods that archaeology utilized. This law states that a layer superimposed on another layer should be younger, having been laid down after the lower, or older, layer. This study of stratigraphy is a keystone to archaeological dating but constitutes relative rather than absolute dating. One of the better-known methods of absolute dating is that of carbon 14 dating. Carbon 12 and carbon 14, an isotope of carbon 12, are elements that exist in all living organisms. Once the organism dies, whether it is plant or animal, the input of carbon 14 from the environment stops, and the remaining carbon 14 begins to decay. The amount of carbon 14 left relative to the amount of carbon 12 is used to calculate the amount of time that the organism has been dead, using the known half-life of carbon 14 (5,730 years).

Archaeomagnetism (the term is the archaeological equivalent of geology's "paleomagnetism") is another dating method, but one that uses changes in the earth's magnetic field as recorded by archaeological artifacts such as kilns. The earth experiences continual changes in the intensity and polarity of its magnetic field. If a clay artifact has been heated to its Curie point, or temperature, its magnetic particles will align in the direction of the polarity of the earth's magnetic field in which they cool. Geological identification of the polarity pinpoints the time of firing. Thermoluminescence dating is also a method used on clay. A piece of pottery is heated to 500 degrees Celsius and the ensuing emission of light measured as an indication of the length of time since its firing, as the energy of the thermoluminescence increases as it is stored up over time. Another method for dating inorganic objects, in this case volcanic rock, is potassium-argon dating. When volcanic rock is newly solidified, it contains no argon, but it does contain potassium 40. As the potassium 40 decays, it becomes argon 40. Because the half-life of potassium 40 is known (1 billion years), the amount of argon 40 gives the absolute age of the rock.

Geological techniques are also used for locating and recording archaeological sites. Remote sensing is a technique by which data are collected on a site in a "remote" rather than a hands-on way. Photographic images are a major part of remote sensing. Aerial photography, for example, is used to photograph the landscape from airplanes or satellites. Images and patterns that record electromagnetic radiation provide another source of remote-sensing data, as does soil resistivity surveying. Soil resistivity surveying is a method used to map buried features by finding electrical conductivity differences between the features and the soil around them. The ease or resistance with which the current penetrates the soil is the basic principle. To test the resistivity, four electrodes are inserted into the ground. Two generate the current, and two measure the drops in voltage; an equation taking into account the distance between the electrodes, the amperage, and the drop in voltage then gives the total resistance to conductivity.

Petrology, or the study of different aspects of rocks, is a standard feature of archaeological geology. Most techniques focus on the study of thin sections or powdered samples of rock—for example, through the use of scanning electron microscopes and X-ray diffraction, respectively. In addition, archaeologists also utilize geological studies of cryoturbation (freeze-thaw cycles in soil), argilliturbation (shrinking and swelling cycles in clays), aeroturbation (disturbances by gas, wind, and air), aquaturbation (disturbances from the movement of water), and seismiturbation (disturbances by earthquakes). Study of these different types of environmental disturbance helps identify the different site-disturbing processes at work.

## Applications of the Method

. Many aspects of the geological sciences can be applied to archaeological sites. It is the nature of the site that determines the appropriate method to use. For example, a historical archaeological site, or one that is dated to within the parameters of recorded history, would not probably be a site at which radiocarbon dating would be useful: The artifacts would not be old enough for a dating method that yields figures in thousands of years. On the other hand, a prehistoric site such as the possibly Iron Age Caer Cadwgan, a probable hillfort in Wales, would benefit primarily from radiocarbon dating: The site is probably about three thousand years old, and charcoal and bone, excellent types of samples for carbon 14 testing, are the main elements found in excavation at this site. This site has also yielded small glass beads, items that would perhaps be datable by thermoluminescence.

Historical sites in general, however, are not the prime candidates for archaeological geology that prehistoric sites are. Prehistoric archaeology, on the other hand, depends completely on geological analysis for some conclusions because it predates any written records; there are no fortuitously preserved documents to fall back on for verification. Archaeological geology can accomplish much, but it is most useful for four principal processes during an excavation: locating a site, recording and analyzing the features of a site, and dating a site.

The archaeological use of soil resistivity for locating sites or individual features was first applied to locate prehistoric stone monuments just after World War II. The differences in ground conductivity are used to locate anomalies, which can range from buried ditches to stone walls. The method was first developed in geology to locate ore deposits, faults, and sinks (sunken land where water can collect). Remote sensing can be a useful method for several different goals. Remote sensing can be used to locate sites, monitor changes in the archaeological record, reveal the distribution of archaeological sites, or map sites. Aerial photography can be used to locate sites, and it can then be used to map a site and record its features for planning an excavation. On some sites in North Africa, the camera will be sent up in a balloon to take the photographs, as the site may be too small or the budget of the excavation too limited for airplane-carried camera work.

Archaeology is a destructive process; once a site is excavated or even surface collected, it cannot be restored. Remote sensing can, sometimes, take the place of excavation in what is termed nondestructive archaeology. It can also be a useful substitute for excavation when there is not time for a full-scale dig to be mounted, as during times when a formation may be temporarily visible (for example, winter snows revealing significant gradations in the land), but conditions may not be right for excavation. Remote sensing can also preserve at least an image of a site that must be destroyed, as during construction of a road. With this use, it is an invaluable tool in rescue archaeology.

Petrology is a useful tool in general for archaeology. Petrology can be used on many different types of sites, from prehistoric to historic. It can be used to give a provenance, or origin, for building and sculptural stones as old as Stonehenge or as young as the classical Greek marbles. Archaeomagnetism can be used not only to date artifacts but also to distinguish sources for substances. Obsidian sources, for example, have been found to each have different magnetization strengths. It is possible then that the source of ore for coins, which may contain trace amounts of iron, may also be able to be discovered. Archaeomagnetic dating of lava has been used to date the end of the Minoan civilization (about 1500 B.C.), which was destroyed by the volcanic eruptions at Santorin (or Thera) in Greece. It is used mainly for early humankind sites, or up to 10,000 years old.

Thermoluminescence can also be used to date lava as well as burnt flint (implements heated by accident or on purpose to improve certain qualities), burnt stones (heated on a fire and then placed in a food container as a "pot-boiler"), glass (volcanic glass especially), sediments (buried soils), and ceramics. This method is popular because of its absolute dates for a wide range of ages: 50-500,000 years old. Potassium-argon dating is also used for inorganic samples but only ones that predate humankind. Samples can only be as young as 100,000 years old. Another limitation, however, is that because it is used to date lava, in order to be of any use the site must be connected to a particular volcanic eruption, and sites such as Santorin and Pompeii are not common (and too young anyway). The usefulness of potassium-argon dating to archaeology is its ability to fix dates for reversals of the earth's magnetic field, which in turn are used to date archaeological sites through archaeomagnetism.

Using petrology to establish the provenance of a rock artifact is of great importance in prehistoric archaeology. The evaluation of rock types found can help to identify the mining or quarrying skills of a culture, its determination of the usefulness of various kinds of rocks, and even some of the places to which people may have traveled. If a certain type of rock is not native to the area in which it is found yet occurs in large quantities, it may be inferred that perhaps significant trade or travel was taking place. The value that a culture may have placed on a particular rock may also be determined, judging by its use (whether ceremonial or practical, for example). Use-wear as opposed to earth-moving processes that have changed the shape of the rock are another object of study. Petrological methods such as X-ray diffraction can be used to identify the origin of rocks on a site. Studying the rocks from a number of different sites can be a way of tracing the trade routes of a culture.

## Context

The main point of archaeology is to investigate humankind's past and to be able to draw some conclusions about what it was like. Yet, one of the criticisms of archaeology has been that it is too heavy on description and too light on substantiated conclusions. Science in general, and geology in particular, helps to give a factual basis to archaeological theorizing. While logic, reasoning, and even perhaps intuition do have a place in archaeology, piecing together the abstract parts of a culture such as religion and philosophy is not as straightforward as piecing together the sherds of a broken pot. Science thus provides archaeology with the backbone to present its conclusions with some degree of surety. The usefulness of any research is limited unless there is some certainty about the conclusions reached.

As more and more archaeological sites are threatened by construction (as the Rose Theatre in London), environmental pollution (as marble structures such as the Parthenon on the Acropolis in Athens), and other man-made hazards, definitive scientific methods must be developed and utilized while a site is still available for study.

## Bibliography

Aitken, M. J. *Thermoluminescence Dating*. San Diego, Calif.: Academic Press, 1985. Aitken has prepared a comprehensive work on thermoluminescence dating. He includes the theoretical and mathematical basis for this method, as well as its applications. This work is specifically aimed at readers without knowledge of physics, but it is still fairly technical and most suitable for college-level students.

Brothwell, Don, and Eric Higgs, eds. *Science in Archaeology*. With a foreword by Grahame Clark. 2d ed. New York: Praeger, 1970. Despite the date of the book, it is helpful because it has chapters on many of the scientific methods that are in use, including thermoluminescence, potassium-argon, and radiocarbon (carbon 14) dating. This volume is useful for seeing the wide range of scientific methods that are applied in archaeology and the beginning of New Archaeology. Suitable for undergraduate college-level students.

Butzer, Karl W. *Archaeology as Human Ecology: Method and Theory for a Contextual Approach*. New York: Cambridge University Press, 1982. Butzer sets out the principles and objectives of geoarchaeology as a subdiscipline of archaeology. His emphasis is on the environmental sciences in general as necessary for the best empirical data in archaeology.

Kelley, Jane H., and Marsha P. Hanen. *Archaeology and the Methodology of Science*. Albuquerque: University of New Mexico Press, 1988. Kelley and Hanen have prepared this volume as a way to reconcile the philosophies of science and archaeology. They include case histories that target the methodological problems of interpreting even sound empirical data. Useful for college-level students seeking to discover how the sciences fit into archaeology.

Kempe, D. R. C., and Anthony P. Harvey, eds. *The Petrology of Archaeological Artefacts*. New York: Clarendon Press, 1983. A very useful book for different techniques of archaeological geology and their various applications, including specific examples. As the title indicates, petrology is the main focus. Technical, so best suited to advanced college-level readers.

Parkes, P. A. *Current Scientific Techniques in Archaeology*. New York: St. Martin's Press, 1986. An up-to-date work that includes archaeometry in great detail. Technical but well written. Suitable for college-level readers.

Schiffer, Michael. *Formation Processes of the Archaeological Record*. Albuquerque: University of New Mexico Press, 1987. This book includes chapters on the earth processes that can disturb and change the archaeological record, such as earthquakes and freeze-thaw cycles. Contains photographs and is suitable for the general reader.

_____, ed. *Advances in Archaeological Method and Theory.* 11 vols. San Diego, Calif.: Academic Press, 1978-1987. This series is a current and comprehensive review of changes in scientific archaeological methods and new applications of those methods. Each chapter is by a different contributor, and many include specific examples of studied sites.

*J. Lipman-Boon*

## Cross-References

Aerial Photography, 17; Secular Variation of Earth's Magnetic Field, 540; Earth's Magnetic Field at Present, 548; Electron Microscopy, 601; Geochronology: K-Ar and Ar-Ar Dating, 833; Geochronology: Radiocarbon Dating, 840; The Geologic Time Scale, 874; Paleosols, 2011; Petrographic Microscopes, 2034; Remote Sensing and the Electromagnetic Spectrum, 2166; Sediment Transport and Deposition, 2290; X-Ray Powder Diffraction, 2751.

# THE ARCHEAN EON

*Type of earth science:* Geology
*Field of study:* Stratigraphy

*The Archean eon is the earliest on the geologic time scale. Within this time, the basic structure and chemical composition of the planet evolved. The complexity and fragmentary character of the rocks of this period have made their history opaque until twentieth century advances in technology.*

*Principal terms*

ACCRETION: the gradual accumulation of matter in one location, typically because of gravity

BASALT: a fine-grained, dark mafic igneous rock composed chiefly of plagioclase feldspar and pyroxene

BASIN: a regionally depressed structure available for the collection of sediments

BRECCIA: a rock formed by the amalgamation of various rock fragments

GNEISS: a coarse-grained metamorphic rock that shows compositional banding and parallel alignment of minerals

GRANITE: a coarse-grained, light-colored igneous rock composed of chiefly three types of minerals: two types of feldspars, quartz, and variable amounts of darker minerals

GREENSTONE: a field term used to describe any altered basic igneous rock that owes its color to the presence of various green minerals

MARIA: Latin plural meaning "sea," originally describing the moon's dark areas; the light-colored areas of the moon are called the highlands

PLATE TECTONICS: the study of the movement and deformation of large segments or plates of the earth's surface over the underlying mantle

SILICATE: a substance whose structure includes silicon surrounded by four oxygen atoms in the shape of a tetrahedron

## Summary of the Phenomenon

The Archean eon is the earliest in the history of the earth and accounts for about 50 percent of all geologic time. The time of its exact beginning is unclear, but an estimate of 4-4.5 billion years ago is a good starting point; it continued until approximately 2.5 billion years ago. The Archean was a time of major evolution in the earth's chemical and physical structure, which gave the planet its basic character. The current paradigm, first enunciated in 1905 by the American geologist Thomas C. Chamberlin (1843-1928) and the astronomer Forest R. Moulton (1872-1952) at the University of Chicago, describes the earth and the solar system in the beginning as a gas cloud rotating about a center. Shock waves from two nearby and independent supernovae caused the cloud to collapse as the rate of rotation increased. With greater rotation, the cloud progressively flattened into a disk shape.

The dominant physical process at this time was the condensation of tiny particles consisting mostly of silicate and nickel-enriched iron. The resulting rotational eddies concentrated the particles, and they clustered at discrete distances from the protosun. The particles literally fell together under their own mutual gravitational attraction, creating larger particles which in turn grew through impact with other masses. This process continued until planetesimal bodies (kilometers in size) accreted and acted as gravitational "dust mops" sweeping through space, collecting more mass. Astronomers currently believe that once accretion through gravitational attraction began to create density centers, the centers reached their present masses rather quickly, requiring something on the order of ten thousand years. The impact-accretion action resulted in the fragmentation and heating of the protoearth, differentiating the preplanetary material. A segregated interior began to develop, and the process accelerated as larger masses retained more and more of the impacting fragments. When the protoearth reached a sufficient mass, a segregation by density occurred similar to the overall density segregation of the solar system. At or near this time, the sun ignited. Its gravitational influence, temperature gradient, and solar wind produced a strong chemical/density segregation among the planets. The "rocky" planets—Mercury, Venus, Earth, the Moon, and Mars—formed close to the sun, while the frozen gas planets—Jupiter, Saturn, Uranus, and Neptune—formed in the outer orbits. By 1954, Harrison Brown had proposed an impact hypothesis to account for the initial accretion and differentiation of the earth into core, mantle, and crust. Following a large number of gravitational impacts, the earth accreted as a homogeneous mixture of silicates and iron-nickel. Radioactive heating caused the dense iron-nickel to melt and sink to the center of the earth, where it formed the core. The remaining lighter silicates formed the mantle and the crust. A slightly different impact hypothesis, described by Robert Jastrow in 1963, requires the existence of a dense iron-nickel condensate phase at the earth's core; a mantle and crust of silicates accreted around the core by gravitational impact. As with any either-or model, the mechanism of accretion and differentiation probably incorporates features from both hypotheses.

Meteorites may aid our understanding of the Archean eon. Their chemical composition suggests that the condensation and/or accretion from the nebular disc was not homogenous, falling instead into three general groups. These groups—called iron, stony-iron, and stony—appear to represent an early crystallization of two distinct chemical phases. Iron meteorites consist chiefly of iron with 4-20 percent alloyed nickel and small amounts of other elements such as chromium. The stony irons, as the name suggests, consist of roughly equal amounts of rock and iron. Stony meteorites are largely silicate minerals. The marked difference in the two earliest known groups (4-4.5 billion years old) found in the primordial solar system increases the likelihood that the earth accreted as a partially differentiated body. A comparative study of earth's sister planet, the moon, further strengthens the impact model of the earth's early history. Because of the close ratio of the two masses compared to other planet-satellite systems and the fact that the earth and moon revolve around a common center, astronomers often describe the earth-moon relation as a dual planet system rather than as a planet-satellite system. They assume that the earth and moon formed contemporaneously and in close proximity to each other. The moon, however, lacks the destructive erosional and tectonic forces found on earth; therefore it functions as a time capsule that mirrors an earlier earth phase. During the later stages of the moon's evolution, a molten stage appeared. The heat energy that caused the melting came from the impacts of the planetesimals and the decay of radioactive elements. Shortly after its crust cooled, a period of intense meteoric bombardment left the moon with numerous craters, resulting in highland-type terrain. Near the end of this cratering period, several large (100 kilometers in diameter), asteroid-sized objects struck the lunar surface, breaking through the thin crust. This allowed the darker colored basaltic lava to escape to the surface, flooding the low-lying areas; these darker areas are the maria. Equally large meteoroids must have struck the earth in the same fashion and during this time period. All maria basalts sampled so far have ages in the range of 3-4 billion years and are contemporaneous with the oldest dated earth rocks. In 1958, radioactive decay studies by L. T. Aldrich and G. W. Wetherill showed that the oldest surviving relics of terrestrial rocks date from about 3.8 billion years. Two explanations proposed in the late 1970's may account for the age differences of terrestrial rocks, lunar rocks (highlands) at 4.1 billion years and meteorites at 4.5 billion years. According to J. V. Smith, the earth's mantle was so cool after accretion (about 4.5 billion years) that it did not heat up sufficiently from gravitational pressure to produce magmas for another 700 million years. The second explanation is B. M. Jahn and L. E. Nyquist's plate tectonic model of subduction. It requires the crust's continuous generation and destruction and its recycling into the mantle via convection currents until some of the crustal material became stable. Meteor bombardment may have destroyed some of this early thin crust, but tectonics was probably the dominant factor.

Geologists have experienced difficulty in estimating the number of meteors that struck the earth. Nor are they certain that these meteors were of similar size and energy as those that formed the lunar craters in the early Archean time period. R. A. F. Grieve and H. Frey have extrapolated much of the physical and statistical modeling for the Archean from the moon, whose early Archean crust equivalent is preserved. Maria lava dates obtained from the Apollo missions indicate an age of 3.1-3.8 billion years for these forty well-defined maria basin structures, suggesting that perhaps up to three thousand basins might have existed on earth. These statistical models of the early 1980's project the formation of at least two thousand—and more likely twenty thousand—basins on earth with ages between 3.9 and 4.4 billion years. Through time, the frequency of these impacts should have decreased nearly exponentially. Meteors with diameters greater than 100 kilometers are the most significant geologic agents of the early Archean. Geologists estimate that several thousands of 100-kilometer meteors impacted the earth's early Archean surface and converted 30-50 percent of the crust into impact basins. These impacts could produce walls 3 kilometers above the surrounding terrain, with depths of 10-12 kilometers. An early ocean basin probably had this type of topography. The energy expended upon impact fractured the thin Archean crust to a depth of 25 kilometers and allowed molten material from the mantle to escape to the surface and flood the basin. The resulting structure became an ideal trap for the accumulation of sediments. Its stratigraphy would have included several kilometers of impact melts, crustal breccia, volcanics, and highland sediments. With the passage of time, the basins subsided, underwent a second partial melting, and produced a new generation of magmas. If the recycling continued, the magmas could have produced rocks higher in silicon and aluminum, more like the continental cores. Geologists believe that once the basins became tectonically stable, their stratigraphy included a mixture of metamorphosed rock intruded by granites and capped by crustal sediments. Such an interpretation can explain the formation of the protocontinent nuclei. Further tectonic development of the early crust led to the partial aggregation of nuclei, which, with the evolution of the greenstone belts, produced the familiar Archean Shields. Greenstone belts are unique to the Archean eon. They consist largely of volcanic rocks and sedimentary rocks derived primarily from volcanics. Their stratigraphy is often metamorphosed, producing the mineral chlorite, which has the characteristic green color from which the belts derive their name. Because the composite features of the greenstone belts are without a counterpart in modern geology, the geologic conditions of their formation were very different from what we observe today. The Canadian Shield demonstrates the greenstone stratigraphy and tectonics. Characteristically, it exhibits alternating linear belts (compressed basins) of greenstone-granite and gneiss. It also contains a series of elliptically shaped basins such as the Abitibi. While no large continents existed during the Archean eon, the nuclei necessary for their formation were present as protocontinents. These protocontinents were separated by numerous marine basins that accumulated lava and volcanic sediments. They later became greenstone belts. The thin Archean crust often broke under the active tectonic forces in the mantle and interjected magma into the protocontinents.

Geologists have had difficulty unraveling the true nature of the Archean stratigraphy. The two main problems are that the greenstone-granite terrains contain extensive metasedimentary sequences and that the combined igneous-metasedimentary successions grade laterally and vertically from intermediate- to high-grade metamorphic rocks. Large-scale magmatic intrusion and the structural response to the meteor impacts characterize the tectonics and stratigraphy of the Archean. The stratigraphic succession—the product of these tectonic forces—suggests that a deep crustal fracture system controlled the geology of this time and that meteorite impact produced the surface topography.

## Methods of Study

Scientists have used a diverse range of analytical techniques to study the Archean eon. Because tectonics or erosion has destroyed much of the earth's original Archean material, we look to our sister planet, the moon, to sample and observe this early stage of planetary development. The imagery from various lunar orbiter missions of the 1970's yielded a clarity and perspective of the moon previously unknown. Few outside the field of geology realized that these images also were revealing a snapshot of the early earth. Voyager photos of September 18, 1977, provided our first look at the earth and moon as a dual planet system. Moon rock samples obtained by Apollo astronauts during the missions of the early 1970's indicated chemical compositions and histories similar to the oldest of the earth's rocks and provided the first evidence supporting a parallel history.

Geologists have a variety of tools and techniques to unravel the Archean story. These range from viewing thin sections of rock samples under a microscope to the use of remote-sensing earth-orbiting satellites beginning in July, 1972. Because fossils are virtually nonexistent in the Archean, geologists rely on radioactive dating techniques for sequencing its events. Field mapping and sample collecting are their primary geological tools.

## Context

Until the twentieth century, the time before the fossil record was known simply as the Precambrian era; the Cambrian was the first period dated by fossils with hard parts. Precambrian time included about 90 percent of all geologic time. Currently, geologists recognize two eons within this period: the Archean, beginning at 4.6 billion years and ending at 2.5 billion years, and the Proterozoic, beginning at 2.5 billion years and ending at about 600 million years ago.

During the Archean eon, the earth underwent significant physical and chemical alterations. The physical changes set the stage for the development of continents and ocean basins; chemical changes would allow life to flourish on the earth's surface. Unfortunately, many details of this period remain hidden from science.

Even though this eon spans a major portion of the earth's history, the rocks left for study represent less than 20 percent of the total rock area exposed at the earth's surface. To complicate the investigation further, erosion has destroyed many of these rocks, and metamorphism (the altering of the surface by heat and pressure) has transformed others beyond any techniques to recognize their original characteristics. In the twentieth century, however, radiometric dating and the Apollo missions to the moon have enhanced greatly human understanding of the Archean. The moon is a snapshot of that earlier time on earth.

Perhaps of greatest importance of the Archean eon to twentieth century civilization and technology are the mineral resources of the Archean. Within these rocks lie much of earth's iron ore and other strategic metals, such as nickel, molybdenum, silver, iridium, gold, titanium, and manganese. Therefore, it is of great importance for geologists and mining engineers to unravel the stratigraphy of these complex rock sequences.

## Bibliography

Hartman, William K. "The Early History of the Planet Earth." *Astronomy* 6 (August, 1978): 6-14.

_____. "The Moon's Early History." *Astronomy* 4 (September, 1976): 6-24. This pair of introductory articles incorporate the latest astronomical and cosmological paradigms. *Astronomy* magazine is noted for its excellent photographs and illustrations. Very readable and a good starting point for the well-read amateur.

Kauffmann, William J., III. *Universe*. New York: W. H. Freeman, 1985. The chapters on the moon, the earth, and modern cosmology provide appropriate background for the general reader interested in the Archean eon. This freshman textbook is well written and includes excellent visuals.

Press, Frank, and Raymond Siever. *Earth*. New York: W. H. Freeman, 1986. An excellent freshman-level textbook in geology. Well written and profusely illustrated.

Ringwood, A. E. *Origin of the Earth and Moon*. New York: Springer-Verlag, 1979. More advanced readers will find this a good introduction to the early Archean.

*Scientific American* 249 (September, 1983). The entire issue deals with the study of the earth. There are many excellent and readable articles accompanied by superb illustrations.

Stanley, Steven. *Earth and Life Through Time*. 2d ed. New York: W. H. Freeman, 1989. A freshman-level textbook for the earth sciences, incorporating the latest cosmology in its discussion of the early earth. Suitable for the interested amateur.

*Anthony N. Stranges*
*Richard C. Jones*

## Cross-References

Earth's Age, 490; Earth's Core, 504; Earth's Crust, 518; Earth's Differentiation, 525; Earth's Mantle, 555; Earth's Oldest Rocks, 561; Earth's Origin, 569; Earth's Structure, 589; Lunar Maria, 1408; Lunar Rocks, 1414; Meteorites: Nickel-Irons, 1652; Meteorites: Stony Irons, 1659; Ocean Basins, 1785; Elemental Distribution in the Solar System, 2434; The Origin of the Solar System, 2442.

# ASTEROIDS

*Type of earth science:* Planetology
*Field of study:* Small solar system bodies

*Asteroids are the numerous small bodies in orbit around the sun, primarily between Mars and Jupiter. They provide important clues to the nature and earliest history of the solar system, including the effect of their collisions on the surfaces of planets and moons.*

### Principal terms

ALBEDO: the fraction of incident light that is reflected from the surfaces of planets, moons, and asteroids

ASTEROID BELT: the region between the orbits of Mars and Jupiter containing the majority of asteroids

CHONDRITE: a stony meteoritic material containing glassy spherical inclusions called chondrules, which are usually composed of iron, aluminum, or magnesium silicates

COMET: an object, with an elongated and randomly oriented orbit, consisting of rocky and icy materials that form a glowing head and extended tail when it nears the sun

DIFFERENTIATION: the sinking of heavy elements, such as nickel and iron, into the core of a planet during its molten stage

METEORITE: the remnant of an interplanetary body that survives a fall through the earth's atmosphere and reaches the ground

PHOTOMETRY: the technique of measuring the brightness of astronomical objects, usually with a photoelectric cell

PLANETESIMALS: the first small bodies to condense from the solar nebula, from which the planets are thought to have formed

## Summary of the Phenomenon

Although the discovery of the first asteroid was accidental, it was not completely unexpected. In 1766, the German astronomer Johann Titius (1729-1796) found that the positions of the planets could be approximated very closely by a simple empirical rule: Add 4 to each number in the sequence 0, 3, 6, 12, 24, 48 . . . and divide the sum by 10 to obtain the planetary distances from the sun in astronomical units (the distance from the earth to the sun is 1 AU), with the exception of the fifth entry, where an apparent gap occurs at 2.8 AUs. This rule was publicized by Johann Bode (1747-1826) and led to a search for a missing planet in the gap between Mars, at 1.5 AUs and Jupiter, at 5.2 AUs. On January 1, 1801, the Sicilian astronomer-monk Giuseppe Piazzi (1746-1826) accidentally discovered a moving object during a routine star survey. He named it Ceres, for the patron goddess of Sicily. Soon its orbit was calculated by Carl Friedrich Gauss (1777-1855) and, at 2.77 AUs, was found to conform closely to the Titius-Bode rule.

Since Ceres seemed to be too small to be a planet, the search continued, and in March of 1802, the German astronomer Heinrich Olbers (1758-1840) found a second small body at the same predicted distance. He named it Pallas. In 1803, Olbers proposed that meteorites come from an exploded planet near 2.8 AUs. This possibility led to a continuing search that resulted in the discovery of Juno in 1804 and Vesta in 1807, the latter by Olbers again. It took some time until a fifth small body was discovered in 1845, but by 1890, the total had reached three hundred. These bodies came to be called "asteroids," for their faint, starlike images. In 1891, the German astronomer Max Wolf (1863-1932) began using a long-exposure camera to detect asteroids, and over the next few years, some five hundred were revealed by their photographic trails. By 1984, the three thousandth asteroid had been numbered in the official catalog of the Institute of Theoretical Astronomy in Leningrad, after its orbit had been calculated and confirmed. Asteroids are usually referred to by number and name, such as 3 Juno or 1,000 Piazzia. About one hundred newly numbered asteroids are cataloged each year, and recent sky surveys indicate as many as 500,000 asteroids large enough to appear on telescopic photographs.

Most asteroids are found in the asteroid belt, which extends from 2.1 to 3.4 AUs, about half are between 2.75 and 2.85 AUs. Asteroids revolve around the sun in the same direction as the planets but tend to have more elongated orbits. Their orbits are inclined up to 30 degrees from planetary orbits, but they are more regular than comet orbits. The smallest asteroids are a few kilometers wide; the largest, 1 Ceres, about 1,000 kilometers wide. In 1867, the American astronomer Daniel Kirkwood (1814-1895) discovered gaps in the asteroid belt where relatively few asteroids are found. These so-called Kirkwood gaps occur where the asteroid orbits have periods that are simple fractions of the twelve-year period of giant Jupiter, resulting in their being affected by repeated gravitational forces called resonances. Such depletions occur, for example, at about 3.3 AUs (where the periods have a six-year, 1:2 resonance with Jupiter) and 2.5 AUs (a four-year, 1:3 resonance); other resonances, however, act to stabilize certain asteroids, such as the Hilda group at 4 AUs (2:3 resonance), which is named for 153 Hilda.

Some asteroids have orbits departing greatly from the main belt. In 1772, the French mathematician Joseph Lagrange (1736-1813) showed that points in Jupiter's orbit 60 degrees ahead of and behind the planet are gravitationally stable (1:1 resonance). In 1906, Max Wolf discovered the first so-called Trojan asteroid, 588 Achilles, at the Lagrange point 60 degrees ahead of Jupiter. Subsequent discoveries have revealed several hundred Trojan asteroids. Those ahead of Jupiter are named for Greek heroes, and those behind are named for Trojan heroes; there is one Greek spy (617 Patroclus) in the Trojan camp, and one Trojan spy (624 Hektor) in the Greek camp. Hektor is the largest known Trojan asteroid and the most elongated of the larger asteroids, at about 150 by 300 kilometers. At least two objects have orbits that extend beyond Jupiter: 944 Hidalgo, which may be a burnt-out comet nucleus, and 2060 Chiron, whose orbit extends beyond Saturn.

Some asteroids depart from the main belt over only part of their orbit. They include the Mars-crossing Amor group, with elongated orbits that carry them inside Mars' orbit but outside Earth's orbit, and the Earth-crossing Apollo group, which cross inside Earth's orbit. (The groups were named for their first examples, discovered in 1932.) Estimates indicate about thirteen hundred Apollos ranging in size from 0.4 to 10 kilometers with an estimated average Earth-collision rate of about one in 250,000 years. The closest known approaches were Hermes, in 1937, at about 780,000 kilometers, and 1566 Icarus, in 1968, at about 6 million kilometers. Smaller Apollos may be an important source of meteorites, and 100-meter objects capable of making a 1-kilometer crater strike Earth about every two thousand years. Aten-type asteroids are Earth-crossers with elliptical orbits smaller than Earth's. Some asteroids appear to be grouped in families that may be the fragments resulting from an earlier collision between asteroids.

The properties of asteroids are mostly determined by remote-sensing techniques used to study their reflected light and other radiation characteristics. More than five hundred asteroids have been studied by remote sensing, which has indicated compositions similar to those of meteorites. Comparison with reflected light from meteorites suggests several classes. The rare E-type asteroids have the highest albedo (23 to 45 percent reflection). They appear to be related to enstatite (a magnesium silicate mineral) chondrites and are concentrated near the inner edge of the main belt. About 10 percent of asteroids are S-type; they have relatively high albedos (7 to 23 percent) and are reddish in color. They appear to be related to stony chondrites, are found in the inner to central regions of the main belt, and they generally range in size from 100 to 200 kilometers. The largest S-type is 3 Juno, at about 250 kilometers, but much smaller Apollo asteroids are also in this category. A few asteroids in the middle belt are classified as M-type, since their reflected light (7 to 20 percent) shows evidence of large amounts of nickel-iron metals on their surface, like iron or stony-iron meteorites.

About three-quarters of all asteroids are C-type, with relatively low albedos (2 to 7 percent) and grayish colors similar to that of the Moon. They are found in the outer belt and among the Trojans, and they resemble the rare carbonaceous chondrite meteorites, containing water-bearing silicate and carbon-based minerals along with some organic compounds (about 1 percent). The largest asteroid, 1 Ceres, is in this category, and there is some evidence that it has a mixture of ice and carbonaceous minerals on its surface. Dark reddish, D-type asteroids are found in the same regions and have similar albedos. About 10 percent of asteroids remain unclassified and are designated as U-type. In general, asteroids with low-temperature volatile materials lie farther from the sun, whereas those in the inner part of the main belt are richer in high-temperature minerals and show little evidence of volatile water and carbon compounds.

Many asteroids exhibit periodic variations in brightness that suggest irregular shapes and rotation. Their measured rotational periods range from about three to thirty hours. There is some evidence that S-type asteroids rotate faster than C-type asteroids but slower than M-type asteroids. Large asteroids (greater than 120 kilometers) rotate more slowly with increasing size, but small asteroids rotate more slowly with decreasing size, suggesting that large asteroids may be primordial bodies while smaller ones may be fragments produced by collisions. Calculations show that rotation rates longer than two hours produce centrifugal forces weaker than gravity, which indicates that loose debris can exist on the surface of even the fastest known rotating asteroid, the Apollo object 1566 Icarus, which has a 2.25-hour rotation rate. Studies of the polarization of light reflected from asteroids indicate that many do have dusty surfaces, and computer models suggest the possibility that larger asteroids have a deep layer of dust and rock fragments, or regolith, similar to that on the surface of the moon. Those with diameters larger than 100 kilometers are believed to have undergone a process of differentiation in which heavier metals sank to the core, leaving a stony surface of lighter materials that was later pulverized by collisions to form a layer of dust.

Asteroid elongations can be estimated from the change in brightness, which can vary by a factor of three or more. Kilometer-scale asteroids have been observed with lengths up to six times greater than their width. Main-belt asteroids tend to be less elongated than Mars-crossers of the same size, perhaps because of more erosion from collisions in the belt. Asteroids larger than about 400 kilometers tend to be more nearly spherical, since their gravitational pressures exceed the strength of their rocky materials, causing deformation and plastic flow into a more symmetric shape. An asteroid's size occasionally can be determined quite accurately by timing its passage in front of a star. In a few cases, the light from such stars has been obscured more than once, suggesting that asteroids with satellites may exist. Some evidence indicates that the unusual Trojan asteroid 624 Hektor (150 by 300 kilometers) may be a dumbbell-shaped double asteroid.

The distribution of asteroid sizes and masses supports the idea that many have undergone a process of fragmentation. Typical velocities of encounter of about 5 kilometers per second in the main belt are quite adequate to fragment most asteroids. Ceres contains nearly half the mass of all the asteroids, but it is more than three times smaller than the Moon and about fifty times less massive. About 80 percent of the total mass of all asteroids is contained in the four largest ones, and only about ten are larger than 300 kilometers. Studies suggest that the main belt was several times more massive in the past but that in the process of fragmentation, the smallest dust particles were removed by radiation pressure from the sun.

## Methods of Study

Since no spacecraft has passed close enough to an asteroid to photograph its surface or measure its mass, indirect methods of remote sensing must be used to determine their properties by studying the reflected light and other radiation that comes from their surfaces. These methods include photometry, infrared radiometry, colorimetry, spectroscopy, polarimetry, and radar detection. They can be augmented by comparative studies with meteorites, whose composition and structure can be analyzed by direct methods in the laboratory. Such methods include chemical, spectroscopic, and microscopic analysis, and processes of fragmentation can be studied by producing high-speed collisions between comparable materials in the laboratory. Such comparative studies must recognize various differences between meteorites and asteroids. The masses of only the three largest asteroids have been determined from their gravitational effects on other bodies; their densities are between 2.3 and 3.3 grams per cubic centimeter.

Photometry is the study of how light is scattered by various surfaces. The varying brightness of reflected sunlight from asteroids can be measured by photoelectric observations to determine their rotation periods and approximate shapes. One test of this method was made in 1931, when the Amor asteroid 433 Eros came close enough (23 million kilometers) for scientists to observe the tumbling motion of this elongated object (7 by 19 by 30 kilometers) and to confirm its 5.3-hour rotation. The size of an asteroid can be estimated from its brightness together with its distance, orbital position, and albedo. The albedo is important, since a bright, small object may reflect as much light as a dark, large object. Since a dark object absorbs more heat than a light object, albedos can be determined by comparing reflected light with thermal radiation measured by infrared radiometry. Photometric measurements also give information on surface textures. Colorimetry involves measuring the range of wavelengths in the reflected light to determine surface colors. Most asteroids are either fairly bright, reddish objects (with albedos of up to 23 percent) composed largely of silicate-type materials or grayish objects, at least as dark as the Moon (11 percent albedo), composed of carbonaceous materials.

Spectroscopy is the analysis of the spectrum of light and can be used to infer the composition of many asteroids. Optical and infrared reflectance spectra exhibit absorption bands at characteristic frequencies for given material. Asteroids' surface composition is determined by comparing their spectra with the spectra of light reflected from meteorites of known composition. Examples of this method applied to U-type asteroids include the identification of pyroxene (a silicate mineral) in the infrared spectrum of Apollo asteroid 1685 Toro and the matching of the surface of Vesta with a basaltic achondrite that resembles lava. Most asteroids appear to have unmelted surfaces with little or no evidence of lava eruptions. About two-thirds of the Trojans are D-type asteroids with no known meteorite counterparts because of their distance from Earth. Their spectra have been matched with the spectra of coal-tar residues, suggesting possible organic compounds.

Polarimetry uses measurements of the alignment of the vibrations of the reflected sunlight and its variation with direction to estimate albedos. Polarization measurements have also been interpreted as evidence for dust-covered surfaces, but they leave uncertainty about the depth of the dust layer. Radar observations of Eros during a close approach to Earth in 1975 were made at a wavelength of 3.8 centimeters and indicated that the surface must be rough on a scale of centimeters. Since optical polarimetry suggests that Eros is dusty, the radar results imply that the dust must be too thin to smooth rock outcrops of more than a few centimeters.

Radar measurements also provide independent estimates of the size of Eros, confirming photometric estimates of its dimensions.

The best method to study asteroids would be by means of a space probe. When Pioneers 10 and 11 passed through the asteroid belt, scientists found that it has no more dust than any other part of the solar system. The Galileo mission was originally planned to pass near 29 Amphitrite in December of 1986, but this opportunity was missed because of delays caused by the destruction of the *Challenger* space shuttle in January of that year. Several countries are continuing to make plans for an asteroid mission.

## Context

Asteroids usually cannot be seen with the unaided eye, but they provide important clues for understanding planet formation, and they can have major effects on the earth and its history. At one time, it was assumed that the asteroid belt was formed by the breakup of a planet between Mars and Jupiter; however, the combined mass in the belt is much less than that of any planet (only 0.04 percent Earth's mass), and the observed differences in the composition of asteroids at different locations in the belt make it unlikely that they all came from the same planet-sized object. It now appears that asteroids are original debris that was left over after planet formation and that has undergone complex processes such as collisions, fragmentation, and heating. Apparently, the strong tidal forces caused by Jupiter's large mass prevented small bodies between it and Mars from combining to form a single planet in their region.

It appears, therefore, that asteroids are among the oldest objects in the solar system, left over from the time immediately before complete planet formation. Studies of these objects should provide clues to the structure and composition of the primitive solar nebula. The different types of asteroid found in different regions of space seem to support the theory of planetesimal origin through a sequence of condensation from a nebular disk around the sun. Asteroids farther from the sun, beyond the main belt, may have contained more ice; those that formed closer, within the belt, may have been primarily stony or stony-iron materials. Some of these planetesimal precursors of asteroids were probably perturbed during close passes by neighboring planets into elongated Apollo-like orbits that cross Earth's orbit. Other objects on similar orbits may have been comets that remained in the inner solar system long enough to lose their volatile ices by evaporation. Processes of collision and fragmentation among these objects provide direct evidence about the earliest forms of matter.

Special interest in Apollo asteroids arises from their potential for Earth collisions. Objects as small as 100 meters hit Earth about once every two thousand years, and the 30 percent that fall on land can produce 1-kilometer craters. Such impacts would devastate much wider areas by their shock waves, and dust thrown into the upper atmosphere could have marked effects on climate. Growing evidence suggests that asteroid collisions in the past might have contributed to major extinctions of species, such as the dinosaurs, and perhaps even caused reversals of Earth's magnetism. Thin layers of iridium, often found in meteorites, have been identified in Earth's crust at layers corresponding to such extinctions. Satellite photography has revealed about one hundred apparent impact craters on Earth with diameters up to 140 kilometers. It is likely that many more succumbed to processes of erosion. Knowledge of Apollo orbits might make it possible to avoid such collisions in the future.

Asteroids also offer the possibility of recovering resources with great economic potential. Some contain great quantities of nickel-iron alloys and other scarce elements; others may yield water, hydrogen, and other materials useful for space construction. Estimates of the economic value of a kilometer-sized asteroid reach as high as several trillion dollars. A well-designed approach to space mining might someday help to take pressure off Earth's ecosystem by providing an alternative to dwindling resources, and space-borne manufacturing centers might alleviate pollution on Earth.

## Bibliography

Baugher, Joseph F. *The Space-Age Solar System*. New York: John Wiley & Sons, 1988. This book is an excellent and highly readable introduction to the solar system, with an emphasis on exploration and results from interplanetary spacecraft. An eight-page chapter on asteroids provides a good overview, supplemented by chapters on comets, meteorites, and species extinctions. A ten-page bibliography provides about five hundred references on planetary studies. The style of the book is suitable for high school and college-level readers.

Chapman, Clark R. *The Inner Planets*. New York: Charles Scribner's Sons, 1977. This book concentrates on the rocky inner planets; it includes a chapter on asteroids. The author is a leading expert on asteroids and planetary cratering. The book is written in an informal style with much anecdotal material about researchers in the field. Suitable for the general reader.

Delsemme, A. H., ed. *Comets, Asteroids, Meteorites*. Toledo, Ohio: University of Toledo, 1977. This book is the result of an international colloquium on the interrelations, evolution, and origins of comets, asteroids, and meteorites. It contains about seventy-five articles, including eighteen specifically on asteroids by leading experts. Although the text is quite technical, much of it can be read by college students interested in detailed information and a firsthand account of research results.

Gehrels, T., ed. *Asteroids*. Tucson: University of Arizona Press, 1979. The most authoritative and comprehensive book on asteroids available in English. It contains about fifty articles on every aspect of asteroid research, including extensive references to original research papers. Most articles are technical, but the first seventy-five pages provide a readable introductory survey. Tabulations in the last section provide data of various kinds on all asteroids that have been studied.

Hartmann, William K. *Moons and Planets*. Belmont, Calif.: Wadsworth, 1983. A college-level textbook on planetary astronomy by one of the leading authorities in the field. The chapter on asteroids is one of the best summaries at the introductory level. It has excellent charts, diagrams, and reproductions of the author's original paintings of imaginary space scenes. Additional material relating to asteroids is included in chapters on comets, meteorites, planetary evolution, and cratering. An appendix on planetary data includes some asteroid data for comparison, and an extensive bibliography includes about seventy entries on asteroids.

Veverka, Joseph. *Planetary Geology in the 1980s*. NASA SP-830-I. Washington, D.C.: National Aeronautics and Space Administration, 1985. This book is a summary of a report compiled by the Planetary Geology Working Group of NASA. It contains introductory chapters on planetary geology, a chapter on the geology of small bodies, and a chapter on remote sensing. The book concludes with recommendations for future research and some three hundred references on planetary geology. It is suitable for general readers with scientific interests.

*Joseph L. Spradley*

## Cross-References

# ASTROBLEMES

*Type of earth science:* Planetology
*Field of study:* Large solar system bodies

*Space Age discoveries about the surface character of other terrestrial planets have led to the realization that Earth must have been heavily scarred by impacts with planetesimals in the past. Erosion processes and plate tectonics have obliterated most of the ancient craters, but new interest in the phenomenon and evidence that major impacts may have had a significant role in shaping the course of evolution have spurred a search for astroblemes, circular surface features considered to have been large impact craters.*

*Principal terms*
   ASTROBLEME: the remnant of a large impact crater on Earth; erosion will
      have altered the superficial appearance, but confirmation can be
      made from deeper structural damage and the presence of
      characteristically shattered and shocked rock
   BRECCIA: rock composed of consolidated rock fragments that have been
      lithified by the impact process
   COESITE: a high-density form of quartz formed under the pressures and
      temperatures involved in impact cratering
   EJECTA: material excavated from the target body by the cratering process
      and redistributed on the surface of the land around the crater
   METAMORPHISM: alteration in the characteristics of rocks and minerals
      owing to the effects of intense heat and pressure
   PLANETESIMAL: any solid minor body orbiting the sun; included are
      many thousands of asteroids and an unknown but very large number
      of meteors
   REGOLITH: soil layers composed of impact-generated rock fragments,
      usually severely altered by heat and stress

## Summary of the Phenomenon

Impact cratering is one of the most fundamental geologic processes in the solar system. Craters are found on the surfaces of all the solid planets and satellites thus far investigated by spacecraft. Mercury and the Moon, bodies whose ancient surfaces have not been reworked by subsequent geologic processes, preserve a vivid record of the role that impact cratering has played in the past. It is inconceivable that Earth somehow escaped the bombardment that caused such widespread scarring, or that it does not continue to be a target for planetesimals still roaming the solar system.

As recently as a quarter-century ago, only a handful of sites on the earth were accepted to be of impact origin. Recently the number of confirmed astroblemes was well in excess of one hundred and increasing at the rate of several per year. In addition, there are many "probable" and "possible" impact features under study. Nevertheless, an enormous discrepancy exists between the number of identified or suspected impact sites on the earth and the number that might be expected.

It is assumed that the flux of incoming bodies is the same for the earth as it is for the moon. Making allowances for the fact that the earth is the largest "target" of any of the terrestrial planets and that two-thirds of its surface is covered by water, planetologists calculate that the land areas of the earth should have been scarred by at least fifteen hundred craters of 10 kilometers or more in diameter. In actuality, only about half of the known astroblemes are in this size range. On a global scale, 99 percent of the predicted large impact craters seem to be missing. This statistic is not a valid indicator of the impact history of the earth, however, because, although the impact phenomenon is a geographic process, the probability for discovering impact sites is strongly modified by the geologic stability of various regions of the earth and by the intensity of the search programs in those areas. Roughly one half of all the confirmed astroblemes have been found in Canada, which constitutes only 1 percent of the earth's surface. In part, this is owing to the stability of the Precambrian rock of the Canadian Shield, but it also reflects a diligent research effort by Canada's Department of Energy, Mines, and Resources. In general, the number of large impact sites found in the well-explored areas of the earth agrees with the accepted rate of crater formation on the other terrestrial planets in the past two billion years.

The obvious difference between the surface appearances of the earth and moon is explained not by any difference in the rate at which impact craters have formed, but in the rate at which they are destroyed. Most of the numerous craters on the moon are more than 3.9 billion years old, while earth's oldest surviving astroblemes were formed less than 2 billion years ago. Studies have shown that erosion effectively removes all traces of a 100-meter (diameter) crater in only a few thousand years, and that a 1-kilometer-wide crater, such as the well-known Barringer Meteor Crater in Arizona, will disappear within a million years. Only craters with diameters greater than 100 kilometers can be expected to leave any trace after a billion years of erosion. This explains not only the absence of widespread cratering on the landscape but also the fact that, among the astroblemes known to exist, medium and large scars are more common than small ones.

Significant craters can be produced only by objects having masses of hundreds of thousands to billions of tons. The Barringer Crater, 1.2 kilometers wide and 200 meters deep, is believed to have been formed by a one-million-ton planetesimal that was perhaps 50 meters in diameter. A 27-kilometer-wide astrobleme known as Ries Crater in West Germany required an impacting body greater than 1 kilometer in diameter with a mass in excess of 1 billion tons. Planetesimals as large as these two examples are not characteristic of the vagrant meteors that wander through the solar system and occasionally streak into the earth's skies as shooting stars.

Most of the past impacts on the earth and the moon appear to be attributable to a family of asteroids known as the Apollo-Amor group (after two specific members of the family). Members of this group are in orbits that graze the orbit of the earth and become subject to orbital perturbations that lead them across the earth's path periodically. It is estimated that the average Apollo-Amor object intersects the orbit of the earth once every five thousand years, although usually the planet is at some other point on its orbit when this happens. The probability of a collision between the earth and any given Apollo-Amor object is small, but several studies have shown that this family contains between 750 and 1,000 asteroids larger than 1 kilometer in diameter. Statistical analysis suggests that such monsters must collide with the earth an average of once every 600,000 years.

The number of Apollo-Amor objects of a given size seems to follow an inverse-square relationship, leading scientists to believe that there are some 100,000 members of the family of at least 100 meters in diameter. Collisions with bodies of this size can be expected once every twenty-five centuries, although two out of every three of these bodies probably strike the ocean. The inverse-square relationship also suggests that there may have been at least a few members of the group as big as 100 kilometers in diameter, and the surface of the moon bears testimony to long-ago impacts with objects of that size. None of the Apollo-Amor asteroids known today is close to this big, so it may be that all of those in this size range have already impacted and no longer pose a threat.

Impact events involve tremendous transfers of energy from the incoming planetesimal to the earth's surface. A projectile's energy of motion increases only linearly with its mass but as the square of its velocity, so surprisingly large craters result from relatively small bodies traveling at hypervelocities. Depending on the directions of motion of the earth and of the planetesimal, impacts on the planet may involve relative velocities as high as 50 kilometers per second. At velocities surpassing 4 kilometers per second, the energy of the shock wave created by the impact is far greater than the strength of molecular adhesion for either the planetesimal or the earth, so that on impact the planetesimal acquires the properties of a highly compressed gas and explodes with a force equivalent to a similar mass of blasting powder.

The shock wave from this explosion intensely compresses the target material and causes it to be severely deformed, melted, or even vaporized. (In all but the smaller impacts, the entire projectile is also vaporized.) The shock wave swiftly expands in a radial fashion, pulverizing the target material and intensely altering the nature of the target rock by extreme and almost instantaneous heat and pressure. This is immediately followed by decompression and what is called a rarefaction wave that restores the ambient pressure. The rarefaction wave moves only over free surfaces, so it travels outward over the ground surface and into the atmosphere above the impact and becomes the excavating force that lifts vast quantities of the pulverized target material upward and outward to create the crater cavity.

The rarefaction wave excavates a hole whose depth is one-third of its diameter and whose profile follows a parabolic curve, but this depression is short-lived and is therefore called the transient cavity. After the passage of the rarefaction wave, a large amount of pulverized target material from the walls of the transient cavity slumps inward under gravity, and some of the ejecta lofted straight up into the atmosphere falls back into the excavation. Together, these sources contribute to a lens-shaped region of breccia that fills the true crater's floor and leaves a shallower, flat-floored apparent crater as the visible scar of the impact. Apparent craters generally exhibit a depth of only one-tenth to one-twentieth of their diameters. Meanwhile, the rarefaction wave carries ejecta particles outward over the surrounding landscape, where they fall to earth as a blanket of regolith that is distinguishable from the local target rock by the effects of shock metamorphism.

## Methods of Study

Impact phenomena are rare enough on the human time scale that no crater-forming events are known to have occurred in recorded history. Owing to this passage of time, and to the fact that most existing astroblemes have been severely altered by erosion, impact cratering has been studied by the unique modifications that a powerful impact shock makes in the rocks and minerals at the site, by the deformation and structural damage to buried strata, and by the presence of certain rare elements and minerals in the sediments surrounding suspected impact sites.

Much attention has been given to the effects of the shock wave on terrestrial rocks, since shock metamorphism is considered to be the most enduring and positive identifier of ancient astroblemes. Shock metamorphism differs from endogenic metamorphism by the scales of pressure and temperature involved and by the very short duration of the exposure to those pressures and temperatures. Endogenic metamorphism usually involves pressures of less than 1 gigapascal (100,000 atmospheres) and temperatures not greater than 1,000 degrees Celsius. The pressures involved in shock metamorphism are exponentially greater, reaching several hundred gigapascals for an instant in the vicinity of the impact. Rock exposed to pressures in excess of 80 gigapascals and temperatures of several thousand degrees Celsius is immediately vaporized. Lesser pressures and temperatures at increased distances from the point of impact produce signs of melting, thermal decomposition, phase transitions, and plastic deformation.

Pockets of melt glass up to several meters thick are commonly found in the breccia within the crater, indicating that pressures there reached 45-60 gigapascals. Coesite and its denser relative, stishovite, are forms of quartz that occur naturally only at impact sites. Shatter cones, conically shaped crystals created at pressures of from 2 to 25 gigapascals, are another prominent feature of shock metamorphism and are particularly well developed in fine-grained isotropic rock. Microscopic examination of impact-shocked porous rock reveals that quartz grains are deformed so as to fill the pores and interlock like the pieces of a jigsaw puzzle. Even at a considerable distance from the impact point, quartz grains tend to be elongated in the direction of the shock wave's passage.

Theories concerning cratering dynamics can also be tested by analogy to some of the craters produced by the detonation of nuclear devices. This latter technique has adequately explained the morphology of the smaller astroblemes, those with diameters that do not exceed 2-4 kilometers. Larger impact events involve additional dynamics that are not mimicked by nuclear devices thus far tested. Astroblemes greater than 2 kilometers in diameter in sedimentary rock or 4 kilometers in diameter in crystalline rock display a pronounced central uplift owing to an intense vertical displacement of the strata under the center of the impact. An additional feature distinguishing complex craters is that their depths are always a much smaller fraction of their diameters than is the case with simple craters.

Photographic imaging of the earth from space has revealed some young and well-preserved astroblemes in remote and poorly explored areas of the earth, such as the Sahara Desert. More important has been the satellite's ability to reveal structures that still preserve a faint but distinct circularity when seen from orbit, although at ground level they are so eroded that their circularity has escaped detection. One of the largest astroblemes yet discovered was found from Landsat satellite images in this way. New imaging technologies, including advanced radar and sonar mapping, promise to extend the capabilities of space surveillance and remote sensing in recognizing possible impact sites.

## Context

The degree to which the earth is in danger of being struck by a massive planetesimal began to be appreciated about the middle of the twentieth century. In 1980, a team led by Nobel physicist Luis Alvarez announced dramatic evidence suggesting that an asteroid impact that occurred 65 million years ago created such planetary trauma that it might explain a mysterious massive extinction of life forms known to have occurred on the earth at that time. At several sites around the world, the researchers had discovered that the sediments at the boundary layer between the Cretaceous and Tertiary periods contained up to one hundred times the normal abundance of the metal iridium, which is rare in the crustal rocks of earth but 1,000 to 10,000 times more abundant in the makeup of many asteroids. This Cretaceous-Tertiary boundary layer is coincident with the point at which fully 70 percent of the life forms then existing on earth, including the dinosaurs, became extinct. Further study has also revealed that this same sediment layer is rich in shock-metamorphosed quartz grains, known only to occur naturally from impact explosions.

Debate continues as to whether an asteroid impact was the primary cause of the mass extinctions at the close of the Cretaceous period or merely a contributing factor, but there is general agreement that a colossal impact occurred at that time. The volume of material represented in the boundary sediments suggests that the planetesimal was perhaps 10 kilometers in diameter and would have created a crater of as much as 200 kilometers in width. No such astrobleme has yet been found (the largest known on earth are 140-160 kilometers in diameter), but preliminary evidence from the global distribution of the ejecta points to the possibility that the impact may have occurred in the North Atlantic, where the scar would be difficult to detect, assuming that it has not already been obliterated by sea-floor spreading.

Although the precise scenario for what is called the K-T Event (from the German spelling of Cretaceous-Tertiary) is not known, a majority of planetologists now consider the evidence that it involved a major impact to be convincing. Meanwhile, several other iridium spikes (abnormally high concentrations of the metal) have been found in the sedimentary beds coinciding with other recognized mass extinctions.

Three related discoveries suggest the possibility that impact cratering may not be an entirely random process, so far as its distribution through time is concerned. Paleontologists David Raup and Jack Sepkoski have shown evidence based on a rigorous analysis of the marine fossil record that mass extinctions appear to occur with regularity every 26 million years. Independently, the team of Walter Alvarez (also a member of the team that discovered the K-T iridium anomaly) and Richard Muller have discovered evidence that the ages of the major known terrestrial astroblemes seem to be periodically distributed at intervals of roughly 28 million years. For some time, researchers have sought a mechanism that could account for the numerous polarity reversals in the earth's magnetic field over geologic history, and some have suggested that major impact events may be the cause. Several studies have reported an apparent fine-scale periodicity in the earth's magnetic field reversals with a cycle of 30 million years. Although the intervals are not in perfect agreement, they are very close, considering the difficulty of precisely dating extinctions and the exact ages of astroblemes.

These discoveries suggest that there may be an as yet undiscovered member of the solar system which moves in such a way as periodically to disrupt the Oort Cloud, the cloud of comets believed to exist on the fringes of the solar system, causing a barrage of planetesimals to descend upon the inner planets. Although the existence and location of such a body remain speculative and controversial, it has been characterized as a dwarf companion star of the sun and is called Nemesis.

## Bibliography

Grieve, Richard A. F. "Terrestrial Impact Structures." *Annual Review of Earth and Planetary Science* 15 (1987): 245-270. A thorough summary of what is known about the cratering process on earth, written by a leading authority on the subject. It is intended for the scientific reader, but its illustrations, extensive bibliography, and the introductory and summary sections of the text are of value even to those who are not familiar with the concepts and terminology in the body of the article.

Hartmann, William K. "Cratering in the Solar System." *Scientific American* 236 (January, 1977): 84-99. A comprehensive explanation of the role attributed to impact cratering in shaping the surfaces of all of the terrestrial planets. The author explains the basis for estimating the frequency of impacts for various sizes of planetesimals and the logic behind using crater counts to estimate the ages of planetary surfaces. The article also explains the theory that the first half-billion years of solar system history involved an extremely heavy bombardment of all the inner planets.

Kerr, Richard A. "When Disaster Rains Down from the Sky." *Science* 206 (November 16, 1979): 803-804. Written in descriptive terms easily comprehended by laymen, this article summarizes research by several investigators attempting to compute the frequency with which the earth is struck by crater-forming bodies. It places particular emphasis on the Apollo asteroid group and examines suggestions that the Apollo family is supplied with new planetesimals by the decay of former comets.

Morrison, David, and Tobias Owen. *The Planetary System*. Reading, Mass.: Addison-Wesley, 1987. With this single source, the subject of impact cratering can be studied in its broader context, as a major surface-shaping phenomenon throughout the solar system. Written as an introductory textbook for a descriptive undergraduate course in planetary science, it is readable, well illustrated, and up to date.

Muller, Richard. *Nemesis: The Death Star*. New York: Weidenfeld & Nicolson, 1988. Despite its tabloid title, this is an excellent discussion of the chain of discoveries leading to the Nemesis theory by the Berkeley physicist who developed it. Organized in two parts, the first recaps the evidence for a major impact at the K-T boundary, and the second tells how further research led Muller to postulate the existence of Nemesis. The book is intended for lay readers and gives insight into how the scientific discovery process works, as well as explaining the theory.

Murray, Bruce, Michael C. Malin, and Ronald Greeley. *Earthlike Planets*. San Francisco: W. H. Freeman, 1981. Although terrestrial impact craters are not specifically discussed, the impact mechanics that produce craters are presented here in terms that are suitable for general readers. It is also an excellent discussion of cratering as a ubiquitous aspect of the surfaces of all the inner planets.

Raup, David M. *The Nemesis Affair*. New York: W. W. Norton, 1986. The author is a significant figure in the field of paleontology and has done leading research on the apparent periodicity of extinctions and magnetic reversals. His narrative is a fascinating personal account of the ideas and the individuals who led the scientific community from extreme skepticism to general acceptance that impact "catastrophism" may have played a major role in the evolution of the earth and its life forms.

Wetherill, George W. "Apollo Objects." *Scientific American* 240 (March, 1979): 54-65. A clearly written explanation of the role that the family of near-earth asteroids is believed to have in causing impact cratering on Earth, the Moon, Mars, and Venus. The discussion contains good information on the problems of determining the number of Apollo asteroids and the frequency with which Earth and other terrestrial planets are hit.

*Richard S. Knapp*

## Cross-References

# THE ATMOSPHERE'S EVOLUTION

*Field of study:* Atmospheric sciences and meteorology

*The chemical composition of the atmosphere has changed significantly over the 4.6-billion-year history of the earth. The composition of atmosphere has been controlled by a number of processes, including the "outgassing" of gases or volatiles originally trapped in the earth's interior during its formation; the geochemical cycling of carbon, nitrogen, hydrogen, and oxygen compounds between the surface, the ocean, and the atmosphere; and the origin and evolution of life.*

*Principal terms*

CHEMICAL EVOLUTION: the synthesis of amino acids and other complex organic molecules—the precursors of living systems—by the action of atmospheric lightning and solar ultraviolet radiation on atmospheric gases

PHOTOSYNTHESIS: the utilization of carbon dioxide and water vapor by chlorophyll-containing organisms in the presence of sunlight to metabolically produce carbohydrates used by the plant for food; oxygen is a by-product in the photosynthesis process

PRIMORDIAL SOLAR NEBULA: an interstellar cloud of gas and dust that condensed under gravity to form the sun, the moon, earth, the other planets and their satellites, asteroids, comets, and meteors some 4.6 billion years ago

SOLAR ULTRAVIOLET RADIATION: biologically lethal solar radiation in the spectral interval between approximately 0.1 and 0.3 micron (1 micron = 0.0001 centimeter)

VOLATILE OUTGASSING: the release of the gases or volatiles, such as water vapor, carbon dioxide, and nitrogen, trapped within the earth's interior during its formation

## Summary of the Phenomenon

Some 4.6 billion years ago, a cloud of interstellar gas and dust, called the primordial solar nebula, began to condense under the influence of gravity. This condensation led to the formation of the sun, the moon, Earth, the other planets and their satellites, asteroids, meteors, and comets. The primordial solar nebula was composed almost entirely of hydrogen gas, with a smaller amount of helium, still smaller amounts of carbon, nitrogen, and oxygen, and still smaller amounts of the rest of the elements of the periodic table. About the time that the newly formed earth reached its approximate present mass, gases that were originally trapped in the earth's interior were released through the surface, forming a gravitationally bound atmosphere. (It is believed that the atmospheres of the other terrestrial planets, Mars and Venus, also formed in this manner.) The release of these gases is called volatile outgassing. The period of extensive volatile outgassing may have lasted for many tens of millions of years. The outgassed volatiles or gases had roughly the same chemical composition as do present-day volcanic emissions: 80 percent water vapor by volume, 10 percent carbon dioxide by volume, 5 percent sulfur dioxide by volume, 1 percent nitrogen by volume, and smaller amounts of hydrogen, carbon monoxide, sulfur, chlorine, and argon.

The water vapor that outgassed from the interior soon reached its saturation point, which is controlled by the atmospheric temperature and pressure. Once the saturation point was reached, the atmosphere could not hold any additional gaseous water vapor. Any new outgassed water vapor that entered the atmosphere would have precipitated out of the atmosphere in the form of liquid water. The equivalent of several kilometers of liquid water released from the earth's interior in gaseous form precipitated out of the atmosphere and formed the earth's vast oceans. Only small amounts of water vapor remained in the atmosphere—ranging from a fraction of a percent to several percent by volume, depending on atmospheric temperature, season, and latitude.

The outgassed atmospheric carbon dioxide, being very water soluble, readily dissolved into the newly formed oceans and formed carbonic acid. In the oceans, carbonic acid formed ions of hydrogen, bicarbonate, and carbonate. The carbonate ions reacted with ions of calcium and magnesium in the ocean water, forming carbonate rocks, which precipitated out of the ocean and accumulated as sea-floor carbonate sediments. Most of the outgassed atmospheric carbon dioxide formed carbonates, leaving only trace amounts of gaseous carbon dioxide in the atmosphere (about 0.035 percent by volume). Sulfur dioxide, the third most abundant component of volatile outgassing, was chemically transformed into other sulfur compounds and sulfates in the atmosphere. Eventually, the sulfates formed atmospheric aerosols and diffused out of the atmosphere onto the surface.

The fourth most abundant outgassed compound, nitrogen, is chemically inert in the atmosphere and thus was not chemically transformed, as was sulfur dioxide. Unlike carbon dioxide, nitrogen is relatively insoluble in water and, unlike water vapor, does not condense out of the atmosphere. For these reasons, nitrogen built up in the atmosphere to become its major constituent (78.08 percent by volume). Therefore, outgassed volatiles led to the formation of the earth's atmosphere, oceans, and carbonate rocks.

The molecules of nitrogen, carbon dioxide, and water vapor in the early atmosphere were acted upon by solar ultraviolet radiation and atmospheric lightning. In the process, molecules of formaldehyde and hydrogen cyanide were chemically synthesized in the early atmosphere. These molecules precipitated and diffused out of the atmosphere into the oceans. In the oceans, the formaldehyde and hydrogen cyanide entered into chemical reactions, called polymerization reactions, which eventually led to the chemical synthesis of amino acids, the building blocks of living systems. The synthesis of amino acids from nitrogen, carbon dioxide, and water vapor in the atmosphere is called chemical evolution. Chemical evolution preceded and provided the material for biological evolution.

For many years, it was thought that the early atmosphere was composed of ammonia, methane, and hydrogen, rather than of carbon dioxide, nitrogen, and water vapor. Experiments show, however, that ammonia and methane are chemically unstable and are readily destroyed by both solar ultraviolet radiation and chemical reaction with the hydroxyl radical, which is formed from water vapor. In addition, ammonia is very water soluble and is readily removed from the atmosphere by precipitation. Hydrogen, the lightest element, is readily lost from a planet by gravitational escape. Thus, an early atmosphere composed of methane, ammonia, and hydrogen would be very short-lived, unless these gases were produced at a rate comparable to their destruction or loss rates. Today, methane and ammonia are very minor components of the atmosphere—methane at a concentration of 1.7 parts per million by volume and ammonia at a concentration of 1 part per billion by volume. Both gases are produced solely by microbial activity at the earth's surface. Clearly, microbial activity and microbes were nonexistent during the earliest history of the planet. The atmospheres of the outer planets—Jupiter, Saturn, Uranus, and Neptune—all contain appreciable quantities of hydrogen, methane, and ammonia. It is believed that the atmospheres of these planets, unlike the atmospheres of the terrestrial planets—Earth, Venus, and Mars—are captured remnants of the primordial solar nebula. Because of the outer planets' great distance from the sun and their very low temperatures, hydrogen, methane, and ammonia are stable and long-lived constituents of their atmospheres. This is not true of hydrogen, methane, and ammonia in the earth's atmosphere.

Some have suggested that at the time of its formation, the earth may have also captured a remnant of the primordial solar nebula as its very first atmosphere. Such a captured primordial solar nebula atmosphere would have been composed of mostly hydrogen (about 90 percent) and helium (about 10 percent), the two major elements of the nebula. Even if such an atmosphere had surrounded the very young earth, it would have been very short-lived. As the young sun went through its T Tauri phase of evolution, very strong solar winds (the supersonic flow of protons and electrons from the sun) would have quickly dissipated this remnant atmosphere. In addition, there is no geochemical evidence to suggest that the early earth ever possessed a primordial solar nebula remnant atmosphere.

There is microfossil evidence for the existence of fairly advanced microbial living systems on the earth by about 3.8 billion years ago. Photosynthesis evolved in one or more of these early microbial species. In photosynthesis, the organism utilizes water vapor and carbon dioxide in the presence of sunlight and chlorophyll to form carbohydrates, used by the organism for food. In the process of photosynthesis, oxygen is given off as a metabolic by-product. The production of oxygen by photosynthesis was a major event on the earth and transformed the composition and chemistry of the early atmosphere. As a result of photosynthetic production, oxygen built up to become the second most abundant constituent of the atmosphere (20.90 percent by volume). It has been estimated that atmospheric oxygen reached only 1 percent of its present atmospheric level 2 billion years ago, 10 percent of its present atmospheric level about 550 million years ago, and its present atmospheric level as early as 400 million years ago.

The evolution of atmospheric oxygen had very important implications for the evolution of life. The presence and buildup of oxygen led to the evolution of respiration, which replaced fermentation as the energy production mechanism in living systems. Accompanying and directly controlled by the buildup of atmospheric oxygen was the origin and evolution of atmospheric ozone, which is chemically formed from oxygen. The evolution of atmospheric ozone resulted in the shielding of the earth's surface from biologically lethal solar ultraviolet between 0.2 and 0.3 micron. The development of the atmospheric ozone layer and its accompanying shielding of the earth's surface permitted early life to leave the safety of the oceans and go ashore for the first time in the history of the planet. Prior to the evolution of the atmospheric ozone layer, early life was restricted to a depth of several meters below the ocean surface. At this depth, the ocean water offered shielding from solar ultraviolet radiation. Theoretical computer calculations indicate that atmospheric ozone provided sufficient shielding from biologically lethal ultraviolet radiation for the colonization of the land once oxygen reached about one-tenth of its present atmospheric level.

Calculations indicate that the atmospheres of Venus and Mars also evolved as a consequence of the volatile outgassing of the same gases that led to the formation of Earth's atmosphere—water vapor, carbon dioxide, and nitrogen. In the case of Venus and Mars, however, the outgassed water vapor never existed in the form of liquid water on the surfaces of these planets. Because of Venus' closer distance to the sun (108 million kilometers versus 150 million kilometers for Earth), its lower atmosphere was too hot to permit the outgassed water vapor to condense out of the atmosphere. Thus, the outgassed water vapor remained in gaseous form in the atmosphere and, over geological time, was broken apart by solar ultraviolet radiation to form hydrogen and oxygen. The very light hydrogen gas quickly escaped from the atmosphere of Venus, and the heavier oxygen combined with surface minerals to form a highly oxidized surface. In the absence of liquid water on the surface of Venus, the outgassed carbon dioxide remained in the atmosphere and built up to become the overwhelming constituent of the atmosphere of Venus (about 96 percent by volume). The outgassed nitrogen accumulated to comprise about 4 percent by volume of the Venus atmosphere. The carbon dioxide and nitrogen atmosphere of Venus is very massive—it produces an atmospheric surface pressure of about 90 atmospheres (the surface pressure of Earth's atmosphere is only one atmosphere). If the outgassed carbon dioxide in the atmosphere of Earth did not leave via dissolution in the oceans and carbonate formation, its surface atmospheric pressure would be about 70 atmospheres, with carbon dioxide comprising about 98-99 percent of the atmosphere and nitrogen about 1-2 percent. Thus, the atmosphere of Earth would closely resemble that of Venus. The carbon dioxide-rich atmosphere of Venus causes a very significant greenhouse temperature enhancement, giving the surface of Venus a temperature of about 750 Kelvins, which is hot enough to melt lead. The surface temperature of Earth is only about 288 Kelvins.

Like Venus, Mars has an atmosphere composed primarily of carbon dioxide (about 95 percent by volume) and nitrogen (about 3 percent by volume). The total atmospheric surface pressure of Mars, however, is only about 7 millibars (one atmosphere is equivalent to 1013 millibars). It is thought that because of Mars' greater distance from the sun as compared to Earth's (228 million kilometers versus 150 million kilometers), the temperature of the surface of Mars was too low to support the presence of liquid water. There may be very large quantities of out-gassed water in the form of ice or frost below the surface of Mars. In the absence of liquid water, the outgassed carbon dioxide remained in the atmosphere. The smaller mass of the atmosphere of Mars compared to the atmosphere of Venus and Earth may be attributable to the smaller mass of Mars and, therefore, the smaller mass available for the trapping of gases in the interior of Mars during its formation. In addition, it appears that the amount of gases trapped in the interiors of Venus, Earth, and Mars during their formation decreased with increasing distance from the sun. Venus appears to have trapped the greatest amount of gases, and was the most volatile-rich planet, Earth trapped the next greatest amount, and Mars trapped the smallest amount.

## Methods of Study

Information about the origin, early history, and evolution of the earth's atmosphere comes from a variety of sources. Information on the origin of Earth and other planets is based on theoretical computer simulations. These computer models simulate the collapse of the primordial solar nebula and the formation of the planets. Recent astronomical observations of what appears to be the collapse of interstellar gas clouds and the possible formation of planetary systems have provided new insights into the computer modeling of this phenomenon. Information about the origin, early history, and evolution of the atmosphere is based on theoretical computer models of volatile outgassing, the geochemical cycling of the outgassed volatiles, and the photochemistry/chemistry of the outgassed volatiles. The process of chemical evolution, which led to the synthesis of organic molecules of increasing complexity, the precursors of the first living systems on the early earth, is studied in laboratory experiments. In laboratory experiments on chemical evolution, mixtures of gases simulating the earth's early atmosphere are energized by solar ultraviolet radiation and atmospheric lightning. The resulting products are analyzed by chemical techniques. A key parameter affecting atmospheric photochemical reactions, chemical evolution, and the origin of life was the flux of solar ultraviolet radiation incident on the early earth. Astronomical measurements of the ultraviolet emissions from young sunlike stars have provided important information about ultraviolet emissions from the sun during the very early history of the atmosphere.

Geological and paleontological studies of the oldest rocks and the earliest fossil records have provided important information on the evolution of the atmosphere and the transition from an oxygen-deficient to an oxygen-sufficient atmosphere. Studies of the biogeochemical cycling of the elements have provided important insights into the later evolution of the atmosphere. Thus, studies of the origin and evolution of the atmosphere are based on a broad cross section of science, involving astronomy, geology, geochemistry, geophysics, and biology as well as atmospheric chemistry.

## Context

Studies of the origin and evolution of the atmosphere have provided new insights into the processes and parameters responsible for global change. Understanding the history of the atmosphere provides better understanding of its future. Today, several global environment changes are of national and international concern, including the depletion of ozone in the stratosphere and global warming caused by the buildup of greenhouse gases. The study of the evolution of the atmosphere has provided new insights into the biogeochemical cycling of elements between the atmosphere, biosphere, land, and ocean. Understanding this cycling is a key to understanding environmental problems. Studies of the origin and evolution of the atmosphere have also provided new insights into the origin of life and the possibility of life outside the earth.

## Bibliography

Cloud, Preston. *Cosmos, Earth, and Man: A Short History of the Universe*. New Haven, Conn.: Yale University Press, 1978. A very readable, nontechnical account of cosmic evolution covering the evolution of stars, the earth, life, and humankind. The volume defines various scientific terms such as elementary particles, chemical bonding, isotopes, periodic table, and mass. The author assumes that the reader does not have a scientific background, only an interest in our cosmic roots.

Henderson-Sellers, A. *The Origin and Evolution of Planetary Atmospheres*. Bristol, England: Adam Hilger, 1983. A technical treatment of the variation of the climate of the earth over geological time and the processes and parameters that controlled it. The chapters in the book include the mechanisms for long-term climate change, the atmospheres of the other planets, planetary climatology on shorter time scales, and the stability of planetary environments.

Holland, H. D. *The Chemical Evolution of the Atmosphere and Oceans*. Princeton, N.J.: Princeton University Press, 1984. A comprehensive and technical treatment of the geochemical cycling of elements over geological time and the coupling between the atmosphere, ocean, and surface. The book covers the origin of the solar system, the release and recycling of volatiles, the chemistry of the early atmosphere and ocean, the acid-base balance of the atmosphere-ocean-crust system, and carbonates and clays.

Levine, Joel S., ed. *The Photochemistry of Atmospheres: Earth, the Other Planets, and Comets*. Orlando, Fla.: Academic Press, 1985. A series of review papers dealing with the origin and evolution of the atmosphere, the origin of life, the atmospheres of Earth and other planets, and climate. The book contrasts the origin, evolution, composition, and chemistry of Earth's atmosphere with the atmospheres of the other planets. It contains two appendices that summarize all atmospheric photochemical and chemical processes.

Lewis, John S., and Ronald G. Prinn. *Planets and Their Atmospheres: Origin and Evolution*. New York: Academic Press, 1983. A comprehensive, textbook treatment of the formation of the planets and their atmospheres. This monograph begins with a detailed account of the origin and evolution of solid planets via coalescence and accretion in the primordial solar nebula and then discusses the surface geology and atmospheric composition of each planet.

Schopf, J. William, ed. *Earth's Earliest Biosphere: Its Origin and Evolution*. Princeton, N.J.: Princeton University Press, 1983. A comprehensive group of papers on such subjects as the early earth, the oldest rocks, the origin of life, early life, and microfossils. Chapters include those on the oldest known rock record, prebiotic organic syntheses and the origin of life, Precambrian organic geochemistry, the transition from fermentation to anoxygenic photosynthesis, the development of an aerobic environment, and early microfossils. Very technical.

*Joel S. Levine*

## Cross-References

The Atmosphere's Structure and Composition, 128; Cambrian Diversification of Life, 183; Colonization of the Land, 246; The Evolution of the Earth's Composition, 496; The Fossil Record, 760; Fossils of the Earliest Life Forms, 782; The Geochemical Cycle, 818; Micropaleontology: Microfossils, 1674; Ocean-Atmosphere Interactions, 1779; The Origin of the Oceans, 1863; The Origin of Life, 1961; Paleobiogeography, 1984; Paleoclimatology, 1993; Elemental Distribution in the Solar System, 2434; The Origin of the Solar System, 2442.

# THE ATMOSPHERE'S GLOBAL CIRCULATION

*Field of study:* Atmospheric sciences and meteorology

*Global circulation is considered to be the average air flow around the world; although winds at any one place and time may vary considerably from this average, it can explain the why and how of the earth's prevailing winds. These systems are responsible for transferring heat and momentum poleward from the tropics.*

*Principal terms*

CONVERGENCE: the movement of winds toward a central point of an area

CORIOLIS EFFECT: a phenomenon caused by the earth's rotation in which moving objects unattached to the earth move to the right of their path of motion in the Northern Hemisphere and to the left in the Southern Hemisphere

DIVERGING AIR: the condition that exists when a net horizontal outflow of air from a region occurs

DOLDRUMS: a nautical term used in reference to the light and variable winds of the equatorial zone

HADLEY CELL: a circulatory pattern of winds driven by heat energy, proposed by George Hadley in 1735 to explain the trade winds

HORSE LATITUDES: the zones of latitude at about 30-35 degrees that are characterized by light winds and hot, dry weather

POLAR JET: a stream of air blowing from a westerly direction at about 12 kilometers over the middle latitudes

TRADE WINDS: winds in the tropics that blow from the subtropical highs to the equatorial low

TROPOPAUSE: the boundary layer between the troposphere and the stratosphere

TROPOSPHERE: the lowest layer of the atmosphere, where weather occurs and temperature decreases with height

## Summary of the Phenomenon

The global circulation is the complex pattern of atmospheric motions that results from the unequal heating of tropical and polar areas and from the earth's rotation. The global circulation, like all winds, is set in motion by variations in atmospheric pressure. Differences in atmospheric pressure from place to place occur in response to the unequal heating of the earth's surface; warm air is less dense than cold air, so low pressures are normally associated with areas of warm air and high pressures with areas of cold air.

To understand how the global circulation is set in motion in response to pressure variations and how the system functions, atmospheric scientists use what is called the three-cell theory. The theory is based on a conceptual model of the earth's wind and pressure systems. It assumes the earth is a rotating sphere with a uniform surface, usually all water. A uniform surface makes a complex matter much easier to understand, because the differential heating and cooling of land and water does not come into play. One other assumption is made: that the sun is always over the equator so that the wind and pressure zones do not shift seasonally.

The global circulation is driven by energy received from the sun. Because the sun angles are higher in lower latitudes, the tropics receive an excess of energy from the sun. The excessive sun energy is absorbed by the earth's surface and is converted to heat energy, which in turn heats the surface air, making it less dense so that the air rises. Air that rises thermally constitutes low pressure, so a broad region of low pressure exists in the equatorial region. This region is called the equatorial low, or doldrums. Moreover, because the rising air must be replaced, air is drawn in from either side of the equatorial low and converges near the equator. Thus, the low-pressure area is a convergence zone and also is called the intertropical convergence zone (ITCZ).

The rising air can ascend only as far as the tropopause (the isothermal layer bounding the troposphere); then the air spreads out horizontally and flows pole-ward. Because the earth rotates on its axis from west to east, air moving at this elevation soon converges and moves from west to east. The convergence aloft occurs about 30 degrees north and south latitude. When convergence occurs aloft, high pressure is generated at the surface. The surface high is accomplished by the converging air aloft spilling earthward and spreading out across the earth's surface. Thus, a high-pressure area is further defined as a region of descending and spread-ing air. These high-pressure regions at 30 degrees north and south latitude are called the subtropical highs, or horse latitudes.

A part of the spreading surface air at the subtropical highs flows over the surface toward the equator. The pressure gradient (change in pressure over distance) between the subtropical highs and the equator is the force that sets the wind in motion. The winds, however, do not flow directly to the equator. The Coriolis effect deflects the wind to the right of the pressure gradient path in the Northern Hemi-sphere and to the left of the path in the Southern Hemisphere. (The Coriolis effect is a pseudo-force that results from the earth turning out from beneath objects moving over the earth's surface.) The winds flowing from the subtropical highs to the equator, because of the Coriolis effect, become northeast winds in the Northern Hemisphere and southeast winds in the Southern Hemisphere. These winds in both hemispheres are often referred to as the trade winds.

Not all of the air settling in the horse latitudes flows toward the equator. Some of the air moves poleward. The winds thus formed in the middle latitudes in either hemisphere also are affected by the Coriolis effect, so that in the Northern Hemi-sphere the prevailing southwesterlies are created and in the Southern Hemisphere the prevailing northwesterlies are formed.

The poles, by the nature of their very cold temperatures, are regions of high pressure. Surface air flows equatorward from the polar regions and, owing to the Coriolis effect, the winds take on a northeasterly direction in the Northern Hemisphere and a southeasterly direction in the Southern Hemisphere.

The easterly winds in the high latitudes and the westerly winds in the middle latitudes in each hemisphere come together at about 60 degrees north and south latitude. These regions of convergence are areas of low pressure and are called the subpolar lows. Moreover, the mild air of the westerlies and the cold air of the easterlies do not mix readily and are separated by a boundary called the polar front. The converging air at 60 degrees rises and spreads out at the tropopause, flowing equatorward on the south side of the subpolar low to converge with equatorial air above the subtropical highs and blowing poleward on the north side to subside into the polar highs.

In summary, there are four areas of high pressure: the two subtropical highs and the two poles. There are likewise three areas of low pressure: the equator and the two subpolar lows. Surface wind patterns consist of the trade winds between the subtropical highs and the equator, the westerlies from the subtropical highs to the subpolar lows, and the polar easterlies from the poles to the polar front. Thus there are three circulation cells in the Northern Hemisphere and three cells in the Southern Hemisphere, which are the mirror image of the Northern Hemisphere cells—hence the name "three-cell theory." When continents, ice fields, and mountains are interspersed among the ocean surfaces, however, circulation patterns differ somewhat from the three-cell model. Pressure systems, instead of being continuous, take on a more cellular configuration and are called semipermanent highs and lows.

In winter, there are two high-pressure areas between 25 degrees and 30 degrees north latitude: the Bermuda-Azores high in the Atlantic and the Pacific high over the Pacific Ocean. Air turns clockwise around these systems, so westerlies are to the north and trade winds to the south. In the Southern Hemisphere, with less contrast between land and water, a more well-defined circulation is produced that is nearer the three-cell model. In addition, a cold, nonpermanent high pressure forms over Siberia, and winds blow toward the oceans bounding eastern Asia. Moreover, there are two semipermanent lows: the Icelandic low in the Atlantic and the Aleutian low in the Pacific. These lows are areas of easterly moving, converging storms. In the Southern Hemisphere, the subpolar low conforms to the model and is a trough of low pressure encircling the earth.

Several changes occur in circulation patterns during summer. Many of the cold, shallow highs disappear, and in other areas, low pressures replace highs but some highs remain. The subpolar lows weaken and are hardly discernible. Conversely, the subtropical highs remain strong, maintaining their circulation patterns through the summer. Also during summer at the subtropical highs, high pressure encircles the earth aloft. Air subsides here and is heated by compression, which promotes clear skies and intense surface heating. The surface heats the air, which, in turn, rises a short distance, then flows laterally several hundred meters above the surface, thereby reducing pressure. The system thus developed is a thermal low and is found in the desert regions of the world at this latitude. Also in summer, the continent of Asia warms, and the pressure relationship with the adjacent oceans reverses itself so that low pressure develops over the continent. Air now flows inland from the oceans, bringing the wet monsoon that typifies eastern Asia. Finally, winter systems shift equatorward 5-10 degrees during that season and, during summer, the wind and pressure systems shift poleward.

High-level, high-speed winds called jet streams move generally from west to east with meanders north and south of the average course. There are usually two jet streams recognized in each hemisphere, the polar jet and the subtropical jet. The polar jet stream is the most powerful straight-line wind system on earth, and speeds as high as 510 kilometers per hour have been recorded. The average speed of the polar jet is considered to be about 139 kilometers per hour and tends to have a higher speed in winter than in summer.

The polar jet draws its energy from the hemispherical distribution of solar radiation. During the winter, when the North Pole is tilted away from the sun, the mean position of the jet stream is about 35 degrees north latitude, and, during summer, when the north pole is tilted toward the sun, the average position of the jet stream is at about 50 degrees north latitude.

The subtropical jet is not as influential as the polar jet. Its influence is significant in the winter but disappears from the midlatitudes in summer. The subtropical jet's position does not vary as much as that of the polar jet, and it has lower mean wind speeds. The subtropical jet is the result of steady accumulation of westerly momentum along the poleward edge of the Hadley cell (unit portion of the atmosphere between 30 degrees and the equator) and along poleward slopes of the subtropical high pressure.

## Methods of Study

Global circulation data are collected by a series of meteorological centers located around the world. They consist of three types, based on the scope of their responsibility. National Meteorological Centers (NMCs) such as the National Weather Service stations in the United States collect national data, Regional Meteorological Centers (RMCs) assimilate hemispherical data, and the World Meteorological Centers (WMCs) compile global data.

The World Meteorological Organization (WMO) oversees data collection, data distribution, and forecasting. Four times each day wind data are collected simultaneously at more than eight thousand stations at 0000Z, 0600Z, 1200Z, and 1800Z—the Z is read as "Zulu" and stands for Greenwich mean time (GMT). GMT, used by all meteorologists, is the time at the Greenwich observatory just outside London, England.

WMCs are three in number and are located in Moscow, Washington, D.C., and Melbourne, Australia. These centers are responsible for building a world weather picture. Thus, they receive information from national and regional centers, prepare analyses, and feed appropriate information back to the national and regional centers. A WMC serves as a clearinghouse, a depository, and a laboratory for wind and other meteorological data.

The RMCs collect data from the NMCs and transmit them to the WMCs; they also provide information for national centers. RMCs also serve as research centers because they have extensive raw data for the hemispheres they represent. RMCs function in different ways, depending on the needs of the people in the nations they serve. An RMC may provide local weather forecasts or it may provide access to training facilities for those nations having none. Moreover, RMCs may give aid in applying wind and weather data to national problems.

NMCs have stations, scattered across the nation, where wind observations are taken simultaneously at designated times. These data are then transmitted as quickly as possible to a central location, where they are plotted on maps and charts and then transmitted back to the stations via facsimile machines, using satellites.

Wind data are collected in a number of ways. Photographs and radar images from satellites can show through the presence of cloud banks where certain types of winds are located. An absence of clouds indicates a high pressure, and whorls of cloud indicates a low pressure, each with its concomitant circulation. Special types of radiosondes (small instrument packages with radio transmitters lifted aloft by balloons) called rawinsondes, which use radar, are used to obtain data on upper-air winds. Usually, a radar beam is bounced from a reflector on the rawinsonde, and wind direction and speed are calculated. A radio that receives a signal, then emits a radio signal of its own, may also be used to gather upper wind data. At the surface, wind vanes, which turn with the wind flow, are used for directional information. Data from these vanes may be gathered through observation or by means of remote recording. Wind velocity is acquired with the use of an anemometer, a device with rotating cups that catch the wind. The cups, which rotate at a speed proportional to the speed of the wind, are attached to a vertical shaft that also rotates, and an electrical counting device located at the bottom of the shaft records the wind speed.

## Context

Global circulation is responsible for the interchange of heat energy between the warm tropics and the cold poles. This energy exchange tempers the weather experienced by all and, hence, the climate of the middle latitudes, making this zone on the earth inhabitable by humans and by other life forms as well. The energy exchange as a result of global circulation also modifies temperatures in the high latitudes, which in turn affects weather through air masses generated in high-latitude regions. Without global circulation, both the heat at the tropics and the cold at the polar regions would continue to increase.

Many of the semipermanent highs and lows, which are part of the global circulation, are source regions for the formation of air masses. The air masses generated in these source regions move out into the middle latitudes and create the daily weather. Un-like air masses do not mix and, when they come together, produce a zone of discontinuity commonly called a front, which usually produces inclement weather. Normally, a high pressure pushes in behind a front, tending to produce fair weather. Thus, the alternation of low pressures and high pressures makes the weather variable from day to day.

Global circulation also affects human life in more direct ways. In the days of sailing ships, the prevailing winds, especially the trade winds, were necessary to power the ships across the oceans. Thus, people and goods could be transported from continent to continent. Even today, those who sail for sport are dependent on the wind for power, although not on the same scale as in the past.

The world's climates are closely related to wind systems. If an area has a prevailing wind from the north, it will be colder than an area in the same latitude with a southerly wind. Similarly, if a region is in line for a wind from a nearby ocean, it will have warmer winter temperatures and cooler summer temperatures than a corresponding inland location at the same latitude. Such a location will also have a more moist climate than an inland location.

The high-level jet streams have an impact on aircraft. The presence of the jet stream was first discovered and documented during World War II. A German pilot flying west above the Mediterranean Sea at the level of the jet stream encountered a headwind blowing as fast as his air speed. His plane was held in place until he ran out of fuel and had to ditch into the sea. American pilots flying west toward Japan from aircraft carriers in the Pacific encountered similar conditions. Many bombing missions had to be aborted because of strong headwinds. One benefit of the jet stream to pilots is that they can return to base much faster flying east with the jet as a tail wind. Planes flying from North America to Europe can make the trip in a shorter time than planes flying the reverse course. Had Charles Lindbergh known about the jet stream, he could have cut several hours from the time on his transatlantic flight.

## Bibliography

Battan, Louis J. *Fundamentals of Meteorology*. 2d ed. Englewood Cliffs, N.J.: Prentice-Hall, 1984. In chapter 13, "General Circulation of the Atmosphere," a nontechnical assessment of the relationships between energy, wind, and pressure is presented. The three-cell theory is used to explain global circulation, and the effects brought about by the interchanges between land and sea are described. The chapter concludes with a discussion of the cryosphere (ice regions) and the applications of mathematical modeling of the atmosphere. Suitable for college students.

Chang, Ching-hu. *Atmospheric Circulation Systems and Climate*. Honolulu, Hawaii: Oriental, 1972. Chapters 1 through 4 and chapters 6 and 7 deal primarily with the general circulation system of the earth. The first chapter covers the historical background, introduces the three-cell theory, and presents the momentum balance and the energy exchange in the atmosphere. The succeeding chapters address the various segments of the three-cell theory in more detail. Suitable for college-level students.

Gedzelman, Stanley D. *The Science and Wonders of the Atmosphere*. New York: John Wiley & Sons, 1980. Chapter 16 presents a fine, color-illustrated analysis of the earth's major wind systems. Included is a description of the world's prevailing wind systems and how they are related to ocean currents and the earth's climates. Also covered are the upper-level winds and their relationship to isobaric (equal-pressure) surfaces. Colored diagrams and satellite photographs are used to illustrate the narrative. A good college-level text.

Lockwood, John G. *World Climatic Systems*. Baltimore: Edward Arnold, 1985. The first chapter provides very thorough coverage of the earth's general circulation system. The author presents analyses of the driving forces of world winds and describes the wind systems in low, middle, and high latitudes. The chapter concludes with a discussion of the geological evolution of world wind systems. Suitable for entry-level college students.

Lydolph, Paul E. *Weather and Climate*. Totowa, N.J.: Rowman & Allanheld, 1985. Chapters 5 and 6 give extensive coverage of the general circulation patterns at both the earth's surface and aloft. Both the three-cell theory and actual circulation systems are covered. The chapter is well illustrated with charts and diagrams that show how wind flows and the distribution of worldwide circulation patterns. Ocean currents are also integrated with the wind-flow systems. Suitable for entry-level college students.

Navarra, John G. *Atmosphere, Weather and Climate: An Introduction to Meteorology*. Philadelphia: W. B. Saunders, 1979. An excellent, nontechnical description of the earth's pressure belts and prevailing wind system is presented in chapter 7. Also included is a treatment of eddy theory, the character of the jet stream, the monsoon systems of Asia and Africa, and the global circulation of pollutants. The chapter is well illustrated with diagrams, maps, and photographs. Suitable for entry-level college students.

Weisberg, Joseph S. *Meteorology: The Earth and Its Weather*. 2d ed. Boston: Houghton Mifflin, 1981. Chapter 6, "The Dynamic Atmosphere," has a concise but thorough coverage of the forces that affect wind flow and velocity, the surface pressure zones, and the general theories of global air circulation. The latter part of the chapter discusses upper-level wind patterns and the nature of the jet stream and demonstrates how the jet stream influences surface weather systems.

*Ralph D. Cross*

## Cross-References

# THE ATMOSPHERE'S STRUCTURE AND COMPOSITION

*Field of study:* Atmospheric sciences and meteorology

*An atmosphere is a shell of gases that covers a planetary surface. The earth's current atmosphere is a complex, dynamic system that interacts closely with and controls the surface environment. Early life forms substantially altered this atmosphere, and now more advanced life forms threaten its composition.*

*Principal terms*

CHLOROFLUOROMETHANES (CFMs): also called chlorofluorocarbons, these are chemicals in which chlorine and fluorine replace one or more of the hydrogen atoms in metyhane; in more complex variations, chlorine- and fluorine-based molecules are attached to the carbon base

COSMIC RAYS: high-energy atomic nuclei and subatomic particles, as distinct from electromagnetic radiation

EXOSPHERE: the outermost layer of the earth's atmosphere

GREENHOUSE EFFECT: a planetary phenomenon in which the atmosphere acts as a hothouse, trapping more heat radiation than it emits; the atmosphere traps solar energy until the mean surface temperature is raised several degrees

HETEROSPHERE: a major realm of the atmosphere in which the gases hydrogen and helium become predominant

HOMOSPHERE: a major realm of the atmosphere whose chemical makeup is similar to the sea-level proportions of nitrogen, oxygen, and trace gases; it overlaps the troposphere, stratosphere, and mesosphere

INFRARED RADIATION: electromagnetic radiation lower in energy than visible light but higher than radio and microwaves; generally beyond 770 nanometers in wavelength

IONOSPHERE: the ionized layer of gases in the earth's atmosphere, occurring between the thermosphere and the exosphere (it starts at about 50-100 kilometers above the surface of the planet)

MESOSPHERE: the layer of the earth's atmosphere occurring above the stratosphere and below the thermosphere (about 40-85 kilometers above sea level)

MIDDLE ATMOSPHERE: a general term encompassing the stratosphere and the mesosphere

PALEOSCIENCE: the scientific method as applied to the study of ancient or prehistoric events

PHOTODISSOCIATION: the splitting of molecules by light, generally in the ultraviolet spectrum

THERMOSPHERE: the highest layer of the earth's atmosphere except for the exosphere; it begins at about 85 kilometers above sea level

TROPOSPHERE: the layer of the earth's atmosphere that lies just above the earth's surface; it extends upward to about 8-18 kilometers

ULTRAVIOLET LIGHT: electromagnetic radiation higher in energy than visible light but lower than X rays; generally in the 310-110 nanometer wavelength range

## Summary of the Phenomenon

"Atmosphere" usually refers to the earth's protective, life-giving layer of gases that completely covers the surface of the planet. Although virtually all planets have atmospheres of some sort, the earth's atmosphere is unique among those known in this solar system, as it is uniquely suited to support a broad range of life forms.

The atmosphere of the earth generally is described as containing 78 percent nitrogen and 21 percent oxygen; the remainder contains 0.9 percent argon, 0.03 percent carbon dioxide, and traces of hydrogen, methane, nitrous oxide, and inert gases. In addition, the atmosphere carries varying amounts of water vapor and aerosol particles such as dust and volcanic ash, depending on local and global events. The early atmosphere was almost entirely hydrogen gas, which was quickly lost by solar heating and was replaced by carbon dioxide and nitrogen from crustal materials. Water was added to the environment by comets. As early as 3.5 billion years ago, primitive algae-like life forms emerged and fed on the carbon dioxide by using photosynthesis to "crack" carbon dioxide and water molecules and to form simple sugars that did not then exist. This process over billions of years gradually brought about a drastic change in the gas ratios, dropping carbon dioxide to only 0.03 percent and raising free molecular oxygen to 20 percent.

Gases are compressible, and they absorb or pass varying amounts of electromagnetic radiation; therefore, the atmosphere is not a static object but is instead a highly dynamic system whose complexity has come to be appreciated only in the last few decades. Phenomena such as weather and climate are short- and long-term events involving the exchange of energy and transport of mass within the atmosphere and with the solid earth, liquid oceans, and space.

The atmosphere has no clear upper boundary, but it generally is considered to be 300 kilometers, the altitude at which it responds more to electromagnetic effects and acts less like a fluid body. It can be described in three major characterizations—temperature, chemistry, and electrical activity—with major sections designated as spheres and their boundaries as pauses.

Temperature changes with altitude and, as there is less overlying gas, with pressure and exposure to radiation. The lowest region of the atmosphere, enclosing virtually all life and weather on earth, is the troposphere, extending to an altitude of 8-18 kilometers (*tropo* is Greek for "turn" and refers to the fact that this region turns with the solid earth). The bottom of the troposphere is the boundary layer, where the atmosphere interacts directly with the surface of the earth. The boundary layer often is turbulent, as moving air masses (winds) encounter and flow around or over obstructions and exchange heat with the ground or with the water. Pressure at the surface varies because the altitude of the surface varies and because of weather phenomena, but the standard is taken as 1.013 bar (or 14.7 pounds per square inch); for meteorological purposes, it is expressed as the height of a column of mercury in a tube standing in an open pool of mercury. Temperature and pressure in the troposphere decrease at about 2 degrees Celsius per kilometer until the tropopause is reached. Life becomes increasingly difficult to maintain with altitude (humans require oxygen above 2-4 kilometers and must wear pressure suits above 10.6 kilometers). Some 75 percent of the gases and 90 percent of the water vapor in the atmosphere are contained below the tropopause. Thunderstorm clouds can sometimes be seen stopping at the tropopause and spreading horizontally.

At the tropopause, temperature reaches a minimum of about −50 degrees Celsius, then rises sharply as one enters the stratosphere to peak at about 15 degrees Celsius at the stratopause, about 50 kilometers high. Above this level, it declines again in the mesosphere to a low of −60 degrees Celsius at the mesopause, 85 kilometers high. Only 1 percent of the atmosphere is in the mesosphere and above; 99 percent lies below. Particles from atomic nuclei to meteors generally are destroyed in the mesosphere. Nuclei—better known as cosmic rays—encountering gas molecules will be shattered into secondary and tertiary particles. Most meteors are heated and evaporated by friction when they encounter the mesosphere. Above the mesosphere, the thermosphere (the hot atmosphere) extends to approximately 300 kilometers in altitude, and temperatures soar to between 500 and 2,000 degrees Celsius, depending on solar activity. Because the atmosphere is so thin, however, the total heat present is minuscule. Finally, beyond the thermosphere is the exosphere (outer layer), which extends from 300 kilometers to the solar wind (also called the interplanetary medium).

From a chemical standpoint, the atmosphere is divided into two major realms: the homosphere and the heterosphere. The homosphere—which overlaps the troposphere, stratosphere, and mesosphere—has a chemical makeup that is largely similar to the familiar sea-level proportions of nitrogen, oxygen, and trace gases, even though the absolute numbers of atoms and molecules drop sharply. Some important differences do start to appear. Ozone and other chemicals rarely encountered at lower altitudes become major constituents of the atmosphere in this realm. Ozone is formed in the stratosphere by short-wavelength ultraviolet sunlight splitting oxygen molecules (photodissociation). These free oxygen atoms then form ozone with oxygen molecules. Molecular nitrogen also is dissociated.

Although the stratosphere and mesosphere (sometimes treated together as the middle atmosphere) are quite tenuous compared to the troposphere, gases in them form an optically dense layer that absorbs or reflects short-wavelength ultraviolet and X-ray radiation that would be damaging to life on the surface. Ozone is especially important with regard to ultraviolet radiation. Nevertheless, this region is quite fragile and can be destroyed by chlorofluoromethanes (Freon and related compounds) used in spray cans and refrigeration systems. Studies indicate that these gases migrate upward in the atmosphere and neutralize thousands of times their own mass in ozone molecules before they are broken down after several decades or even centuries. The result is believed to have led to the formation of ozone "holes" over the two polar regions and is expected to cause the eventual destruction of the entire ozone layer. Atomic oxygen becomes more common in the mesosphere. In the heterosphere, the gas mixture changes drastically, and hydrogen and helium become dominant.

From an electrical standpoint, there are the neutral atmosphere and the ionosphere. The neutral atmosphere, below 50 kilometers, is largely devoid of electrical activity other than lightning, which might be regarded as localized "noise." Above 50 kilometers, atoms and molecules are ionized largely by sunlight (ultraviolet radiation in particular) and to a lesser extent by celestial X-ray sources, collisions with other atoms, and geomagnetic fields and currents. Although the ionosphere as a whole is electrically neutral, it comprises positive (ion) and negative (electron) elements that conduct currents and that respond to magnetic disturbances. The ionosphere starts at about 50-100 kilometers in altitude and extends outward to more than 900 kilometers as it gradually merges with the magnetosphere and its components. It is sometimes called the Heaviside layer after Oliver Heaviside (1850-1925), who predicted a layer of radio-reflection ionized gases. The ionosphere is divided into C, D, E, and F layers, which in turn are subdivided ($F_1$, for example).

The ionosphere is one of the most active regions of the atmosphere and one of the most responsive to changes in solar activity. Ions and electrons in the ionosphere form a mirrorlike layer that reflects radio waves. Radio waves are absorbed by the lower (D) region of the ionosphere (which also reaches down into the mesosphere). The D-layer dissipates at night in the absence of solar radiation, allowing radio waves to be reflected by the F-layer at higher altitudes, thus causing radio "skip." These effects vary at different wavelengths. Intense solar activity can alter the characteristics of the ionosphere and make it unreliable as a radio reflector, either through the input of high-energy radiation or by the injection of particles carried by the solar wind.

Such particle injections would go unnoticed but appear as the aurora borealis and aurora australis (northern and southern dawns, respectively). The earth's magnetic field shields the planet from most charged radiation particles. At the polar regions, however, where the magnetic field lines are vertical (rising from the surface), the environment is magnetically open to space. Many charged particles from space or from the solar wind will be funneled into the polar regions. When the particles strike the atmosphere, they surrender their energy as light with spectral lines unique to the electrochemical interactions taking place. These auroral displays generally take place at 120-300 kilometers in altitude, with some occurring as high as 700 kilometers.

The aurora is the best-known atmospheric light display. Other "dayglow" and "nightglow" categories are caused by lithium, sodium, potassium, magnesium, and calcium layers at altitudes from about 60 to 200 kilometers. These metals are believed to have been deposited by meteors as they are evaporated on atmospheric entry. A layer of hydroxyl radicals (OH molecules) causes an infrared glow at about 100 kilometers, and dull airglows are caused by poorly understood effects at 100-300 kilometers in altitude.

Although the principal division of the atmosphere is vertical, there are horizontal differences related to latitude and to weather. Two major phenomena which affect the atmosphere are the jet streams and waves. The jet stream is a high-speed river of air moving at about 10-20 kilometers in altitude and at 100-650 kilometers per hour. Its location plays a major role in the movements of larger air masses that make up weather fronts in the troposphere. More than twenty wave phenomena take place in the atmosphere in response to different events. The three principal categories are gravity, Rossby, and acoustic. Gravity waves are not associated with relativity but with vertical oscillations of large air masses causing ripples, like a bottle bobbing in a pond. Rossby (or planetary) waves are associated with the wavelike distribution of weather systems. Acoustic waves are related to sound.

## Methods of Study

The atmosphere has been studied first from the ground upward as scientific instruments were carried into flight to record data at higher altitudes, then from space downward as they were placed aboard satellites to provide global information. Ironically, the middle atmosphere is poorly understood because it is too thin to support flight but too thick to allow orbital speeds.

The earliest types of instruments used for atmospheric study remain among the most important. Barometers, thermometers, anemometers, and hygrometers pro-vide the most immediate records of atmospheric change and warnings of impending events. Vertical profiles of atmospheric conditions are obtained by transporting such instruments up into the air on balloons and on suborbital rockets. The term "sound-ing rocket" comes from the earliest days of atmospheric study, when scientists were "sounding" the ocean of air just as they would the ocean of water: Small charges were attached to balloons, and the time sound took to reach the ground was a crude measure of atmospheric density. Balloon-borne instrument packages continued to be called radiosondes ("radio sounders").

Instrumentation carried aboard spacecraft is of a different nature. Many of the most revealing devices have been spectrometers of various types that analyze light reflected, emitted, or adsorbed by the atmosphere. Reflections of ultraviolet light by the atmosphere led to the discovery of the ozone "holes"; drops in reflectivity meant that ultraviolet was passing through rather than being returned to space (typically, such measurements also require observation of the solar ultraviolet out-put). Optical instruments usually are most effective when they view the atmosphere "edge-on" so as to increase the brightness of the signal (somewhat like viewing a soap bubble at the edges). Atmospheric studies can be difficult when viewing straight down, because the weak signals from airglow and other effects are washed out by the brighter glow of the earth or the stellar background. Special techniques can be employed. The U.S. space shuttle has twice carried sensors designed to monitor carbon monoxide pollution in the atmosphere. Gas cells containing carbon monoxide at different pressures acted as filters that blocked all signals but the wavelengths corresponding to carbon monoxide at the same pressure (that is, altitude) as that in the cell.

The most powerful tools used in studying the atmosphere have been the weather satellites, which observe the atmosphere from geostationary orbit (affording continuous views of half a hemisphere) and from lower polar orbits. Images from these satellites reveal the circulation of the atmosphere by the motion of clouds. Other sensors (called sounders) provide temperature profiles of the atmosphere at various altitudes.

The most extensive analyses of the atmosphere have been carried out by the Atmosphere Explorers, the Orbiting Geophysical Observatories, the Atmosphere Density Explorers, and the Dynamics Explorers. Operating in the upper reaches of the atmosphere, these spacecraft have delineated the structure and composition of the atmosphere and the changes it experiences with seasons and solar activity. The more sensitive chemical assays, however, have been conducted by instruments carried aboard the manned Spacelab 1 and 3 missions on the space shuttle. An Imaging Spectrometric Observatory carried on Spacelab 1 produced highly detailed emission spectra of the atmosphere between 80 and 100 kilometers in altitude. Unexpected emissions from nitrogen were detected at higher altitudes, indicating some photochemical effects that are not yet understood. Atmospheric Trace Molecules Observed by Spectroscopy (ATMOS), on Spacelab 3, measured the altitude ranges of some thirty chemicals and identified five, such as methyl chloride and nitric acid, in the stratosphere, where previously they were only suspected. Others were ruled out as factors in middle-atmosphere chemistry, since they were not detected.

Radar observations of rocket launches in the 1960's revealed that rocket exhaust often will create an electron "hole" in the ionosphere, usually when water vapor from rocket exhaust neutralizes free electrons. This effect usually lasts only a few minutes or hours, depending on the extent of the depletion. The Spacelab 2 mission in 1985, however, used a series of thruster firings over select ground stations to burn holes in the ionosphere in order to observe the rate at which they generate and their effect on communications (or, in one case, in order to observe radio stars at normally blocked frequencies).

## Context

The various paleosciences have revealed that the atmosphere as it currently exists is a relatively recent phenomenon brought about by the gradual alteration of the environment by life forms. Awareness of this global alteration is helping humans understand the effects they are having on the environment over a relatively short timespan—essentially since the onset of the Industrial Revolution. The widespread use of fossil fuels and the burning of forests to clear land for agriculture has converted the carbon that plants spent billions of years converting into solid carbon compounds back into gaseous carbon dioxide. Furthermore, the plants that were "sinks," or absorbers, of carbon dioxide are available in lesser quantities to perform the ancient task of liberating oxygen. Sulfur compounds are naturally introduced by volcanoes, biological decay, and oceanic processes, but large quantities have been added by industrial processes, including coal burning. One product, sulfur dioxide, combines with water vapor at low altitudes to form sulfuric acid; at high altitudes it, too, can alter the ozone layer and the terrestrial radiation balance. In addition, the ratios of nitrogen compounds are altered by inefficient combustion and by widespread use of nitrogen-giving fertilizers; these products, too, have an adverse effect on ozone.

The immediate concern is not that the oxygen supply will be depleted—although that is a credible, long-term possibility—but that the increased amounts of carbon dioxide in the atmosphere will cause a greenhouse effect. In a greenhouse, long-wavelength radiation is admitted by a transparency, absorbed by the soil or ground, reemitted as longer-wavelength radiation, and reflected inward (or trapped) by the transparency. Glass serves this purpose for a greenhouse; carbon dioxide has the same effect in the earth's atmosphere. Other man-made gases that enhance the greenhouse effect are nitrous oxide, methane (which is also produced naturally), and chlorofluoromethanes (which also deplete ozone, thus allowing more radiation to enter). Because so little is known about the causes of different effects—many of the measurements which must be taken were learned only in the 1960's and 1970's—there are some uncertainties in predicting what will happen. It is expected, however, that within the next century, the carbon dioxide content of the atmosphere will double (the same as in the last eighteen thousand years) and will thus increase global temperatures by 2 degrees Celsius. This temperature increase will shift weather patterns and will cause large portions of the polar ice caps to melt, thus flooding coastal regions.

The atmospheric system is now being understood as an interactive agent with the space environment and with the ocean and the solid earth. Links between solar activities and weather and climate have been sought for decades (especially with sunspot cycles), but little more than contradictory hints have been discovered. Interactions between the oceans and the air are more substantial: Winds drive waves and thus ocean currents; in return, the oceans act as a heat source or sink for the atmosphere. The most famous interaction is the El Niño/Southern Oscillation event. El Niño ("the child"; it usually happens around Christmas) is an upwelling of cold water off the Pacific coast of South America that occurs every two to seven years. Besides having a disastrous effect on the fishing industry, it causes changes in circulation and precipitation patterns in the atmosphere over the Pacific basin.

Comparative planetology analyzes the differences and similarities between and among the planets. Earth, Venus, and Mars are used most often in comparative atmospheric studies. These three "terrestrial" planets are similar in size and in general chemistry but totally different in environment, largely because of their different atmospheres. Venus has a dense atmosphere composed largely of carbon dioxide and topped by clouds of sulfuric acid, which has led to surface temperatures of 900 degrees Celsius and to pressures ninety times greater than that of the earth. The circulation pattern, though, is unaltered by precipitation and oceans and thus can be used as a model in studying the earth. Efforts to understand how Venus became a "runaway greenhouse" have suggested a similar scenario for the earth. Mars, in contrast, has a tenuous atmosphere (0.01 bar at the surface) composed of carbon dioxide and traces of water vapor and oxygen. Studies of Mars focus on how its climate and atmosphere evolved and whether it was once earthlike.

## Bibliography

Beer, Tom. *Atmospheric Waves*. New York: John Wiley & Sons, 1974. A technical survey of the various types of wave phenomena in the atmosphere. The introductory chapter is of value to the general reader.

Bird, John. *The Upper Atmosphere: Threshold of Space*. NASA NP-105. Washington, D.C.: Government Printing Office, 1988. A well-illustrated color booklet that describes the atmosphere. Written on a popular level. Diagrams clearly show different layers and altitudes in the atmosphere.

Brasseur, Guy, and Susan Solomon. *Aeronomy of the Middle Atmosphere: Chemistry and Physics of the Stratosphere and Mesosphere*. Boston, Mass.: D. Reidel, 1984. A broad, technical survey of the knowledge of the middle atmosphere. Introductory sections are of value to the general reader.

Lewis, Richard S., ed. *Illustrated Encyclopedia of Space Exploration*. New York: Harmony Books, 1984. Chapters on Venus, Earth, and Mars include discussions and comparisons of the atmospheres and the effects on their respective environments. Other chapters cover the outer planets. College-level book; well illustrated.

National Aeronautics and Space Administration Advisory Council. *Earth System Science: A Closer View*. Report of the Earth System Sciences Committee. Washington, D.C.: Government Printing Office, 1988. A detailed and intriguing examination of the earth from core to outer space, presenting the atmosphere as one of the most important systems comprising our environment.

National Research Council. *Space Science in the Twenty-first Century: Imperatives for the Decades 1995-2015*. Washington, D.C.: National Academy Press, 1988. A National Academy of Sciences survey of the state of man's knowledge of the atmosphere and the environment. Includes recommendations for missions to expand that knowledge.

Neal, Valerie, et al. *Science in Orbit: The Shuttle and Spacelab Experience: 1981-1986*. NASA NP-119. Washington, D.C.: Government Printing Office, 1989. A comprehensive book detailing experiment results from science investigations aboard the U.S. space shuttle. Separate chapters deal with atmospheric and plasma physics activities. Well illustrated.

Reiter, Elmar R. *Jet Streams: How Do They Affect Our Weather?* Garden City, N.Y.: Doubleday, 1967. A popular description of the jet stream and meteorology, written for the private pilot. Includes discussion of how the jet stream was discovered and initially explored.

*Dave Dooling*

## Cross-References

# ATMOSPHERIC INVERSION LAYERS

*Field of study:* Atmospheric sciences and meteorology

*Temperature inversions occur frequently around the world. They are marked by a temperature increase with increasing altitude and occur most often in conjunction with a stagnating high pressure. Temperature inversions can be hazardous to humankind, and they frequently cause unpleasant atmospheric conditions.*

### Principal terms

ADIABATIC: characterizing a process in which no heat is exchanged between a system and its surroundings

ADVECTION: the process of transport of air solely by the horizontal motion of the atmosphere

AIR DRAINAGE: the flow of cold, dense air down slopes in response to gravity

ALBEDO: the percentage of reflectivity from the earth environment, being greatest from white surfaces and decreasing toward black

LAPSE RATE: the rate of decrease in temperature with increasing height

NEGATIVE LAPSE RATE: an increase in temperature with increasing height

RADIATIONAL COOLING: the cooling of the earth's surface and the layer of air immediately above it by a process of radiation and conduction

RADIOSONDE: a balloonborne instrument package for the simultaneous measurement and transmission of weather data

STAGNATING ANTICYCLONE: a high pressure that remains over an area for three to four days

TURBULENCE: an irregular, perhaps random, motion of air appearing as eddies

## Summary of the Phenomenon

A temperature inversion is an increase in temperature with an increase in altitude above the earth's surface in the troposphere, the lowest layer of the atmosphere. Normally, temperatures decrease with increasing altitude in the troposphere. To comprehend temperature inversions in the troposphere, it is first essential to understand how the troposphere is heated. The sun is the source of energy for heating the troposphere, but the sun does not heat this layer of the atmosphere directly. Only a minuscule amount of solar radiation is absorbed by the gases that make up the troposphere; rather, most of the energy used to heat this layer is derived from the surface of the earth.

The sun radiates mostly short wavelengths, and short wavelengths tend to pass through the atmosphere without much interference on the part of atmospheric gases. These gases, including variable gases such as water vapor and carbon dioxide, are transparent to shortwave energy; that is, these gases allow shortwave energy to pass through to the earth's surface without much of the shortwave energy being absorbed. The shortwave energy is absorbed by the earth's surface, and the earth radiates longwave energy back toward the sky. The terrestrial radiation is intercepted by clouds and gases such as water vapor, carbon dioxide, and methane, which absorb the longwave energy and reradiate it back toward the earth. In this way, there is a continual exchange of longwave energy between the earth and atmosphere and, thus, heat is held within the troposphere. Therefore, the surface of the earth is the direct source of heat energy for heating the troposphere, and temperatures decrease with height.

Temperature inversions occur largely because of the mobility of air. The gases that comprise the atmosphere are fluids and, therefore, behave as fluids. The air is capable of flowing much the same way that water does. Fluids are subject to various densities in response to differing temperatures. The warmer the fluid's temperature, the less dense is the fluid. It is logical, therefore, to assume that the colder, denser air is near the bottom of the troposphere and that the warmer air overlies it. This is not the case, however, except when a temperature inversion is present. The vertical variation of temperature in the troposphere is called the lapse rate. A normal or positive lapse rate is present when the temperatures decrease with increasing altitude, while a temperature increase with height results in a negative lapse rate and indicates the presence of a temperature inversion. Temperature inversions are of two general kinds: ground inversions and upper air inversions.

Ground inversions occur frequently and commonly extend upward for 100 meters or more. They can develop from several different causes. The primary cause of ground temperature inversions is radiational cooling, which occurs at night. During the day, the ground is heated and builds up a store of energy. After the sun has set, the earth's surface continues to radiate heat energy, thereby cooling the ground surface. When two bodies—such as the atmosphere and the earth—are in contact, heat energy is conducted from the warmer body to the cooler body. Thus, energy from the air is conducted into the ground, thereby cooling the air immediately above it. Air is a poor conductor of heat energy, so only about the first 100 meters experience a temperature decrease as a result of radiational cooling. Such nighttime-induced temperature inversions are more likely to occur on nights with clear skies than on nights with cloudy skies, as the amount of radiation lost by the earth at night is reduced by cloud cover. Calm wind conditions or light breezes also are more conducive to developing a ground inversion, because strong winds cause air to whirl, and mixing of the air breaks up the inversion. In addition, ground inversions are more likely to develop and to last longer in the cold climates of the world because a snow or ice cover reflects sunlight, and the small amount of heat absorbed is utilized in the melting process, thus cooling the surface very rapidly and producing an inversion. Therefore, ground inversions are more frequent and longer-lasting in high latitudes, especially at the North and South poles, than in middle latitudes. Likewise, the fall and winter seasons in the Northern Hemisphere, when temperatures are coldest, are more likely times for ground inversions to develop and to be more long-lasting than are other times of the year.

Normally, ground inversions are local in character and are found most frequently in valleys or other topographic depressions. Thus, a second method of inversion formation is the result of a phenomenon called air drainage. On cold nights, over rolling topography, cold air, being denser than warm air, responds to the pull of gravity and slides downslope and collects in depressions. Continued cooling can cause inversions to extend over larger areas both vertically and horizontally, if the vertical cooling is great enough to extend above the summits of the rolling terrain. Evidence of the initial development of a ground inversion often is heavy dew or frost. Frequently, ground fogs occur in association with inversions because of cooling of the air. This is particularly true in an air drainage situation where fogs first appear in depressions in the surface.

A third way in which ground inversions are formed is from a warm air mass moving into a region. A warm current of air may move in over a cool ground surface or over a cooler layer of surface air. The lower portions of the air mass are cooled, and stable or nonturbulent conditions result, producing an inversion.

Frequency of ground inversions varies across the United States (frequency being expressed as a percentage of the total time a region has inversions). During winter, Southern California and Arizona have inversions about 55 percent of the time; the central United States experiences inversions about 45 percent of the time; and Utah, Wyoming, Montana, and other Rocky Mountain states also have frequent ground inversions. The southeastern United States also experiences frequent ground inversions, which occur about 45 percent of the time. Most of these winter inversions occur at night. Summer inversions are less frequent than winter inversions, but they do occur. The central United States has inversions only about 35 percent of the time in summer, and the East Coast has inversions only about 20 percent of the time.

Upper-air inversions are more persistent and last for longer periods of time, usually several days rather than a few hours. These inversions normally occur above the surface at heights of 50-2,000 meters. Inversions develop above the surface in the troposphere as a result of several physical processes. One phenomenon that leads to the formation of an upper-air inversion is the subsidence, or sinking, of air. Air that subsides in the troposphere is compressed because of increasing pressure at lower levels. Compression of air causes it to heat adiabatically (from within) at a lapse rate of 10 degrees Celsius per kilometer. One such region of subsiding air is in a high pressure area or anticyclone. Here the upper atmospheric layers descend farther and heat more, thus developing an upper-air inversion. Therefore, regions that experience a high frequency of high-pressure areas have numerous upper-air inversions.

A second means of producing an upper-air inversion is through the movement of air masses. An air mass is a body of air with uniform physical characteristics horizontally. Air mass source regions affecting North America consist of the Pacific high and the Bermuda-Azores (Atlantic) high at about 30 degrees north latitude, the Arctic high at the North Pole, and the Canadian high and the Aleutian low at about

60 degrees north latitude. Often warm, moist air from the Pacific and Atlantic highs invades the United States. At the same time, polar or Arctic continental air may move southward and encounter the warm, moist air. The colder air, being denser, will push beneath the warmer air, lifting it aloft. The result is an upper-air inversion positioned above the boundary of the two air masses.

A third phenomenon that causes an upper-air inversion is the daily heating and cooling cycle. Generally, an inversion can develop when cloudy conditions during the day interfere with heating the surface more than cloudy conditions interfere with cooling it at night. If insufficient heating occurs during the day to offset the night-time cooling, an upper-air inversion is left in the troposphere.

Still another upper-air inversion is called the trade wind inversion and occurs in the low latitudes lying between the subtropical high (Pacific and Atlantic highs) and the equatorial low. Here the inversion is formed by the subsiding of air in the Hadley cell (where air rises near the equator and sinks near 30 degrees latitude, producing the trade winds in each latitude).

## Methods of Study

Every twelve hours, at midnight and at noon Greenwich mean time (the time at the observatory in Greenwich, England), hundreds of soundings of the atmosphere are taken. Soundings or readings of temperature and other weather elements are made by sending helium-filled balloons aloft. Attached to the balloons are a package of weather instruments and a radio transmitter called a radiosonde. Information on temperature, humidity, and pressure is sensed by the instruments and transmitted back to weather stations on the ground, where the data are recorded and plotted.

Over the oceans and sparsely settled regions of the world, where radiosondes are not sent aloft, weather data are obtained remotely from satellites. The data acquired from radiosondes and satellites are plotted on a special chart from which the meteorologist can make interpretations about the stability of the atmosphere and can determine the presence of temperature inversions and at what level they exist. When a temperature inversion is present, the atmosphere is said to be stable because the vertical movement of air is restricted. Once the temperatures received from the soundings are plotted on the special chart at the various elevations, a linear graph of temperature changes with height is the result. From the chart, the meteorologist can quickly interpret the rate of temperature change (lapse rate) for various layers in the troposphere. A temperature increase with height (negative lapse rate) is discerned easily on the chart and the depth of the inversion easily can be seen.

The lines on the chart show how much rising air would decrease in temperature with increasing altitude in noncloudy air (with a dry adiabatic rate of 10 degrees Celsius per kilometer) and how much it will decrease in cloudy air (with a wet adiabatic rate of 6 degrees Celsius per kilometer). By comparing the temperature soundings with these latter lines, the meteorologist can determine just how stable or unstable particular layers of the troposphere are. For example, in a hypothetical situation, suppose that a meteorologist has identified four layers of air on the special chart. The first layer of the sounding had temperatures decreasing at the rate of 12 degrees Celsius per kilometer, which is greater than the dry rate mentioned above. With this rate of temperature decrease, the layer would be absolutely unstable, and air could rise readily within it. Hence, no temperature could exist in this layer. Suppose that the second layer had an increase in temperature of 2 degrees Celsius per kilometer. This increase indicates a negative lapse rate, and because 2 degrees Celsius per kilometer is much less than the wet rate, the layer would be considered absolutely stable and definitely indicates the presence of a temperature inversion. Then suppose that the third layer has a temperature decrease of 8 degrees Celsius per kilometer. This rate is in between the dry and the wet adiabatic rates and is considered conditionally unstable, which means that air would have to be lifted to an elevation where clouds are forming to be able to rise on its own. Again, a temperature inversion is not present in this layer. Finally, assume that the top layer has a temperature decrease of 4 degrees Celsius per kilometer. This rate is less than the wet adiabatic rate and would be absolutely stable, but it would not have a temperature inversion within it because the temperature is decreasing even though it is absolutely stable. In other words, temperature inversions cause stable layers in the atmosphere, but not all stable layers contain temperature inversions. Thus the meteorologist collects, analyzes a vertical profile of the atmosphere, and detects temperature inversions in the atmosphere, which, in turn, contributes to a weather forecast.

## Context

Air beneath an inversion will not rise because it is colder than the inversion layer. Likewise, air will not rise within a ground inversion layer because air gets warmer with height, and air has to get cooler with height for air currents to rise within it. Owing to this resistance to air rising, pollution is concentrated near the earth's surface when an inversion is present. Pollution has always been present in the atmosphere naturally, but it began to worsen when humankind discovered fire. Burning coal causes pollution because much soot and sulfur dioxide is released to the atmosphere.

England's pollution problems culminated in the worst pollution disaster of all time in 1952. A temperature inversion formed over London on December 5, and fog developed in the humid air and gradually thickened over a five-day period. The people heated their homes more than usual to combat the wetness in the air. This additional burning of coal and oil added more soot and sulfur dioxide to the air, and four thousand people died as a direct result of the polluted air. Finally, in 1956, Great Britain passed a clear air act partly in response to this disaster.

The United States has had its own pollution disasters. On October 26-30, 1948, a high-pressure area stagnated over Donora, Pennsylvania, which had several industries that issued pollutants into the air. With the temperature inversion associated with the stagnating high pressure, the pollution thickened near ground level and could not be dispersed. By October 30, the situation had reached crisis proportions and people began to die. In all, seventeen people died; although that may seem to be a relatively small number, had Donora had the same population as London and had the ratio of deaths to population total carried over to a city that size, eight thousand people would have died.

Pollution disasters have occurred in other countries as well, and many countries have considerable pollution problems in their cities even though they have yet to suffer a disaster. An upper-air inversion is one of the reasons that Los Angeles has extreme air pollution levels, because the Pacific high area covers that part of the state for extended periods of time. The inversion layer associated with this high is lower than the mountains to the east, so the air and thus the pollution are entrapped above the city. This situation in effect places a "lid" over the city, and winds from the Pacific Ocean cannot carry away the pollutants because of the highlands to the east. In Florida, temperature inversions during the cold season often result in freezes that threaten the citrus crop. The freezes result from temperature inversions entrapping cold air at ground level. Other parts of the country experience such a threat to crops as well.

Fogs are quite frequently associated with temperature inversions. On calm, clear nights when radiational cooling is ongoing and the air is moist, radiation fog will form. This type of fog, which is usually quite patchy, is frequent in topographic depressions where air drainage results. Fog may also form when a warm, moist mass of air moves in over a cold ground surface. The air is cooled from below, an inversion is formed, and the water vapor in the air condenses. This type of fog is usually deeper and more extensive than is radiation fog. Fogs are a hazard to transportation.

## Bibliography

Ahrens, C. Donald. *Meteorology Today: An Introduction to Weather, Climate, and the Environment*. 3d ed. New York: West Publishing, 1988. Chapter 5, "Seasonal and Daily Temperature," provides a good background of temperature characteristics necessary to understanding temperature inversions. A good discussion of the various types of inversions is also included. A section entitled "Focus on a Special Topic" describes radiation inversions in detail. Suitable for entry-level college students.

Battan, Louis J. *Fundamentals of Meteorology*. Englewood Cliffs, N.J.: Prentice-Hall, 1984. Chapter 5 provides a fairly thorough, nontechnical analysis of atmospheric stability and vertical air motions. Included is a discussion of temperature inversions along with associated factors of stability, instability, temperature lapse rates, vertical motions, and turbulent diffusion. Diagrams showing temperature inversion profiles of both types in the atmosphere are included, as well as a table showing seasonal temperature inversion frequency.

Eagleman, Joe R. *Meteorology: The Atmosphere in Action*. New York: Van Nostrand Reinhold, 1980. Chapter 5 contains a reasonably good analysis of both ground and upper-air inversions. As in most meteorology books, much space is devoted to factors affecting stability in the atmosphere, an understanding of which is necessary to comprehend temperature inversions. The chapter also covers lapse rates, adiabatic rates, stability in saturated and nonsaturated air, and applications of stability.

Gedzelman, Stanley D. *The Science and Wonders of the Atmosphere*. New York: John Wiley & Sons, 1980. Chapter 13 provides very good coverage of temperature inversions and other factors in addition to characteristics related to stability/instability in the atmosphere. The author demonstrates temperature inversions with the use of thermodynamic charts (a chart showing temperature, pressure, and adiabatic rates). He also discusses some actual soundings taken in the atmosphere.

Spiegel, Herbert J., and Arnold Gruber. *From Weather Vanes to Satellites: An Introduction to Meteorology*. New York: John Wiley & Sons, 1983. Chapter 3 presents the factors of energy exchange between sun, earth, and atmosphere necessary to understand temperature inversions. Chapter 4 covers temperature causes and characteristics and distributions in the atmosphere. Adiabatic rates (cooling rates of air irrespective of surrounding air) and lapse rates are described, an understanding of which is necessary to study temperature inversions. The chapters are well written, nontechnical, and easy to understand.

*Ralph D. Cross*

## Cross-References

Air Pollution, 24; The Atmosphere's Global Circulation, 121; The Atmosphere's Structure and Composition, 128; Climate, 217; Clouds, 224; Storms, 2477; Tornadoes, 2527; Weather Forecasting, 2717; Wind, 2730.

# ATMOSPHERIC OZONE

*Field of study:* Atmospheric sciences and meteorology

*One of the natural gases in the atmosphere is ozone, which occurs in the strato-sphere. Ozone absorbs ultraviolet radiation from the sun. When chlorofluorocar-bons, which are used as a primary refrigerant and in making plastic, are broken up, they release chlorine ions. Each chlorine ion can destroy more than 100,000 mol-ecules of ozone. Scientists are concerned with possible ultraviolet damage to all organisms if this ozone depletion continues.*

### Principal terms

ATMOSPHERE: five clearly defined regions composed of layers of gases and mixtures of gases, water vapor, and solid and liquid particles, extending up to 300 miles above the earth

BIOSPHERE: the total living material—plants and animals and their environment—of a specific area of the earth

CHLOROFLUOROCARBONS: chemicals used worldwide as a primary refrigerant and in the production of foam plastic products

FOOD CHAIN: an arrangement of the organisms of an ecological community according to the order of predation in which each uses the next, usually lower, member as a food source

OZONE: a naturally occurring gas in the lower atmosphere produced by the ionization of oxygen

PHYTOPLANKTON: free-floating microscopic aquatic plants that convert sunlight into food for themselves and for other organisms in the food chain

ULTRAVIOLET SOLAR RADIATION: radiation composed mainly of ultraviolet A (UV-A) and ultraviolet B (UV-B), which are categories based on their wavelengths

## Summary of the Phenomenon

The atmosphere consists of five clearly defined regions. The two regions closest to the earth's surface are the troposphere and the stratosphere. In the lower region, there is a slow, constant increase in temperature with increase in altitude. At approximately 60 kilometers above the earth's surface, the stratosphere is known as the stratopause; the temperature of the stratopause varies less than does the tem-perature of the troposphere. There is a clear separation between the stratosphere and the troposphere; the exchange between tropospheric and stratospheric air re-quires several months, or even years, which indicates the difference in circulation of air within the two zones.

The air near the earth's surface has a clearly defined chemical composition. The lowest air is composed of 78.1 percent molecular nitrogen, 21 percent molecular oxygen, 0.9 percent argon, and small amounts of carbon dioxide. In the lowest level of the atmosphere there are small, variable amounts of water vapor and trace quantities of methane, nitrous oxide, carbon monoxide, hydrogen, ozone, helium, neon, krypton, and xenon. Where there is sufficient mixing by turbulence, the air consists mainly of molecular nitrogen and oxygen.

Ozone, a naturally occurring triatomic form of oxygen, is an irritating, pale blue gas that is explosive and toxic, even at low concentrations. Ozone is extremely unstable and highly reactive. It is 1.5 times as dense as is diatomic oxygen, the most common form of oxygen molecule, composed of only two atoms. Oxygen molecules consisting of two oxygen atoms are photodissociated by light in the shorter wavelengths (between 2,000 and 3,000 angstroms) into two oxygen ions ($0+$). An ion is an atom or group of atoms that carries an electric charge as a result of having lost or gained one or more electrons. Therefore, ions are by nature relatively unstable and quickly bond to any appropriate atom or element. The production of $0+$ ions leads immediately to the production of molecules of ozone.

Ozone and molecular oxygen absorb nearly all the ultraviolet radiation coming into the atmosphere from the sun. The ozone layer is essential for the protection of life on earth. In 1985, British researchers reported a sharp drop in ozone over Antarctica and described a hole in the ozone layer within which the ozone concentrations fell by as much as 50 percent. It has been estimated that world ozone levels have dropped by an estimated 3-7 percent in the seven years after the ozone hole was first discovered. As early as 1975, scientists at the University of California, Irvine, had suggested that chlorofluorocarbons (CFCs) were causing the protective layer of ozone to become thinner over the Antarctic. This suggestion was based on data they had collected. In 1977, the British Antarctic Survey at Halley Bay had reported a drop in ozone levels far out of line with existing models. This thinning occurs during twenty-two to thirty days every September and October, making a sort of "hole" in the usually more uniform ozone layer. The first documentation of the connection between CFCs and ozone, based on data collected by the Jet Propulsion Laboratory in Pasadena, California, indicated that chlorine compounds bloom as the ozone hole appears in September and October of each year. It has been hypothesized that the chlorine compounds condense onto ice crystals during the polar winter, and as spring arrives in September, the chlorine is warmed by the sun and converted into an active form that can destroy ozone. There has been much scientific speculation about the cause of the declining ozone layer. The main culprit is widely held to be CFCs. Research has shown that a chlorine-containing molecule related to CFCs is abundant in the hole. The fact that there is no fluorine in the upper atmosphere from natural sources, supports the view that the chlorine compounds found there are probably CFCs, which are of man-made origin.

CFCs are nontoxic, inert gases that are simple and cheap to manufacture and that vaporize at low temperatures; thus, they are used worldwide as a primary refrigerant and as propellant gases for spray cans. Because they are a good insulator, CFCs are used as ingredients in plastic foam products. When these CFCs are broken up, however, either physically or by intense ultraviolet radiation at higher altitudes, they release chlorine ions. The free chlorine ions act as an initiator of a chain reaction that brings about the breakdown of ozone; each ion can destroy more than 100,000 molecules of ozone. Chemists think that there is even a product of this chain reaction that perpetuates further chain reactions of ozone breakdown. During the first several years after their initial use, the atmospheric concentrations of CFCs were increasing at a rate of several hundred percent a year. Later research has indicated that the hole is an uneven one, with 1.5- to 2-mile-thick slices of ozone-poor air sandwiched within layers of only minimal depletion. Researchers from the University of Wyoming found great differences in adjacent layers. In some cases, a layer that had lost more than 75 percent of its ozone was adjacent to another layer with a loss of less than 25 percent. The great speed with which the depletion occurred has puzzled scientists: In some situations, they found that about half of the ozone was gone after twenty-five days.

There are three main theories that scientists propose as the cause of ozone depletion. Some scientists put forth a chemical explanation: The depletion is caused by chemical events exacerbated by the presence of CFCs. A second group suggests that high solar-cycle activity produces ozone-destroying active forms of nitrogen above the stratosphere, but the absence of depletion above 12 miles makes the solar-cycle theory unlikely. Scientists known as dynamicists argue that the ozone hole is formed by air movements of mixing and blending of air masses. As one scientist with the National Oceanic and Atmospheric Administration points out, the dynamic theory does not hold up, based on chemical measurements made inside the ozone hole that showed very low levels of nitrous oxide. This compound is found in relative abundance in the troposphere (the region of atmosphere in contact with the earth's surface); if an air mass moved from the troposphere into the stratosphere, as the dynamicists claim, there should be plenty of nitrous oxide. Most scientists think that very likely a combination of these effects, possibly in addition to unknown factors, is the cause of the rapid depletion. No model so far proposed can adequately explain the ultimate cause of this very rapid depletion.

## Methods of Study

Researchers utilize a great diversity of devices and techniques in their study and interpretation of atmospheric ozone. One popular technique is the use of models. A good model is one that simulates the interrelationships and interactions of the various parts of the known system. The weakness of models is that, often, not enough is known to give an accurate picture of the total system or to make accurate predictions. Most modeling is done on computers. Scientists estimate how fast chemicals such as CFCs and nitrous oxide will be produced in the future and build a computer model of the way these chemicals react with ozone and with one another. From this model, it is possible to estimate future ozone levels at different altitudes and at different future dates.

Similar processes appear to be at work in the Arctic stratosphere, leading to ozone depletion, as in the Antarctic; however, the National Oceanic and Atmospheric Administration (NOAA) Aeronomy Laboratory in Boulder, Colorado, reported a discrepancy between observed ozone depletion and predicted levels, based on models that account accurately for the Antarctic depletions. This report suggests that some other mechanism is at work in the Arctic. Thus, good models can be very useful in studying new data. There are two models favored by most scientists in this area. Some scientists put forth a chemical model that says the depletion is caused by chemical events promoted by the presence of chlorofluorocarbons created by industrial processes. Acceptance of this model was promoted by the discovery of fluorine in the stratosphere. Fluorine does not naturally occur there, but it is related to CFCs. The other model assumes that the ozone hole was formed by dynamic air movement and mixing. This model best fits data gathered by ozone-sensing balloons that sample up to 30 kilometers altitude and then radio the data back to earth. Ozone depletion is confined to air between 12 and 20 kilometers. While the total ozone depletion is 35 percent, different strata showed various amounts of depletion from 70 to 90 percent. Surprisingly, about half the ozone was gone in twenty-five days. This finding does not fit the chemical model very well.

Besides ozone-sensing balloons, satellites are of much help. The National Aeronautics and Space Administration (NASA) obtains measurements with its Nimbus 7 satellite. Ozone measurements made by this satellite helped to develop flight plans for the specialized aircraft NASA also deploys in ozone studies. NASA's ER-2 aircraft is a modified U-2 reconnaissance plane that carries instruments up to 20 kilometers altitude for seven-hour flights to 80 degrees north latitude. A DC-8, operating during the same period, is able to survey the polar vortex, owing to its greater range. In addition, scientists utilize many meteorological techniques and instruments, including chemical analysis of gases by means of infrared spectroscopy, mass spectroscopy and gas spectroscopy combined, gas chromatography, and oceanographic analysis of planktonic life in the southern Atlantic, Pacific, and Indian oceans. As new research methods become available, they are applied to this essential study.

## Context

Atmospheric ozone provides a gauze of protection from the lethal effects of ultraviolet radiation from the sun. This ability to absorb ultraviolet radiation protects all life forms on the earth's surface from excessive ultraviolet radiation, which destroys the life of plant and animal cells. Currently, between 10 and 30 percent of the sun's ultraviolet B (UV-B) radiation reaches the earth's surface. If ozone levels were to drop by 10 percent, the amount of UV-B radiation reaching the earth would increase by 20 percent.

Present-day UV-B levels are responsible for the fading of paints and the yellowing of window glazing and for car finishes becoming chalky. These kinds of degradation will accelerate as the ozone layer is depleted. There could also be increased smog, urban air pollution, and a worsening of the problem of acid rain in cities. In humans, UV-B causes sunburn, snow blindness, skin cancer, cataracts, and excessive aging and wrinkling of skin. Skin cancer is the most common form of cancer—more than 400,000 new cases are reported every year in the United States alone. The National Academy of Sciences has estimated that each 1 percent decline in ozone would increase the incidence of skin cancer by 2 percent. Therefore, a 3 percent depletion in ozone would produce some 20,000 more cases of skin cancer in the United States every year.

Many other forms of life—from bacteria to forests and crops—are adversely affected by excessive radiation as well. Ultraviolet radiation affects plant growth by slowing photosynthesis and by delaying germination in many plants, including trees and crops. Scientists have a great concern for the organisms that live in the ocean and the effect ozone depletion may have on them. Phytoplankton, zooplankton, and krill (a shrimplike crustacean) could be greatly depleted if there were a drastic increase in ultraviolet A and B. The result would be a tremendous drop in the population of these free-floating organisms. These organisms are important because they are the beginning of the food chain. Phytoplankton use the energy of sunlight to convert inorganic compounds, such as phosphates, nitrates, and silicates, into organic plant matter. This process provides food for the next step in the food chain, the herbivorous zooplankton and krill. They, in turn, become the food for the next higher level of animals in the food chain. Initial studies of this food chain in the Antarctic suggest that elevated levels of ultraviolet radiation impair photosynthetic activity. Recent studies show that a fifteen-day exposure to UV-B levels 20 percent higher than normal can kill off all anchovy larvae down to a depth of 10 meters. There is also concern that ozone depletion may alter the food chain and even cause changes in the organism's genetic makeup. An increase in the ultraviolet radiation is likely to lower fish catches and upset marine ecology, which has already suffered damage from man-made pollution. On a worldwide basis, fish presently provides 18 percent of all the animal protein consumed.

The United Nations Environmental Program (UNEP) is working with governments, international organizations, and industry to develop a framework within which the international community can make decisions to minimize atmospheric changes and the effects they could have on the earth. In 1977, UNEP convened a meeting of experts to draft the World Plan of Action on the Ozone Layer. The plan called for a program of research on the ozone layer and on what would happen if the layer were damaged. In addition, UNEP created a group of experts and government representatives who framed the Convention for the Protection of the Ozone Layer. This convention was adopted in Vienna in March, 1985, by twenty-one states and the European Economic Community and has subsequently been signed by many more states. The convention pledges states that sign to protect human health and the environment from the effects of ozone depletion. Action has already been taken to protect the ozone layer. Several countries have restricted the use of CFCs or the amounts produced. The United States banned the use of CFCs in aerosols in 1978. Some countries, such as Belgium and the Nordic countries, have in effect banned CFC production altogether. The group has also worked with governments on a Protocol to the Convention that required nations that signed to limit their production of CFCs. It is the hope and aim of these nations that such international cooperation will lead to a better global environment.

## Bibliography

Begley, Sharon. "A Gaping Hole in the Sky: Chemicals Are Depleting the Thin Ozone Layer That Shields the Earth from Dangerous Radiation." *Newsweek* 112 (July 11, 1988): 21-23. This article discusses the chemicals that have been posited as agents depleting the ozone layer and thus exposing life on earth to harmful radiation. Easy reading level; scientifically accurate.

Lemonick, M. D. "Culprits of the Stratosphere." *Time* 130 (September 21, 1987): 57. A good discussion of the various man-made chemicals that are thought to contribute to the problem of the ozone hole. *Time* magazine frequently offers brief but accurate coverage of new scientific research and discoveries.

National Research Council Staff. "The Search for Ozone-Friendly Refrigerants." In *Causes and Effects of Stratospheric Ozone Reduction: An Update.* Washington, D.C.: National Academy Press, 1982. Considers the chemistry and physics of ozone reduction as well as the biological effects of increased solar ultraviolet radiation. College reading level, though advanced high school students will find helpful information. References, glossary, and a list of chemical symbols. Appendices on methods of detection.

Shell, E. R. "Weather Versus Chemicals." *The Atlantic* 259 (May, 1987): 27-31. A good source for discussion in fairly simple terms of the complex problems of the ozone hole and the widely recognized role of chlorofluorocarbons in this global issue. *The Atlantic* magazine offers thorough discussion of environmental issues on a popular reading level.

*George K. Attwood*

## Cross-References

# AURORAS

*Field of study:* Atmospheric sciences and meteorology

*Auroras, the northern and southern lights, are caused by geomagnetic activity taking place in the earth's atmosphere. By understanding auroras, scientists can gauge the effects of solar activities on the earth's environment.*

### Principal terms

ATMOSPHERE: the layer of gases that cloaks the surface of the earth

ELECTROMAGNETIC SPECTRUM: the range of energies that can be taken by electromagnetic radiation

GEOMAGNETISM: the external magnetic field generated by forces within the earth; this force attracts materials having similar properties, inducing them to line up (point) along field lines of force

IONOSPHERE: the upper level of the atmosphere, which is ionized (electrically charged) by exposure to sunlight

SOLAR WIND: the stream of gases emitted by the sun's surface

## Summary of the Phenomenon

"Aurora" is a general term for the light produced by charged particles interacting with the upper reaches of the earth's atmosphere. The term "aurora borealis" specifically refers to the northern dawn, or northern lights; "aurora australis" refers to the southern lights. The aurora appears in an oval girdling the earth's geomagnetic poles, where the field lines are perpendicular to the surface. In this region, the earth is not shielded from the space environment as it is at lower latitudes (where the field lines are almost parallel to the surface); thus, electrons and ions moving along magnetic field lines can strike the atmosphere directly. Normally, the auroral oval is located about 23 degrees from the north magnetic pole and 18 degrees from the south magnetic pole. Because the north magnetic pole is located in Greenland, the oval is offset toward Canada and away from Europe. Generally, the auroras appear at altitudes between 100 and 120 kilometers high, in sheets 1 to 10 kilometers thick and several thousand kilometers long.

The auroral oval is a product of the earth's magnetic field and is driven by the sun's output of charged particles. The oval can be enlarged as far north or south as 20 degrees latitude; its normal range is around 55-60 degrees. These variations in range and intensity have been correlated with sunspots, showing that solar activity is the engine that drives the aurora and other geomagnetic disturbances. Additionally, scientists usually describe auroral activity in terms of local time relative to the sun rather than the geographic point over which it occurs. Thus, the earth can be considered to be rotating beneath the auroral events (even though the shape of the oval remains skewed). The first indication that the aurora might be linked to solar activity came in 1859, when Richard Carrington observed an especially powerful solar flare in white light. A few hours later, he observed a strong auroral display and suspected that the two might be linked.

Auroras are caused by electron precipitation: Electrons "rain" on the upper atmosphere from this field-aligned current. The analogy is limited, as rain falls at random, while electrons moving in a magnetic field do so in a helix wrapped around a field line, somewhat like the rifling of a gun barrel. The helix of electrons trapped in the earth's magnetic field will become more pronounced as they approach the poles, until finally their direction is reversed (at the "mirror point") and they are reflected back to the opposite pole. Motion back and forth is quite normal.

If the electrons are accelerated into the ionosphere, they encounter oxygen atoms (from molecules dissociated by sunlight) and nitrogen molecules. These collisions will release *Bremsstrahlung* (braking) X rays, which are absorbed by the atmosphere or radiated into space. The oxygen is ionized (and an electron freed) and radiates light when it is neutralized by a free electron. Nitrogen either is excited and radiates when it returns to the "ground" state or is dissociated and excited.

The aurora has been compared to a television picture tube: The face of the tube has been relatively simple to understand, but the circuitry that drives the display remains elusive. As the atmosphere fades gradually into space, starting at about 60 kilometers above the surface of the earth, it forms an electrified layer called the ionosphere, where oxygen and nitrogen molecules are dissociated by sunlight. Because many of these free atoms and molecules are also ionized by sunlight, electric fields and currents move freely, although the net electrical charge is zero.

The structure of the aurora varies widely. Three major forms have been discerned: quiet (or homogeneous) arcs, rayed arcs, and diffuse patches. Homogeneous arcs appear as "curtains" or bands across the sky. They sometimes will occur as pairs or (rarely) sets of parallel arcs and have also been described as resembling ribbons of light. The lower edge of the arc will be sharply defined as it reaches a certain density level in the atmosphere, but the upper edge usually simply fades into space. Pulsating arcs vary in brightness, as energy is pumped in at different rates. Also in the category of quiet arcs are diffuse luminous surfaces, which are like clouds and have no defined structure; they may also appear as a pulsating surface. Finally, the weakest homogeneous display is a feeble glow, which actually is the upper level of an auroral display just beyond the horizon.

Auroras with rays appear as shafts of light, usually in bundles. A rayed arc is similar to a homogeneous arc but comprises rays rather than evenly distributed light. The formation and dissipation of individual rays may produce the illusion that rays are moving along the length of a curtain. Among rayed arcs, the "drapery" most resembles a curtain and is most active in shape and color changes. If the viewer is directly below the zenith of an auroral event, then it appears as a corona, with parallel rays appearing to radiate from a central point. Drapery displays are often followed by flaming auroras that move toward zenith.

A controversial aspect of auroras is whether they produce any sound. Many observers, from antiquity, have reported "hearing" the aurora; however, sensitive sound-recording equipment has yet to capture this sound. This leaves open the question whether the sound is a psychological perception, an electrostatic discharge, or some other phenomenon.

The colors of the aurora—pink, red, green, and blue-green—are distinct and correspond with specific chemistry rather than being a continuous spectrum typical of a uniformly hot body (such as the sun). Major emissions come from atomic oxygen (at 557.7 and 630 nanometers wavelength) and molecular nitrogen (391.4, 470, 650, and 680 nanometers). These emissions come from distinct altitudes. The green oxygen line (557.7 nanometers), which peaks at 100 kilometers altitude, is caused by an energy state that decays in 0.7 second. The red oxygen line (630 nanometers), which peaks at about 300 kilometers, comes from an energy state that decays in 200 seconds. While oxygen is energized to this level at lower altitudes, its energy will be lost to collisions with other gases long before it can decay naturally. From such comparisons, geophysicists were able to deduce some of the vertical structure of the atmosphere. X rays and ultraviolet light are also emitted but cannot be detected from the ground. The Dynamics Explorer 1 satellite has recorded the aurora at 130 nanometers in hundreds of images taken several earth radii above the North Pole.

The brightness of the aurora can vary widely. Four levels of international brightness coefficients are assigned, ranging from IBC I, which is comparable to the brightness of the Milky Way, to IBC IV, which equals the illumination received from a full moon. Auroras usually are eighty times brighter in atomic oxygen than in ionized nitrogen molecules, indicating their origins higher in the atmosphere. Doppler shifting is commonly recorded in the spectra around 656.3 nanometers (hydrogen-alpha), indicating the motion of protons that are neutralized and re-ionized as they accelerate up or down the field lines. It is theorized that, as with many natural effects, only a small fraction (about 0.5 percent) of the energy that goes into the auroras actually produces light. The remainder goes into radio waves, ultraviolet rays, and X rays, and into heating the upper atmosphere.

Single images from the Dynamics Explorer satellite have confirmed the indication by ground-based camera chains that the aurora is uneven in density and brightness. One image, for example, shows that the auroras thin almost to extinction on the dayside but expand to several hundred kilometers in thickness between about 10:00 P.M. and 2:00 A.M. local time. "Theta" auroras have been recorded in which a straight auroral line crosses the oval in the center, giving the appearance of the Greek letter θ. This phenomenon may be caused by the splitting of the tail of the plasma sheet (which extends well into the tail of the magnetosphere) or by the solar wind's magnetic field when it has a direction opposite the earth's.

Imagery by the spin-scan auroral imagers aboard the Dynamics Explorer 1 satellite showed that auroral substorms start at midnight, local time, and expand around the oval. Observations of hundreds of substorms showed that they have the same generalized structure but that no two are alike. The satellite imager also showed expansions and contractions in the aurora in response to changes in the interplanetary magnetic field and in the solar wind. As the solar wind—which is simply a plasma—meets the earth's magnetosphere, a shock wave is formed, and the wind is diverted around the earth. This diversion compresses the earth's magnetic field on the sunward side, while it extends like a comet's tail on the nightside. When the field of the solar wind is oriented toward the south, its field lines reconnect with the field lines of the earth and allow protons (free hydrogen nuclei) and electrons to enter the magnetosphere (they are normally blocked when the field is oriented to the north).

Auroral activity is strongly driven by the solar wind. If the magnetic field of the wind points north—aligned with the earth's magnetic field—then the auroral oval is relatively small, and its glow is hard to see. When the solar wind's magnetic field reverses direction, a substorm occurs. The oval starts to brighten within an hour, and bright curtains form within it. At its peak, the oval will be thinned toward the noon side and quite thick and active on the midnight side. As the storm subsides, about four hours after the field reversed (actually, as it starts to revert to normal), the aurora dims and curtains form. Finally, a large, diffuse glow covering the pole may be left as the field becomes stronger in the northward direction.

The flow of the solar wind past the magnetosphere generates massive electrical currents, which flow mostly from one side of the magnetosphere to the other. Some of the currents, however, connect down the Earth's magnetic field, into and through the auroral oval. Because an electric current is caused by the flow of charged particles (electrons in this case), in the process, electrons are brought directly into the ionosphere around the poles. The primary currents enter around the morning side and exit around the evening side. Secondary currents flow in the opposite direction. Changes in the electrical potential of the magnetosphere, as when it is pumped up by particles arriving in the solar wind, will force the electrons through the mirror point; they are then accelerated deeper into the ionosphere. This auroral potential structure, as it is called, is thin but extends around the auroral oval for thousands of kilometers, even to the point of closing on itself.

Electrojets also form in the auroras at low altitudes from an effect known as "E-cross-B drift" (written $E \times B$). At high altitudes, electrons and protons flow freely because there is a low gas density and no net current change. At lower altitudes, around 100 kilometers, the protons are slowed by collisions with atoms and molecules, but the electrons continue to move unopposed. The result is a pair of electrojets, eastward (evening) and westward (morning), which flow toward midnight, then cross the polar cap toward noon. These electrojets heat the ionosphere, especially during active solar periods, when the aurora is more intense.

This $E \times B$ drift in the auroral ovals appears to be a major source of plasma for the magnetosphere. It appears that the ions (which are positively charged) are accelerated upward along the same magnetic field lines where electrons (negatively charged) precipitate. Hydrogen, helium, oxygen, and nitrogen make up this ion flow. Each has the same total energy, so their paths vary according to mass. The net effect is that of an ion fountain blowing upward from the auroras then spread by a wind across the poles.

A little-known subset of the aurora is the sub-auroral red (SAR) arcs, which appear at the midlatitudes; the magnetic field lines on which they occur are different from those on which auroras appear. SAR arcs always emit at 660 nanometers (from oxygen atoms) and are dim and uncommon. Modern instrumentation has shown that the SAR arcs are a separate phenomenon from the polar auroras. These arcs may be caused by cold electrons in the plasmasphere interacting with plasma waves or with energetic ions. SAR arcs are believed to originate at approximately 19,000-26,000 kilometers altitude during especially strong geomagnetic storms, although the arcs themselves appear at altitudes around 400 kilometers as the energy from the storm leaks or is forced downward.

The aurora also appears in the radio spectrum. Studies in the twentieth century showed that the aurora could be sounded by radar at certain frequencies. Satellites in the 1970's started recording bursts of energy in the low end of the AM radio spectrum. This radiation is called auroral kilometric radiation (AKR), because its wavelength is up to 3 kilometers, reflected outward by the ionosphere. Such bursts can release 100 million to 1,000 million watts at a time, making them far more powerful than conventional broadcasts by humans. The bursts originate in a region of the sky about 6,400-18,000 kilometers high, in the evening sector of the auroral oval. Because the radiation is polarized, it is likely that AKR is caused directly by electrons spiraling along magnetic field lines in a natural mimic of free-electron lasers in the laboratory.

## Methods of Study

The space age owes its birth in some measure to the aurora, for it was the desire to study the earth-space interface around the globe at high altitude that resulted in the launching of the first satellites, during the International Geophysical Year in 1957-1958. Until then, ground-based photography and instrumentation were almost the only methods of studying the aurora (aircraft and rockets played a lesser role). Ground-based instrumentation in the 1940's and 1950's confirmed that auroras were linked to the geomagnetic field, for studies showed that the aurora occurred in a circle around the north magnetic pole. Photography of the aurora has always been difficult because the display is dynamic, sometimes changing from second to second. Not until the 1950's were electronic devices available to analyze the entire auroral spectrum visible from the ground.

Satellites in the 1970's and 1980's have expanded the array of instruments available to investigators. While field and particle instrumentation has been used to analyze gases and plasmas, imaging instruments have been equally revealing. Notable cameras of various sorts have been carried by Dynamics Explorer 1, the U.S. Air Force HiLat (high latitude) satellite, and the Swedish Viking satellite. In addition, some imaging was performed by polar-orbit weather satellites, but with lesser spectral and spatial resolution. The Skylab crews observed some auroral activity. The Spacelab 3 crew in 1985 photographed the aurora from above the atmosphere. Combining images taken a few seconds apart allowed formation of stereo pairs so that the structure could be studied better. In other experiments, small electron guns have been carried into space aboard rockets and spacecraft to fire electrons back at the atmosphere in an attempt to generate artificial auroras.

A key finding by the satellites was that auroras are often more active on the dayside of the earth, although sunlight and sky completely overwhelm it, and that large quantities of radiation are generated in the ultraviolet. This radiation is not seen at the earth's surface, because the atmosphere absorbs the light.

## Context

Auroras are the most visible manifestation of the interaction between the earth and space. The study of plasmas has been enhanced by observations made of them. A clear understanding of the aurora will provide a means of diagnosing activities in the magnetosphere and the effects of solar activities on the terrestrial environment.

Auroras also serve as a means to study stars and planets. The same basic physics takes place in stars' atmospheres as in the auroras and the magnetosphere of earth, although the energies and chemistries may be vastly different. Thus, the terrestrial aurora can serve as a vast laboratory for testing theories. Planets with magnetic fields also have auroral activity. Much of Jupiter's radio noise is caused by auroral kilometric radiation, and the Einstein Observatory recorded X rays that apparently came from *Bremsstrahlung* radiation in the Jovian atmosphere. The Voyager 1 spacecraft observed a 29,000-kilometer-long aurora on the nightside of Jupiter, plus lightning pulses in and above the clouds coincident with the auroral activity.

## Bibliography

Akasofu, Syun-Ichi. "The Dynamic Aurora." *Scientific American* 260 (May, 1989). A detailed, college-level treatment of the current understanding of auroras, written by the physicist who is generally accepted as the world expert.

Delobeau, Francis. *The Environment of the Earth*. New York: Springer-Verlag, 1971. A technical description of the terrestrial environment, written as a reference for space scientists. Although the work is dated by subsequent discoveries, its description of auroral chemistry is still valid.

Dooling, Dave. "Satellite Data Alters View on Earth-Space Environment." *Spaceflight* (July, 1987). An article focusing on the exploration of the magnetosphere by the Dynamics Explorer satellites, with details on auroral imaging and radiation.

Eather, Robert H. *Majestic Lights: The Aurora in Science*. Washington, D.C.: American Geophysical Union, 1980. A well-illustrated, informative booklet describing auroras through history and their modern scientific interpretation. Written for general audiences.

Petrie, William. *Keoeeit: The Story of the Aurora Borealis*. Oxford: Pergamon Press, 1963. Highly detailed description of the history of auroras (largely from the Canadian and Eskimo point of view) and of the structure of auroral displays. Also tells much of the ground-based exploration of the aurora.

*Dave Dooling*

**Cross-References**

The Atmosphere's Structure and Composition, 128; Earth-Sun Relations, 399; Earth's Magnetic Field at Present, 548; The Jovian Planets' Atmospheres, 1290; Magnetic Reversals, 1439; Magnetic Stratigraphy, 1446.

# THE BASIN AND RANGE PROVINCE

*Field of study:* Mountain ranges

   *Alternating linear ranges and valleys characterize the Basin and Range province of western North America. This topography resulted from crustal stretching that caused large normal faults. The crustal stretching, which occurred over the last 40 million years, is superimposed on a complex record of older geologic events.*

   *Principal terms*
      DETACHMENT FAULT: a horizontal or gently dipping, regionally extensive fault; the hanging wall usually contains numerous smaller, steeper normal faults that end at the detachment fault
      DIP: the angle between a sloping surface, such as a fault, and a horizontal plane
      DUCTILE SHEAR ZONE: a planar zone of rock that accommodates relative movement like a fault, but the movement has occurred by processes of solid-state flow rather than by fracture
      FAULT: a fracture or system of fractures across which relative movement of rock bodies has occurred
      FAULT SLIP: the direction and amount of relative movement between the two blocks of rock separated by a fault
      HALF-GRABEN: an asymmetrical structural depression formed along a normal fault where the downthrown block is tilted toward the fault
      HANGING WALL and FOOTWALL: the rock bodies located respectively above and below a fault
      INTERNAL DRAINAGE: the condition in which a river system has no outlet; instead it drains into a saline lake or playa (a lake basin that contains water only shortly after a rainstorm)
      LITHOSPHERIC PLATES: rigid blocks that make up the outer shell of the earth, 100-200 kilometers thick and generally similar in size to the continents, forming a mosaic that covers the earth's surface
      NORMAL FAULT: a fault across which slip caused the hanging wall to move downward relative to the footwall
      PLATE TECTONICS: the theory that earth movements reflect the relative movements between a small number of rigid lithospheric plates, along narrow zones of deformation called plate boundaries
      STRIKE-SLIP FAULT: a fault across which the relative movement is mainly lateral
      THRUST FAULT: a fault, usually dipping less than 30 degrees, across which the hanging wall moved upward relative to the footwall

## Summary of the Phenomenon

The Basin and Range province comprises three different but related entities: a geologic province of western North America, the alternating linear mountain ranges and valleys that characterize that province, and the fault-block bedrock structure responsible for the distinctive topography. The Basin and Range province includes the area between the Rocky Mountains on the east and the Sierra Nevada and Cascade Mountains on the west, from southern Montana, Idaho, and Oregon south to northern Mexico. Crustal stretching in a roughly east-west direction across this area in the last 40 million years is responsible for the distinctive topography and crustal structure. The stretching is the most recent chapter of a long, complex geologic history.

Alternating elongate mountain ranges and valleys (basins) define Basin and Range topography, which occurs not only in the Basin and Range province but also in other areas of young continental stretching, such as southern Greece and the Yunan province in China. Ranges and basins are usually similar in extent, commonly 50-200 kilometers in length and 20-30 kilometers in width. Climate throughout the Basin and Range province is arid or semiarid. As a result, the ranges are generally rugged, sparsely vegetated, and drained by ephemeral and occasional perennial streams. Topographic relief from range tops to basin bottoms is usually 1-3 kilometers. Internal drainage is common, either in an individual basin or with several basins linked in a single internal drainage system. An example of the latter is the Great Salt Lake in Utah, which is the terminus of a drainage system that includes most of the basins and ranges of northwestern Utah. Ranges and basins are defined on one or both sides by young, and in some instances seismically active, normal faults. The range side of the fault is the upthrown block and the basin side the downthrown block, so the fault movements are expressed directly in the topography; however, erosion of the ranges and sedimentation in the basins cause topographic relief to be much less than the total displacement across the faults, which can exceed 10 kilometers. Typical Basin and Range faults dip from 30 to 70 degrees. Internal drainage results because subsidence along active normal faults ponds the water running off in streams. The common fault pattern is one in which basins and ranges are faulted on one side only to form a series of half-grabens, or asymmetrical structural depressions. Between the half-grabens are asymmetrical tilted-block ranges that are straight and steep on the faulted side and more gently sloping on the other side which, downslope, forms the bedrock floor of the next basin. Series of tilted-block ranges and half-graben basins are sometimes called "domino-style" fault systems, because the fault-bounded blocks resemble a series of dominos that have been stood on end next to each other and then toppled together. Strike-slip faults also are common in the Basin and Range province, commonly acting to link together the ends of normal faults. Some of these strike-slip faults are very large. For example, the Furnace Creek fault zone that runs along northern Death Valley in California, linking normal faults in Death Valley to others farther north, may have accommodated 70 kilometers of strike slip.

Much study of the Basin and Range has focused on ranges called metamorphic core complexes (MCCs) that are not domino-style fault blocks. There are more than twenty MCCs in the Basin and Range, and more may exist but are yet unrecognized. Both the structure and topography of MCCs are controlled by a detachment fault that separates an upper level, usually composed of sedimentary and volcanic rocks, from a lower level made up of metamorphic and plutonic rocks formed deeper in the crust. Rocks of the upper level generally have been intensely stretched along numerous normal faults, such that they have increased in width by several hundred percent. Rocks beneath the detachment fault commonly have flowed at high temperatures and great depth. Analysis of the flow structures indicates that much or all of this flow also represents a large amount of horizontal stretching. Upper-level faulting and lower-level flow are therefore believed to be related. The detachment fault in an MCC is usually dome-shaped, so that the fault dips gently off the flanks of the range in every direction. Differences in erosion resistance between rock types above and below the detachment fault resulted in the domelike shape of the ranges, which is quite different from that of the more typical fault-block ranges. It is widely accepted that MCCs record extreme horizontal stretching, but since their recognition in the 1970's, their origin and significance have been intensely debated and remain controversial. There are two main issues: the relationship between MCCs and "normal" Basin and Range domino-style faults, and the significance of detachment faults. Regarding the former, one view is that MCCs and domino-style Basin and Range faults represent distinct extensional processes and that an MCC forms instead of large domino-style faults when the crust in an area is especially hot and susceptible to flow. Others consider MCCs to be exposures of what underlies the domino-style fault systems at depth; that is, the domino-style faults end downward at a detachment fault like those exposed in MCCs. In this view, greater than normal stretching in some areas caused the upper crust to be stretched so thin that deeper rocks and structures were exposed as MCCs. Researchers are similarly split into two camps regarding the significance of the detachment faults. One group considers the detachment faults to represent a horizontal zone along which the cooler upper crust that deforms by faulting is mechanically separated (detached) from the hotter lower crust that deforms by flow. In this case, the detachment fault would act to accommodate differences in the movement patterns of rocks above and below it; it need not accommodate large displacement, but merely local adjustments. The other view is that the detachment fault represents a large, gently dipping normal fault that cuts down through the crust. In this view, as much as 50-60 kilometers of horizontal displacement has occurred along detachment faults in MCCs, thus bringing together originally widely separated upper- and deeper-crustal rocks. Consensus tends to favor the latter view of each issue, that is, that MCCs represent the deeper parts of domino-fault systems and that detachment faults are major dislocations that cut through the crust and accommodate tens of kilometers of slip. Much future work will be needed before either of these issues will be considered resolved.

The structure summarized in the foregoing has been superimposed in the Basin and Range upon a long and complex previous geologic history. Indeed, much of the knowledge of that history can be attributed to the Basin and Range faulting which has uplifted and exposed crustal sections many kilometers thick to allow the geologic record to be read. The oldest rocks in the Basin and Range are scattered occurrences of ancient, deep-seated metamorphic and plutonic rocks as much as 2.5 billion years old. These rocks are exposures of the ancient crust of the North American continent. In the Late Precambrian eon, part of the west side of the North American continent was faulted away and carried by plate tectonics to some other part of the globe. This event formed a new western continental margin facing a new ocean basin. This ancient continental margin presently runs southwestward across southern Idaho and central Nevada, so that the eastern and southern parts of the Basin and Range formed from crust of the ancient continent, but the western Basin and Range was part of a deep ocean basin. From this time until the middle of the Paleozoic era, this continental margin resembled the modern east coast of North America: a broad, gently sloping shelf, generally tectonically stable and largely covered by shallow seawater. During the Late Paleozoic and Early Mesozoic eras, lithospheric plate movements caused two major lithospheric blocks to collide successively with this continental margin. The collisions resulted in periods of mountain building along the North American continental margin, known as the Antler and Sonoman orogenies. Other results of these plate collisions included the building outward of the North American continent, such that by 250 million years ago, all of what now lies in the Basin and Range was part of continental North America, and strike-slip faulting that shifted some crustal blocks hundreds of kilometers along the continental margin, substantially changing the shape of the coastline in the process. Following the Sonoman orogeny, the western continental margin of North America changed completely. By 200 years ago, the continental margin was the site of underthrusting of oceanic lithosphere (subduction), causing the construction of a high mountain chain along western North America that was similar to the modern Andes in South America. What is now the Basin and Range province covered an area analogous to modern Peru, Bolivia, and northern Argentina, including the eastern parts of the Andes, its foothills, and some of the adjacent plains. The mountain range was an area of volcanism and magmatic intrusion, now represented by large masses of granite in the Sierra Nevada and much of the Basin and Range. Thrust faulting occurred along the east side of the mountain chain, as it does today on the east side of the Andes. Such thrust faults are especially well known in the areas around Las Vegas, Nevada, and Salt Lake City, Utah.

Formation of the Basin and Range is part of a comparatively recent change in the tectonic pattern of western North America. From about 30 million years ago to the present, the Andes-like plate boundary (still active in the Pacific Northwest) has been changing into a strike-slip plate boundary (transform fault) that includes the San Andreas fault of Southern California. Somewhat earlier, large-scale stretching of the lithosphere began in the Basin and Range. Most of the MCCs formed between 40 and 20 million years ago. At the same time, numerous large volcanic centers appeared in and around the Basin and Range. These volcanic centers were the sources of enormous explosive eruptions that blanketed much of the Western United States with hot ash. Volume estimates of these eruptions reach and even exceed 3,000 cubic kilometers, greatly exceeding the largest known historic eruptions on earth. Both extension and explosive volcanism continue to the present, as evidenced by modern earthquakes along Basin and Range faults and by a few major volcanic centers that are still active. Most geologists, however, believe that both the rate of extension and the intensity of volcanism have decreased.

## Methods of Study

The Basin and Range province is one of the foremost areas worldwide for study of the processes by which the continental crust stretches. It is a natural laboratory in which the earth has done an experiment, and the geologists' job is to analyze the results (and to determine just what the experiment was). Three main types of techniques are brought to bear in such studies: field studies of surface geology, laboratory analysis of samples collected in the field, and geophysical field studies. The first step is basic fieldwork, which involves mapping the rock bodies and structures exposed at the surface. The geologist uses this information to make inferences about the spatial relationships of rock bodies and the geologic history that led to those arrangements. In spite of being one of the best-studied continental rifts in the world, at least half of the Basin and Range province's surface geology has yet to be studied in detail. Fundamental questions remain about continental extension processes. Therefore, the surface geology of the Basin and Range will continue to be an important source of new insights for years to come.

Laboratory analytical techniques provide more precise and detailed information about rocks than can be gathered in the field. A complete summary cannnot be attempted here because relevant techniques span all of earth science; however, isotopic geochronology and thermobarometry are particularly important. Isotopic geochronology is based upon measuring the progressive decay of radioactive elements, and the consequent buildup of the products of that decay. This is the principal method of determining numerical ages of ancient rocks, and therefore it is vital in determining when ancient events occurred, for comparing ages from one area to another in order to look for spatial patterns, and for determining the rates of at which processes have operated. Thermobarometry uses chemical compositions of minerals in rocks to estimate the temperature and pressure conditions under which the minerals grew. Mineral compositions are generally determined using the electron microprobe on a polished chip of the rock. Thermobarometry is used to find where in the crust deep-seated igneous and metamorphic rocks formed.

Important geophysical field techniques include seismology and studies of potential fields such as gravity and magnetism. Seismologists study the transmission of sound waves through the earth, including sound waves from earthquakes, and from artificial sources such as explosions. The variations in the time it takes for sound waves to travel from their sources to various receivers (seismometers) and variations in the characteristics of the waves recorded at different seismometers allow seismologists to map out the internal structure of the earth in terms of the rocks' sound-transmitting properties. For example, it is mainly through seismological studies that we know the thickness of the earth's crust (about 30 kilometers in most of the Basin and Range). Variations in the earth's gravity field from one place to another can be used to investigate variations in the densities of rocks at depth, and similar variations in the magnetic field indicate changes in the magnetic properties of rocks at depth. It is by combining such geophysical studies with observations of the surface geology that our present understanding of the structure and evolution of the Basin and Range has been achieved.

## Context

The Basin and Range province is significant from the standpoints of economic opportunities and geologic hazards. A large portion of the metallic mineral wealth of the western United States (particularly copper, silver, gold, lead, and zinc) is located in the Basin and Range. Many of these deposits formed in association with volcanic activity during Basin and Range crustal stretching. To date, oil and gas exploration in the Basin and Range has been less fruitful, although small oil fields have been found in central and northern Nevada. The Basin and Range, however, remains a poorly explored "frontier" area, and many petroleum geologists are optimistic about future discoveries.

Two types of geologic hazards are particularly significant in the Basin and Range province: earthquakes and explosive volcanic eruptions. Studies of Basin and Range earthquakes (such as the 1983 Borah Peak earthquake in Idaho) and of recently active Basin and Range faults that have not caused a historic earthquake (for example, the Wasatch fault in northern Utah) indicate that the major range-bounding faults are capable of releasing large, damaging earthquakes with magnitudes of 7 to 7.5 on the Richter scale. An earthquake of this size results from a slip event in which the fault blocks "slip" a few meters with respect to each other. If geologists are correct that most of the displacement along major Basin and Range faults occurs in these large earthquakes, then each major fault in the province has been the source of thousands of major earthquakes over the last 25 million years. Although large explosive volcanic centers were widespread throughout the Basin and Range 25 million years ago, the only such centers presently active lie at the edges of the province, at Yellowstone National Park and Long Valley in California, and at the Valle Grande at Bandelier National Monument in New Mexico. As noted above, major eruptions from this type of volcanic center dwarf all historic eruptions. Scientists can predict little about the catastrophic results of another major eruption from one of these systems, other than that they almost certainly would be staggering.

## Bibliography

Davis, George H., and Evelyn M. VandenDolder, eds. *Geologic Diversity of Arizona and Its Margins: Excursions to Choice Areas*. Tucson: Arizona Bureau of Geology and Mineral Technology, 1987. This volume contains geological descriptions and road logs for thirty-three field trips in Arizona, about nineteen of which concern the Basin and Range province. The trips are intended for professional geologists, but some of the content is accessible to others. The observations and interpretations presented are up-to-date, describing a number of key areas for understanding the southern Basin and Range.

McPhee, John. *Basin and Range*. New York: Farrar, Straus & Giroux, 1981. This is a popular account of a journalist's introduction to geology and geologists, mainly in the context of the Basin and Range province. The book is readable and entertaining, and the geological descriptions are reasonably accurate, if superficial.

Newman, Gary W., and Harry E. Goode, eds. *Basin and Range Symposium*. Denver: Rocky Mountain Association of Geologists, 1979. This volume contains a potpourri of information about the Great Basin, which includes most of the northern Basin and Range. The bulk of the text is fifty-one technical papers, directed mainly toward resource exploration. The papers range from general to specific, from quite short to fairly long, and from excellent to poor in quality. The book also includes an informal history of exploration and development of the Great Basin, and a road log for a four-day geological excursion in southern and eastern Nevada. The levels of various sections range from the general reader to the professional geologist.

Stewart, John H. *Geology of Nevada*. Reno: Nevada Bureau of Mines and Geology, 1980. This book was written to accompany the 1:500,000-scale geologic map of Nevada (available from the U.S. Geological Survey and the Nevada Bureau of Mines and Geology), by a geologist who has spent much of his career studying the Basin and Range. It is organized based on the complete geological history recorded in Nevada, so that only the latter part deals with Basin and Range topography, structure, and volcanism per se. For college-level students.

Weide, David L., and Marianne L. Faber, eds. *This Extended Land: Geological Journeys in the Southern Basin and Range*. Las Vegas: University of Nevada Press, 1988. This volume contains descriptions and road logs for eighteen field trips in southern Nevada and adjacent areas. As with the field-trip guidebook for Arizona (above), the trips are intended for professionals, but some of the book's contents are accessible to the general reader.

*John M. Bartley*

## Cross-References

Continental Rift Zones, 275; Earth's Structure, 589; Normal Faults, 676; Thrust Faults, 683; Transform Faults, 690; The Geomorphology of Dry Climate Areas, 882; Mountain Belts, 1725; The Worldwide Distribution of Oil and Gas, 1923; Plate Margins, 2063; Plate Tectonics, 2079; Seismic Reflection Profiling, 2333; Subduction and Orogeny, 2497; Thrust Belts, 2519; Yellowstone National Park, 2757.

# BIOPYRIBOLES

*Type of earth science:* Geology
*Field of study:* Mineralogy and crystallography

  *Biopyriboles are important rock-forming minerals, third in abundance only to feldspars and quartz. They are especially abundant in igneous and metamorphic rocks. Important groups of biopyriboles include micas, exemplified by biotite mica; pyroxenes; and amphiboles—hence the name "biopyribole."*

  *Principal terms*
    AMPHIBOLE: a group of generally dark-colored, double-chain silicates crystallizing largely in the orthorhombic or monoclinic systems and possessing good cleavage in two directions intersecting at angles of about 56 and 124 degrees
    BIOPYRIBOLE: a rock-forming mineral that is a member of the sheet or chain silicates
    CHAIN SILICATE: a group of silicates characterized by joining of silica tetrahedra into linear single or double chains alternating with chains of other structures; also known as "inosilicate"
    CLEAVAGE: The tendency of a mineral or chemical compound to break along smooth surfaces parallel to each other and across atomic or molecular bonds of weaker strength
    CRYSTAL SYSTEM: one of any of six crystal groups defined on the basis of length and angular relationship of the associated axes
    MICA: a group of complex, hydrous sheet silicates crystallizing largely in the monoclinic system and possessing pearly, elastic sheets with perfect one-directional cleavage
    MONOCLINIC: a crystal system possessing three axes of symmetry, generally of unequal length; two axes are inclined to each other obliquely, and the third is at right angles to the plane formed by the other two
    ORTHORHOMBIC: a crystal system possessing three axes of symmetry that are of unequal length and that intersect at right angles
    PYROXENE: a group of generally dark-colored, single-chain silicates crystallizing largely in the orthorhombic or monoclinic systems and possessing good cleavage in two directions intersecting at angles of about 87 and 93 degrees
    SHEET SILICATE: a group of silicates characterized by the sharing of three of the four oxygens in each silica tetrahedron with neighboring tetrahedra and the fourth with other atoms in adjacent structures to form flat sheets; also known as "phyllosilicate" or "layer" silicate

SILICATE: a chemical compound or mineral whose crystal structure possesses silica tetrahedra (a structure formed by four charged oxygen atoms surrounding a charged silicon atom)

## Summary of the Phenomenon

Biopyriboles include numerous but related groups of minerals. They are important constituents of both igneous rocks, whose minerals largely form as a result of cooling and crystallization of a melt (liquid), and metamorphic rocks, whose minerals are largely crystallized in a solid state at elevated temperatures or pressures. Some biopyriboles also occur as fragments in sedimentary rocks and sediments. The three most important mineral groups in biopyriboles are micas, pyroxenes, and amphiboles.

Biopyriboles are silicate minerals, meaning that they are composed of atoms of the chemical elements silicon and oxygen as well as atoms of other chemical elements. The silicon atom is surrounded by four oxygen atoms attached or bonded to it. This forms a structure known as a silica tetrahedron, which can be represented as a four-sided solid with triangular faces. This silicon-oxygen bond is very strong. These silica tetrahedra may be repeated in various ways; biopyriboles are expressed by the chain (line) and sheet (plane) structures. Pyroxenes and amphiboles are examples of chain silicates and micas of sheet silicates.

Other atoms with attached or bonded oxygen (or in some cases oxygen attached to hydrogen, or hydroxyl) may also occur as chains or sheets alternating with the chains or sheets of silica tetrahedra. In sheet silicate groups, the sheet or plane of silica tetrahedra might alternate with aluminum bonded to its oxygens. For some sheet silicate minerals, other layers (potassium atoms bonded to oxygen or hydroxyl, for example) may be layered within. In chains, silica tetrahedra may alternate with structures of iron atoms with attached oxygens. In some groups (amphiboles), two chains of silica tetrahedron alternate with one or more other chains.

The following is a useful outline of the major groups of biopyriboles.

A. Sheet Silicates
   1. Mica Group (examples: biotite and muscovite)
   2. Chlorite Group
   3. Serpentine Group (examples: antigorite and chrysotile asbestos)
   4. Talc Group (examples: talc and pyrophyllite)
   5. Clay Mineral Group (examples: kaolinite, smectite, and illite)
   6. Brittle Mica Group
B. Chain Silicates
   1. Single silica tetrahedron chains
      a. Orthorhombic pyroxenes (examples: enstatite and hypersthene)
      b. Monoclinic calcic pyroxenes (examples: diopside and augite)
      c. Monoclinic alkali pyroxenes (example: jadeite)
      d. Pyroxenoids (example: wollastonite)
   2. Double silica tetrahedra chains

a. Orthorhombic amphiboles (example: anthophyllite)
b. Monoclinic magnesium-iron amphiboles (example: cummingtonite)
c. Monoclinic calcic amphiboles (examples: tremolite and hornblende)
d. Monoclinic alkali amphiboles (examples: glaucophane, riebeckite—
   form "blueschists")
C. Complex Biopyriboles

Biopyriboles are found as crystals or as crystalline masses. Crystals may be defined as inorganic or organic solids which are chemical elements or compounds. These are formed by growth and are bounded by faces or surfaces with a definite geometric relationship to one another. This relationship is expressive of an orderly internal arrangement of atoms and molecules. Crystalline masses are intergrowths of crystals that show incomplete expression of external faces, generally because there was either not enough space or some substance in the solution or melt inhibiting crystal growth.

Crystals belong to systems, based on the relationship of three lines or axes to each other. Most micas, pyroxenes, and amphiboles fall into the orthorhombic and monoclinic systems under normal geologic conditions in the earth's crust (a very few are hexagonal or triclinic).

The micas are one of the most common groups of rock-forming minerals. They are characterized by the following properties: the formation of thin, sheetlike crystals, which are stronger within the sheets than between them; a tendency to break in one smooth direction parallel to the sheets, a property called "cleavage"; crystallization in the monoclinic system for most species; considerable elasticity; and a luster that is vitreous (glasslike) to pearly. Two of the most common members of this group are biotite and muscovite mica.

Biotite mica occurs in black, brown, or dark green flakes and is a potassium-magnesium-iron-aluminum hydroxyl silicate. The magnesium and iron atoms can substitute for each other in the octahedral layers (which alternate with a silica tetrahedron and potassium-hydroxyl layer), because charged atoms (ions) of magnesium and iron have nearly the same size as well as the same charge. The mineral occurs widely in most igneous and metamorphic rocks but is most abundant in granite, which is composed of interlocking crystals of feldspar, quartz, and commonly mica. It is also abundant in the coarsely layered (foliated) metamorphic rock mica schist.

Muscovite mica occurs in clear to smoky yellowish, greenish, or reddish flakes and is a potassium-aluminum hydroxyl silicate. Aluminum occurs both in the octahedral layer and (substituting for silica) in the tetrahedral layer. Muscovite mica is especially abundant in granite and occurs in large sheets and crystals in the very coarse rock granite pegmatite. It is also prominent in mica schist and occurs microscopically in slate. Flakes of muscovite can occur as fragments in some sandstones, which are sedimentary rocks.

The chlorite group is similar to the micas in that these minerals also tend to have sheetlike crystals that show cleavage parallel to the sheets and possess a pearly luster. The color of chlorite flakes is commonly dark to bright green, although it can also occur in brown, pink, purple, and colorless crystals. The potassium, sodium, and lithium that are present in mica are absent in chlorite. Its crystals are flexible but not elastic.

Chlorite may occur as fine-grained masses in clay or claystone. The largest crystals occur in altered ultramafic rocks, such as serpentinite, and in the metamorphic rock chlorite schist. Varieties of this mineral group also may occur associated with metallic ore deposits. Chlorite differs in the arrangement and number of octahedral layers from the related serpentine and talc groups.

The serpentine mineral group is hydrous and somewhat complex. It includes magnesium-rich sheet silicates, which commonly occur as an alteration of the magnesium-iron silicates olivine and pyroxenes in altered ultramafic rocks known as metaperidotites. Serpentines may also form as an alteration of olivine (forsterite) pyroxene or other minerals in marble. The various kinds vary from rather soft to moderately hard. The most common are antigorite, with a platy-massive structure, and chrysotile asbestos, which is fibrous. Serpentines are most commonly green, but brown, red, blue and black varieties are known. They are economically important in some areas and occur in mountain belts such as the Alps and the Appalachian Piedmont.

The talc group consists of sheet silicates that are rich in magnesium, aluminum, or iron. They are characterized by a very pearly luster, great softness, so they can be scratched with a fingernail, and a soapy or greasy feel; they occur in thin sheets or scaly or radiated masses. Talc is a hydrous magnesium silicate that can form through the alteration of olivine, pyroxene, or serpentine. It is common in altered ultramafic rocks; it also occurs as talc schist and in some marbles. Pyrophyllite, the aluminum-rich analogue of talc, occurs in schists or through metamorphic alteration of aluminous rocks. The iron-rich analogue minnasotaite occurs in metamorphosed iron formations.

Clay minerals are of the most widespread groups of sheet silicates. They include chlorite, kaolinite (china clay), smectite (also known as montmorillonite) and illite. Clays can occur as mixed sheets, for example, of chlorite and illite or illite and smectite.

Kaolinite is usually white and soft and is a hydrous aluminum silicate, prized for use in china. It consists of silica tetrahedron layers alternating with aluminum hydroxide octahedral layers. Smectite is unusual: It has a layer that takes up water or liquid organic molecules, and therefore its mineral structure is expandable. Illite has a structure similar to that of muscovite mica, but some of the potassiums are replaced by hydroxyl. It is sometimes included in the mica group.

All these minerals may be important constituents of sedimentary rocks (especially chlorite, illite, and smectite) and of soils. Claystones and mudstones are largely made up of clay minerals. Other members of this group occur associated with metallic ore deposits and hot springs or geyser areas.

The brittle mica group is less common, but consists largely of hydrous calcium-bearing, iron-rich, or aluminous sheet silicates. Samples are characteristically easily broken across, as well as between, sheets, hence the term "brittle mica." One aluminous variety, margarite, occurs in attractive lilac or yellow crystals associated with corundum (aluminum oxide) or as veins in chlorite schist.

The chain silicate group includes orthopyroxenes, clinopyroxenes, pyroxenoids, orthoamphiboles, and clinoamphiboles. The pyroxene group is characterized by single silica tetrahedron chains alternating with octahedron chains and other chains with cubic structures. The octahedron chains tend to have smaller internal atoms than those of the cubic chains. Octahedron chain atoms include magnesium, iron, or aluminum, and cubic chain atoms include calcium and sodium. Sometimes the larger atoms such as calcium are called X-type, and the smaller atoms such as magnesium are called Y-type. Other letter classifications may be used by crystallographers. Pyroxenes have two directions of smooth breakage (cleavage), nearly at right angles to each other. Most pyroxenes tend to be green, brown, or green-black in color and are moderately hard.

Orthorhombic pyroxenes (also called orthopyroxenes) occur mostly in dark-colored high-temperature igneous rocks such as pyroxenites and gabbros. They range from light bronze-brown to dark green-brown in color and may have a bronzy luster. In this group, ferrous iron atoms can substitute freely for the magnesium atoms in the structure. Two important orthopyroxenes are enstatite and hypersthene.

Monoclinic pyroxenes (also called clinopyroxenes) occur in dark-colored igneous rocks and in siliceous or aluminous marbles metamorphosed at high temperatures. There are two main groups, the calcium-rich or calcic types and the sodium-rich or alkali types. Substitution of sodium and calcium atoms can occur to a certain extent between the two types. The calcic pyroxenes are usually green or brown; sodic pyroxenes may be light or bright green or, if iron-rich, blue-black to black. Common examples of calcic clinopyroxenes are diopside and augite. Magnesium and ferrous iron atoms substitute freely. Two important sodium-alkali pyroxenes are jadeite, an important carving and gem material, and aegirine.

Pyroxenoids are similar in some respects to pyroxenes; the former are also high-temperature minerals, but differ in that octahedral and cubic chains both have Y-type atoms so that monoclinic or even triclinic structures result. They also tend to be more tabular and less blocky than are pyroxenes in their structure. Wollastonite, a calcium silicate found in siliceous marbles, is an important example of this group.

Minerals having double silica tetrahedral chains are called amphiboles. Amphiboles are distinguished from pyroxenes, which are closely similar in color, hardness, and occurrence, by the two directions of cleavage, 124 and 56 degrees instead of close to 90 degrees, as is the case for pyroxenes. Orthorhombic amphiboles (orthoamphiboles) include the magnesium-iron amphibole anthophyllite and the aluminum-magnesium-iron amphibole gedrite. These types are restricted largely to magnesium-rich, calcium-poor metamorphosed ultramafic and mafic plutonic and volcanic rocks. Anthophyllite-gedrite varies from purple or clove-brown to yellow-brown or gray in color and may be columnar or fibrous in structure.

One group of clinoamphiboles (monoclinic amphiboles) is a magnesium-iron silicate similar to the anthophyllite group. The magnesium-rich end member is called cummingtonite, and the iron-rich member is known as grunerite. Cummingtonite usually occurs as fibrous or radiating crystals and is brown to gray in color. The largest group of clinoamphiboles is the calcic amphiboles. In all the calcic amphiboles, the amount of calcium exceeds that of alkalis (sodium and potassium). In the tremolite group, which is analogous to the diopside group in the clinopyroxenes, calcium and magnesium or ferrous iron are the major constituents of the cubic and octahedral chains respectively, although sodium-rich tremolites occur. These amphiboles vary from colorless to green and occur mostly in marble and metamorphosed dark igneous rocks. The hornblende group of calcic amphiboles, which is somewhat analogous to the augite group of clinopyroxenes, can have a much more varied composition: Some sodium may substitute for calcium, and aluminum and ferric iron may substitute for magnesium and ferrous iron in the octahedral chains and aluminum for silica in the tetrahedral chains. Hornblendes are commonly black to dark green and occur in a wide array of igneous and metamorphic rocks.

The alkali amphiboles are rich in sodium (or, very rarely, potassium), and most range in color from dark to light blue or violet to blue-black. Important members are the sodium-magnesium-iron-aluminum amphiboles riebeckite (blue) and glaucophane (blue to violet). Glaucophane is an important constituent of blueschist, which is formed at high pressures and is especially common in some parts of California and Japan.

Complex biopyriboles consist of combined anthophyllite-talc structures. First described from Vermont, they occur elsewhere as well. Other combinations of amphibole-talc structures are possible. Multiple chain units are characteristic of this group.

## Methods of Study

Many methods have been used to study and analyze biopyriboles, including simple physical tests and comparison with other minerals, optical examination and testing under compound and polarizing microscopes, X-ray diffraction and other X-ray methods, scanning and high-resolution transmission electron microscopy, electron microprobe, and differential thermal analysis.

Simple physical techniques can determine color, cleavage directions, crystal form, hardness (resistance to abrasion), density, and other properties. The major biopyribole groups and the more common or distinctive kinds of micas, amphiboles, and pyroxenes can be identified with such techniques. Examination under a binocular or compound microscope can extend this process to smaller grains or crystals. Association of other minerals rich in certain elements may also be helpful in identification.

Polarizing microscopes are more powerful tools that force light to travel in a

certain direction through a sample by means of polarizers and producing interference and refraction (bending) effects in the light. The chemical makeup of many
pyroxenes can be studied in this way, but the more complex amphiboles and sheet
silicates require more sophisticated methods.

In X-ray diffraction, X rays are generated by electron bombardment and produce
multiple reflections off atomic planes in crystals, allowing determination of the
dimensions of spacing of these planes and hence identification of the mineral.
Micas, clays, serpentines, and other sheet silicates are often readily differentiated
and analyzed by X-ray diffraction. Special cameras for X-ray diffraction permit the
study of structure, mineral unit cell dimensions, and atomic position of the elements.

Scanning electron microscopy produces an electron photograph of the surface of
a fine-grained material or small crystals. This method is necessary, in conjunction
with X-ray diffraction, for unequivocal identifications of fine-crystalline clay and
serpentine group minerals. Transmission electron microscopy permits resolution to
a few angstroms (atomic dimensions), thus allowing direct studies of mineral
structure. This method is necessary for studying detailed molecular structure of the
chain silicates and complex biopyriboles.

The electron microprobe, useful for chemical analysis, focuses an intense beam
of electrons on some coated material (usually gold or carbon); the material then
emits characteristic X rays, whose wavelength and intensity can be examined with
an X-ray spectroscope. Through calculations and with adequate corrections applied,
an analysis can be produced, provided there is a mineral standard for comparison.

Differential thermal analysis uses a thermocouple method for measuring temperature differences between the material being tested and a standard material. A useful
method to detail heat-absorbing (endothermic) dehydration reactions for minerals,
especially for clay minerals and sheet silicates, thermal analysis aids in the identification and structural analysis of these minerals.

## Context

Biopyriboles are important constituents of rocks in both the crust and the mantle
of the earth. Some of the rocks containing pyroxenes and amphiboles, such as
traprock and diorite, are used for road and railroad gravels, building stone, and
monuments. Clay minerals, especially kaolinite and a hydrated type called hal-
loysite, are used to make fine china and pottery and are a constituent of ceramics,
brick, drain tile, and sewer pipe. Kaolinite is also used as a filter in medical
research and as a filler in paper. Bentonite (smectite or montmorillonite) is used in
drilling muds that support the bit and drilling apparatus in oil exploration.

Muscovite mica has been used as an electric insulating material and as a material
for wallpaper, lubricants, and nonconductors. Lepidolite is a source of lithium and
is used in the manufacture of heat-resistant glass. Talc is highly important in the
cosmetics industry. As the massive variety, soapstone, it is used for tabletops and in
paint, ceramics, paper, and insecticides. Pyrophyllite, the aluminum analogue, is

used for the same purposes. Serpentine has been used as an ornamental and building stone. The variety chrysotile is the main source of asbestos, used in the past for fireproof fabrics and construction material. Health considerations have largely forced the discontinuance of its manufacture and use.

Pyroxenes are not so widely used, but clear and transparent colored varieties of diopside and spodumene have been used as gemstones, and both jadeite and rhodonite are prized gem materials for carving. Spodumene is also a major source of lithium for ceramics, batteries, welding flux, fuels, and the compound lithium carbonate, used to treat manic-depressives.

Fibrous varieties of anthophyllite (also called amosite), tremolite, and riebeckite (also called crocidolite) were used in the past as sources of asbestos. For health reasons, the use of these substances has been discontinued.

Pyroxenes and amphiboles are particularly useful to geologists, by themselves or in conjunction with other minerals such as garnet. The partitioning of elements such as magnesium and iron in the crystal structure occurs at different values under different temperatures, and pressure and thermodynamic equations can be used to determine probable temperatures and pressures of formation and help geologists decipher the geologic history of the region where these minerals occur. Micas and some amphiboles can be used in potassium-argon dating to determine the age of the mineral's formation, which is useful in decoding geologic history.

## Bibliography

Deer, W. A., R. A. Howie, and J. Zussman. *Rock-Forming Minerals*. Vol. 2, *Chain Silicates*, and vol. 3, *Sheet Silicates*. New York: Longman, 1963. These volumes, part of a five-volume set, discuss in detail the crystallography, properties, chemistry, occurrence, and origin of the pyroxenes and amphiboles and the micas and other sheet silicates. The work's quality is excellent; it is very well written and well organized. Suitable for college-level students.

Klein, Cornelis, and C. S. Hurlbut, Jr. *Manual of Mineralogy*. New York: John Wiley & Sons, 1985. A general text of mineralogy, revised many times since James D. Dana first published the prototype in 1862. Extremely useful, it lists properties, occurrence, and uses of the amphiboles, pyroxenes, and sheet silicates and gives background information in crystallography and descriptive mineralogy. Suitable for the high school and college reader.

Leake, Bernard E. "Nomenclature of Amphiboles." *The American Mineralogist* 63 (November, 1978): 1023-1052. A complete, but rather technical, description of amphiboles and their classification. Appropriate for the college-level reader.

Robinson, George. "Amphiboles: A Closer Look." *Rocks and Minerals* (November/December, 1981). An excellent and readable summary of the properties and occurrence of this complex group. Suitable for both the high school and college reader.

*David F. Hess*

## Cross-References

Electron Microscopy, 601; Experimental Petrology, 662; Igneous Rock Classification, 1138; Ionic Substitution in Minerals, 1245; Crystallization of Magmas, 1420; Water in Magmas, 1433; Metamorphic Rock Classification, 1553; Physical Properties of Minerals, 1681; The Structure of Minerals, 1693; Radioactive Decay, 2136; Earth Resources, 2175; X-Ray Powder Diffraction, 2751.

# BIOSTRATIGRAPHY

*Type of earth science:* Geology
*Field of study:* Stratigraphy

*Biostratigraphy is that branch of the study of layered rocks—stratigraphy—that focuses on fossils. Its goals are the identification and organization of strata based on their fossil content. Biostratigraphy thus investigates one of the principal bases of the geologic time scale of earth history.*

### Principal terms

CORRELATION: the determination of the equivalence of age or stratigraphic position of two strata in separate areas, or, more broadly, determination of the geological contemporaneity of events in the geologic histories of two areas

FOSSILS: remains or traces of animals and plants preserved by natural causes in the earth's crust, excluding organisms buried since the beginning of historical time

INDEX FOSSIL: a fossil that can be used to identify and determine the age of the stratum in which it is found

SEDIMENTARY ROCKS: rocks formed by the accumulation of particles of other rocks or of organic skeletons or of chemical precipitates or some combination of these

STRATIGRAPHY: the study of layered rocks, especially of their sequence and correlation

STRATUM (pl. STRATA): a single bed or layer of sedimentary rock

## Summary of the Methodology

Biostratigraphy is the method of identifying and differentiating layers of sedimentary rock (strata) by their fossil content. Strata with distinctive fossil content are termed biostratigraphic units, or zones. Zones vary greatly in thickness and in lateral extent. A zone may be a single layer a few centimeters thick and of very local extent, or it may encompass thousands of meters of rocks extending worldwide. The defining feature of a zone is its fossil content: The fossils of a given zone must differ in some specific way from the fossils of other zones.

Zones are usually recognized after fossils have been collected extensively over the lateral and vertical extent of a rock sequence or at many sequences over a broad region. The positions of the fossils in the strata are carefully recorded in the field. Fossils that co-occur in a single layer are noted, as are fossils found isolated in the strata. In the laboratory, the biostratigrapher, usually a paleontologist, then tabulates the vertical and lateral ranges of the fossils collected. It is from these ranges that the paleontologist recognizes zones. Different types of zones are recognized depending on the way in which the fossils in the strata prove to be distinctive.

Assemblage zones are strata distinguished by an association (assemblage) of fossils. Thus, not one type but many types of fossils are used to define an assemblage zone. All dinosaur fossils, for example, can be thought of as defining an assemblage zone that encompasses earth history from about 220 to 66 million years ago.

Range zones are strata that encompass the vertical distribution, or range, of a particular type of fossil. Thus, one fossil type, not many, is used to define a range zone. In contrast to the example just given, one type of dinosaur, *Tyrannosaurus rex*, lived only between 68 and 66 million years ago. Its fossils thus define a range zone that corresponds temporally to this two-million-year interval.

Acme zones are rock layers recognized by the abundance, or acme, of a type (or types) of fossil (or fossils) regardless of association or range. Horned dinosaurs (*Triceratops* and its allies) reached an acme between 70 and 66 million years ago; that is, during this period they were most diverse and most numerous. This acme zone thus overlaps the *Tyrannosaurus rex* range zone and represents a small portion of the dinosaur assemblage zone.

Finally, interval zones are recognized as strata between layers where a significant change in fossil content takes place. For example, the mass extinctions that took place 250 and 66 million years ago bound a 184-million-year-long interval zone that is popularly referred to as the "age of reptiles."

Biostratigraphy developed independently in England and France just after 1800. In England, William Smith, a civil engineer, worked in land surveying throughout the country. From his vast field experience, he recognized that a given stratum usually contains distinctive fossils and that the fossils (and the stratum) could often be recognized across a large area. Smith's work culminated in his geological map of England (1815), based on his tracing of rock-fossil layers across much of the country.

Meanwhile, in France, Georges Cuvier and Alexandre Brongniart studied the succession of rocks and fossils around Paris. They too discovered a definite relationship between strata and fossils and used it to interpret the geological history of the rocks exposed near Paris. In this history, Cuvier saw successive extinctions of many organisms coinciding with remarkable changes in the strata. To him, these represented vast "revolutions" in geological history, which Cuvier argued were of worldwide significance. It is now known that Cuvier was mistaken, but the discovery that a particular fossil type (or types) was confined to a particular stratum became the basis for biostratigraphy. This allowed geologists to identify strata from their fossil content and to trace these strata across broad regions of the earth's crust.

Almost simultaneous with the development of biostratigraphy was the development of biochronology. Biochronology is the recognition of intervals of geologic time by fossils. It stemmed from the realization that during earth's history, different types of organisms lived during different intervals of time. Thus, the fossils of any organism represent a particular interval of geologic time. (Such fossils are called index fossils because they act as an "index" to a geologic time interval.) Biochronology thus identifies intervals of geologic time based on fossils. These time-distinctive fossils are the fossils by which zones are defined, which is to say that each zone represents, or is equivalent to, some interval of geologic time.

The time value of zones made them more useful in tracing strata and deciphering local geological histories. Biostratigraphy now became one of the central methods of stratigraphic correlation. With the aid of fossils, it became possible to determine the ages of strata and thus demonstrate the synchrony or diachrony of these strata in different areas. Through its use in stratigraphic correlation, biostratigraphy became one of the bases for constructing what is called the relative geological time scale of earth history composed of eons, eras, periods, epochs, and ages. This time scale is the "calendar" by which all geologists temporally order their understanding of the history of the earth.

## Applications of the Method

Biostratigraphy is generally used as a method of stratigraphic correlation, the process of determining the equivalence of age or stratigraphic position of layered rocks in different areas. Stratigraphic correlation by biostratigraphy is extremely important in deciphering geological history; it reveals the sequence of geological events in one or more regions. Understanding geological history is of interest for its own sake to scientists and laypersons alike. It is crucial to the discovery of mineral deposits and energy resources within the earth's crust. In addition, it provides insight into the biological events that have taken place on this planet for the last 3.9 billion years.

A good example of the use of biostratigraphy in this last regard comes from the study of dinosaur extinction. When dinosaurs were first discovered in England in 1824, and when the term "dinosaur" was coined by the British anatomist Sir Richard Owen in 1841, nobody realized that dinosaurs had lived on earth for only 150 million years and that their extinction had taken place rather rapidly about 66 million years ago. By 1862, however, enough dinosaur fossils had been collected around the globe that a biostratigraphic pattern was beginning to emerge. In that year, the American geologist James Dwight Dana, in his classic *Manual of Geology*, noted that all dinosaurs disappeared before the end of the Mesozoic era, which is now considered as the interval of earth history between 250 and 66 million years ago. This biostratigraphic generalization was possible because geologists noticed that many Mesozoic rocks (but no older or younger rocks) were full of dinosaur fossils, and thus the Mesozoic came to be termed "the age of reptiles." It might just as well be referred to as the "dinosaur zone," except of course for the first 30 or so million years of the Mesozoic, during which dinosaurs apparently did not exist.

More than a century of research has confirmed Dana's biostratigraphic generalization and considerably refined it. Scientists now generally agree that the last dinosaurs disappeared worldwide 66 million years ago, give or take one or two million years. It is also known that dinosaurs first appeared about 220 million years ago. Thus, scientists are able to recognize a dinosaur zone and erect many types of zones based on the ranges and acmes of specific types of dinosaurs. This biostratigraphy of dinosaurs is the basis for informed discussion of the sequence and timing of events during the evolution of the dinosaurs. For example, scientists are now confident that *Stegosaurus* lived long before *Tyrannosaurus* and that stegosaurs as a group of dinosaurs became extinct long before the end of the Mesozoic.

Although discussion here has relied heavily on dinosaurs for examples of biostratigraphy at work, the fossils of these giant reptiles are not ideal for use in biostratigraphy, because it is not easy to identify most dinosaur fossils precisely and because most dinosaurs were not animals with broad geographic ranges. Indeed, the fossils of most use in biostratigraphy, index fossils, are those that are easy to identify precisely and that represent organisms that had wide geographic ranges, enjoyed broad environmental tolerances, and lived only for a brief period of geologic time.

Usually an entire skull or skeleton is needed to identify a dinosaur fossil precisely; the isolated bones most often found are not enough, although they do indicate the fossil is that of a dinosaur. Most dinosaurs (there are some notable exceptions) seem to have lived in one portion of one continent; indeed, fossils of the horned dinosaur *Pentaceratops* (a cousin of *Triceratops*) have been found only in New Mexico. There is strong evidence that some dinosaurs preferred coastlines, whereas others preferred dry areas. Thus, many, if not most, dinosaurs did not live in a wide range of environments. Finally, although many dinosaurs apparently lived for only brief intervals of geologic time, the fossil record of most of these giant reptiles is not extensive enough to pin down their exact interval of existence.

The factors that mitigate the use of most dinosaur fossils in biostratigraphy are quite different for microscopic fossils of pollen grains and the shelled protozoans known as foraminiferans. These microscopic fossils fit well the four criteria listed above that identify fossils most useful in biostratigraphy. Indeed, such "microfossils" (studied by micropaleontologists) are some of the mainstays of biostratigraphy.

## Context

Biostratigraphy, the recognition of strata by their fossil content, is a cornerstone of stratigraphic correlation. By using fossils to identify bodies of rock, they can be traced over broad areas, and their sequence in distant areas can often be determined. Stratigraphic correlation by biostratigraphy is critical to deciphering geological history; without it, the search for mineral deposits and energy resources would be considerably more difficult. Furthermore, understanding the history of geological disasters—earthquakes, volcanic eruptions, meteorite impacts, and the like—and thereby being able to predict future disasters, relies on knowledge of the sequence and timing of geological events, knowledge often derived from biostratigraphy. Deciphering the history of life on this planet, including the myriad appearances, changes, and extinctions of earth's biota during the last 3.9 billion years, largely depends on the sequence and timing established by biostratigraphy.

Biostratigraphy has also given rise to biochronology, the recognition of intervals of geologic time based on fossils. As a result, scientists have been able to construct a relative global geologic time scale, and it is within the context of this time scale that all geological and biological events in earth history have been placed.

## Bibliography

Ager, Derek V. *The Nature of the Stratigraphical Record*. 2d ed. New York: Halsted Press, 1981. A witty and unabashed look at stratigraphy; some of the discussion centers on biostratigraphy. An extensive bibliography, index, and a few well-chosen illustrations illuminate the text.

Barry, W. B. N. *Growth of a Prehistoric Time Scale*. Rev. ed. Palo Alto, Calif.: Blackwell Scientific Publications, 1987. Largely devoted to the history of how the global geologic time scale was formulated, much of this book is a history of biostratigraphy. Well illustrated, with a good bibliography and an index.

Brenner, R. L., and T. R. McHargue. *Integrative Stratigraphy Concepts and Applications*. Englewood Cliffs, N.J.: Prentice-Hall, 1988. Chapter 11 of this college-level textbook provides a detailed look at biostratigraphic concepts, methods, and applications. Well illustrated, with extensive reference lists and an index.

Eicher, D. L. *Geologic Time*. 2d ed. Englewood Cliffs, N.J.: Prentice-Hall, 1976. Chapter 4 provides a less technical look at biostratigraphy than do Brenner and McHargue. Very readable, well illustrated, with some references and an index.

Hedberg, H. D., ed. *International Stratigraphic Guide*. New York: John Wiley & Sons, 1976. The international "rule book" for stratigraphy. It sets procedures and standards to be met when naming stratigraphic units. It also defines many terms used in stratigraphy and has an extensive bibliography. Chapter 6 is devoted to biostratigraphy.

Stanley, S. M. *Earth and Life Through Time*. 2d ed. New York: W. H. Freeman, 1989. An excellent introductory-level college textbook on historical geology. It reviews the history of life and the many fossil forms found in strata in the earth's crust. Chapter 5 includes a discussion of biostratigraphy. Lavishly illustrated, with extensive references, glossaries, appendices on fossil groups, and an index.

*Spencer G. Lucas*

## Cross-References

The Cretaceous-Tertiary Boundary, 303; The Fossil Record, 760; The Geologic Time Scale, 874; Micropaleontology: Microfossils, 1674.

# BUILDING STONE

*Type of earth science:* Economic geology

*Building stone is any naturally occurring stone that is used for building construction. The three rock types (igneous, metamorphic, and sedimentary) are all utilized in building stone. The physical characteristics of each type of rock, such as hardness, color, and texture, determine how the stone is used.*

*Principal terms*

GRANITE: an igneous rock that is known for its hardness and durability; in modern times, it has been used on the exterior of buildings, as it is able to resist the corrosive atmospheres of urban areas

IGNEOUS: rock that was formed from a molten material originating near the base of the earth's crust

LIMESTONE: a sedimentary rock that can be easily shaped and carved; currently it has gained acceptance as a thin veneer

MARBLE: a metamorphic rock that has been used since Grecian times as a preferred building stone; it is known for its ability to be carved, sculptured, and polished

METAMORPHIC: rock that was formed by heat and pressure; tectonic, or mountain-building, forces of the earth's crust create and alter the mineral composition and texture of the original rock material

SANDSTONE: a sedimentary rock that is known for its durability to resist abrasive wear; it is likely to be used for paving stone

SEDIMENTARY: most commonly, rock that was formed by marine sediments in an ocean basin; it usually shows depositional features and may include fossils

SLATE: a metamorphic rock that has a unique ability to be split into thin sheets; some slates are resistant to weathering and are thus good for exterior use

## Summary of the Phenomenon

Building stone is any kind of rock that has supplied humankind with the material to erect monuments and edifices throughout history. The pyramids of Egypt, the temples of Greece, the skyscrapers of the modern world have all utilized various forms of building stone. The ancients used blocks of stone stacked like building blocks, whereas the modern builder uses a thin veneer of stone anchored to the exterior of a building frame. Special physical properties of the various stone materials lend themselves to these various usages. Because of these special physical properties, only a small percentage of the earth's rock material can be classified and utilized as building stone. Granite, an igneous rock that forms the core of the continents, is a good example. Granite is abundant, but because of mineralogic variations or structural weakness, only a small percentage of the granite areas will yield quarry blocks of suitable dimensions for building stone.

Building stone is quarried, or excavated, in most countries and, from its point of origin, may be shipped around the world. Quite commonly, granite blocks from Brazil are shipped to Canada for sawing and finishing and then shipped to a construction site in one of the cities in the United States. Similarly, building stone from the United States has been shipped to Italy for sawing and finishing and then shipped to England for installation on buildings. The average quarry block weighs 15 to 20 tons. These quarry blocks are sawn into slabs that vary in thickness from a half inch to four inches. Whether the building stone is a limestone, marble, granite, slate, or a sandstone, the quarry block must be solid enough to yield slabs of competent rock. These slabs are further cut on diamond saws to the desired shape and dimensions and then finished to the requirements of the architect or owner.

Buildings constructed before or around the turn of the century were built with cubic pieces 6 inches thick or greater. Cubic stone forms both the supporting structure for the walls and the exterior protection to the building. Most buildings built since the 1950's, however, require that the building stone be cut into thin panels less than 3 inches thick and fastened to the exterior of the steel supporting structures. This later use of stone demands that more engineering and design criteria be used to establish acceptable versus nonacceptable building stone. The processes by which the architect, engineer, and geologist select and qualify a particular stone for usage help to determine the aesthetic and physical character-istics of the stone. The architect usually establishes the design criteria for the size and shape of the stone. He or she looks at the stone from the point of view of aesthetics—for example, focusing on its color and texture. The engineer and geolo-gist then determine the suitability of the selected stone for realizing the design plan.

## Methods of Study

Geologists and engineers who are involved with quarrying and fabricating build-ing stone look for deposits of stone that are uniform in texture, color, and structural integrity. The exploration of new areas is accomplished by researching and review-ing existing geological maps, aerial photographs, and geological libraries. Ground sleuthing or field mapping and reconnaissance are the next steps in delineating a potential quarry locality. Rock sample collection, mineralogic identification, and physical property testing are conducted to determine whether the characteristics of the stone would be suitable for the specific use. The end use of the building stone varies from a dimension stone block size of 100 cubic feet to a rubble stone size of 1 cubic foot. Some blocks smaller then 100 cubic feet can be used to produce tiles and novelties but, for the most part, the major emphasis is on quarrying the larger blocks of stone.

Quarrying large blocks of stone requires geological uniformity of the rock type over an ample enough area. This area needs to be adequate in size to open a quarry that will yield uniform material for an extensive period of time (ten to twenty years). To find an area of this size, the geologist must understand the various tectonic forces that have acted over geological time. Most metamorphic and sedimentary rocks have been folded and faulted during geological time. Most igneous rocks have internal stresses that were created during the molten or plastic stage of injection into the earth's crust. Such forces will cause cracks and weakness in the rock masses that diminish the potential use for dimension stone.

The color characteristic of the stone, so critical to the architect's design criteria, is studied by polished hand samples or test block extraction from the potential quarry area. The mineralogic content of the various granites will determine the color consistency and stability. Petrologic microscope work and thin section studies are an important part of the search for suitable granite. Color stability in a building stone is as important a factor as color uniformity; there are numerous dark limestones that fade to a pale gray that are unsuitable for exterior use but are beautiful, for example, in an interior lobby.

Texture and mineral fabric are also important considerations in studying the suitability of a particular stone for building stone. The use of the stone will depend on whether it has a fine or coarse texture. Interlocking mineral grains, a well-cemented matrix, and nonsoluble minerals are also important characteristics to identify. Many fine-textured marbles are "sugary" and soft because of poorly interlocked calcite grains, whereas a similar fine-grained marble may be tough and durable to atmospheric corrosion because of a well-interlocked mineral fabric and subsequent low porosity to surface water.

The major criterion in determining whether a building stone will be suitable for a project is the soundness of the deposit. The soundness is a measure of the combination of natural fractures and the strength of the stone. Geological conditions during the formation of the various rock types will determine the soundness. In a sedimentary rock, the bedding (foundation or stratification) and jointing (fracturing without displacement) will determine the block sizes capable of being produced. In an igneous and metamorphic rock, the schistosity (tendency to split along parallel planes), cleavage (tendency to split along closely spaced planes), and jointing will be contributing factors in determining the degree of soundness. Also, in an igneous and metamorphic rock mass, the internal stresses need to be measured and understood before determining block sizes that may be capable of being produced. In the years prior to diamond cutting tools and hydraulic handling equipment, cleavage, jointing, and bedding were used to help pry out blocks of stone. With the development of such tools, the quarry workers can cut out more solid masses of rock for building stone.

Rock strength is another criterion of a building stone that needs definition. Specific laboratory equipment is used by a test engineer to determine the flexural and compressive strength for each building stone. Depending on the planned usage, water absorption and abrasive wear test data are also important for knowing how a particular rock will react in certain applications. The test program may also include producing test specimens of the finished product and installing them in mock-up panels.

## Context

Building stones have been used by humans to produce comfortable habitations ever since cave dwellers blocked up cave entrances for protection and warmth. In the modern world, architects utilize building stone to clad the exterior of modern buildings as a protective shield for the structural steel supports. Designers take polished building stone and clad interior lobbies for durability and beauty in the entrances of these same buildings. Slate, marble, granite, limestone, and sandstone are all utilized as building stone. These materials occur throughout the world in easily exploitable deposits. From the mid-1800's to the mid-1900's, the building stone industry in North America was both the impetus and nucleus for towns, railroads, and machine tool industries across the continent. From the 1900's through the 1930's, many technological advances in quarry drilling and finishing equipment were fostered by the building stone industry. The 1950's through the 1970's saw many adaptations to the demands of architects and designers. Innovative technology was developed to gain the competitive advantage over other producers as well as to satisfy the need to exploit deeper and more solid deposits of stone. This technology went from the muscle power of workers in the mid-1800's to the use of steam, electricity, and compressed air by the early 1900's. The equipment and tools developed from the early 1900's into the 1930's remained relatively unchanged into the 1950's. Since the 1950's, the more sophisticated use of carbides and diamonds for cutting and a high grade of steel for drilling has allowed for the more efficient excavation of stone. The use of hydraulics and electronics have also allowed for a higher degree of automation and cost savings for the manufacturer.

In North America, the building stone industry has shrunk from more than a thousand active quarries in the 1920's, with more than a dozen localities where quarries, mills, and shops were an integral part of the local economy, to a situation in which active quarries number in the hundreds and there are few areas where integrated quarries, mills, and shops are an important part of the local economy. Yet, the trend toward the increased use of stone in the late 1980's has suggested to many that the building stone industry would once again become an important factor in local economies.

## Bibliography

Barton, William R. *Dimension Stone*. Information Circular 8391. Washington, D.C.: Government Printing Office, 1968. A very good description of the dimension (building) stone industry in North America before major technological advances. Appropriate for high school students.

Bates, Robert L. *Stone, Clay, Glass: How Building Materials Are Found and Used*. Hillside, N.J.: Enslow, 1987. A good, concise (64-page) reference for junior high school students and above.

Bates, Robert L., and Julia A. Jackson. *Our Modern Stone Age*. Los Altos, Calif.: William Kaufmann, 1982. A good reference on industrial minerals. Building stone is included in the discussion.

Meade, Lance P. "Defining a Commercial Dimension Stone Marble Property." In *Twelfth Forum on the Geology of Industrial Minerals*. Atlanta: Georgia Department of Natural Resources, 1976. An objective discussion of the important criteria for developing a dimension stone property. For the college-level reader.

Newman, Cathy, and Pierre Boulat. "Carrara Marble: Touchstone of Eternity." *National Geographic* 162 (July, 1982): 42-58. An excellent photo essay on building stone quarrying. The Italian quarries described provided Michelangelo with the marble for his sculptures.

*Lance P. Meade*

## Cross-References

Igneous Rock Bodies, 1131; Igneous Rock Classification, 1138; Metamorphic Rock Classification, 1553; Metamorphic Textures, 1578; Earth Resources, 2175; Physical Properties of Rocks, 2225; Sedimentary Rock Classification, 2304; Stress and Strain, 2490.

# CAMBRIAN DIVERSIFICATION OF LIFE

*Type of earth science:* Paleontology and earth history

*The abrupt appearance of a great variety of animal fossils about 570 million years ago and about 3 billion years after the origin of life is termed the Cambrian diversification. Study of this spectacular development provides insights into the processes of evolution.*

### Principal terms

COELOMATE: an organism possessing an internal cavity termed the coelom

EUKARYOTE: a cell that has a nucleus surrounded by a well-defined membrane; the type of cell present in the metazoans

METAZOAN: A grade of organization of living organisms in which the cells are specialized for various functions and cooperate for the good of the whole organism

PHANEROZOIC: the time period from 570 million years ago to the present; that period of time during which sediments accumulated containing obvious and abundant remains of animals and plants

PRECAMBRIAN: the time period that includes nearly 90 percent of geologic time, ranging from 4.6 billion years ago, when the earth formed, to 570 million years ago, when the Cambrian period started

TRACE FOSSILS: traces of animal activity, such as burrows or trackways, preserved in the sediment

## Summary of the Phenomenon

Although the remains of microscopic organisms are known from rocks more than 3 billion years old, the remains of complex animals are not known before about 680 million years ago, while plants and animals with preserved hard parts did not become established until about 570 million years ago. The abrupt appearance of a great variety of animal fossils at the end of the Precambrian (the time period ranging from about 4.6 billion years ago to the start of the Cambrian period, 570 million years ago) is termed the Cambrian diversification and was a spectacular radiation heralding the start of the Phanerozoic (the time period ranging from the Cambrian to the Quaternary period). By the middle of Early Cambrian time, most of the major invertebrate animal groups had appeared in the oceans, and this rapid appearance is a striking feature of the fossil record. The diversification has been documented and shows a period of about 80 million years during which the variety of life increased exponentially, suggesting that each group originated by the simple splitting into two of an ancestral group. Unfortunately, although there is fossil evidence of early metazoans (complex animals), it is sparse, and reconstruction of the events during which simpler animals groups gave rise to more advanced animal groups is based primarily on comparative anatomy and embryology of modern forms.

The earliest record of metazoans occurs in the Ediacaran interval, which is a stratigraphic unit deposited during the last 100 million years of the Proterozoic. Prior to that there is only evidence of unicellular organisms. Initially these were prokaryotic (single cells lacking nuclei), but about 1.5 billion years ago, the first eukaryotic organisms (cells with a nucleus) had developed. The earliest metazoans were probably loose aggregates of eukaryotic cells that were not differentiated by function; however, the organisms found in the Ediacaran interval are already more complex. The fauna was first described from the Pound quartzite in the Flinders Ranges of South Australia. The fossils are impressions, left as the animals were stranded on mud flats and subsequently covered by sand, and they are interpreted as having been made by metazoans lacking hard parts. Many of the impressions are circular in outline with concentric or radial striations and have been considered to be jellyfish, though none can be tied with confidence to living organisms. In addition there are large (up to 1 meter long) elongate leaf-shaped forms considered to be related to modern sea pens, which are frondlike representatives of one of the coral groups. Other impressions are regarded as having been made by polychaete worms (bristle worms), while much rarer are impressions of supposed arthropods and animals of uncertain affinities. Whether these impressions should be interpreted in terms of living jellyfish, corals, and worms has been questioned, but they are clearly evidence of the existence of early metazoans. This fauna significantly predates the earliest Cambrian faunas and is now known from five continents. The presence of the same or similar forms as far apart as South Australia and northern Russia is striking evidence of the widespread distribution of this early shallow-marine fauna. In this fauna, scientists can glimpse a fleeting stage in metazoan diversification, a stage that may have given rise to the more diverse and abundant invertebrates of the Cambrian and later periods but which ultimately became extinct before the end of the Proterozoic.

Trace fossils also provide evidence of the early development of metazoans and can be particularly valuable, as impressions left by animals in sediment may be preserved when the animals themselves may not be. Trace fossils do not become abundant or diverse until near the Precambrian/Cambrian boundary, and most of these early traces probably resulted from the burrowing activity of soft-bodied infaunal worms. Trace fossils take the presumed origin of mobile metazoans further back into the Precambrian than do the Ediacara fauna but only to about 100 million years before the start of the Cambrian. As the Ediacara fauna indicates that a number of major groups had already developed, the initial radiation of Metazoa had clearly taken place earlier. Study of the relationships of modern metazoan groups can help to shed light on the course of this diversification.

Several grades or levels of organization are recognized in metazoans living at present. The simplest forms are ones in which the cells are not separated by function; some modern sponges can serve as examples of this grade. Most simple metazoans have cells that are separated by function, however, and the simplest grade is represented by the Cnidaria (corals and jellyfish), in which the body wall is separated into two layers: the outer ectoderm and the inner endoderm. The next grade, which includes all higher organisms, consists of forms in which the body wall is in three layers, the mesoderm being sandwiched between the ectoderm and endoderm. In more advanced invertebrate animals, the mesoderm forms a lining to the ectoderm and overlies a fluid-filled cavity termed the coelom, which may have originally functioned as a hydrostatic skeleton but in higher organisms has also been used as space for the placement of internal organs. The coelomates (organisms with a coelom) can be divided into several major groups on the basis of embryology, indicating the early subdivisions of the basic stock. These include a lophophorate group encompassing Brachiopoda and Bryozoa, in which a food-gathering apparatus termed a lophophore is present; a large group including both Echinodermata and Chordata (the group that includes vertebrates); and a further group that includes Arthropoda and Annelida (segmented worms). The larvae of marine annelids are very similar to those of Mollusca, and the mollusks may, therefore, have split off early from the main line of descent of segmented animals. Although the time of origin of these groups is unknown, it can be concluded that coelomates were present already in the Late Precambrian and that the origination of arthropods was closer to the age of the Ediacara fauna than that of the annelids or the cnidarians that form the majority of the population.

The Ediacara fauna vanishes from the sedimentary record before the end of the Precambrian, although the presence of trace fossils indicates that metazoans were still present. The base of the Cambrian is recognized as the appearance of fossils of animals that secreted a skeleton, and this basal stage of the Cambrian, the Tommotian stage, contains a diverse fauna of small shelly organisms, many tubelike and composed of calcium phosphate. This fauna also includes sponges, brachiopods, gastropods, primitive mollusks, and hyolithids (conical shells usually considered to be mollusks, though their soft parts cannot be reconstructed with any degree of confidence). The best-known sequences through the Precambrian/Cambrian boundary are in Siberia, where sedimentation occurred without a major interruption through this period. In these sequences, small shelly fossils occur only rarely in the Precambrian, although they are abundant in the Tommotian, pointing to an explosive development of life in the earliest Cambrian.

Above the Tommotian stage, a number of groups of larger animals with hard skeletons appear. They are characteristic of later Cambrian faunas, appear very abruptly, and are fully organized and differentiated on their first appearance. One of the most conspicuous groups is the trilobites, many-legged arthropods that crawled along the sea floor, often forming conspicuous trace fossils. Brachiopods, two-valved filter-feeding organisms, are also common, and echinoderms were represented by a remarkable variety of types. Although the animals with hard skeletons were very diverse, there is also evidence that the soft-bodied fauna was equally diverse. One indication of this diversity is provided by the fauna preserved in the Middle Cambrian Burgess shale of British Columbia. The black shale of the Burgess shale accumulated in an oxygen-free environment, which prevented the destruction of the animals that were washed in with it. The majority of organisms in this fauna are nontrilobite arthropods, but there are also numerous polychaete and priapulid worms, which were already highly diversified and which might have caused the burrows found in rocks of latest Precambrian age. In addition, there are many animals of unknown affinity, often forms found only in the Burgess shale. This fauna indicates the presence of complex communities composed of highly organized animals; the diversity in the range of feeding adaptations, for example, is quite as varied as that found in modern animals. This complex fauna is quite unlike that of the earliest Cambrian or of the Ediacaran and demonstrates the explosiveness of the early radiation.

A number of explanations of this sudden diversification have been put forward. Environmental factors were certainly very important, and one suggestion is that the diversification may have been related to an increase in suitable environments at the end of the Precambrian. That would have been caused partly by the breakup of continental areas, which would have provided greater lengths of coastline and, therefore, a rapid increase in the availability of habitats for the shallow-marine organisms. In addition, the end of an extensive period of glaciation that took place at the end of the Precambrian would have resulted in the flooding of coastal areas, providing increased shallow-marine environments. The end of the glacial period would also have resulted in a warming trend that would have opened up new marine environments and possibly helped to trigger the expansion of marine diversity.

It has also been suggested that an increase in oxygen levels may have contributed to the sudden development of complex metazoans. Large and thin animals such as those present in the Ediacara fauna may have been adapted to respire by diffusion in oxygen concentrations as low as 8 percent of present levels. Oxygen levels of up to 10-15 percent of present levels may have been present in the earliest Cambrian, which may have been sufficient to allow the increased diversification of invertebrate organisms. Further evidence for oxygen levels is also available in the appearance of hard skeletons at the base of the Cambrian. External skeletons are useful protection, suggesting their development in response to predation; however, they are also useful as solid surfaces for the attachment of muscles and as supports to lift organisms above the bottom. Calcium and phosphate ions are both essential to the processes within metazoan cells, and it may be that skeletal parts originated as reserves of these materials. Calcium phosphate is a hard tissue commonly found in earliest Cambrian faunas; organisms using calcium carbonate did not become common until the end of the Cambrian. At present, an atmospheric oxygen level of at least 16 percent is required before marine organisms can secrete calcium carbonate skeletons, suggesting that increased oxygen levels in the Cambrian may have contributed to the development of diverse organisms at that time. It appears, therefore, that a variety of environmental factors including increase of shallow-marine areas, a warming trend, and increasing oxygen levels may all have contributed to the explosive Cambrian diversification of invertebrate organisms.

## Methods of Study

The evidence for the early evolution of complex organisms rests on the fossils present in the sediments. Studies of these remains give scientists insights into the way in which early life developed. Preservation of organisms is an unusual occurrence, however, and particularly rare when the organisms are completely soft-bodied. Preservation potential is enhanced by the presence of some hard parts, skeleton or shell, that will resist erosion and decay. The potential for preservation can be additionally enhanced if the organism lives in an environment in which sedimentation is taking place, thus improving the chances of incorporation in the sediment. Because of these constraints on preservation, scientific knowledge of shallow-marine faunas through time is much greater than knowledge of faunas in other environments.

The earliest metazoan faunas are those from the Ediacaran. These organisms were soft-bodied, and their preservation is therefore an extremely uncommon event. The fossils consist of natural molds and casts formed when the animals were covered by drifting sands in nearshore environments. The specimens can be studied directly by scientists, as they are normally clearly exposed on the bedding planes of the sediments when the rocks are split. In some cases where molds only are present, a latex cast may be made to facilitate detailed study. Preservation of the early Cambrian fauna in the Burgess shale is rather different, however, and a greater variety of techniques can be used in its study. The specimens are compressed into thin films of carbon and are exposed on the bedding planes of the shale when it is split. In many cases, the splitting results in breakage through the specimen so that parts of the original adhere to two separate rock slabs (termed the part and the counterpart). Such compression means that in complex animals such as arthropods, delicate preparation may be necessary to remove surfaces so that other surfaces and structures may be examined. Such preparation is conducted under a binocular microscope, and small engraving tools and needles are used to remove the matrix. Interpretation of the specimens involves producing drawings and photographs, and the Burgess shale material provides special problems here, as the specimens are preserved as black carbon films on a black shale. Ultraviolet light may be used to enhance the reflectivity of the specimens relative to the surrounding matrix; they may also be photographed under a liquid (water or ethyl alcohol), as this process will also enhance differences between the specimen and the matrix. Drawings are normally made using a camera-lucida attachment on a binocular microscope. This attachment allows the scientist looking through the microscope to see both the specimen and his or her drawing hand and pencil, thus enabling the tracing of the specimen and production of an accurate illustration.

Study of the data as a whole requires analysis of large amounts of information so that evolutionary trends can be assessed and periods of rapid diversification or higher than normal extinction can be recognized. These studies are dependent on the original description and identification of the fossils, but manipulation of the data is accomplished by computers.

## Context

Fossilization is an unusual occurrence; therefore, knowledge of past organisms tends to be tantalizingly incomplete. This incompleteness of the fossil record is more marked as one goes back through time, and knowledge of the earliest stages in the development of complex organisms is thus very patchy indeed. Nevertheless, scientists are interested in assessing and interpreting such information as is available because of the light it sheds on the evolutionary process and on the origin of complex metazoans that ultimately gave rise to humans.

A picture of early metazoan evolution has been developed in which, during the Late Precambrian (about 680 million years ago), a shallow-marine fauna of soft-bodied organisms had developed and was present worldwide. These organisms showed similarities to modern organisms such as jellyfish, sea pens, and annelid worms, though their direct relationship to the modern forms has been questioned. The organisms were often large but thin and filmlike, suggesting that they may have been adapted to obtain oxygen by diffusion in the low oxygen concentrations of that time. This fauna disappears from the fossil record before the end of the Pre-cambrian, although the evidence of trace fossils shows that complex organisms were still present. At the base of the Cambrian period (570 million years ago), small shelly fossils start to appear. They are mostly composed of calcium phosphate, suggesting that oxygen levels were higher but not yet high enough for the wide-spread use of calcium carbonate as a skeletal material. Shortly after there was a major evolutionary radiation of invertebrate groups that is termed the Cambrian diversification. During this radiation, most of the major invertebrate groups appear, suddenly and already well differentiated. This appearance implies a previous soft-bodied development of the groups for which scientists have no fossil evidence or, alternatively, a very sudden development—probably both these processes were involved in the diversification. The role of preservation in providing scientists with basic data is highlighted by the occurrence of the Burgess shale fauna in the Middle Cambrian, in which soft-bodied organisms from this early radiation are preserved together with organisms whose hard parts make them more commonly preserved. This fauna demonstrates the presence of a large and diverse suite of organisms, many of which belong to groups that became extinct fairly soon and for which we have no other fossil record.

The reasons for the diversification of metazoans in the Cambrian are complex but are mostly related to the development of a more hospitable environment at this time. The continents were breaking up and, therefore, greater lengths of coastline with shallow-marine habitats were present. In addition, the end of an extensive period of glaciation resulted in a warming trend and also a worldwide sea-level rise caused by the melting of the glaciers that also extended shallow-marine environments. At the same time, the increase in oxygen levels may have triggered the development of more complex organisms.

## Bibliography

Clarkson, E. N. K. *Invertebrate Paleontology and Evolution*. London: Allen & Unwin, 1979. Somewhat detailed but does provide a good overview of the development and radiation of the Metazoa. Also provides sections on the Ediacara and Burgess shale faunas. Suitable for high school or college students.

Glaessner, M. F. *The Dawn of Animal Life: A Biohistorical Study*. New York: Cambridge University Press, 1984. A rather detailed account of the Ediacara fauna and its significance. Suitable for college-level students.

Stanley, S. M. *Earth and Life Through Time*. 2d ed. New York: W. H. Freeman, 1989. A general text on paleontology and historical geology that provides considerable background on the evolution of the Metazoa in its environmental context. Suitable for high school or college students.

Stearn, C. W., and R. L. Carroll. *Paleontology: The Record of Life*. New York: John Wiley & Sons, 1989. A general paleontology text that provides an extremely clear section on the early development and diversification of the Metazoa. Suitable for high school or college students.

Whittington, H. B. *The Burgess Shale*. New Haven, Conn.: Yale University Press, 1985. A very readable and well-illustrated account of the history of study of the Burgess shale, its fauna and significance. Suitable for college-level students.

*David K. Elliott*

## Cross-References

Eukaryotes, 623; The Fossil Record, 760; Ediacarian Fossils, 776; Fossils of the Earliest Life Forms, 782; Fossils of the Earliest Vertebrates, 789; The Paleozoic Era, 2018.

# CARBONATES

*Type of earth science:* Geology
*Field of study:* Mineralogy and crystallography

*Carbonate minerals are characterized by having the carbonate ion in their composition. The common carbonate minerals are divisible into the calcite, aragonite, and dolomite groups.*

### Principal terms

ANION: a negatively charged ion

ARAGONITE: a carbonate with the orthorhombic crystal structure of the calcium carbonate compound; it forms in marine water or under high-pressure, metamorphic conditions

CALCITE: a carbonate with the hexagonal crystal form of the calcium carbonate compound; a common mineral found in limestone and marble

CATION: a positively charged ion

CRYSTAL: a solid with an internally ordered arrangement of component atoms

DIVALENT ION: an ion with a charge of 2 because of the loss or gain of two electrons

DOLOMITE: a double carbonate that includes magnesium and has a hexagonal structure; it is abundant in ancient rocks

ION: an atom that has lost or gained one or more electrons

ISOSTRUCTURAL: having the same structure but a different chemistry

POLYMORPHS: different structures of the same chemical compound

## Summary of the Phenomenon

Carbonates are one among several classes of mineral. Minerals are the stuff of which rocks are made. They are natural substances with a definite chemical composition and an ordered internal arrangement. Minerals can be divided into chemical groups based on their atoms and into structural groups based on the atoms' ordered arrangement.

All carbonates contain the carbonate ion as their defining anionic group. An ion is an atom that has lost or gained electrons and so has become chemically reactive. When an ion has lost an electron, it has a positive charge and is called a cation; when an ion has gained an electron, it has a negative charge and is called an anion. The number of electrons lost or gained is the charge of the ion. The charge and the radius (size) of an ion determine how it is chemically bonded to another ion, how strong the bonding is, and the number of ions that can be coordinated to it or surround it. Scientists have found that the carbonate ion contains one carbon ion in the middle of a triangle formed by three oxygen ions, which occupy the corners of the triangle. Two-thirds of the charge on each oxygen ion is used for bonding with the central carbon ion. As a result, only one-third of the charge on each oxygen ion is available for bonding with cations, and the carbonate ion group acts as if it were a single ion with an overall double negative charge. To form a carbonate mineral, the negative charge on the carbonate ion must be neutralized by cations such as calcium, magnesium, strontium, manganese, and barium.

Atoms in a mineral lie on imaginary planes, which are called atomic planes. These planes cut across other planes, forming definite and knowable intersection angles. Those atomic planes that contain many atoms tend to develop into crystal faces. Minerals are crystalline, and the crystal faces of a mineral are related to the internal arrangement of atoms. The bonds between atoms of the same atomic plane tend to be stronger than the bonds across the atomic planes. Consequently, minerals break or cleave along preferred planes, or cleavage planes, when struck by a hammer. A set of parallel cleavage planes yields one cleavage direction. Some minerals have more than one cleavage direction; others have none, since the bond strength between atoms is the same in all directions. Common carbonate minerals have three cleavage directions.

The atoms of a mineral are symmetrically related to one another. Since crystal faces are related to the internal arrangement of the atoms, these crystal faces are also symmetrically related. Scientists have found that all minerals can be grouped into thirty-two crystal classes based on their symmetry relations. A small group of atoms forms the basic building block of crystals. This basic building block is called a unit cell; it is an arrangement of the smallest number of atoms which, as a unit, may be repeated over and over again to form a visible crystal. The volume of a unit cell can be determined from the lengths of its lines and the angles subtended by them. Depending on the cell's shape, these imaginary lines may be parallel to its edges or may pass through opposite corners, sides, or edges. The lines are called crystallographic axes. The various kinds of unit cell have led scientists to regroup the thirty-two crystal classes of minerals into six crystal systems. The common carbonates belong to two of the six: the orthorhombic and hexagonal systems. The orthorhombic crystal system is characterized by having three crystallographic axes which are unequal in length and which are perpendicular to one another. The hexagonal system has four axes, all of which pass through a common center. Three of these axes lie on the same plane, are of equal length, and are separated from one another by 120 degrees. The fourth axis is different in length from the others and is perpendicular to them.

The three common carbonates, calcite, aragonite, and dolomite, belong to three structural types. Calcite and aragonite are polymorphs of the same compound; that is, the same chemical compound occurs in different structures. Aragonite is orthorhombic and less symmetrical than calcite, which is hexagonal. Calcite and dolomite are both hexagonal, but they do not have identical structures. In calcite, calcium atomic planes lie between carbonate ion planes. In dolomite, alternating calcium planes are occupied by magnesium atoms. As a result, calcite has a higher symmetry content than dolomite, although both belong to the same crystal system. Also, dolomite shows more internal order than calcite, because it requires the positioning of more different atoms in specific atomic sites.

All carbonates which contain divalent cations whose ionic radii are less than or equal to that of the calcium ion are isostructural to calcite, which has a hexagonal structure. Different chemical compounds which have identical structures are said to be isostructural. Siderite, magnesite, and rhodochrosite are isostructural to calcite.

Calcite is by far the most common of all carbonate minerals. It is commonly off-white, colorless, or transparent. It may exhibit different crystal shapes, but in all cases, a careful examination will reveal the hexagonal crystal structure. It is fairly resistant to abrasion, although it can be scratched by a steel knife. Its resistance to scratching is partly why marble, which is composed of calcite, is used as a building stone. Calcite fizzes and dissolves in acid. Clear calcite crystals exhibit sets of parallel cleavage lines that intersect with other sets in such a way as to give the impression that calcite is rhombus-shaped.

In its most abundant form, calcite is synthesized by aquatic organisms that are common in shallow marine environments of warm latitudes, such as the Gulf Coast. As the marine organisms die, their shells, which are made of calcite, settle at the bottom. These shells may be broken into smaller fragments by browsing organisms or wave action. The fragments may become cemented together by calcite and form a rock called limestone. Many caves and some sinkholes are found in regions where the rocks are limestone. Caves are formed because calcite is dissolved by groundwater. Sinkholes are formed when the roofs of caves collapse.

In the dolomite group, alternating calcium atomic planes are occupied by other divalent ions, such as magnesium in dolomite, iron in ankerite, and manganese in kutnohorite. Since the magnesium, iron, and manganese ions are smaller than the calcium ion, the dolomite group structure is not as highly symmetrical as the calcite structure. Consequently, although both the calcite and the dolomite group minerals are hexagonal, they belong to different classes among the thirty-two classes of crystals. Of the dolomite group minerals, the mineral dolomite is by far the most common. It is fairly common in ancient carbonate rocks called dolostones. Dolomite is white to pinkish and is similar to calcite in many ways; however, it does not fizz readily when diluted acid is dropped on it.

In the aragonite group, carbonate ions do not lie on simple atomic planes. Adjacent carbonate ions are slightly out of line; also, adjacent carbonate ions face in opposite directions. Divalent cations whose ionic radii are larger than or equal to the calcium ion form carbonate minerals which are isostructural to aragonite. Of the minerals in the aragonite group, aragonite is the most common. It is generally white and elongate. It is the carbonate mineral that readily precipitates from marine water, but it is not a stable mineral, and in time it changes to the more symmetrical and hexagonal structure of calcite. Aragonite is the least symmetrical polymorph of calcium carbonate and is found in metamorphic rocks which were formed under high pressure and comparatively low temperature.

## Methods of Study

Carbonates are generally light-colored, soft, and easy to scratch with a knife as compared with most other common rock-forming minerals. They form a white powder when scratched. They are harder than fingernails, however, and cannot be scratched by them. When acid is poured on carbonate powder, it fizzes, liberating carbon dioxide. Carbonates such as calcite do not even have to be powdered for the acid test, because they fizz readily. The cleavage planes and the angles between cleavages are another physical method by which carbonate minerals can be distinguished. Clear crystals such as those of calcite can produce double refraction of objects, another property that identifies carbonates without the aid of instruments.

Better mineral identification is done by scientists after a rock is cut to a small size, mounted on glass, and ground to a very thin section of rock (0.03 millimeter thick), which is then capable of transmitting light. The thin section is placed on a stage of a transmitted-light polarizing microscope. A lens below the stage polarizes light; it allows the transmission only of light which vibrates in one direction, say, east to west. Another lens, above the stage, allows the passage only of light that vibrates in the other direction, north to south. When glass is placed on a stage and the lower polarizer is inserted across the light source, the color of the glass can be seen. When the upper polarizer is also inserted, however, the glass appears dark, because no light is transmitted. The optical properties of most minerals, including the carbonates, are different from those of glass. Other accessories are used in addition to the polarizing lenses in order to determine minerals' optical properties. Magnification by microscope permits the better determination of minerals' physical properties, such as their shape and cleavage.

The crystal structure of carbonate crystals can be determined with the aid of a contact goniometer. Its simplest version is a protractor with a straight edge fastened at its middle. The goniometer is used to measure the angles between crystal faces, from which scientists can determine the crystal structure.

X-ray diffraction can ascertain the crystal structure of any substance, including carbonates. Diffraction peaks characteristic of each mineral can be displayed on a chart recorder when X rays bombard a sample. Each diffraction peak results from the reinforcement of X-ray reflections from mutually parallel atomic planes within the sample. Several diffraction peaks from one mineral indicate equivalent numbers of sets of atomic planes within the minerals. The difference in the peak heights corresponds to the density of atoms in the pertinent atomic planes. The detection device does not have to be a chart recorder; it can be a photographic paper or a digital recorder that can be appropriately interfaced to a computer for the quick identification of minerals.

## Context

Carbonates are a fairly common group of minerals which form in environments that range from arid lands to shallow seas. Hot springs are one place where calcite precipitates. Travertine, or tufa, is a banded rock that precipitates at the mouth of springs. Caliche, deposits of carbonate that precipitate from groundwater in arid climates, is a source of serious problems to irrigation farmers. Sinkholes that form by the collapse of roof rocks of near-surface caves in the limestones of warm and humid regions are a problem not only to farmers but also to homeowners. It is not unusual for part of a house, or the whole of it, to sink suddenly into a depression caused by a collapse into an underground cave.

Carbonates are important for their regulation of the pH, or acidity content, of ocean waters. Carbonate minerals dissolve when the acid content of water is raised and precipitate when the acid content is reduced. In this way, the pH of ocean water is regulated to a steady value of 8.1.

Carbonates are also known for their industrial applications, which range from dolomite tablets to building materials such as cement and mortar. One of the finest building rocks is marble, which is composed of carbonate minerals. Marble often is delicately banded with different colors. The banding arises because the minerals are lined up in directions perpendicular to the natural pressure under which an impure limestone was metamorphosed and converted to marble. If the original limestone was pure and composed entirely of calcite, the marble that is metamorphosed from it would be white and not banded. Polished marble is used as a building material or often as decorative stone for doors or exteriors. Polished travertine is also used as building stone, but it is placed in the interiors of buildings because of banded porous zones that can accumulate rainwater. Regular limestone is used in buildings and, most commonly, in retaining walls alongside houses and roads. Most limestone is used for cement. Cement is up to 75 percent limestone; the rest is silica and aluminum.

## Bibliography

Bathurst, Robin G. C. *Carbonate Sediments and Their Diagensis*. 2d ed. New York: Elsevier, 1975. This is an excellent book on carbonate rocks. Chapter 6 discusses the chemistry and structure of the more common carbonate minerals.

Deer, W. A., R. A. Howie, and J. Zussman. *Rock Forming Minerals*. Vol. 5, *Nonsilicates*. 4th ed. London: Longman, 1965. A work of reference useful for advanced students. Carbonates are discussed on pages 226 through 322.

Klein, Cornelis, and C. S. Hurlbut, Jr. *Manual of Mineralogy*. 20th ed. New York: John Wiley & Sons, 1985. An excellent book on the study of minerals. The details of carbonates are treated in chapter 10. Suitable for college-level students.

Mason, Brian, and L. G. Berry. *Elements of Mineralogy*. San Francisco: W. H. Freeman, 1968. An excellent and easy-to-read book on the study of minerals. Used by many colleges. Carbonates are discussed in chapter 7.

Parker, Sybil P., ed. *McGraw-Hill Encyclopedia of the Geological Sciences*. 2d ed. New York: McGraw-Hill, 1988. This reference has complete entries on all the common carbonate minerals, including aragonite, dolomite, limestone, and calcite. Written at a college level. Illustrated.

Prinz, Martin, George Harlow, and Joseph Peters, eds. *Simon and Schuster's Guide to Rocks and Minerals*. New York: Simon & Schuster, 1978. Rocks and minerals are described and illustrated with color photographs in this easy-to-read book.

*Habte Giorgis Churnet*

## Cross-References

Building Stone, 178; Cement, 196; Igneous Rock Classification, 1138; Igneous Rocks: Carbonatites, 1173; Ionic Substitution in Minerals, 1245; Karst Topography, 1310; Physical Properties of Minerals, 1681; The Structure of Minerals, 1693; Non-Silicates Other Than Oxides and Carbonates, 1741; Physical Properties of Rocks, 2225; X-Ray Powder Diffraction, 2751.

# CEMENT

*Type of earth science:* Economic geology

*Cement is a common construction material used to bond mineral fragments in order to produce a compact whole. The most common types of cement result from the reaction of lime and silica. These are called hydraulic cements because of their ability to set and harden under water.*

*Principal terms*

AGGREGATE: a mineral filler such as sand or gravel that, when mixed with cement paste, forms concrete

ALUMINA: sometimes called aluminum sesquioxide, alumina is found in clay minerals along with silica; tricalcium aluminate acts as a flux in cement manufacturing

CLINKER: irregular lumps of fused raw materials to which gypsum is added before grinding into finely powdered cement

CONCRETE: a composite construction material consisting of particles of an aggregate bound by a cement

GYPSUM: a natural mineral, hydrated calcium sulfate; it helps control the setting time of cement

HYDRATION: a chemical combination with water; the hydration of calcium silicates is the major reaction in the hardening of cement

HYDRAULIC CEMENT: any cement that sets and hardens under water; the most common type is known as Portland cement

LIME: a common name for calcium oxide; it appears in cement both in an uncombined form and combined with silica and alumina

SILICA: silicon dioxide; it reacts with lime and alkali oxides and is a key component in cement

## Summary of the Phenomenon

Cement is an important construction material because of the ready availability of its raw materials, the ability to shape it prior to setting, and its durability after it has hardened. Cement combined with the proper aggregate makes concrete, a durable, load-bearing construction material. By far the most common type of cement is that which is called Portland cement. Portland cement consists primarily of lime, silica, and alumina. These materials are carefully ground, mixed, and heated to produce a finely powdered gray substance. In the presence of water, these ingredients react to form hydrated calcium silicates that, after setting, form a hardened product. Such a product is classified as a hydraulic cement because of its ability to set and harden under water.

Cement must be manufactured (except in rare cases where deposits of cementlike rock are found) from raw materials that are found rather easily in nature. Cement manufacturers have a number of sources for lime, including limestone, marl, marine shells, and alkali wastes. Alumina and silica can be found in clay, shale, slate, ashes, and blast furnace slag. The first step in preparing the raw materials for cement production is to grind them into a fine powder and then mix them in predetermined ratios. The mixing can be done dry or wet, as a slurry. After mixing, the raw materials are burned in a large rotating kiln. This kiln can be from 4 to 8 meters in diameter and from 90 to 200 meters long and is slightly inclined. As the mixture flows through the kiln, it reaches a maximum temperature ranging from 1,400 degrees Celsius to 1,500 degrees Celsius, at which point the raw materials interact to form calcium silicates. The mixture leaves the kiln in the form of rough lumps or pellets, called clinker, no larger than 5 centimeters in diameter. After the clinker cools, the manufacturer adds gypsum and grinds the two components into a fine powder known as Portland cement.

Adding water to dry cement creates a paste that eventually hardens. The reaction of water with cement is known as the hydration process. This reaction involves much more than water molecules attaching themselves to the constituent elements of cement. Rather, the constituents are reorganized to form new, hydrated compounds. One of the first reactions involves the aluminates, particularly tricalcium aluminum ($3CaAl_2O_3$, hereafter abbreviated as $C_3A$). Although $C_3A$ is undesirable in cement, it is necessary as a flux during the manufacturing process. If allowed to react unchecked with water, it would lead to flash setting, not allowing time for working the cement or concrete product. To preclude this difficulty, a carefully controlled amount of gypsum is added to the cement at the time of manufacture. The resultant sulfo-aluminates slow the hydration of $C_3A$, giving the more important calcium silicates time to react with water.

Hydration of the calcium silicates occurs more slowly than that of the aluminates but forms the basic, strength-giving structure of hardened Portland cement. Two different calcium silicates $3CaO \cdot SiO_2$ (abbreviated as $C_3S$) and $2CaO \cdot SiO_2$ (abbreviated as $C_2S$) are present in the cement. Both forms of calcium silicates react with water to produce the hydrated calcium silicate ($C_3S_2H_3$). This product is sometimes called tobermorite because of the resemblance its molecular arrangement bears to that of the natural but rare mineral of the same name (taken from Tobermorey, Scotland). Another product of the reaction is calcium hydroxide, or $Ca(OH)_2$, which is integral to the microstructure of the hardened cement. It is important to note that as the exact ratios of the different constituents vary, so does the composition of the product. What is actually being produced, at different places and by different manufacturers, is a family of hydrated calcium silicates rather than one precise formula.

Having reviewed the chemical properties of cement, it is now necessary to examine its physical properties, from which hardened cement derives its mechanical properties. From the time water is added to the time the cement paste sets and fully hardens, cement goes through four general phases. Four main compounds are present through all these stages: a gel of the above-mentioned hydrated compounds, crystals of calcium hydroxide, unhydrated cement, and water. The proportions of these compounds change with time; the cement gains rigidity as the percentage of hydrated calcium silicate increases, with the attendant drop in the amount of free water.

These compounds eventually arrange themselves in loose, crumpled layers. For the first few minutes after adding water to cement, the two form a paste in which the cement is in suspension within the water. At this stage, the cement dissolves in the water. The next stage, sometimes called the dormant period, lasts for one to four hours. During this time, the cement forms a gel and begins to set, thus losing its pliability. The individual cement grains build a coating of hydration products, and loose, crumpled layers of hydrated calcium silicate begin to form. In the microscopic spaces between the cement grains, water is held by the surface forces of the cement particles. Larger spaces, called capillary pores, hold free water, which the cement slowly absorbs for use in the hydration process. During the third stage, which peaks about six hours after water is added to the cement, the coating of hydration products around the cement grains ruptures, exposing unhydrated cement to water, thus further building the calcium silicate layers. As these layers grow, they entrap water, which continues to react with the cement particles. They also contain calcium hydroxide (a by-product of the hydration of calcium silicates), which fills the larger pores and thus apparently contributes to the overall strength of the cement. The fourth stage produces the final setting and the hardening of the cement. The hydration process may continue for years, and there will in all probability be a small percentage of the cement that never hydrates. Hydration of $C_3S$ and $C_2S$ occurs at different rates. In the first four weeks, the hydration of the $C_3S$ contributes most to the strength of the hardening cement, while after that the hydration of the $C_2S$ contributes more to the cement's strength. After about a year, the hydration rates of the two compounds are roughly equal.

While Portland cement is by far the most common type of cement, there are others. Most of these, such as high-early-strength cements, slag cements, Portland-pozzolan cements, and expansive cements, are variations upon the basic Portland cement. Manufacturers can produce these specialized cements through slight variations in the basic chemical composition of Portland cement and through the use of various additives. Each of these cements is designed for specific uses, and their advantages include lower cost, higher strength, and faster setting times. Another type, high-alumina cement, is not based on Portland cement. Formed by the fusion of limestone and bauxite, high-alumina cement hardens rapidly and withstands the corrosive effects of sulfate waters (unlike basic Portland cement). Its early promise as a structural material has diminished because of a number of failures, but its ability to withstand high temperatures makes it quite useful in constructing furnaces.

## Methods of Study

The quality of Portland cement can be measured by four principal physical characteristics: fineness, soundness, time of set, and compressive strength. The desired specifications for each may vary from one country to another and will certainly vary for the different types of cement, but generalizations about them may safely be made. The fineness of the cement plays a large role in determining the rate of hydration. The finer the cement, the larger the surface area of the cement particles, and the faster and more complete the hydration. Originally, fineness was tested by measuring the percentage of cement retained by a specified sieve. A number 200 sieve (with openings 74 microns across), for example, would retain not more than 22 percent of a good Portland cement. Sieve tests were not totally reliable, however, because of clogging and because they did not give a good indication of the distribution of the different sizes of particles.

A new method has been developed that measures fineness in terms of the specific surface (the surface area of cement particles measured in square centimeters per gram of cement). The two most common ways of measuring specific surface are the Wagner turbidimeter test and the Blaine air permeability test. To use the turbidimeter, a sample of cement is dispersed in kerosene inside a tall glass container. A beam of light is then passed through the kerosene at given elevations at a specified time, and the concentration of cement is measured by a photoelectric cell. The specific surface can then be calculated from the photoelectric cell readings.

The air permeability test relies on the fact that the number and size of pores are functions of the size of the particles and their distribution. A given volume of air is drawn through a bed of cement, and the time it takes for the air to pass through the cement is used to calculate the specific surface of that sample.

Soundness is another important characteristic of cement. A sound cement is one that will not crack or disintegrate with time. Unsoundness is often caused by the delayed hydration and subsequent expansion of lime. The usual method of testing cement for soundness is in an autoclave. A small sample is placed in the autoclave after curing for twenty-four hours and is subjected to extremely high pressure for three hours. After the sample has cooled, it is measured and compared to its original length. If it has expanded less than 0.8 percent, the cement is usually considered sound.

Time of setting is tested on fresh cement paste as it hardens. The ability of the paste to sustain a given weight on a needle of a given diameter (usually a 300-gram load on a 10-millimeter diameter needle) can easily be correlated to its setting time.

Concrete, like other masonry products, is much stronger in compression (for example, a vertical pillar in which gravity pushes the pillar in on itself) than in tension (for example, a horizontal beam that is bowed such that the bottom half wants to pull apart). Thus it is most useful to study the compressive strength of concrete. The usual test is to make a two-inch cube of cement and sand (in a 1:2.75 mixture) and compress it until it breaks. Much can be learned by measuring the breaking load, type of fracturing, and other results of this test.

## Context

Cement has been used for construction purposes since at least 4000 B.C. The

Romans used a hydraulic cement based on slaked lime and volcanic ash in many of their construction projects, some of which are still standing. Hydraulic cement disappeared with the Roman Empire and did not reappear until the middle of the eighteenth century. The famed British engineer John Smeaton rediscovered the use of hydraulic cement in 1756 as he rebuilt the Eddystone Lighthouse. Since that time, cement has become a crucial building material.

One important use of cement is as mortar, or cement mixed with sand. Mortar is the substance that binds bricks, stone, and other masonry products. Cement is also the primary ingredient in grout, such as that used between tiles. The most important and common use of cement, however, is in making concrete.

Concrete is the product of mixing cement paste with a mineral aggregate. The aggregate, which acts as a filler, can be a wide variety of materials but is usually a sand or gravel. As a construction material, concrete has many advantages. First, it is inexpensive and readily available. The energy costs alone are a fraction of what they would be for a substance such as steel, and the raw materials for concrete are often available near the construction site, thus saving considerable transportation costs. Another important advantage of concrete is the ability to form it in a wide variety of shapes and sizes, quite often on the job site. Concrete is also known for its long life and low maintenance, as a result of the strong binding characteristics of cement and its resistance to water. Finally, concrete's high strength in compression and proven long-term performance make it a good choice for many structural components.

Concrete for structural uses comes in four major forms. Ready-mixed concrete is transported to a construction site as a cement paste and is then poured into forms to make roadways, driveways, floor slabs, foundation footings, and many other types of structural foundations. Precast concrete can be used for anything from a birdbath to wall slabs for a building, which are cast at a concrete work and then transported to their intended site. A common example of a precast member might be the beams of a highway overpass. Reinforced concrete is any concrete to which reinforcement (usually steel rods) has been added in order to increase its strength. Prestressed concrete is a relatively new form of concrete. Developed in the 1920's, prestressed concrete is put under compression through the use of jacks or steel cables, such that a beam is always in compression, whereas an unstressed beam in the same place would be experiencing tension.

These forms of concrete are used, often in combination, in a variety of ways. Slabs, walls, pipes, dams, spillways, and even elegant vaulted roofs (known as thin-shell vaulting) are all made of concrete. Cement, especially as it is used in concrete, has played a crucial role in shaping the physical environment. Concrete is the most widely used manufactured construction material in the world. In most modern countries, the ratio of concrete consumption to steel consumption is at least ten to one. Although concrete is often taken for granted, the world is literally built upon it.

## Bibliography

Blanks, Robert F., and Henry L. Kennedy. *The Technology of Cement and Concrete.* New York: John Wiley & Sons, 1955. A somewhat dated but still useful work on cement and concrete. The introductory chapter has some helpful information on the history, economy, and general background on the subject. These same themes are woven into the remainder of the text.

Mehta, P. Kumar. *Concrete: Structure, Properties, and Materials.* Englewood Cliffs, N.J.: Prentice-Hall, 1986. This book is well illustrated with tables, charts, photographs, and drawings. Definitions are abundant and clear. Also contains numerous examples, all illustrated with photographs, of modern-day projects, ranging from sculpture to dams.

Mindess, Sidney, and J. Francis Young. *Concrete.* Englewood Cliffs, N.J.: Prentice-Hall, 1981. A carefully written and detailed explanation of concrete covering the different cements, chemical reactions, aggregates, and all aspects of making and using concrete. Chapter 2, "Historical Development of Concrete," includes a brief but useful historical overview of cement. Each chapter has a separate bibliography.

Neville, A. M. *Properties of Concrete.* 2d ed. New York: John Wiley & Sons, 1973. Another work on concrete that includes a lengthy discussion of cement. This is a fairly technical work, but it is clearly written and contains good definitions. Chapter 1 is a detailed discussion of Portland cement, and chapter 2 discusses other types of cement. References are included at the end of each chapter.

Orchard, Dennis Frank. *Concrete Technology.* Vol. 1, *Properties of Materials.* 4th ed. London: Applied Science Publishers, 1979. Despite its title, almost one-third of this book discusses cement. Harder reading than some other books on the subject and with less detail but gives a suitable overview for the general reader. Refers to specifications and practices in both Great Britain and the United States.

Portland Cement Association. *Principles of Quality Concrete.* New York: John Wiley & Sons, 1975. Designed to educate persons for employment in the concrete industry, this work explains cement and concrete in the simplest terms. Provides a brief historical overview of the development of cement and concrete as well as of innovations such as reinforcing and prestressing. Also contains useful discussions of applications of cement and concrete.

Troxell, George Earl, Harmer E. Davis, and Joe W. Kelly. *Composition and Properties of Concrete.* 2d ed. New York: McGraw-Hill, 1968. This book contains a section on cement. It is written clearly enough and with sufficient definitions of terms and other aids to allow the general reader to explore the subject.

*Brian J. Nichelson*

## Cross-References

Building Stone, 178; Earth Resources, 2175; Future Resources, 2182; Sand, 2253; Silica Minerals, 2365.

# THE CENOZOIC ERA

*Type of earth science:* Geology
*Field of study:* Stratigraphy

*During the Cenozoic era, the last 66.4 million years of earth history, all aspects of the modern earth environment developed. Scientists are able to distinguish between environmental changes caused by a normal progression of geologic phenomena and those changes that are related to human activity through study of the geologic record from this era.*

### Principal terms

EPICONTINENTAL SEA: any body of marine water that is present on the continents; epicontinental seas were more extensive in the past than at present

EPOCH: a relative time unit and a subdivision of a period

GLACIERS: systems of moving ice that can occur at any time in high elevations and periodically will occur on the continents in the high latitudes during periods known popularly as ice ages

MAGNETIC REVERSAL: a change in the earth's magnetic field from the north-oriented magnetic pole to the south-oriented magnetic pole

PALEOCLIMATE: a climate that existed in the geologic past, usually one that existed before adequate climatic records were kept and thus most often a prehistoric climate

PERIOD: a relative time unit and a subdivision of an era

REGRESSION: a very slow fall in sea level that may result in the exposure of the continental shelves

TECTONICS: the general term for deep-earth geologic phenomena such as mountain building, volcanism, earthquakes, continental collisions, and sea-floor spreading

TRANSGRESSION: a very slow rise in sea level that usually results in the flooding of the continents

## Summary of the Phenomenon

The Cenozoic era began approximately 66.4 million years before the present and extends into modern time. It is subdivided into two periods, the Tertiary and the Quaternary, and these two periods are subdivided into seven epochs. The subdivisions of the Cenozoic era are not equal in duration; rather, the periods and epochs, as well as the Cenozoic era itself, are relative time units and do not have a fixed time value, as do absolute time units such as hours, days, and years. Relative time units are based on geologic events and phenomena such as fossils. Their position in geologic history is determined by the relative position of these events and phenomena in the rock record. The values in years are determined by radiometric methods after the relative units are recognized.

The Cenozoic era represents a time in earth history when the modern earth environment began to develop. The geologic setting, geography, atmosphere, climate, oceans, and fauna and flora all began to exhibit a decidedly modern appearance. In previous eras of earth history, many environmental conditions were very different from those of the present as were the fauna and flora. Despite the differences, there is a progression in geologic history that can be followed. The earth of the Cenozoic era most closely resembles the present-day earth, because the Cenozoic era is closer in time and contains the recent epoch of earth history. The further back one goes in time, the greater the differences. In order to understand fully and appreciate the development of the earth through the Cenozoic era, a brief survey of the conditions and phenomena of the epochs of the Cenozoic era from the oldest to the youngest is necessary.

The Paleocene epoch (between 66.4 and 57.8 million years ago) is the first epoch of the Cenozoic era. The transition from the preceding Cretaceous period of the Mesozoic era is one of the most pronounced in the geologic record. Great physical and accompanying biological changes took place. Whatever the cause of such changes, the setting of the Paleocene was very different from that of the Cretaceous. Worldwide, the beginning of the Paleocene is marked by a regression of the seas, a fall in sea level. This change resulted in reduced shallow seas for the dwelling of marine organisms and a decrease in humid conditions on the continents. The geographic setting was also changing with the continued enlargement of the Atlantic Ocean Basin and the northerly drift of North America. This northerly drift resulted in the increase of the temperate zone in North America at the expense of the subtropical zones, causing a cooling of the climate from the tropical conditions of the Cretaceous period. Another important geographic change in the Paleocene epoch was the decrease in size of Tethys, the worldwide warmwater ocean roughly parallel to the equator. In North America, mountain building that began in the late Cretaceous continued in the Rocky Mountains region. Although sea level fell worldwide in the earliest Paleocene, a large transgression, or sea-level rise soon began. This transgression was large enough that the sea reached all the way into the present-day High Plains of North and South Dakota. It is estimated that sea level was more than 250 meters above its present level during this episode. When this transgression and the following regression ended, the sea never again rose to this level. Since the end of this transgression-regression interval, sea level has never risen above the coastal plains.

Life of the Paleocene epoch was very different from that of the Cretaceous period. Marine life was not as diverse in the Paleocene, and many prominent forms of marine invertebrates that were common in the Cretaceous were extinct by the Paleocene. Many of the marine organisms looked very much like modern marine invertebrates and, in fact, are the ancestors of modern biota. On land, a fauna that had been previously dominated by the dinosaurs was now dominated by the mammals. Most of these mammals were small and did not closely resemble many of the modern mammals. Others, such as the rodent *Paramys*, which resembled a modern squirrel in appearance, are clearly the ancestors of modern mammal faunas. The flora of the Paleocene was dominated by the flowering plants.

The Eocene epoch (between 57.8 and 36.6 million years ago) contained two major tectonic events of global significance. The first major event was the beginning of the closure of Tethys. This was caused by the collision of two continents, India and Asia. Although mountain building did not begin in the area at this time, the two continents were in close proximity to each other. Mountain building did begin in the Mediterranean region during the Eocene as a result of the African plate moving relative to the Eurasian plate. Another significant tectonic development was the separation of Australia from Antarctica. This event allowed the development of a cold current around the Antarctic continent and a climatic isolation of this landmass. In North America, volcanic activity was extensive throughout the West.

Environmental conditions of the Eocene showed a continued cooling and drying trend from the Paleocene. Large basins between the mountains that were built during the Paleocene were filled with river and lake sediments during the Eocene. Sea level remained higher than at present, but the epicontinental seas in North America were confined to the coastal plain regions.

One of the major innovations in marine life during the Eocene epoch was the whale. The whales developed from land carnivores that had adapted to a marine existence. On land, the most significant development was the appearance of the grasses. These plants enabled the widespread development of savannas (semiarid grasslands) and a wide variety of grazing animals. Included among these are the earliest members of the horse, elephant, and rhinoceros lineages. Also present were the first very large mammals, the titanotheres, and early ancestors of the camels. The Eocene also saw the first development of the dog, cat, and weasel families and the existence of numerous birds.

The Oligocene epoch (between 36.6 and 23.7 million years ago) saw a continuation of the tectonic and environmental conditions that were present in the Eocene. An important change occurred in the earth's sea level at about the middle of the Oligocene. Sea level fell radically to a point well below present sea level. This change appears to be related to the development of continental glaciers in Antarctica and resulted in a further cooling and drying of the continents.

Life of the Oligocene is characterized by the success of the large land mammals such as titanotheres and rhinoceros. One member of the rhinoceros family, *Indrichotherium*, was the largest mammal to walk the earth, standing about 5.5 meters tall at the shoulder. The mammal fauna of the Oligocene continued to become more modern in appearance; monkeys and other apes began to develop at this time.

The Miocene epoch (between 23.7 and 5.3 million years ago) represents a time of marked change in earth history. Although throughout the Cenozoic era the fauna and flora have been very modern in appearance, the Miocene marks a time when faunas and floras began to resemble modern ones closely. In the marine realm, invertebrates resembled modern ones, and, in fact, many modern species of invertebrates trace their origins to the Miocene epoch. The expansion of the whales in the

Miocene was the greatest marine-related change. On land, the flora began to be dominated by small, nonwoody plants. These plants were well adapted to life under somewhat dry, cool conditions. Many of the modern common families of wild-flowers began their rapid expansion in the Miocene. Small mammals, such as the rodents, and the perching birds expanded. Large mammals were present, but very large forms, such as the titanotheres, were extinct by the Miocene. In the Miocene, two major additions to the carnivores, the bear and hyena families, developed.

The tectonic and environmental conditions of the Miocene are closely akin to modern processes. One major worldwide tectonic event was the beginning of the uplift of the Himalaya as India began to move beneath the Asian continent. Another important event was the closure and evaporation of the entire Mediterranean Sea. Whether this event, known as the Messinian Event, was caused by tectonic pro-cesses or was related to a worldwide drop in sea level, or some combination of the two, is still debated among scientists. No matter what the cause, such a phe-nomenon represents a major change in the earth's environment. As a result of this major change, development of widespread continental glaciation began in the Southern Hemisphere. Global conditions produced by this process were lower sea level and dryer conditions in the Northern Hemisphere.

The Pliocene epoch (between 5.3 and 1.6 million years ago) represents a time of equable climate over much of the earth, partly because of a rise in sea level that began at this time. Other major events that began in the Pliocene were the renewed uplift of the Rocky Mountains and the uplift of many of the other mountain ranges throughout the American West. Two new locations for sea-floor spreading began to develop. The Red Sea began to expand at this time, as did the Gulf of California. Continued volcanism between North and South America caused a land bridge to develop between the two land masses. A sharp climatic change began in the late Pliocene with the widespread development of continental glaciers. Life of the Pliocene resembled the life of the Miocene in many ways. One important develop-ment was the first well-preserved fossils of the hominids, the family to which the human species belongs.

The Pleistocene epoch (between 1.6 million years ago and 10,000 years ago) is a time in earth history dominated by glaciers. The Pleistocene is commonly referred to as the "ice age," but there were many advances and retreats of the great conti-nental ice sheets during this epoch. Much of the modern earth surface acquired its present appearance as features such as the Great Lakes and many present-day river systems were formed. During the Pleistocene epoch, the last of the truly large mammals became extinct. Forms such as mammoths, mastodons, and giant sloths disappeared from the fauna. Some of these extinctions appear to be related to the expansion and success of the human species. A part of this expansion includes the arrival of humans in the Americas more than 30,000 years ago, possibly over a land bridge between Siberia and Alaska which was the result of lower sea level in the present-day Bering Sea.

The Holocene epoch began about 10,000 years ago. This date is approximately the time that the last glacier retreated from the temperate latitudes. The Holocene epoch is not recognized by all geologists as different from the Pleistocene. The question is whether the present conditions on the earth mark a fundamental change in the earth's climate or whether they simply mark another warm period between glacial episodes. One thing the Holocene does characterize is the importance of man as a geologic agent and the ability of humans to reshape the environment. For this reason, many geologists recognize the Holocene as a unique epoch in earth history.

## Methods of Study

The Cenozoic era is studied by a variety of geologic techniques. As the goal of geologists studying the Cenozoic is to reconstruct the conditions of the earth during that era, almost all geologic phenomena should be studied. Three very important aspects of the Cenozoic era that are commonly studied are the life of the Cenozoic, the environment of the Cenozoic, and the age of the Cenozoic. Each one of these fields of study is interdependent on the others, and it is not desirable to separate them completely.

The first thing that must be established in any study of geologic history is a time framework. Such a framework need not be absolute in millions of years but will at least involve an understanding of the ordering of events. Each of the epochs recognized has characteristic marine and nonmarine fossils. By studying the fossils of a deposit, scientists can understand the relative age of that deposit. Fossils are not the only way that a time framework can be established. Changes in the earth's magnetic field can be used to order events. The earth's magnetic field has reversed its polarity from the present North orientation to a South orientation many times during the past. Such magnetic reversals leave a signature in the rock record, and this record is especially good in deposits of the Cenozoic era. Magnetic reversals are most effectively used in association with the fossil record. Another important method of determining the age of deposits is the use of radioactive isotopes. This method produces an age in millions of years and is useful for dating deposits that contain no fossils or for putting an absolute age on deposits which do; however, it cannot be done on all deposits. Minerals with suitable isotopes must be in a deposit to date it. Additionally, this procedure is expensive and time-consuming and may not add anything to an age obtained by studying fossils or magnetic reversals.

Once a time framework is established, other studies may proceed. Detailed studies of the life of the Cenozoic era involve the collection and description of fossils. When possible, fossils are studied as groups or assemblages. By studying assemblages as well as individuals, some insight into the interactions of animals and plants of the Cenozoic era can be gained. Once some idea about the interrelationships are established, scientists have some idea of the physical and chemical conditions under which the organisms lived.

The record of physical and chemical conditions through time gives scientists an accurate picture of the environment of the Cenozoic era, how it changed through time and how it developed into the present-day environment. When the environment of the Cenozoic era is studied, two major aspects of the earth are examined: the climate and the oceans. The techniques used to study these two phenomena are similar because of the interaction between the ocean and the atmosphere. One of the most useful ways to study the climate and the oceans of the Cenozoic era is through the use of fossil microorganisms such as foraminifera, radiolaria, and diatoms preserved in deep-sea sediments. A remarkably accurate record of the Cenozoic era is present in the ocean basins, and by detailed study of the fossil assemblages, the changing conditions of the earth's climate and oceans can be determined. First, the distribution of the modern microorganisms to be studied is mapped, and the physical and chemical conditions associated with these microorganisms are noted. Then, the fossil record is examined, and the fossil assemblage and the conditions it represents are recorded. The result should be an accurate reflection of the earth's climatic and oceanographic changes through time. While one would expect older fossils to differ from recent ones, good comparisons can be made, as many of the modern species have a well-documented ancestry through the Cenozoic era.

Chemical properties of the shells of these microorganisms can also provide insight into the climatic conditions of the past. An example of this is with the shells of foraminifera. All shells of foraminifera contain oxygen, and the ratio of the common isotope of oxygen, oxygen 16, to a heavier isotope of oxygen, oxygen 18, in the shells is a reflection of this ratio in seawater. It is known that this ratio varies through time with changing climatic conditions. A decrease in the amount of oxygen 18 is associated with an expansion of glaciers and thus with a global cooling. Through study of these chemical properties, an accurate picture of the advances and retreats of glaciers during the Cenozoic era has been constructed.

## Context

The Cenozoic era represents approximately the last 66 million years of earth history, and, as such, it contains the record of development of the modern environment. Understanding the past environment and the development of the present environment is essential to any attempt to study modern environmental changes. It must be kept in mind that the modern environment is not static and that changes in the environment will be a continuation of those processes that have been operating throughout the Cenozoic era. The question that must be asked is whether the changes observed in the modern environment are a part of the normal evolution of the earth's environment or whether they are the direct or indirect result of human activity.

The question of whether the Holocene epoch is a new episode in earth history or simply a warm interval between ice ages is one example of such a conflict. Warm periods are known to occur between every glacial episode and would not be unusual after the last one. The question itself seems trivial in the light of many recent environmental problems. Yet the foundation of this question is whether humans are independent geologic agents, capable of intentionally or unintentionally reshaping the earth's environment. Certainly not all alteration of the environment would be completely unwelcome, but it must be remembered that the earth is an interdependent system and that a change in one aspect of the environment will likely cause an unforeseen change elsewhere.

An understanding of geologic history can help scientists to understand changes in the earth's environment such as the rise of global sea level. Much concern has been expressed about this potential global disaster, and, in fact, there is great cause for concern. When the geologic history of the Cenozoic era is reviewed, it is apparent that rises and falls in sea level are a normal part of earth history, especially as a warm interval approaches. Yet, the human effect on this process is significant. By changing the composition of the earth's atmosphere through waste gases, a global warming trend has been greatly expanded. This warming trend is causing a melting of the remaining glaciers in Greenland and Antarctica, and the meltwater is causing a rise in global sea level. This process was occurring naturally, but the rate at which it is operating has been greatly increased because of human activity.

If society is to confront the changing environment effectively, scientists must be able to distinguish between changes that are related to normal processes of development resulting from a continuing trend from the geologic past and those changes that are directly caused or influenced by human activity. As environmental improvements are considered, it must be clear to environmental planners what changes can and cannot be made, and, should a change be made, what are the likely consequences in other areas of the earth's environment. Only with a clear understanding of the earth's history during the Cenozoic era can any of these problems be approached in a systematic way.

## Bibliography

Cooper, John D., Richard H. Miller, and Jacqueline Patterson. *A Trip Through Time: Principles of Historical Geology.* Columbus, Ohio: Merrill, 1986. A basic introduction to historical geology. Excellent discussions of the Cenozoic history of western North America, illustrations that are clear, and a text that is fairly easy to read. Designed as an introductory text for college students, but the readership level is such that any interested individual can gain information from this book. A glossary is included.

Lane, N. Gary. *Life of the Past.* 2d ed. Columbus, Ohio: Merrill, 1985. A basic introduction to the study of paleontology, fossils, and life of the past. An excellent text for the amateur or student interested in the animals of geologic history. In a clear style, the characteristics of the different fossil groups are explained. Illustrations of the different groups are included. Each chapter is followed by a series of key words, and an extensive glossary is included at the end of the text. Written for a general audience with a high school education, but more advanced students will find the book useful.

Levin, Harold L. *The Earth Through Time.* 3d ed. Philadelphia: W. B. Saunders,

1988. A thorough, well-illustrated text on historical geology. The text is well organized and proceeds in a logical manner. Illustrations are abundant, and selected ones are in full color. Although the book is written for first-year college students, the general reader will find much of interest. Two of the four appendices are especially helpful: One is a classification of living things, and the other is a summary of important rock sections of various ages, including the Cenozoic. A glossary and an index are included.

_____. *Life Through Time*. Dubuque, Iowa: Wm. C. Brown, 1975. A clearly written text intended for general readers. Provides a simple introduction to the development of life through time. Includes a catalog of organisms and an extensive glossary. Drawings and photographs, although they are not abundant, are clear and uncomplicated.

Mintz, L. W. *Historical Geology*. 3d ed. Columbus, Ohio: Merrill, 1981. Intended as an introduction to historical geology from the standpoint of a dynamic earth. The text is written for first-year college students, but one of its attractive features is the abundance of illustrations. Although not in color, the line drawings are clear and provide excellent examples of life of the Cenozoic as well as other eras.

Stanley, Steven M. *Earth and Life Through Time*. 2d ed. New York: W. H. Freeman, 1989. This book is a beautifully illustrated and thorough treatment of earth history. Provides a detailed account of the evolution of the earth and its life forms. A major feature of this text is the worldwide approach used to discuss major events. Examples from outside North America are discussed. Also, very clear illustrations of the positions of the continents through time are included, as well as illustrations of animals and plants in their environments. Although a bit more difficult to read than other texts on historical geology, it can be understood by college students, and the illustrations make this book worthwhile for any interested person.

Wicander, E. Reed, and J. S. Monroe. *Historical Geology*. St. Paul, Minn.: West Publishing, 1989. Intended as a basic introduction to historical geology for first-year college students. Beautifully illustrated, containing many full-color diagrams and photographs. Also contains many case histories written in clear, nontechnical language. Although designed for college students, the writing style is accessible to the general reader.

*Richard H. Fluegeman, Jr.*

## Cross-References

Biostratigraphy, 173; Geochronology: K-Ar and Ar-Ar Dating, 833; Geochronology: Radiocarbon Dating, 840; Geochronology: Rb-Sr Dating, 848; The Geologic Time Scale, 874; Ice Ages, 1115; Mammals, 1453; Mass Extinctions, 1514; The Mesozoic Era, 1535; Meteorite and Comet Impacts, 1623; Ocean-Atmosphere Interactions, 1779; Sea Level, 2267; Stable Isotopes: Oxygen 18/Oxygen 16, Deuterium/Hydrogen, and Carbon 13/Carbon 12 Ratios in Rocks, 2456; Stratigraphic Correlation, 2485; Transgression and Regression, 2534.

# CLAYS

*Type of earth science:* Geology
*Field of study:* Petrology, sedimentary

*Clays are fine-grained materials with unique properties, such as plastic behavior when wet. They form by weathering of silicate rocks at the earth's surface, by diagenetic reactions, and by hydrothermal alteration. An understanding of clays is important in solving problems in petroleum geology, engineering, and environmental science.*

*Principal terms*

AUTHIGENIC MINERALS: minerals which formed in place, usually by diagenetic processes

CATION EXCHANGE CAPACITY: the ability of a clay to adsorb and exchange cations, or positively charged ions, with its environment

CHEMICAL WEATHERING: a change in the chemical and mineralogical composition of rocks by means of reaction with water at the earth's surface

CLAY MINERAL: a mineral with a layered crystal structure that contains silicon, aluminum, and water

CLAYS: materials that have a very fine grain size (less than .002 millimeter) and unique properties, such as plastic behavior when wet

DETRITAL MINERALS: minerals which have been eroded, transported, and deposited as sediments

DIAGENESIS: the conversion of unconsolidated sediment into consolidated rock after burial by the processes of compaction, cementation, recrystallization, and replacement

HYDROLYSIS: a chemical weathering process which produces clays by the reaction of carbonic acid with aluminosilicate minerals

PHYLLOSILICATE: a mineral with silica tetrahedra arranged in a sheet structure

SHALE: a sedimentary rock with a high concentration of clays

## Summary of the Phenomenon

The definition of clays varies depending on the scientific discipline or application. An engineer's definition, which is based on particle size, differs from a mineralogist's definition, which is based on crystal structure. In the broadest sense, clays are materials that have a very fine grain size (less than 0.002 millimeter) and behave plastically when wet. A more specific definition of a clay mineral is a hydrous aluminum phyllosilicate, or, more simply stated, a mineral that contains water, aluminum, and silicon and has a layered structure. The term "clays" will be used for the broad definition, "clay mineral" for the specific definition. Rock flour, or material that was ground to a fine powder by glaciers, would fit the definition of clays; however, it may contain minerals such as quartz and feldspars that do not fit the definition of a clay mineral. Mica is a hydrous aluminum phyllosilicate, but it often occurs as large crystals, so it does not fit the definition of clays. Certain minerals such as zeolites and hydroxides (goethite and gibbsite) have a very fine grain size and physical properties similar to clay minerals, so they are often included with the clay minerals. Unique properties of clays, including their plastic behavior when wet and ability to adsorb water and ions in solution, can be attributed to their small crystal size, high surface area, and unique crystal structure.

There are two basic elements of the clay mineral structure: a tetrahedral sheet and an octahedral sheet. A silica atom surrounded by four oxygen atoms forms the basic building block of all silicate minerals, the four-sided silica tetrahedron. In phyllosilicate minerals, the silica tetrahedra are linked together by sharing the three oxygen atoms at the corners of the tetrahedra, forming a continuous sheet. The tetrahedral sheet has a negative charge and a general chemical formula of $Si_4O_{10}^{4-}$. An octahedron is an eight-sided figure that consists of a cation, or a positively charged ion, surrounded by six hydroxyl anions, or negatively charged ions ($OH^-$). The octahedra are linked together to form a sheet by sharing the hydroxyl anions on the edges of the octahedra. The octahedral sheets are neutral, and there are two types: trioctahedral and dioctahedral. The trioctahedral sheet is composed of divalent cations such as $Mg^{2+}$ and $Fe^{2+}$. For every six hydroxyl anions, the trioctahedral sheet contains three cations, resulting in a sheet where all the available octahedral sites contain a cation. The dioctahedral sheets contains trivalent cations such as $Al^{3+}$ and $Fe^{3+}$. The dioctahedral sheet has only two cations per six hydroxyl anions, resulting in only two-thirds of the available octahedral sites being filled with cations. The general chemical formulas for the trioctahedral and dioctahedral sheets are $Mg_3OH_6$ and $Al_2OH_6$ respectively. Layers in clay minerals are made of combinations of tetrahedral and octahedral sheets. The unshared oxygen of the silica tetrahedra take the place of some of the hydroxyl anions in the octahedral sheet, resulting in neutralization of the negative charges on the tetrahedral sheet. There are two types of layers: a 1:1 or T-O layer made up of one tetrahedral sheet and one octahedral sheet and a 2:1 or T-O-T layer which contains one octahedral sheet sandwiched between two tetrahedral sheets.

The prototype clays have neutral layer charges, with the layers held together by weak van der Waals bonds. Kaolinite and serpentine are 1:1 prototype clay minerals. Kaolinite is dioctahedral and serpentine is trioctahedral. Kaolinite, a pure white clay, is the major constituent of fine porcelain. Serpentine can occur as chrysotile asbestos, which was widely used as insulation material before it was recognized as a health hazard. Talc and pyrophyllite are the trioctahedral and dioctahedral 2:1 prototype clay minerals. The waxy or slippery feel of talc is the result of cleavage along the weak van der Waals bonds between the layers. Because of the various types of ionic substitutions in the tetrahedral and octahedral sheets, the layers may develop a negative charge, which needs to be balanced by interlayer materials. A lower-valance cation may substitute for a higher-valance cation in the tetrahedral or octahedral sheets. Layers can also develop a negative charge if some of the sites in a trioctahedral sheet are left vacant. In the mica group of clay minerals, the charge on the 2:1 layer is $-1$ and is balanced by a positively charged potassium ion that occurs between the layers. Muscovite is a dioctahedral 2:1 phyllosilicate, and biotite is trioctahedral. The perfect cleavage of micas is in the direction parallel to the tetrahedral sheets and allows them to be peeled into paper-thin sheets. Micas usually occur as larger crystals and therefore are not considered true clay minerals; however, illite, a common clay mineral, has a structure and chemical formula similar to muscovite, a mica. The chlorite clay minerals have an extra octahedral sheet between the 2:1 layers to balance the excess negative charges. The vermiculite and smectite groups of clay minerals have layer charges which are less than 1 and are balanced by hydrated cations between the layers; a hydrated cation is a positively charged ion, such as sodium, that is surrounded by water. In smectites, this water is held very loosely between the 2:1 layers and can be easily lost or gained depending on the humidity of the environment, causing these clays to shrink or swell.

Clay minerals occur in soils, sediments, sedimentary rocks, and some metamorphic rocks. Sedimentary rocks cover approximately 80 percent of the earth's surface, and shales are the most common type of sedimentary rock. Because shales are composed predominantly of clays, their abundance makes clays one of the most important constituents of the earth's surface.

Most clays form by the breakdown and weathering of minerals rich in aluminum and silicon at the earth's surface. Physical weathering is the breaking and fragmentation of rocks with no change in the mineralogical or chemical composition. This process can form clay-sized particles, but it does not form clay minerals. Physical weathering, however, increases the surface area of minerals, which favors chemical weathering. A change in the chemical and mineralogical composition of rocks by reaction with water at the earth's surface is called chemical weathering. The process called hydrolysis is a chemical weathering reaction that results in the formation of clays. A weak acid and water react with aluminosilicate minerals, resulting in the production of a clay mineral plus ions in solution. (The weak acid is called carbonic acid; it forms when carbon dioxide, a common gas in the atmosphere, is dissolved in rainwater.) The type and amount of clay that forms by this reaction depends on the nature of the rock being weathered (the parent material) and the intensity of weathering.

Clays produced by weathering are eventually eroded, transported, and deposited as sediments. Most clays are transported in suspension. The brown, muddy waters of rivers are a reflection of the clays being carried in suspension. Clays are deposited and accumulate in quiet water environments, where the energy is low enough to allow the clays to settle out of suspension. Several processes enhance the deposition of clays. When fresh river water mixes with salty ocean water, the negative charges on clay surfaces are neutralized, causing them to flocculate. Clay floccules, or aggregates of clay-sized particles that behave like larger silt- or sand-sized grains, rapidly settle out of suspension. Biodeposition is a process whereby organisms ingest clays with their food; the resultant fecal pellets settle to the bottom as sand-sized particles.

There are two types of clays in sedimentary rocks: detrital and authigenic. Minerals which are transported and deposited as sediments are called detrital. Authigenic minerals form within the rocks during diagenesis, a process whereby sediments buried within the earth's crust undergo increases in temperature and pressure, resulting in compaction and cementation of loose sediments and the formation of sedimentary rocks. Water expelled from the sediments during this process may react with other minerals in the sediment to form clay minerals. Kaolinite, chlorite, illite, and smectite formed by diagenesis have been observed in sandstones. Diagenesis may also result in one clay mineral being converted into another clay mineral. A reaction which commonly occurs is the alteration of smectite to form illite as a result of an increase in temperature. This reaction is important to petroleum geologists because intermediate mixed-layered illite/smectite clays form at different temperatures. The clay mineralogy of a shale can be used to determine the maximum burial temperature of a rock. Clay minerals may also form in metamorphic rocks as a result of hydrothermal alteration. Hydrothermal fluids are hot, chemically active fluids that accompany igneous intrusions. In addition to forming clay minerals as they pass through a host rock, hydrothermal fluids are responsible for producing important ore deposits such as copper ores. Economic geologists may use the distribution of hydrothermal clay minerals to locate valuable ore deposits.

## Methods of Study

Clay minerals are difficult to identify and analyze because of their small crystal size. Because they can be observed neither with the naked eye nor by standard petrographic microscopes, they require the use of sophisticated equipment for their identification. Analysis is further complicated by the fact that it is difficult to obtain pure samples of the clay minerals because they often occur as mixtures with other minerals. Before a clay mineral can be analyzed, it must be isolated from the sample by means of special physical and chemical techniques.

The tool a clay mineralogist uses most often is an X-ray diffractometer (XRD). This instrument focuses a beam of X rays onto the sample. The crystal structure of the minerals acts as a diffraction grating, and the instrument records X rays that are diffracted from the mineral. The geometry of the XRD unit is such that mineralogists can determine the spacing between planes of atoms in the crystal structure by measuring the position of "reflections" produced by X rays diffracted by the mineral. Clay mineralogists prepare specially oriented samples which enhance the reflections between the layers of clay minerals, called basal reflections. The basal reflections are used in determining the type of clay mineral present. Other instruments that are used to investigate clay minerals include the scanning electron microscope (SEM) and the transmission electron microscope (TEM). The very high resolution of these microscopes allows the scientist to observe clay minerals at a very great magnification. The scientist is thus able to observe the outward crystal form of clay minerals and their texture or orientation with respect to other grains in the sample. The SEM is very helpful in distinguishing between detrital and authigenic clays in sedimentary rocks.

A property that is helpful in identifying clays and understanding their behavior is the cation exchange capacity (CEC). Because of their small size and unique crystal structure, clay surfaces are negatively charged and have the ability to adsorb positive ions on their surfaces and within clays between the layers. These cations are easily exchanged with solutions. If a clay that is saturated with cations is placed in a solution saturated with sodium ions, it will exchange its cations for the sodium ions. The ability of a clay to adsorb and exchange cations is called the "cation exchange capacity" and depends on the type of clay mineral. Kaolinite, chlorite, and illite have relatively low CECs; smectite has a relatively high CEC. This property is especially important to soil scientists, because it controls the availability of nutrients necessary for plant growth.

## Context

Clay minerals are studied by geologists, soil scientists, chemists, materials scientists, and chemical and civil engineers. A knowledge of clay mineralogy is helpful in solving problems in petroleum geology, civil engineering, and environmental science. Clays have a variety of applications in industry. They are a readily available natural resource and are relatively inexpensive. Approximately 50 million tons of clay materials worth more than $1 billion are used industrially each year.

Sedimentary rocks that produce oil and gas by the heating of organic matter after it is buried are called source rocks. The source rock for most oil and gas is shale. By determining the type of diagenetic clay minerals present, the petroleum geologist can determine if the source rock has been heated to a temperature that is high enough to produce oil or gas. Rocks that contain oil or gas which can be easily extracted are called reservoir rocks. The best reservoir rocks are sandstones with a high porosity and permeability. Some sandstones contain clay minerals that occur between the sand grains as a cement or within the pores. Clay minerals have the potential to reduce the porosity and permeability of a reservoir. It is important to know the type and amount of clay minerals in a reservoir in order to evaluate its quality. A knowledge of clays is important to engineering because the concentration of clays in a soil determines it stability. Soils which contain high percentages of smectites could cause damage to the foundations of buildings because smectites swell when saturated with water and subsequently shrink when dried out.

Clays may be used as liners for sanitary landfills because the small grain size of clays allows them to be packed together very closely, forming an impermeable layer. The liner prevents toxic leachate, which forms when rainwater reacts with solid waste, from moving out of the landfill and contaminating surface water and ground-water supplies. Chemical engineers have developed what are called designer clays by altering the properties of naturally occurring clays. These clays act as catalysts in the breakdown of toxic substances to form less toxic products. Designer clays are helpful in the destruction and disposal of toxic wastes such as dioxin and in the cleaning of existing toxic waste sites.

Clays are the basic raw material of the ceramics industry. When clays are mixed with water, they become plastic and are easily molded. A hard ceramic material is produced by firing the molded clay. In addition to the familiar pottery and dinner-ware, fired clays are used in the production of brick, tiles, sewer pipes, sanitary-ware pottery, kiln furniture, cement, and lightweight aggregates. Kaolinite is used as a coating on fine paper, in paints, and as a filler in plastics and rubber. The petroleum industry uses kaolinite as a cracking catalyst in the refinement of petro-leum. Swelling clays such as smectite are used as binders in animal feed and iron ore pellets (taconite), as drilling muds, as industrial absorbents, and as pet litter.

## Bibliography

Blatt, Harvey, Gerard Middleton, and R. Murray. *Origin of Sedimentary Rocks*. 2d ed. Englewood Cliffs, N.J.: Prentice-Hall, 1980. This comprehensive textbook covers the classification, origin, and interpretation of sedimentary rocks. The formation and classification of clays are discussed in detail in the chapter on weathering. The chapter on mudrocks gives an excellent discussion of the dis-tribution of clay minerals. Suitable for college-level students.

Eslinger, Eric, and David Pevear. *Clay Minerals for Petroleum Geologists and Engineers*. Tulsa, Okla.: Society of Economic Paleontologists and Mineralogists, 1988. Covers the major geologic aspects of clay mineralogy. The crystal structure, classification of clay minerals, origin by weathering and diagenesis, and distribu-tion of clays are discussed in detail. Application of clay mineralogy to exploration and production of petroleum is also covered. The appendix contains a summary of sample preparation and X-ray diffraction analysis of clays. A suitable text for college-level students with a science background.

Klein, Cornelis, and Cornelius S. Hurlbut, Jr. *Manual of Mineralogy*. 20th ed. New York: John Wiley & Sons, 1985. A general textbook on mineralogy, covering crystallography, physical properties of minerals, and systematic mineralogy. A very good discussion on X-ray diffraction is given in chapter 6. Phyllosilicate minerals are discussed in chapter 11. Suitable for college-level students.

Longstaffe, F. J. *Short Course in Clays and the Resource Geologist*. Toronto: Miner-alogical Association of Canada, 1981. A collection of papers by well-recognized experts in the field of clay mineralogy. The first three chapters cover the crystal structures of clay minerals and their identification by X-ray diffraction. Subse-quent chapters give case histories and specific examples of applications of clay mineralogy to petroleum geology. Suitable for college-level students with a science background.

Welton, J. E. *SEM Petrology Atlas*. Tulsa, Okla.: American Association of Petroleum Geologists, 1984. An atlas of scanning electron microscope (SEM) graphs of authigenic minerals which occur in sandstones. In addition to the SEM images, the chemical composition of the minerals is given. Text is kept to a minimum; however, a summary of sample preparation and scanning electron microscope analysis is given in the introduction. Suitable for all levels.

*Annabelle M. Foos*

## Cross-References
Cement, 196; Diagenesis, 354; Electron Microscopy, 601; Hydrothermal Mineralization, 1108; Industrial Nonmetals, 1225; Landfills, 1351; The Structure of Minerals, 1693; The Origin of Oil and Gas, 1901; Silica Minerals, 2365; Soil Chemistry, 2382; Soil Formation, 2394; Soil Liquefaction, 2402; Expansive Soils, 2421; Weathering and Erosion, 2723; X-Ray Powder Diffraction, 2751.

# CLIMATE

*Field of study:* Atmospheric sciences and meteorology

*Climate is the long-term total of atmospheric variations. Over shorter periods of time, climate is referred to as weather. Climate always refers to a specific geographical location and is determined by many factors, including wind belts, topography, elevation, barometric pressure and movement of air masses, amount of solar radiation available, proximity to oceanic influences, and planetary cycles.*

*Principal terms*
   AIR MASS: a mass of air in the lower atmosphere that has generally uniform properties of temperature and moisture
   ATMOSPHERE: the envelope of gases surrounding the earth, consisting of five clearly defined regions
   GENERAL CIRCULATION MODELS (GCMs): comprehensive, mathematical-numerical formulas, in climate studies, that attempt to express the basic dynamical equations thought to govern the large-scale behavior of the atmosphere and include the numerical methods and resolution used to solve those equations
   GREENHOUSE EFFECT: a situation in which levels of carbon dioxide and water vapor in the atmosphere of a planet lead to a trapping of solar energy, which results in increased temperatures
   PARAMETERIZATION: the arbitrary assignment of a value to physical processes which occur on scales too small to be resolved by a general circulation model
   PRECIPITATION: phenomena such as rain, snow, and hail deposited on the earth's surface from moisture in the atmosphere

## Summary of the Phenomenon
From early times, humans have attempted to classify climates. The ancient Greeks in the sixth century B.C. visualized the earth as having three temperature zones based on the sun's elevation above the horizon. (The Greek work *klima*, meaning "inclination," is the origin of the word "climate.") They called these three zones torrid, temperate, and frigid. This system did not consider the differences between climates over land and over water, the effects of topography, and other atmospheric elements such as precipitation.

Many people confuse weather with climate. The two phenomena are related, but weather is concerned with day-to-day atmospheric conditions, such as air temperature, precipitation, and wind. Climatology is concerned with the mean (average) physical state of the atmosphere, along with its statistical variations in both time and space over a period of many years. In addition to the description of climate, climatology includes the study of a wide range of practical matters determined by climate and the effects and consequences of climatic change. As a result, it has become an interdisciplinary science, important to a wide range of other fields, such as geophysics, biology, oceanography, geography, geology, engineering, economics, statistics, solar system astronomy, and political and social sciences.

For centuries, the content of the atmosphere and the amount of solar radiation reaching the earth's surface have been fairly constant. Until the middle of the 1950's, it was assumed that the climates of the earth also were relatively unchanging; scientists now understand that climate is never constant. Climate consists of the ocean, atmosphere, cryosphere (areas of permanent ice), land surface, and biomass. The various components of climate are coupled to each other in a nonlinear feedback process—that is, a change in one of these factors produces a feedback or effect on the other factors. Therefore, all or any of these processes can change the statistical state of the system called climate.

The science of climatology has developed along two main lines. Regional climatology studies the discrete and characteristic qualities of a particular region of the globe. The second approach of climatology is a physical analysis of the basic relationships existing among various atmospheric elements of temperature, precipitation, air pressure, and wind speed. A third branch now widely used, which originated in the 1960's, is called dynamical climatology. This branch uses models to simulate climate and climatic change based on the averaged forms of the basic equations of dynamic meteorology.

The classification of climates is of two types: genetic and empirical. A genetic system is based on air masses and global wind belts, which control climates. The empirical classification system utilizes the observed elements of climate, such as temperature. An empirical classification system called the Köppen system uses five categories: tropical forest climates; dry climates; warm, temperate rainy climates with mild winters; cold forest climates with severe winters; and polar climates. Another empirical classification system, which may be more useful in describing world climates, is based on decreasing temperature and increasing precipitation. This system of classification is convenient for use in many other sciences, as well. The first category is the desert climate, which has the highest temperatures and the lowest precipitation. The next category is the savanna, which may be either temperate or tropical. In either case, this climate is characterized by nearly treeless grassland. The steppes of Eastern Europe are an example of a temperate savanna, with plants adapted to very hot conditions and extremely limited water supply. The grassy plains of western African are typical tropical savanna. The next category or climate type is temperate and tropical Mediterranean climate. An example of temperate Mediterranean climate is the coast of southern California. Tropical Mediterranean climate is found typically in the northern region of Africa. The next climate type is the temperate and tropical rain forests. An example of a temperate rain forest is the Olympia Peninsula in Washington State. Brazil offers a good example of a tropical rain forest. The two last climate types are the coldest and have a great amount of precipitation in the form of snow. The first of these two, the taiga, is characterized by great forests of evergreen cone-bearing trees. Taigas occur only in the temperate zone or at great elevation. Large portions of Canada are typical of this climate type. The last region is the tundra. This coldest climate type may have small amounts of precipitation. Again, this region is found in either the temperate zone or the highest elevations on earth. The best example is northern Canada and most of Alaska.

Climate is not a steady, unvarying cycle of weather, it fluctuates and varies over a period of time. One of the major factors causing these variations is the role of atmospheric circulation. The atmosphere extends out from the earth's surface for hundreds of miles and consists of five clearly defined regions. The troposphere, the region closest to the earth, extends about 11 miles above the earth's surface. It is in this region that most weather phenomena affecting climate take place.

In the tropics there is intense solar heating, whereas in the polar regions there is little solar heating. These differences of heating and cooling of the atmosphere result in a large-scale global circulation of air that carries excess heat and moisture from the tropical areas of intense heating into the higher latitudes, where there is little excess heat and moisture. The great movements of air masses that are produced alter various local climates.

Global cloud patterns are also extremely important factors in regulating worldwide climate. Heavy cloud cover reduces the amount of solar radiation reaching the surface of the earth, which can have a cooling effect. Yet cloud cover also acts as a kind of blanket to reduce the amount of heat normally lost from the ground. A clear sky in winter always results in colder temperatures at the surface than when there is cloud cover. Even so, only the solar heat that manages to reach the earth's surface is able to be kept under this protective cover. Extended cloud cover will result in less solar heat reaching the earth's surface, leading to a cooler climatic condition.

Modification of the climate of various parts of the globe is also strongly influenced by movement of ocean currents and global wind belts. An oceanic effect termed El Niño has made dramatic climate changes, possibly on a global scale; scientists are not sure of the initial cause of this phenomenon.

It is important to remember that climate has never been stable and unchanging. Many factors can cause changes in local and even global climate; when one factor becomes very active, it inevitably modifies the rate of change and influence of other factors affecting climate.

## Methods of Study

Because the science of climatology is the study of weather patterns for a geographic area over a long span of time, records of scientific data on the weather are valuable for interpreting climate trends. Because of the international agreements and standardized procedures concerning climate that were adopted in 1853, about 100 million observations have been taken from ships since then. The quantities recorded were sea-surface temperature, wind direction and speed, atmospheric pressure and temperature, the state of the sea, and cloudiness. These records offer the best opportunity for delineating the dynamic behavior of the global climate over the last century.

A great variety of instruments are used by meteorologists in gathering weather information. The net radiometer, pyranometer, and Campbell-Stokes sunshine recorder are used for measuring radiation and sunshine. The sling psychrometer is used to determine relative humidity. For remote sensing, a humidity gauge is used in which electrical transmission of the variation depends on the fact that the passage of electrical current across a chemically coated strip of plastic is proportional to the amount of moisture absorbed at its surface. This type is used in radiosondes for upper-air observations.

Measurement of wind velocity and direction employs a simple device called an anemometer. Anemometers have four-bladed propellers that are driven by the wind to record wind speed. When the propellers are mounted at right angles, an anemometer responds to air movement in three dimensions. Weather pilot balloons, or "pibals," are released and then tracked visually using a theodolite, or a right-angled telescopic transit that is mounted in a way to make possible the reading of both azimuthal (horizontal) and vertical angles. The progress of the balloon is then plotted minute by minute on a special board, and the direction and speed is computed for each altitude. This technique does not work, however, for upper-air wind observations when there is a low cloud cover. Under these conditions, rawin observation is used. Here, a metal radar target is attached to the balloon and tracked by a radar transceiver or radio theodolite until the balloon breaks or is out of range.

Precipitation is measured in several ways. Rain measurements are made using a rain gauge. An improved version is the tipping-bucket gauge, which has a small divided metal bucket mounted so that it will automatically tip and empty measured quantities of rainfall. This tipping closes electrical contacts that activate a recording pen. Another type of improved rain gauge is a weighing-type gauge. Here, as precipitation falls on a spring scale, a pen arm attached to the scale makes a continuous record on a clock chart. Snow depth is determined by averaging three or more typical measured depths. Where snow depths become very great, graduated rods may be installed in representative places so that the depth can be read directly from the snow surface. Heat and air pressure are measured by thermometers and barometers, most of which can record data automatically.

Specially equipped planes and satellites can obtain previously inaccessible data of value in determining climate changes. The National Aeronautics and Space Administration (NASA) has supplied a modified U-2 spy plane to carry instruments to 20 kilometers for seven-hour flights up to 80 degrees north latitude. A DC-8 is also used at the same time because of its extended range. The Nimbus 7 satellite is also employed. The U.S. satellite Landsat continually photographs the earth's surface. These photographs are radioed back to earth stations and are computer-enhanced to provide visual information about such things as the amount and type of vegetation, precipitation, and underground waterways. The enhanced photographs also provide information about changing conditions that may cause changes in local and/or global climates.

In order to gain information about the relationship between carbon dioxide and global temperature, scientists have drilled deep into Arctic and Antarctic ice and have obtained core samples of the polar ice pack. By studying the amount of carbon dioxide trapped in air bubbles in very old layers of ice pack, scientists have been able to chart the ebb and flow of carbon dioxide in the atmosphere. Fossilized plant tissues indicate how warm the air was during the same period as the bubbles in the core samples. This clue helps provide a picture of the warming and cooling trends that have occurred in very ancient times, and it also makes possible comparisons with current climate conditions.

Climatologists who hold the view of dynamical climatology have found modeling very useful. This is concerned primarily with general circulation models, or GCMs. The most important part of a GCM is the parameterization of a wide range of physical processes too small to be resolved by the model. These may include all of the turbulent fluxes that occur in the surface boundary layer as well as the occurrence of convection, cloudiness, and precipitation. These relatively small processes must be parameterized in terms of the variables which are resolved by GCMs. It is primarily this parameterization which makes GCMs different from each other and leads to variations between the results of different GCM models. The value of these models, however, depends mostly on the accuracy with which the model actually simulates the natural conditions. Also, sometimes assumptions must be made in modeling, and these assumptions can give a false picture under certain conditions. Models, therefore, are intensely tested against weather data as newer methods of observations and more accurate data become available to ensure the accuracy of the models.

As newer methods for measurement, comparison, and prediction become available, and as all nations become participants in standardized measurements, the understanding of global climate change and more accurate predictions will lead to better management of human activities affecting the climate.

## Context

For centuries, the content of the atmosphere and the amount of solar radiation reaching the earth's surface have been fairly constant. Until the middle of the 1950's, it was assumed that the climates of the earth also were relatively constant and unchanging. Scientists now understand that climate is never constant, and that it is the departures from the expected "norm" that provide the greatest insight into climatic processes and that have the greatest human impact.

The ice ages were a decided departure from the "norm," as was the thirty-year drought in the early twentieth century. This drought in the United States culminated in the "Dust Bowl" disaster, which disrupted human life and crop production in the middle region of the country. The impact on human life caused by the devastating drought of the Sahel region in Africa led, in the early 1970's, to a drastic decrease in the growing season and reduced available water resources nearly to the vanishing point. Loss of the anchovy fisheries along the Peruvian coast in the 1970's (probably the result of the oceanic fluctuations known as El Niño), severe droughts in the United States' farmbelt in the 1980's, and the large-scale flooding in Bangladesh all attest the fact that dramatic climatic fluctuations and changes are in fact the true norm. It is now seen that climate modification may even result in microclimates as small as portions of a backyard garden.

Many factors cause climatic change. Some factors are of natural origin, while many others result from human activity. The globe's tropical rain forests are vital to maintaining a proper carbon dioxide/oxygen balance in the global atmosphere. With the heavy deforestation in South America and Asia in the late twentieth century, the natural means for maintaining the balance of atmospheric carbon dioxide is endangered. Industrial and automobile exhaust also contributes heavily to the buildup of carbon dioxide in the atmosphere, resulting in measurable increases in the global temperature. Carbon dioxide absorbs heat reflected from the earth's surface, creating a greenhouse effect that normally raises the global temperature to a life-supporting level. Even a small increase of 2 degrees Celsius, however, would have a potentially disastrous effect on climatic conditions. Global warming would mean that as the oceans warmed, they would expand; ocean temperature and the direction of upper-level winds are the main factors in the development of hurricanes. Some scientists argue that the warming of the oceans has already increased the frequency and the force of hurricanes. These storms result in loss of life, money, and property.

One of the main dangers of a warming climate is flooding from rising sea levels. Scientists have calculated that if the average temperature increases by about 37 degrees Celsius, the sea levels could increase by approximately 81 centimeters, enough to flood huge areas of unprotected coastal land. Nearly 30 percent of all human beings live within about 60 kilometers of a coastline. A rise in sea level of only 20 inches could have a profound effect, flooding many of the world's most important cities and ports.

Various forms of pollution over large urban areas such as Los Angeles, Tokyo, and London have caused local climate changes in these areas. Concentrations of ozone built up at ground level from industrial and automobile exhausts cause extreme eye and lung irritation. Oxides of nitrogen, carbon dioxide, sulfur dioxide, and particle-laden air, which can cause a depletion in the amount of total solar radiation, have altered climate conditions over local urban areas. Also, changes in surface characteristics—such as converting forests and prairies to agricultural fields, building cities, damming rivers to create lakes, and spilling oil at sea—all affect climate conditions. Usually, these surface changes appear to have only a minor global effect, though they do alter local conditions significantly.

There is now widespread national and international interest in how human activity is fundamentally altering the global climate. Organizations are seeking to inform the general public regarding society's role in maintaining a healthful climate. One such organization is the Climate Institute in Washington, D.C., which sponsors world conferences where scientists and government leaders from many nations gather. The Climate Institute provides an interchange among climate researchers and analysts, policymakers, planners, and opinion makers.

## Bibliography

Bolin, Bert, and B. R. Doos. *The Greenhouse Effect: Climatic Change and Eco-systems.* New York: John Wiley & Sons, 1986. Published with the support of the United Nations Environment Programme and the World Meteorological Organisation. Rich with information. Students can skip the many technical areas and glean the valuable original scientific information.

Fletcher, J. O. "Climatology: Clues from Sea-Surface Records." *Nature* 310 (August 23, 1984): 630. A study of the large, sudden changes in globally averaged sea-surface temperature in terms of the effect on global climate.

Graham, N. E., and W. B. White. "The El Niño Cycle: A Natural Oscillator of the Pacific Ocean Atmosphere System." *Science* 240 (June 3, 1988): 1293-1302. The article discusses the oceanic phenomenon known as El Niño. The journal *Science* provides excellent scientific materials on the cutting edge of discovery.

Henderson-Sellers, A., and P. J. Robinson. *Contemporary Climatology*. New York: John Wiley & Sons, 1986. Well written and easy to follow. Gives a broad introduction to the science of climatology and its many aspects.

Linden, Eugene. "Big Chill for the Greenhouse." *Time* 132 (October 31, 1988): 90. *Time* magazine frequently offers brief but accurate coverage of current scientific research and discoveries for the average reader. This article discusses the so-called greenhouse effect.

Shell, E. R. "Weather Versus Chemicals." *The Atlantic* 259 (May, 1987): 27-31. A discussion of the problems associated with the ozone hole. *The Atlantic* has thorough discussions of environmental issues on a popular reading level.

*George K. Attwood*

## Cross-References

# CLOUDS

*Field of study:* Atmospheric sciences and meteorology

*Clouds provide an indication of the current weather and a forecast of weather to come as well as information regarding climate and other aspects of the surface of the earth and its atmospheric membrane. They are also a resource field for the investigation of the dynamic intermingling of solid, liquid, and gaseous substances.*

### Principal terms

CIRRUS: trail or streak clouds, ranging from 5 to 13 kilometers above the ground, which are feathery or fibrous in appearance

CONDENSATION: the transformation from water vapor into a liquid when, subject to falling temperatures, droplets form (or condense) around small particles in the atmosphere

CONVECTION: the transmission of heat within a substance; the motion of warm (less dense) particles rising as cooler (denser) particles sink

CUMULUS: clouds with vertical development, or heap clouds, ranging from ground level to 6 kilometers above the ground

RADIATION: the transfer of heat energy through a transparent medium, as occurs when the sun warms the earth

STRATUS: sheet or layer clouds, ranging from 2 to 6 kilometers above the ground (altostratus, or middle) or 0 to 2 kilometers above the ground (stratocumulus, or low)

SUPERSATURATION: a state in which the air's relative humidity exceeds 100 percent, the condition necessary for vapor to begin transformation to a liquid state

## Summary of the Phenomenon

The formation of clouds is essentially a two-part process. The heat provided by the radiation of the sun warms moisture on the earth's surface. This moisture evaporates, or rises as an invisible mist through the cooler air just above the ground, until it reaches a level of air which is too cold to maintain it in the form of mist. At this point, the second part of the process begins. The atmosphere is filled with numerous particles that provide a surface to which individual water molecules (the components of mist) adhere. These particles become the centers, or nuclei, for water droplets or ice crystals, depending on the temperature of the atmosphere. They are usually composed of combustion products, meteoritic dust, volcanic material, and soil or salts of some variety, and they are essential for the aggregation of water molecules. When a sufficient number of molecules have aggregated, a cloud has come into existence. The size, shape, and growth patterns of the cloud will depend upon the moisture and the atmospheric energy available during its formation.

Although clouds appear to be relatively stable, they are always in motion. They rise or fall, depending on the temperature of the surrounding air, and move with the direction of the winds. Eventually, clouds either dissipate as precipitation, in which the water droplets (in the form of rain or snow) fall back to the earth's surface, or evaporate, in which case the water droplets break down into a vapor or mist which remains in the atmosphere. The parts of the atmosphere in which clouds occur have been divided into three stages, which have been designated high, middle, and low. Because water vapor will rise to greater altitudes the warmer the air, the upper limits of the high stage range from 8 kilometers in the polar regions to 18 kilometers in the tropics. In the temperate zones, which include most of the world's land-masses, the high stage ranges up to approximately 13 kilometers, the point at which the troposphere (the area in which most clouds form) gives way to the stratosphere, which is the domain of the highest of conventional cloud shapes.

Cloud classification generally begins with the highest clouds, the cirrus, which are composed of ice crystals. The air temperature of these clouds is usually below −25 degrees Celsius, and they are formed when air rises slowly and steadily over a wide area. They are usually delicate in appearance, are white in color, and tend to occur in narrow bands. They are thin enough to permit stars or blue sky to be seen through them, and they are responsible for the ring or halo effect that appears to surround the sun. They often signal large, slow-moving warm fronts and rain. They sometimes seem to be gathered in branching plumes or arcs with bristling ends. Since the color of a cloud depends on the location of the light source which illuminates it—usually the sun—the position of the sun at sunset or sunrise may cast these clouds in bright reds or yellow-oranges. A variant of this classification is the cirrocumulus, a cloud composed of ice crystals gathered in columns or prismatic shapes. The cirrocumulus usually is arranged in ripples or waves; it is the cloud that sailors describe when they speak of a "mackerel sky." A close relation is the cirrostratus, which resembles a transparent white veil. Suffusing the blue of the sky with a milky tone, it is composed of ice crystals shaped like cubes. It is the cloud that herdsmen describe as "mares' tails."

On the middle atmospheric level are found the altocumulus clouds. They signal an approaching cyclonic front. The altocumulus clouds reach an altitude of 6 kilometers, where they intersect the lower level of the cirrocumulus, and they tend to resemble the cirrocumulus at their uppermost reaches. Below this point, they tend to be larger and to have dark shadings on their lower boundaries. They are composed primarily of water drops and are formed by a slow lifting of an unstable layer of air. Typically, they look like large, somewhat flattened globules and are often arranged evenly in rows or waves. In the summer, they may appear as a group of small, turretlike shapes, and in that form they often precede thunderstorms. The other basic middle-level cloud is the altostratus. These clouds are formed in air that is ascending slowly over a wide area, and they often occur in complex systems between the higher cirrostratus and the low-level nimbostratus. They are composed of both ice crystals and water droplets, with raindrops or snowflakes in the lower levels of the cloud. They are usually gray or bluish-gray, resembling a thick veil that is uniform in appearance, and often cover a substantial portion of the sky. There is a reciprocal relationship between altocumulus and altostratus clouds, in that a sheet of altocumulus clouds—particularly high, scaly ones—may be forced down and become transformed into altostratus. Conversely, as weather improves, altostratus may be altered toward altocumulus.

Clouds on the lowest levels generally are associated with the onset of precipitation. They often produce what is frequently called a leaden sky—one that is flat and "dirty" in appearance. These clouds range in altitude from 2 kilometers to the air just above the earth's surface. The stratocumulus cloud may appear in sheets, patches, or layers close together, in which case the undersurface has a wavelike appearance. These clouds are formed by an irregular mixing of air currents over a broad area and suggest instability in the atmosphere. They are composed primarily of water droplets, and because they often have a marked vertical development, they can be confused with small cumulus clouds; however, they have a softer, less regular shape than cumulus clouds. Stratus clouds tend to be the lowest level of cloud formation. Sometimes resembling fog, they are usually an amorphous, gray layer, and while they do not produce steady rain, drizzle is not uncommon. They are formed by the lifting of a shallow, moist layer of air close to the ground and are composed almost exclusively of water droplets. They produce the dullest of visible sky conditions.

The cumulus cloud is probably the cloud form most frequently depicted in artistic illustrations of the sky. In fair weather, cumulus clouds are separated into cottonlike puffs with distinctive outlines against a deep blue background. When they are few in number and almost purely white, they are a prominent feature of the most pleasant weather during the spring and summer; however, these clouds also have the potential to change into storm-making systems. They are initially formed by the ascent of warm air in separate masses or bubbles, the air rising with increasing velocity as the cloud takes shape. Their development is driven by convection currents, and while their base is usually about 1 kilometer above the land surface (or somewhat less over the ocean), they may grow vertically to an altitude of more than 7 kilometers; in the case of the cumulonimbus, the classic anvil-shaped thunderhead, they may reach an altitude of more than 15 kilometers. In the transition to cumulonimbus, the warm air rises rapidly into a cooler layer, and the convergence of radically varying temperatures produces a "boiling" at the tops of the clouds. When the rising air encounters strong winds at its upper reaches, it becomes flattened against the stable, colder layer of air that resists the convection from below. This shearing effect is what leads to the classic anvil shape of the thunderhead.

The cumulonimbus is the great thundercloud of the summer sky. It tends to be white, dense, and massive, with a dark base. Generally growing out of cumulus clouds, these are the tallest of conventional cloud forms, created by strong convection currents with updrafts of high velocity within the clouds. The thunderstorm is a product of considerable turmoil within a cumulonimbus cloud. Violent updrafts in the center of the cloud result in an increasing size of water droplets that alternately descend and rise within the cloud until they fall as some form of precipitation. The size of the drops that eventually fall is an indication of the altitude of the cloud as well as the severity of the storm; in their lower regions, cumulonimbus are composed of water droplets, but as they rise, ice crystals, snowflakes, and hail may form. The development of the cumulonimbus is generally cellular (or compartmentalized) so that there is usually some space between clouds of this type, although they may occur in a long "squall line" that is often the boundary between warm and cold airflows. Cumulonimbus clouds, because of the great energy involved in their production, often generate subsidiary clouds as well. On lower levels, the sky seems to take on a convoluted, disorganized appearance, while upper levels often feature extensions that are like cirrus clouds. The forward edge of a cumulonimbus cloud often produces what looks like the front of a wave or rolling scud just under the base of the main cloud.

Although original attempts at cloud classification included the word "nimbus" to describe a separate order of low, rain-producing clouds, the term is now applied as a modifier. In addition to its application to the storm-producing version of the cumulus cloud, there are also nimbostratus clouds, or low, gray, dark clouds with a base close to the ground, which generally contain rain. They are formed by the steady ascent of air over a wide area, usually associated with the arrival of a frontal system. They differ from stratus clouds in that they are much darker and are composed of a mixture of ice crystals and water droplets. These clouds have a ragged base, highly variable in shape and often hard to discern in steady rain. Depending on the temperature, the base will be primarily snowflakes or raindrops.

In addition to the standard forms, other cloud-related phenomena may occur in the atmosphere. A cloud is essentially composed of water in a liquid state or of ice particles suspended in the air or both; however, other substances which may not technically be considered the components of clouds—essentially dry particles (lithometeors)—may be suspended in the atmosphere and gathered in cloudlike masses. Haze, for example, is a suspension of extremely fine particles invisible to the naked eye but sufficiently numerous to produce an opalescent effect. Clouds of smoke are usually composed of the products of combustion gathered in a dense, swirling mass which rises from its source. Particles of sand may be gathered by strong, turbulent winds into clouds that move near the surface of the earth. One other type of cloud, the noctilucent, is a high-altitude form found in the mesosphere at 8 to 90 kilometers above the earth's surface in northern latitudes. Its formation is somewhat mysterious, but a current theory maintains that it is created by turbulence that carries water vapor to unusual heights during the arctic summer. The nuclei for the formation of these clouds may be deposited in the atmosphere by the residue of meteors. Noctilucent clouds are either pure white or blue-white and have pronounced band or wave structures. One theory maintains that this wave configuration is a result of gravity waves in the atmosphere, but the source of these gravity waves is unknown. Noctilucents resemble high cirrus clouds more than any other form.

On rare occasions, clouds have also been observed in the stratosphere. Their composition has not been determined, but at a range of 20 to 30 kilometers above the earth's surface, nacreous or "mother-of-pearl" clouds—so designated because they may display a full spectrum of colors—have been seen in the sky over Scandinavia and Alaska during the winter.

## Methods of Study

Recorded descriptions of the sky and weather-related phenomena date at least as far back as Aristotle's *Meteorologica* (c. 350 B.C.). The first formal system of cloud classification owes its development to the work of Chevalier de Lamarck in France and Luke Howard in London in the early nineteenth century. In 1897, C. T. R. Wilson's cloud chamber experiments simulated the cloud formation process in the laboratory. By 1925, radio wave observations were beginning to augment free balloon ascensions as a method of examining the atmosphere, and in 1928, the first radiosonde apparatus—a kind of electrical thermometer which transmits temperature, pressure, and humidity—were placed into operation. Immediately after World War II, high levels of atmospheric exploration became possible with rockets. This advancement eventually resulted in the most effective instrument for cloud observation ever produced, the weather satellite. In 1960, the first meteorological satellite, Tiros 1, was launched by the United States. It transmitted pictures of cloud patterns back to the earth, and where previously the motion of cloud systems could be developed only from separate ground sightings, the satellite provided an overview of areas more than 1,000 kilometers wide. The use of time-lapse photography permitted an observer to follow the birth and decay of cloud systems and, in conjunction with computer data storage, made it possible to develop a history of the entire range of cloud formation in the atmosphere.

There are seven basic factors which must be considered to determine the fundamental properties of cloud systems. They are, according to Horace Byers, the amount of sky covered, the direction from which the clouds are moving, their speed, the height of the cloud base, the height of the cloud top, the form of the cloud, and the constitution of the cloud. Each of these categories depends upon the location of the observing system. The amount of sky covered will vary considerably, depending on whether a ground observer is reporting or a satellite photograph is being analyzed against a schematic grid. The direction of cloud motion also depends on the point of observation, because relatively specific motion with regard to a fixed point is much easier to chart than the complex series of measurements necessary to describe the motion of a large-scale cloud formation. The upper and lower reaches of a cloud may be measured from balloons, from airplanes, by radar devices on satellites, and in ground stations. The recent refinement of cloud investigation by satellite photography has led to the consideration of what the eminent environmental scientist Richard Scorer calls "messages," which include the fact that cyclonic patterns are more various than had been realized, requiring the assimilation of much more data into an explanation of how large-scale cloud systems are formed and why they exist for a particular duration in time. In addition to measurements that are essentially external, the inner mechanics of a cloud must be studied to determine its basic properties and potential behavior. The inner cloud physics which influence its development and its potential for precipitation involve the supercooling and freezing of water (that is, water droplets which do not form ice crystals below zero degrees Celsius), the origin and specific form of the ice nuclei which lead to the growth of a cloud and which depend on the rise and descent of particles within a cloud, the rate of collisions between particles in a cloud which influence the growth of droplets and crystals, and the reflecting and refracting properties of the components of a cloud which determine the color of a cloud in terms of both visual observation and radiophotometric measurement. Aside from spectographic observations, most cloud physics depends on an understanding of thermodynamics, or the effects of heat changes on the motion and elemental properties of particles in the atmosphere.

## Context

In addition to the physical adjustments that humans have had to make in response to the weather are the psychological effects of light, heat, and other meteorological phenomena. Only recently have these effects been examined in depth. Moreover, the great theater of the skies has presented not only a continuing panorama of endless variety and enthrallment in an aesthetic sense but also a constant demonstration of some of the most basic laws and principles of physics. As Jonathan Weiner has pointed out, one does not need the elaborate equipment of a nuclear physicist to watch the laws of physics in operation. They are in evidence all the time, and the procession and change in cloud forms is one of the most specific manifestations of this process. Meteorologists call cloud systems "weather factories," and amateur weather watchers regard clouds as the "weathermen of the heavens" because analyzing them can provide fairly accurate weather predictions. The prevalence of cloud images on film from weather satellites is a contemporary expression of the importance of cloud motion in weather forecasting. The considerable number of references to clouds in poetry is an indication of the manner in which clouds have captivated the human imagination. John Ruskin made the connection between clouds and spirituality when he called them "drifted wings of many companies of angels," and there are many examples of folk wisdom based on shrewd observation of clouds, such as "Mares' tails, mares' tails, Make lofty ships carry low sails." While modern science has contributed immensely to an understanding of how clouds are formed and of what they are composed, it has not diminished the awesome impact of a great cloud system in motion across the horizon.

## Bibliography

Ahrens, C. Donald. *Meteorology Today.* St. Paul, Minn.: West Publishing, 1985. An up-to-date, clearly written examination of the entire spectrum of meteorological phenomena that might be of interest to the nonspecialist. Cloud systems are discussed within the context of atmospheric science. Extensively illustrated. Suitable for college-level students.

Anthes, Richard, Hans Panofsky, John Cahir, and Albert Rango. *The Atmosphere*. Columbus, Ohio: Charles E. Merrill, 1957. A book for the casual as well as the sophisticated observer of the weather. Chapter 5 follows a weather system across the United States over four days, concentrating on changes in cloud systems. Includes a good chart of the atmosphere and a useful annotated bibliography.

Byers, Horace. *General Meteorology*. New York: McGraw-Hill, 1959. An older but still essentially accurate study. A good chapter on cloud observation includes an introduction to the science prior to satellites and detailed descriptions of cloud classifications.

Lee, Albert. *Weather Wisdom*. Garden City, N.Y.: Doubleday, 1976. An entertaining and informative discussion of the weather and its effects on human life. Includes a lively and lucid discussion of cloud systems, generously supported by quotations from poems about clouds.

Ludham, F. H., and R. S. Scorer. *Cloud Study: A Pictorial Guide*. London: John Murray, 1957. This book, nearly a classic in the field, has been described by Sverre Petterssen, former Director of Scientific Services for the U.S. Air Force Weather Service, as "a charmingly written, well-illustrated discussion, readily understood by nonspecialists." It provides an excellent basis for observation of cloud systems.

Miller, Albert, and Jack Thompson. *Elements of Meteorology*. Columbus, Ohio: Charles E. Merrill, 1970. A solid examination of cloud formation within the larger context of atmospheric phenomena. An excellent appendix has a descriptive explanation of each of the major cloud classifications, including a color photograph for each type.

Moran, Joseph M., and Michael Morgan. *Meteorology: The Atmosphere and the Science of Weather*. 2d ed. New York: Macmillan, 1989. One of the best current texts available for college-level students. Written by two longtime scholars in the field, the book has charts, photographs, and illustrations in addition to clear and informative discussions of weather phenomena.

Neiburger, Morris, James G. Edinger, and William D. Bonner. *Understanding Our Atmospheric Environment*. San Francisco: W. H. Freeman, 1973. A very clearly written, essentially introductory examination of how clouds are formed, with a good table of cloud classifications and photographs. Also contains a somewhat more advanced study of clouds and precipitation and a very useful table of units of measurement and conversion factors.

Parker, Sybil P., ed. *Meteorology Source Book*. New York: McGraw-Hill, 1988. Clear definitions and comprehensive illustrations make this a good source for basic information about meteorology. Different sections have been written by specialists in the field.

Petterssen, Sverre. *Introduction to Meteorology*. New York: McGraw-Hill, 1969. Petterssen, an eminent authority in the field, addresses himself "to readers who wish to make a first acquaintance with the atmosphere and its environs." In addition to a good introduction to basic cloud states, with a list of important terms (mostly derived from the Latin) describing variants in basic cloud types, there are several analytical chapters that consider development and change in cloud systems. Includes an annotated bibliography.

Rogers, R. R. *A Short Course in Cloud Physics*. Elmsford, N.Y.: Pergamon Press, 1976. For the student who wishes to go beyond the preliminary material. Some knowledge of mathematics and physics is required. See also H. R. Pruppacher and J. D. Klett, *Microphysics of Clouds and Precipitation* (1980).

Scorer, R. S. *Cloud Investigation by Satellite*. New York: John Wiley & Sons, 1986. The author, Emeritus Professor and Senior Research Fellow at Imperial College of Science and Technology, University of London, is one of the most distinguished environmental scholars in the world. Although this book is designed primarily for the specialist, it is written clearly enough for the layperson. Reading is enhanced by Scorer's penetrating and engaging style. There is a wonderful variety of photographs of cloud systems.

Trefil, James. *Meditations at Sunset: A Scientist Looks at the Sky*. New York: Charles Scribner's Sons, 1988. Trefil's tone is clear, affable, and enthusiastic, and the chapter "When Clouds Go Bad" is a superb description of a storm—vivid and energetic.

*Leon Lewis*

**Cross-References**

The Atmosphere's Structure and Composition, 128; Storms, 2477; Tornadoes, 2527; Weather Forecasting, 2717; Wind, 2730.

# COAL

*Type of earth science:* Economic geology

*Coal is a sedimentary rock composed of altered plant debris. Its principal uses are for fueling steam power plants, as a source of coke for smelting metals, and for space heating and industrial process heat. Synthetic gas and oil are manufactured from coal on a large scale.*

### Principal terms

BRITISH THERMAL UNIT (BTU): the amount of heat required to raise the temperature of one pound of water by one degree Celsius at the temperature of maximum density for water

CELLULOSE: the substance forming the bulk of plant cell walls

FIXED CARBON: the solid, burnable material remaining after water, ash, and volatiles have been removed from coal

HUMIC ACID: organic matter extracted by alkalis from peat, coal, or decayed plant debris; it is black and acidic but unaffected by other acids or organic solvents

LIGNIN: a family of compounds in plant cell walls, composed of an aromatic nucleus, a side chain with three carbon atoms, and hydroxyl and methoxyl groups

MOLECULE: the smallest entity of an element or compound retaining chemical identity with the substance in mass

ORGANIC MOLECULE: molecules of carbon compounds produced in plants or animals, plus similar artificial compounds

VOLATILES: substances in coal that are capable of being gasified

## Summary of the Phenomenon

Coal is a heterogeneous mixture of large, complex, organic molecules. It is mostly carbon but contains significant amounts of hydrogen, nitrogen, sulfur, and water. Coal is derived from plant debris that accumulated as peat (plant remains in which decay and oxidation have ceased). When covered by sediments, peat begins to lose its water and more volatile organic compounds. It also compacts and progressively becomes more chemically stable. Thereafter, peat may successively alter to lignite, bituminous coal, anthracite, or graphite as deeper burial, deformation of the earth's crust, or igneous intrusion increases temperature and pressure.

Enzymes, insects, oxygen, fungi, and bacteria convert plant debris to peat. If unchecked, they can quickly destroy the deposit. Thus, permanent accumulation is limited to situations where oxygen is excluded and accumulated organic waste products prevent further decay. Rapid plant growth, deposition in stagnant water, and cold temperatures promote peat accumulation. Bacteria, the principal agents of decay, operate under a wide range of acidity and aeration; eventually, they remove oxygen and raise acidity so that decay stops.

Peat is a mixture of degraded plant tissue in humic acid jelly. All protoplasm, chlorophyll, and oil have decayed. Carbohydrates have been seriously attacked: First starch, then cellulose, and finally lignin are destroyed. Epidermal tissue, seed coats, pigments, cuticles, spore and pollen coats, waxes, and resins are most durable, but they occur in relatively small amounts. Thus, peat is dominated by lignin, the most resistant carbohydrate, with an enhanced proportion of durable tissues.

Lignites range from brown coal, which closely resembles peat but has been buried, to black or dark brown lignite, which is similar to higher-ranking coal. Lignite is partially soluble in ammonia. Its resins and waxes dissolve in organic solvents. Water content is high, and there generally is less than 78 percent carbon and more than 15 percent oxygen on an ash-free basis. Woody structure may be obvious and well-preserved. Lignite yields less than 8,300 Btu per pound.

Further compression and heating progressively convert lignite to subbituminous coal. Fibrous, woody structure gradually disappears, color darkens, the coal becomes denser and harder, water content goes down, and carbon content increases. There is a pronounced decrease in alkali solubility and susceptibility to oxidation. Subbituminous coal, ranging from 8,300 to 13,000 Btu per pound, still weathers significantly and is subject to spontaneous combustion. Like lignite, subbituminous coal burns to powdery ash.

Bituminous coals range from 46 to 86 percent fixed carbon and from 11,000 to about 15,000 Btu per pound. They burn to fused or "agglomerating" ash, resist weathering, and do not spontaneously ignite. Anthracite ranges from 86 to 92 percent fixed carbon, having lost almost all water and volatiles. In addition, it is nonagglomerating, and heating values are about 12,500-15,000 Btu per pound.

Coal is composed of vitrain, a shiny, black material with a glassy luster; durain, a dull, black, granular material; clairain, a laminated, glossy black material; and fusain, a dull black, powdery material. Bright coal is dominated by vitrain. Banded coal, which is the most abundant, is dominated by clairain. Dull coals are mostly durain, and fusain is referred to as mineral charcoal. Microscopic study reveals materials derived from woody or cortical tissues called vitrinite or fusinite. Vitrinite is dominant in vitrain and in the "bright" laminae of clairain. Fusinite characterizes durain and the "dull" laminae in clairain. Other microscopic entities, or macerals, include exinite, coalified spores and plant cuticles; resinite, fossil resin and wax; sclerotinite, fungal sclerotia; and alginite, fossil algal remains. Micrinite is unidentified vegetal material. The chemical composition of coal is poorly known because the large, complex, organic molecules in coal break down under attempts to separate them as well as in the process of analysis. The molecular composition of many derivative molecules, however, is known.

Mineral matter in coal includes all admixed minerals as well as inorganic elements in the coal itself. The organic elements—carbon, hydrogen, oxygen, nitrogen, and sulfur, which form the organic matter in the coal—also occur in compounds, such as iron sulfide, which are part of the mineral matter. Ash is altered mineral matter remaining after the coal is burned and is not synonymous with "mineral matter." Carbonate minerals such as calcite (calcium carbonate) lose their carbon dioxide. Sulfides such as pyrite (iron sulfide) break down to yield sulfur dioxide. Clay minerals lose their water and are drastically altered in molecular structure. Furthermore, the minerals and inorganic elements in the coal react with one another to produce an ash of mixed oxides, silicates, and glass.

Clays are the most abundant minerals in coal. Some clay is washed into the coal swamp, but much arises from chemical reactions occurring in the peat and coal during and after coalification. Sulfides generally are half as abundant as is clay, with the iron sulfides—pyrite and marcasite—most widespread. Sulfides of zinc and lead also may be abundant. Pyrite and marcasite may originate during plant decay and coalification as hydrogen sulfide generated from organic sulfur combines with iron. Hydrogen sulfide also may result from decay of marine organisms as the swamp is invaded by the sea, thus producing more pyrite. Coals associated with marine rocks generally have higher sulfur content than do those coals from wholly alluvial deposits. Carbonates of calcium (calcite), iron (siderite), and magnesium (dolomite) generally are half as abundant as are sulfides. Quartz is ubiquitous, ranging from small amounts to as much as one-fifth of the mineral matter. More than thirty additional minerals have been noted as abundant or common in coal.

Trace elements such as zinc, cadmium, mercury, copper, lead, arsenic, antimony, and selenium are associated with sulfides. Others, such as aluminum, titanium, potassium, sodium, zirconium, beryllium, and yttrium, are associated with mineral grains washed into the swamp. Still others find their way into the peat within plant tissues or later are concentrated from waters circulating through either the peat swamp or the coal seam. These elements include germanium, beryllium, gallium, titanium, boron, vanadium, nickel, chromium, cobalt, yttrium, copper, tin, lanthanum, and zinc. Coal ash has been a source of germanium and vanadium, and both uranium and barium have been mined from some coal seams. Iron, selenium, gallium, zinc, and lead occurrences in coal have been investigated as possible sources of these metals, and, inasmuch as release of metals from coal mining or combustion is generally deleterious, their recovery in pollution control may be feasible.

A large, poorly drained area covered by prolific plant growth is required for accumulation of a significant coal seam. Multiple layers of substantial thickness and extent must accumulate to develop a major coal field. No coal formed before the Devonian period (408-360 million years ago), because land plants capable of producing forests were absent. From then until the end of the Carboniferous (360-286 million years ago), forests of primitive plants, including lycopods, notably *Lepidodendrales* (presently represented by club moss), sphenopsids such as *Calamitales* (presently represented by scouring rush), tree ferns, seed ferns, and others, produced extensive peat in the tropical zone from Texas to Nova Scotia and across western Europe to the Ukraine. These peats accumulated in intermontane basins, on alluvial plains, and in deltaic complexes bordering rapidly developing mountain chains in eastern North America, Western Europe, and the Ural Mountains. Somewhat similar forests occupying more temperate climates produced significant coal in Siberia, northern China, and Korea. During the Late Carboniferous and Permian (286-245 million years ago), a different group of plants (the glossopterid flora) grew in coal swamps in Brazil, South Africa, peninsular India, and Antarctica. These areas were combined in Gondwanaland, a large continent centered on the South Pole at that time. Here, peat accumulated in apparent cold-to-temperate conditions peripheral to a series of south polar ice caps.

During the Permian, Triassic (245-208 million years ago), and Early Jurassic (208-144 million years ago), world climates cooled and dried as continents co-alesced in a single, relatively high-standing landmass. Coal swamps were restricted but, in favorable, warm, moist environments remnant from the Carboniferous, coal-measures flora persisted in small peat swamps. At the same time, ancestral conifers, conifers, cycads, and cycadeoids replaced coal-measures plants in more widespread forests, but generated few peat deposits during the Triassic and Early Jurassic.

More favorable coal-forming conditions arose again from the Middle Jurassic, through the Cretaceous (144-66 million years ago), and into the Cenozoic (66 million years ago to present). The continents split up with resultant mountain de-velopment in the western Americas, along the southern margin of Eurasia, and elsewhere. Increased erosion and sedimentation, along with crustal movement, caused widespread alluvial fans, deltas, coastal swamps, and intermontane basins, all of which favored peat accumulation. Warm and moist climates from the Late Jurassic through the Early Cenozoic stimulated plant growth. At first, conifers and cycadlike plants dominated, but in the Middle Cretaceous, these plants were largely replaced by broad-leaved angiosperms closely resembling modern forest flora. Extensive Jurassic coals in China and Iran and very extensive Late Cretaceous and Early Tertiary coal in western North America comprise a second peak of coal accumulation. Many of these accumulations are lignite or subbituminous coal as opposed to generally higher-grade coals formed earlier. Coal deposition continued in suitable environments scattered over most of the world during the later Tertiary. Almost all of these coals are lignite.

Peats form today in two very different environments. Poor drainage in areas of recent glaciation, coupled with low temperature, facilitates peat formation in high latitudes. In warm temperate and tropical regions that are poorly drained, vigorous forests may produce peat. Coastal plains and shoreline deposits, such as the Dismal Swamp and Everglades; deltas and alluvial plains, such as the Mississippi Delta; and tropical alluvial plains, as in the upper Amazon Basin, are all good examples. Most of the high-latitude peat is unlikely to be incorporated in major sedimentary accumulations and, thus, is unlikely to become coal. Other modern peats, however, are an extension of the sort of peat accumulation that occurred in the geologic past and, therefore, provide a guide to understanding coal formation.

Individual coal beds or seams may be very widespread or of limited extent. The Illinois #2 Coal, for example, is recognizable from western Kentucky to north-eastern Oklahoma. Other coal beds cover only a few square kilometers. Coals range from a few millimeters to more than 100 meters thick. They generally are tabular but may be interrupted by filled stream channels or rolls, which are protuberances of overlying rock apparently forced into the coal while in a plastic state. Thin layers of clay (splits) or cracks filled with clay (clay veins) interfere with mining and dilute mined coal with extraneous rock. Coal beds may be subhorizontal or may be steeply inclined, depending on deformation in the area. They also may be continuous or may be offset by faults—fractures of the crust along which movement has occurred. Inclination or interruption of the bed interferes with mining.

## Methods of Study

The distribution and character of coal beds are determined by standard field geologic methods. Surface exposures are plotted on maps, and their geometric orientation is recorded. Thereafter, the coal beds are projected geometrically into the subsurface. Wherever possible, their position is verified in wells and mine shafts so that the full regional extent, depth, and attitude of the coal are illustrated. If detailed information is required for mining, specially drilled coal test holes will be utilized to locate channel fillings and faults interrupting the coal as well as to determine changes in thickness and quality. These test holes make it possible to plan mining efficiently. In addition, the relationship of the coal to rocks above and below will be investigated so that mining methods may be adjusted to potential geologic hazards, such as caving roofs and incursion of underground water.

Standardized, practical tests define quality and/or suitability for specific uses. Burning coal samples under controlled conditions at 750 degrees Celsius produces a standard American Society for Testing Materials (ASTM) ash, which defines the total ash content and its nature. Coals with low-ash content are preferred. The character of the ash—agglomerating produces a glassy clinker, and nonagglomerating produces a powder—determines the type of grate on which the coal can be burned. The heating value of the coal, figured on an ash-free basis, is determined by controlled combustion in a calorimeter: a closed "bomb" fitted with temperature sensors. The amount and quality of volatile materials are analyzed by carbonizing the coal at a standard temperature in a closed vessel and measuring the amount and kinds of substances driven out of the coal. These data are required to classify the coal according to rank and grade and to fix its value in the market.

More precise analytical techniques and tools are employed in research, as opposed to routine coal testing. The physical composition of the coal may be determined by microscopic study of thin sections (slices of coal mounted on glass and reduced to a thickness allowing transmission of light) or by examining polished surfaces with a reflecting microscope. In this way, the components of the coal may be distinguished and examined separately. More detailed study may utilize either transmission or scanning electron microscopy. Coal rank also may be determined very precisely by means of measuring reflectance—in this case, the amount of light reflected from polished vitrinite.

Mineral matter in the coal, as distinguished from ash, may be directly examined by these techniques but also may be recovered from the coal employing a low-temperature asher. The asher is an electronic device that vaporizes combustible materials without significantly raising the temperature of the sample. In this way, clays, carbonates, sulfides, and other minerals that are significantly altered by heat are delivered for study in their original state.

Elemental chemical analysis of coal provides information as to its composition at a level of limited value to coal investigators. The organic compounds in coal, however, suffer substantial alteration under almost any analytical technique that can be applied to them. The volatiles recovered by coal carbonization in the absence of oxygen may be separated by distillation, but they are not the compounds originally present in the coal. Solid organic materials may be selectively dissolved and the resultant materials subjected to organic analysis, but, again, these materials are not the ones that were present in the original coal. In spite of these limitations, however, some conception of the original chemistry of the coal is obtained, and very good information applicable to coal utilization is developed. X-ray diffraction and other spectroscopic techniques have begun to uncover the structure of coal molecules without altering them. Concepts of coal molecular structure, however, remain rudimentary.

## Context

Coal is a major source of heat energy and a significant source of organic compounds of practical use—from drugs to plastics. It fueled the Industrial Revolution and, thus, is responsible for the appearance of modern industrial society. Coal was the principal source of energy until World War I. Although its use declined thereafter under competition from oil and gas, coal is again increasing in relative importance. In contrast to oil and gas, whose reserves are limited and for which production is expected to peak early in the twenty-first century, coal reserves appear to be adequate at least until well into the twenty-second century.

In spite of its large reserves, coal presents several significant problems. Coal is a solid fuel and is inappropriate for use in domestic heating and vehicular transport. Therefore, substantial research on converting coal to liquid and gaseous fuel is needed and is under way. Furthermore, coal combustion produces gaseous and solid wastes that must be managed. Sulfides are converted to metallic oxides and sulfur dioxide, which combine with water in the atmosphere to produce acid rain. This precipitation kills plants, causes respiratory difficulties, and destroys aquatic life. The carbon in coal, as well as in wood or hydrocarbons, combines with oxygen to form carbon dioxide when burned. Enough carbon dioxide has already been produced by burning wood, coal, and hydrocarbons so that a change in global atmospheric composition has been detected. Resultant climatic changes are feared, even though ultimate results are not yet predictable. Other deleterious elements are released, either into the atmosphere or in ash, such as lead, cadmium arsenic, and mercury. Although these elements are emitted in small amounts, the environmental effects must be understood so that appropriate action may be taken. Mine hazards, gas and cave-ins especially, are geologically controlled. Subsidence of underground mines—its extent, timing, and ultimate cost to surface values—also is geologically controlled. Strip-mining reclamation and the problem of mine waters entering both surface and subsurface water supplies are additional geologic concerns.

## Bibliography

Averitt, P. "Coal." In *United States Mineral Resources*, U.S. Geological Survey Professional Paper 820. Washington, D.C.: Government Printing Office, 1973. A concise account of coal formation, its rank, sulfur content, and minor elements occurring in coal. United States and world coal resources also are reviewed. Written for the informed general public.

Francis, Wilfrid. *Coal: Its Formation and Composition*. London: Edward Arnold, 1961. Describes the tissues of coal-forming plants, how they accumulate to form peat, and formation and composition of peat, lignites, and higher-ranking coals. Reviews the composition of coal, including inorganic constituents, and discusses coal-forming processes. Moderately technical. Outdated but usable.

Galloway, W. E., and D. K. Hobday. *Terrigenous Clastic Depositional Systems*. New York: Springer-Verlag, 1983. Discusses the character and processes of nonmarine sedimentary environments, excepting glacial environments, as related to coal deposition. Reviews the character and composition of coal as affected by depositional origin. Written for college students but intelligible to the general reader.

James, P. *The Future of Coal*. London: Macmillan Press, 1982. Summary account of the origin of coal, mining methods, its use and markets, and environmental and health problems associated with coal use. Also a discussion of coal occurrence and use on a worldwide basis. Written for the nontechnical reader.

Stach, E. *Stach's Textbook of Coal Petrography*. 3d ed. Berlin-Stuttgart: Gebruder Borntraeger, 1983. Includes discussion of origin and formation of peat and coal, a detailed account of coal's physical constituents and their origin, a discussion of trace elements in coal, the methods of coal petrography, and practical applications of coal petrography. The most comprehensive account in English. Written for professional coal geologists.

Stewart, W. N. *Paleobotany and the Evolution of Plants*. New York: Cambridge University Press, 1983. A well-illustrated account of the evolution of plants, including those responsible for coal. Written for beginning college-level students.

Van Krevelen, D. W. *Coal: Typology-Chemistry-Physics-Constitution*. Amsterdam: Elsevier, 1961. A comprehensive treatise on the physical and chemical properties of coal, its constitution and classification, and its geology and petrology. Somewhat dated, but still the best single reference. Written at the technical level.

Williamson, I. A. *Coal Mining Geology*. London: Oxford University Press, 1967. General geology as it pertains to coal, along with details of mine geology, coal composition, and Carboniferous fossils and stratigraphy. Written for elementary geology and mining students.

*Ralph L. Langenheim, Jr.*

## Cross-References

Acid Rain, 9; Air Pollution, 24; Alluvial Systems, 31; Coastal Processes and Beaches, 240; Colonization of the Land, 246; Deltas, 332; Environmental Health, 615; Floodplains, 712; Fossil Plants, 753; The Greenhouse Effect, 1004; Earth Resources, 2175; Future Resources, 2182; Sedimentary Rock Classification, 2304; Sedimentary Rocks: Biogenic, 2312.

# COASTAL PROCESSES AND BEACHES

*Type of earth science:* Geology
*Field of study:* Sedimentology

*The shoreline is the meeting place for the interaction of land, water, and atmosphere, and rapid changes are the rule rather than the exception.*

### Principal terms

BEACH: an accumulation of loose material, such as sand or gravel, that is deposited by waves and currents

LONGSHORE CURRENT: a slow-moving current between a beach and the breakers, moving parallel to the beach; the current direction is determined by the wave refraction pattern

LONGSHORE DRIFT: the movement of sediment parallel to the beach by a longshore current

OSCILLATORY WAVE: a wind-generated wave in which each water particle describes a circular motion; such waves develop far from shore, where the water is deep

TSUNAMI: a low, rapidly moving wave created by a disturbance on the ocean floor, such as a submarine landslide or earthquake

WAVE BASE: the depth to which water particles of an oscillatory wave have an orbital motion; generally the wave base is equal to one-half the distance of the length of the wave

WAVE REFRACTION: the process by which the angle of a wave moving into shallow water is changed; the bending which results is also termed wave refraction

## Summary of the Phenomenon

The processes that create, erode, and modify beaches are many. Marine processes, such as waves, wave refraction, currents, and tides, work concurrently to modify, create, or erode a beach. This suggests that a beach is a very sensitive landform, and indeed it is. Generally a beach is a deposit made by waves and related processes. Beaches are often regarded as sandy deposits created by wave action; however, beaches may be composed of broken fragments of lava, sea shells, coral reef fragments, or even gravel. A beach is composed of whatever sediment is available. Beaches have remarkably resilient characteristics. They are landforms made of loose sediment and are constantly exposed to wave and current action. On occasion, the coastal processes may be very intensive, such as during a hurricane or tropical storm. Yet, in spite of the intensity of wave processes, these rather thin and narrow landforms, although perhaps displaced, restore themselves within a matter of days. Coastal scientists are inclined to believe that the occurrence and maintenance of beaches are related to their flexibility and rapid readjustment to the varying intensity of persistent processes.

Sediment deposited on beaches is derived from the continents. Rivers are one source of beach sediment and the coast is another. As rivers erode the land, the sediment they carry ultimately finds its way to the shore. Because the sediment may be transported several tens or hundreds of kilometers, it is refined and broken down even further to finer-sized particles. Once the river reaches the sea, the sediment is distributed by longshore currents along the shoreline as a beach. Beaches also occur where the shoreline is composed of cliffs, such as along the Pacific coast of North America. Here, waves erode the sea cliffs and the sediment is deposited locally as a beach. Under these conditions, the beach deposit is most often gravelly because the sediment is transported only a short distance and has not had an opportunity to break up into finer-sized sediment such as sand.

The most obvious process and energy source working on beaches is waves. Waves approaching a beach are generally created by winds in storm areas at sea. As wind velocities increase, a wave form develops and radiates out from the storm. An oscillatory motion of the water occurs as the wave form moves across the water surface. It is important to note that the water movement within a wave is not the same as the movement on a wave form. In a wave created in deep water which is approaching a beach, the water particles move in a circular orbit, and very little forward movement of the water occurs. The water at the surface moves from the top of the orbit (the wave crest) to the base of the orbit (the wave trough) and then back up. Thus the water particles form an oscillatory wave motion; this motion continues down into the water. Although the size of the orbits in the water column decreases, motion occurs to a depth referred to as the wave base. At this point, the depth of the wave base is less than the depth of the water. As wave crests and troughs move into shallow water, the water depth decreases to a point where it is equal to the wave base. From this point, the orbital motion is confined because of the shallowness of the water and takes on an elliptical path. The ellipse becomes more confined as waves enter shallower water and eventually becomes a horizontal line. At this point, there is a net forward movement of water in the form of a breaker.

As a wave enters shallow water, many adjustments occur, such as a change in the orbital path of water particles described above and a change in the velocity of the wave form. Since the wave base is "feeling the bottom" in shallower water, friction occurs, slowing the wave down. As seen from an airplane, waves entering shallow water do so at an angle, not parallel to the shoreline. Therefore, one part of the wave enters shallow water and slows down relative to the rest of the wave. Thus, a part of the wave crest is feeling bottom sooner than the rest of the wave. Since the wave crests and troughs have different velocities, the wave refracts or bends. In so doing, the wave crests and troughs try to parallel the shallow bottom topography, which they have encountered.

The wave refraction is seldom completed, and the breaking wave surges obliquely up the slope of the beach and then returns perpendicular to the shoreline. The result is a current which basically moves water in one direction parallel to the beach in a zig-zag pattern (a longshore, or littoral, current). It is a slow-moving current which is located between the breaking wave out in the sea and the beach. Because longshore-current movement operates in shallow water and along the beach, it is capable of transporting sediment along the shoreline. "Longshore drift" refers to the movement of sediment along beaches. In a sense, the longshore current is like a river moving sand and other material parallel to the shore. Beaches are always in a state of flux. Although they appear to be somewhat permanent, they are constantly being moved in the direction of the longshore current. Along any shoreline, several thousand cubic meters of sediment are constantly in motion as longshore drift. Along the beaches of the eastern United States, about 200,000 cubic meters are transported annually within a longshore drift system.

A different type of ocean wave is one which is generated on the ocean floor rather than by the wind. Such waves are properly termed tsunamis. Although they popularly have been coined "tidal waves," they are completely unrelated to tides or the movement of planets. Some type of submarine displacement, such as the creation of a volcano, a landslide on the sea floor, or an earthquake beneath the ocean bottom, causes a displacement of water, which triggers waves. The waves are low, subdued forms traveling thousands of kilometers over the ocean surface at extremely high velocities, often in excess of 800 kilometers per hour. As a tsunami approaches shallow water or a confined bay, its height increases. There is no method for direct measurement of heights of tsunami waves; however, in 1946, a lighthouse at Scotch Cap, Alaska, located on a headland 31 meters above the Pacific Ocean, was destroyed by waves caused by a landslide-generated tsunami.

The changing character of a beach is very dynamic because the properties of waves are variable. During storm conditions or when more powerful waves strike a beach during the winter season, for example, the beach commonly is eroded, has a steeper slope, and is composed of a residue of coarser sediment, such as gravel, that is more difficult to remove. During fair-weather or summer conditions, however, beaches are redeposited and built up.

## Methods of Study

The study of beaches and coastal processes is not particularly easy because of constant wave motion and changes in the beach shape. Scientists have, however, developed field methods as well as laboratory techniques to study these phenomena. To study wave motion and related current action, several techniques have been devised to include tracers, current meters, and pictures taken from satellites and aircraft. Two types of tracers are commonly used to determine the direction and velocity of sand movement: radioactive isotopes and fluorescent coatings to produce luminophors. (Luminophors are sediment particles coated with selected organic or inorganic substances which glow under certain light conditions.) In the former type, a radioactive substance such as gold, chromium, or iridium is placed on the surface of the grains of sediment. Alternatively, grains of glass may be coated with a radioactive element. The radioactive sediment can then be detected relatively easily and quickly with a Geiger counter. Both techniques can trace the direction and abundance of sediment along the seashore. Bright-colored dyes or current meters can also be used to document the direction of longshore currents. Surveying instruments are used to determine the high and low topography of beaches and adjacent sand bars. By measuring beach topography before and after a storm, for example, scientists can record changes. In this way, they can document the volume and dimensions of beach erosion or deposition which has taken place during a storm. Measurement of wave height and other wave characteristics can be done with varying degrees of sophistication. Holding a graduated pole in the water and visually observing wave crest and troughs is simplest and cheapest. To achieve more refined measurements, scientists place pressure transducers or ultrasonic devices on the shallow sea floor to record pressure differences or fluctuations of the sea surface. These more precise instruments also record wave data on a graph for later study and analysis.

All the above methods are detailed field techniques. By comparing aerial photographs, detailed maps, satellite pictures, and in some cases government studies in a coastal sector, changes over long periods of time may be detected. Finally, because wave motion cannot be controlled on a shoreline, wave tank studies are used to derive wave theories. Normally, an elongated glass-lined tank with water 1 to 3 feet in depth is used. A wave machine creates waves at one end of the wave tank and sediment is introduced at the other end. The heights and other characteristics of the waves can be varied, as can the type of sediment, to form the beach. In this controlled way, the various beach and wave relationships can be studied.

## Context

More than 70 percent of the population of the United States lives in a shoreline setting, and thus an understanding of how waves interact with beaches is important. Shoreline property is highly prized and hence valuable because of the demand for it. On many beaches, the great investments made in hotels and condominiums suggest that beaches are the most sought-after environment on earth; shoreline frontage is sold by the foot or meter, not by the acre or hectare. Currently, however, such demand and investment are threatened with rising sea levels and continued coastal erosion.

Beaches represent the line of defense against wave erosion. Waves generated in the open sea slow down in shallow water, and the beach deposit absorbs the impact of waves. Beaches are therefore constantly changing and are one of the most ephemeral environments of earth. Thus, a sound knowledge of longshore currents and beach development is necessary prior to nearshore or marine construction. Sea walls and groins, for example, interfere with waves and longshore currents and may cause considerable erosion in selected areas: Sea walls are often constructed perpendicular to a shoreline to slow longshore currents so that a beach can be deposited. Downcurrent, beyond the area of beach deposition, erosion will take place. Similarly, rivers—a major source of the sediment that creates beaches—are sometimes dammed, thus depriving beaches of sediment and resulting in their erosion. Unless planners, developers, and builders understand these processes, major damage can result: Failure to understand coastal processes has on occasion caused a riparian property owner to sue a neighbor who caused beach erosion to take place.

Beaches are in a sense climatic barometers that record changes of sea level. The warmer atmosphere has led to a rising sea level as a result of glacial melting and warmer water temperatures. The impact of rising ocean levels was first noted on eroding beaches along the eastern United States many years ago. That was followed by the discovery of changes in the ozone content of the atmosphere. Beaches do indeed detect changes in the local sand supply, as well as global changes in the atmosphere.

## Bibliography

Bascom, Willard. "Beaches." *Scientific American* 203 (August, 1960).

——————. "Ocean Waves." *Scientific American* 201 (August, 1959). Although older, both of these articles are still current. Well illustrated with photos and diagrams. Technical concepts are explained in language a nonscience layperson can understand. Included is a discussion of tsunami or tidal wave, wave properties, and wave refraction. The more recent article is a continuation of the wave article; it presents aerial photographs of the impact of seawalls and related structures on the beaches.

——————. *Waves and Beaches.* Garden City, N.Y.: Anchor Books, 1964. A good introductory pocket book for nonscientists by an expert. Numerous examples and illustrations have made this softcover book popular. Nonmathematical and nonscience laypersons should have no difficulty with this book.

Bird, Eric. *Coasts: An Introduction to Coastal Geomorphology.* 3d ed. New York: Basil Blackwell, 1984. Includes chapters on waves and on beaches. Although most examples are Australian, the book covers fundamental concepts. A good introduction for anyone who has had a high-school-level earth science course.

Kaufman, Wallace, and Orrin Pilkey. *The Beaches Are Moving: The Drowning of America's Shoreline*. Garden City, N.Y.: Anchor Books, 1979. This thought-provoking book, written in a nontechnical style, deals with the processes working in the coastal zone, such as winds, waves, and tides. The impact of rising sea levels and the modification and urbanization of the coast are highlighted. A narrative text suitable for all ages.

Komar, Paul D. *Beach Process and Sedimentation*. Englewood Cliffs, N.J.: Prentice-Hall, 1976. Extensive treatment of waves, longshore currents, and sand transport on beaches. Equations and mathematical relationships are presented and elaborated upon. College-level material. This book is for those interested in the specifics of coastal processes.

Leatherman, Stephen P. *Barrier Island Handbook*. Amherst: University of Massachusetts Press, 1979. Based on actual field studies along the East Coast of the United States. Numerous photographs, diagrams, and tables. Most suitable for coastal managers and government employees; however, very readable and suitable for nonscientists as well as the general scientist. Emphasizes the dynamic nature of beaches, recreation and construction impacts, and nearshore processes.

Leonard, Jonathan Norton. *Atlantic Beaches*. New York: Time-Life Books, 1972. A regional travel description of the shoreline from Cape Cod, Massachusetts, southward to Cape Hatteras and the Outer Banks, North Carolina. Information is presented in a nonscience narrative form. Color photography is excellent. Useful in planning trips along the East Coast of the United States, as the emphasis is on the scenery of the seascape.

Pethick, John. *An Introduction to Coastal Geomorphology*. Baltimore, Md.: Edward Arnold, 1984. A thorough survey of coastal processes, this 260-page book is divided into three sections: wave energy on the coast and its characteristics, the relationship between currents and the movement of beach material along the shore, and the landforms, such as beaches, mud flats, and estuaries. Most suitable for anyone needing an equation or a technical explanation of selected processes operating in a coastal zone.

Thorsen, G. W. "Overview of Earthquake-Induced Water Waves in Washington and Oregon." *Washington Geologic Newsletter* 16 (October, 1988). A nine-page introduction to the impact of a tsunami on the coasts of Washington and Oregon. An earthquake occurred in March, 1964, in Alaska, and the waves traveled southward along the Pacific coast of North America. The tsunami is discussed in nontechnical language. Damage and economic losses are estimated. Maps and tidal gauge records presented. A good review of wave activity, intended for interested laypersons and teachers.

Walker, H. J. "Coastal Morphology." *Soil Science* 119 (January, 1975). A nontechnical overview of coastal landforms. Discussion includes beaches, deltas, and lagoons. The world view is taken, and maps illustrating processes are included. This fifteen-page article is useful for a nonscientist interested in the causes and distribution of coastal features from a geographical perspective.

*C. Nicholas Raphael*

**Cross-References**

Continental Shelf and Slope, 281; Marine Terraces, 1466; Ocean-Atmosphere Interactions, 1779; Surface Ocean Currents, 1798; Ocean Tides, 1832; Ocean Waves, 1839; Sea Level, 2267; Sediment Transport and Deposition, 2290; Tsunamis, 2548; Wind Power, 2737.

# COLONIZATION OF THE LAND

*Type of earth science:* Paleontology and earth history

*The advent of animals and plants on land during Ordovician time added new complexity to preexisting ecosystems of microbes. The newly increased mass of vegetation on land served to stabilize soils against erosion and further promoted the weathering of their nutrient minerals. Arthropods, too, found a place in this early ecosystem of nonvascular plants on land.*

### Principal terms

ARTHROPODS: a group of animals lacking backbones but with rigid, proteinaceous, and mineralized external skeletons that are jointed at the limbs and at other points of movement; includes crabs, spiders, and insects

CHAROPHYTE: a kind of freshwater green alga with filamentous branches arranged in whorls around a threadlike central stem, characterized by egg cells that are large compared to those of other algae

CUTICLE: an outer thin, waterproof, waxy, and proteinaceous cover to the bodies of land plants and arthropods

MILLIPEDE: a kind of arthropod with an elongate body of many, nearly identical segments, each with a pair of limbs on each side

NEMATOPHYTE: an extinct kind of nonvascular land plant consisting of flat sheets, stems, or trunks, supported by densely interwoven, microscopic, proteinaceous tubes

PHOTOSYNTHESIS: the process by which plants and some microbes create organic matter and oxygen from carbon dioxide and water, using the energy of the sun and a catalytic pigment

RHIZOME: an organ of vascular plants with the anatomy of a stem rather than of a root but running along or under the ground more like a root than a stem

RHYNIOPHYTE: an extinct kind of vascular land plant with rhizomes and simple spore-bearing organs but lacking true roots or leaves

SPORE: a reproductive propagule with a tough, acid- and desiccation-resistant, external, proteinaceous coat in land plants lacking seeds

STOMATE: an opening in the surface of the green parts of vascular land plants that can be closed by the flexing of adjacent cells in order to control gas exchange between the atmosphere and the plant interior

VASCULAR PLANTS: those plants with elongate, woody, water-conducting, tubular cells (tracheids) in their stems or veins of leaves; now includes ferns, conifers, and flowering plants

## Summary of the Phenomenon

The appearance of animals and plants on land by the Middle Ordovician period, some 450 million years ago, was a major event in the evolution of terrestrial ecosystems. Nevertheless, they probably were not the earth's first inhabitants; there is a fossil record of blue-green algae and other microscopic life well back into Precambrian time, as much as 3.5 billion years ago. Indeed, it is doubtful that plants and animals visible to the naked eye could have lived on land without preexisting microbial ecosystems, which served to stabilize minerals in soils, to decompose and circulate organic matter of dead organisms, and to oxygenate the atmosphere by photosynthesis. The increased mass of more complex animals and plants on land during Ordovician time further stabilized soils, invigorated the recycling of organic matter, and boosted atmospheric oxygenation. In addition, large plants provided greater depth and structure to terrestrial ecosystems than was possible with microbes and so may have promoted photosynthetic efficiency, biological diversity, and perhaps also resistance to disturbance by floods and storms. This self-reinforcing boost to terrestrial productivity firmly established life on land.

Because there are marine fossils of plants and animals visible to the naked eye in Precambrian rocks (at least 600 million years old), it has commonly been assumed that the earliest creatures on land during the Ordovician and Silurian periods invaded from the sea. Reasons advanced to explain why the land was unavailable for marine creatures for more than 200 million years include the lack of available oxygen, the poverty of terrestrial microbial photosynthetic productivity, and an unpredictable land surface of flash floods and erosional badlands. This view of an invasion from the sea has been used to explain the origins of earliest land animals, which probably were arthropods, such as millipedes and spiders. A tremendous variety of fossil arthropods have been found in Cambrian, Ordovician, and Silurian deposits of shallow seas and estuaries. Like modern marine crabs, these creatures may have ventured out to a limited extent on land, and some may have become more fully adapted to more difficult conditions there. The external skeletons of arthropods, important for defense in the sea, also are effective for support, movement, and preventing desiccation on land.

On the other hand, millipedes and spiders are not very closely related either to any known fossil or to living aquatic arthropods. A reassessment of the earliest fossil scorpions, formerly regarded as possible early land animals, has shown that they had a breathing apparatus that would have been effective only in water. Substantial evolution on land must have occurred to produce the earliest spiders and millipedes, perhaps from microscopic early microbial feeders that have left no fossil record.

The idea of invasion of the land by marine and freshwater algae is supported to some extent by the close biochemical similarities between modern land plants and charophytes (a kind of pond weed commonly called stonewort because of its calcified egg cells). Charophytes, however, are very different from land plants, and it is unlikely that such soft-bodied aquatic algae in the geological past were any more successful in colonizing the land than are the mounds of rotting seaweed now thrown up on beaches by storms. Land plants differ from stoneworts and seaweeds in many ways: They have a waxy and proteinaceous outer coating (cuticle) to prevent desiccation and to allow the plant body to remain turgid through internal water pressure; they have small openings (stomates) surrounded by cells that can open and close the opening in order to control loss of water and oxygen and intake of carbon dioxide; they have internal systems of support and water transport, which include tubular thick-walled cells (hydroids) in nonvascular plants, such as mosses and liverworts, and elongate cells with helical or banded woody thickenings (tracheids) in vascular plants; they have roots, unicellular root hairs, or rootlike organs (rhizoids) that gather water and nutrients from soil; they have propagules (spores) protected from desiccation and abrasion by proteinaceous envelopes. To some botanists, the coordinated evolution of all these features from aquatic algae is extremely unlikely, notwithstanding the impressive diversity of algae today. This consideration, plus the simple nature of the earliest fossil land plants, has led to the argument that land plants evolved on land from microscopic algae already accustomed to such conditions.

While immigrant versus indigenous evolutionary origins of the earliest land creatures remains a theoretical problem, there is fossil evidence of very early land ecosystems. In Late Ordovician rocks are found the earliest spores of land plants. Most of them are smooth and closely appressed in groups of four, somewhat similar to spores of liverworts and mosses today. This is not to say that they belonged to liverworts and mosses; no clear fossils of land plants visible to the naked eye have yet been found in rocks of this age. Early moss and liverwort ancestors are found in Silurian rocks, but so are extinct nonvascular plants, such as nematophytes. These early experiments in the evolution of land plants had tissues supported by densely interwoven proteinaceous tubes. In life, they had the rubbery texture of a mushroom and a variety of bladelike and elongate forms similar to those of some living algae. Although the botanical affinities of the earliest spores of nonvascular land plants remain unclear, there is evidence that they grew in clumps. Buried soils of Late Ordovician age have been found with surficial erosion scours of the kind formed by wind around clumps of vegetation. The clumps are represented by gray spots from the reducing effect of remnant organic matter. Burrows also have been found in Late Ordovician buried soils as an indication of animals in these early land ecosystems. The fossil burrows are quite large (2-21 millimeters). They are similar in their clayey linings, backfill structures, and fecal pellets to the burrows of modern roundback millipedes. The buried soils are calcareous and strongly ferruginized—indications that they were nutrient-rich, periodically dry, and well drained, as are modern soils preferred by millipedes. Actual fossils of millipedes have not yet been found in rocks older than Late Silurian, so all that can be said at present is that these very early animals on land were in some ways like millipedes.

By Silurian time (some 438 million years ago) there was a considerable diversification of life on land. Spores of fungi and of vascular land plants have been found fossilized in Early Silurian rocks. During Mid-Silurian time, there were small, leafless plants with bifurcating rhizomes and photosynthetic stems terminated by globular, spore-bearing organs. These matchstick-sized fossil plants have been called *Cooksonia*. Although not so well preserved as to show their water-conducting cells, they have been regarded as the earliest representatives of the extinct group of vascular plants called rhyniophytes. In Devonian rocks (some 408 million years old), some well-preserved rhyniophytes are known to have been true vascular plants, but there are other plants similar in general appearance that had simpler thick-walled conducting cells like those of nonvascular plants. By Devonian time, there were also vascular plants with spore-bearing organs borne above lateral branches (zosterophylls), plants with true roots and spore-bearing organs borne in clusters (trimerophytes), and spore-producing plants with woody roots and tree trunks (progymnosperms). The evolution of the earliest vascular plant cover on land, and of the first forests, involved different kinds of plants now extinct.

To fossil millipedes of Silurian age were added during Devonian time spiders, centipedes, springtails (Collembola), and bristletails (Thysanura). The earliest vertebrates on land are known from bones of extinct amphibians (Ichthyostegalia) and from footprints of Devonian age, some 370 million years old.

This great Silurian and Devonian evolutionary radiation promoted environmental changes similar to those initiated by the first colonization of land by plants and animals, as well as some new changes. For example, the formation of charcoal from wildfires in woodlands and the accumulation of peat in swamps were ways of burying carbon that otherwise might have decayed or been digested into carbon dioxide in the atmosphere. Removal of carbon dioxide in this way allowed increased oxygenation of the atmosphere. Oxygenation was kept within bounds by increased flammability of woodlands when oxygen reached amounts much in excess of the present atmospheric level.

Late Devonian ecosystems were very different from modern ones. Major ecological roles, such as insect-eating large animals on land, were still being added. More changes were to come, but the world at that time would have seemed a much more familiar place than the meadows of *Cooksonia* during the Silurian, the patchy cover of Ordovician nonvascular plants, and the red and green microbial earths of earlier times.

## Methods of Study

Understanding of the earliest animals and plants on land can be gained by the traditional methods of paleontology, that is, by breaking open rocks of suitable kind and geological age with hammers and chisels. Unfortunately, fossils relevant to the problem are exceedingly rare, poorly preserved, and often small in size. There have been a few discoveries of cuticle coals, such as the Barzass coal of Siberia, and of permineralized peats (peats infiltrated by minerals), such as the Rhynie chert of Scotland, which are largely composed of early land plants. Individual fossil plants can be extracted easily from cuticle coals using acids and then studied under the microscope. Thin sections of permineralized peat may reveal anatomical details of early land plants. In most cases, however, a large amount of rock must be broken to find a representative sample of these rare early fossils. In recent years, large amounts of especially promising sedimentary rocks have been dissolved in hydrofluoric acid, thus liberating the crushed and carbonized remains of plants and, in some cases, also fossil arthropods. A similar approach is used to liberate the spores of land plants, which often are associated with cuticle sheets, tubular conducting cells, and fragments of arthropods. These microscopic fossil remains are much more abundant and widespread than those that can be seen with the unaided eye. Although it may be difficult to determine the biological affinities of such tiny fossils or fossil fragments, they are abundant enough to give an idea of the geological timing of early land ecosystems.

Early land ecosystems also have left traces in sedimentary rocks deposited near streams, lakes, and seashores. Ancient soils buried in stream deposits can be recognized by a variety of features of modern soils, such as gradual changes down from an erosional surface (soil horizons) and complex systems of cracking found in soils (soil peds). Also found in some of these early soils are rhizome traces and animal burrows, which can be studied by means of field observations, sawn rock slabs, microscopic examination of ground thin sections, and chemical analyses. Stabilization of the landscape by early terrestrial ecosystems also promoted meandering rather than braided streams. The channel patterns of ancient streams are reconstructed by studying sedimentary structures and the composition.

## Context

Although plants and animals that first colonized the land are now long extinct, analogous lowly creatures still form the basis for modern terrestrial ecosystems. Microbes are intimately associated with plant roots and animal activity in soils, but they still play a vital role in obtaining nutrients and recycling organic matter, as did their Precambrian forerunners. Modern lichens, mosses, liverworts, and ferns play a role in colonizing difficult and disturbed habitats, as did the first plants on land. Similarly, millipedes, mites, springtails, and spiders remain important elements of solid faunas, despite the addition of many other kinds of creatures later in geological time. The structural and energetic levels within modern terrestrial ecosystems are to a considerable extent a result of their early Paleozoic history.

Primitive mosses and liverworts and mites and millipedes are quite resistant to modern industrial pollution, compared to other organisms. Chemical analyses to determine enrichment of heavy metals in mosses and population studies of soil mites are proving to be effective indicators of the degree of pollution of industrialized areas. These lowly yet hardy plants and animals are also proving important in the reclamation of polluted sites. They may play a role someday in the improvement of surface conditions on planetary bodies that may be suitable for human colonization, such as Mars.

## Bibliography

Attenborough, David. *Life on Earth*. Boston: Little, Brown, 1979. This short and readable book is a companion to a popular television series of the same name. Programs (and chapters) 3 and 6 introduce biological aspects of the colonization of land.

Halstead, L. B. *The Search for the Past*. Garden City, N.Y.: Doubleday, 1982. This introduction to fossils and the history of life on earth is written as a series of short and well-illustrated essays that assume no scientific background of the reader. Discussion of biological aspects and geological consequences of the colonization of the land is scattered through several sections.

Little, C. *The Colonization of the Land*. Cambridge, England: Cambridge University Press, 1983. This extended account of the invasion of land by a variety of animal groups is aimed at the level of a high school graduate or beginning university student. Includes an extended bibliography of technical works.

Schumm, Stanley A. *The Fluvial System*. New York: Wiley-Interscience, 1977. This book summarizes many years of theoretical and experimental work on river channels and includes interesting speculations on the effects of early land plants on styles of deposition in and around rivers. Some parts of the book are highly mathematical, but most of it is suitable for senior high school and college readers.

Stanley, Steven M. *Earth and Life Through Time*. 2d ed. New York: W. H. Freeman, 1989. This textbook for entry-level college students in geology includes a short section on colonization of the land, with illustrations of a few of the pertinent fossils. Also useful is a concise treatment of basic ideas in the study of fossils and sedimentary rocks.

Stebbins, G. L., and G. J. C. Hill. "Did Multicellular Plants Invade the Land?" *American Naturalist* 115 (1980): 342-353. The short answer to the title of this well written article is no. The argument is theoretical but well reasoned. Because it challenges conventional views, this article would be a useful basis for debate among college or senior high school students.

Stewart, Wilson N. *Paleobotany and the Evolution of Plants*. Cambridge, England: Cambridge University Press, 1983. This successful senior-level university textbook in paleobotany is written from the perspective of plant evolution. One chapter offers speculations on how the land "turned green." Excellent illustrations of most of the fossil plants pertinent to the topic. Many references to technical articles.

Wright, V. P., and Alfred Fischer, eds. *Paleosols: Their Recognition and Interpretation*. Princeton, N.J.: Princeton University Press, 1986. This collection of articles aimed at the senior college student or geological professional has two chapters that discuss the interpretation of fossil soils (paleosols) thought to have supported early land plants. Other chapters introduce various other aspects of the study of paleosols, and all have copious references to technical articles.

*Gregory J. Retallack*

## Cross-References

The Evolution of Life, 655; Fossil Plants, 753; The Fossil Record, 760; Fossilization and Taphonomy, 768; Fossils of the Earliest Life Forms, 782; Paleobiogeography, 1984; Paleosols, 2011; The Paleozoic Era, 2018.

# COMETS

*Type of earth science:* Planetology
*Field of study:* Small solar system bodies

*Comets are small bodies containing water ices and carbon-based organic compounds. They have played important roles in the cratering of solar system bodies and perhaps in the deposition of organic compounds on the primitive earth. Some scientists believe that comets may have contributed to the mass extinctions that mark the boundaries of geologic eras and periods.*

### Principal terms

COMA: an envelope of gas and dust surrounding the comet nucleus that has not yet been pushed into the comet tail by solar wind and by radiation pressure

DUST TAIL: dust particles blown off the cometary nucleus by radiation pressure after sublimation; it appears yellow as a result of reflected sunlight

LONG-PERIOD COMET: a comet whose period of orbital revolution is greater than two hundred years

METEOR SHOWER: the annual passage of earth through a cometary wake or debris field, causing a meteor display as comet dust particles burn up in the upper atmosphere

NUCLEUS: the central core of a comet, composed of frozen gases and dust; the source of all cometary activity

OORT CLOUD: the source of comets, a spherical shell reservoir of comet nuclei containing a trillion comets nearly one light-year away from the sun

PLASMA TAIL: molecules originating within the nucleus that are ionized by sunlight and pushed away from the comet by the magnetic field of the solar wind

SHORT-PERIOD COMET: comets whose orbital revolution periods are less than two hundred years; an example is Comet Halley, at seventy-six years

SUBLIMATION: the process of passing directly from the solid (ice) to gas or vapor state without first melting into a liquid

VOLATILE ELEMENTS AND COMPOUNDS: atoms and molecules that would be easily driven off by moderate heating; includes water, ammonia, methane, and other carbon compounds

## Summary of the Phenomenon

The word "comet" is derived from the Latin *coma*, which means "hair." Comets were "hairy stars" in ancient times. In Japan and China, comets were called "broomstars" (an accurate description of their slow motion against the background stars), as their gossamer tails swept the heavens. Comets are named either for their discoverers or simply by the year and order of appearance (for example, Comet 1990 II). Comets are occasionally among the most spectacular sights in earth's nighttime sky, with their tails stretching across the starry sky. Comets are composed of three basic parts: the solid core or nucleus, the coma (a bright shell of gas which surrounds the nucleus), and two types of tails made of ionized gas and dust.

Sometimes visible as a bright pinpoint speck in a telescope, the nucleus is the solid part of a comet, composed of volatile elements such as water, carbon dioxide, ammonia, and methane. Cometary nuclei are variable in size, ranging from a few hundred meters to more than 10 kilometers in diameter. The surface of a comet is the darkest of any known object in the solar system, appearing coal-black except for bright patches where vents allow eruptive jets of gas and dust. The dark carbonaceous material acts as an insulator to protect the interior ices from vaporization near the sun. At a distance of three astronomical units, or AUs (an astronomical unit is the mean distance of earth from the sun), solar radiation acts on the ices, and the nucleus becomes active. Rapid sublimation (the transition from solid ice directly to the gaseous state without first melting into liquid) begins at a temperature of about 214 Kelvins. The nucleus will be hidden from view by the coma, a gaseous envelope surrounding the nucleus, with a diameter of about 10,000 kilometers.

Although composed mostly of water (nearly 80 percent), the comet's complex chemical composition is revealed by spectral analysis of the coma. At 1 AU, the coma spectrum exhibits emission bands of molecular carbon, cyanogen, oxygen, hydroxyl, and hydrides of nitrogen ($NH$ and $NH_2$). Also present are emission lines of silicon, calcium, sodium, potassium, and nickel, along with molecules common to interstellar space: hydrogen cyanide and methyl cyanide. Surrounding the coma is a gigantic spherical cloud of neutral hydrogen that was discerned by spacecraft in earth orbit during the 1970's. The giant cloud can be observed only from space because it is detectable only in ultraviolet light, which is mostly blocked by earth's atmosphere. Extremely tenuous, the cloud is virtually a vacuum and is about seven times the size of the sun.

As the comet's ices sublimate, a tail may form and stretch for millions of kilometers (up to 1 AU) across the inner solar system. There are actually two distinct types of comet tail. The Type I tail is made of ionized gas erupting from jets on the nucleus. Under the influence of a stream of charged particles from the sun called the solar wind, the bluish-appearing plasma tail is the result of fluorescence of the carbon monoxide radical and always points directly away from the sun. The yellowish-appearing dust tail (Type II) is reflected sunlight from dust grains being pushed out of the coma by solar radiation pressure.

Cometary dust grains are left behind as debris in the wake of passage. Large particles eventually spiral into the sun, while particles much less than a centimeter in size are swept out of the inner solar system by the solar wind. Despite millions of years of solar "house dusting," comets continually replenish the tiny debris swarms. Millions of these particles continuously rain down on the earth's atmosphere. Interplanetary dust is visible in postsunset and predawn hours around the spring and autumn equinoxes, respectively. The "gegenschein," or zodiacal light, is seen as a triangular wedge of lightened sky stretching from the horizon where the sun has set or will rise.

When the earth passes through cometary paths, meteor showers occur as tiny particles vaporize in an incandescent display high in the upper atmosphere. One of the most spectacular showers occurs in the predawn hours of August 12 as the Perseid meteors associated with Comet Swift-Tuttle. Occasionally, larger chunks of cometary material enter the upper atmosphere and appear as spectacular fireballs called bollides. It is believed that a large chunk of Encke's comet was responsible for the mysterious blast that leveled trees 30 kilometers from the impact center near the Stony Tunguska River in Siberia. The presence of carbonaceous chondrite dust but no meteorites or impact crater at the site, along with orbital coincidence with the trajectory of Comet Encke, is powerful evidence for cometary interactions with the earth.

Comets do not always survive passage through the inner solar system. How many trips a comet will make around the sun depends on its mass and on how close it passes to the sun at its nearest point (perihelion). Halley's comet, for example, loses about one-tenth of 1 percent of its total mass with each trip around the sun. In 1976, the spectacular Comet West was observed breaking up as it neared the sun. Heating from the sun, the comet's own gas jets, and spin and tidal forces all interact to pull unstable cometary nuclei apart.

Two general groups characterize the orbits of comets and offer clues to their origin. Short-period comets have orbits with periods of revolution less than two hundred years. Long-period comets have orbital periods of thousands and millions of years, taking them well beyond the planetary system. Originally, the 113 known short-period comets may have come from this far outer region but were perturbed into shorter-period orbits by interactions with the massive gravitational fields of the outer planets, especially Jupiter. Studying the orbits of long-period comets led to the discovery that most seem to originate from a region about 65,000 AUs from the sun—nearly a quarter of the distance to the nearest star. A spherical cometary reservoir, called the Oort cloud (named for Jan Oort, a Dutch astronomer who proposed its existence in 1950), is believed to be populated by about a trillion comets with a total mass equivalent to that of the earth.

## Methods of Study

Aristotle was one of the first great thinkers to formulate an observationally based theory of the nature of comets. Aristotelian cosmology held that the heavenly bodies—the moon, sun, five known planets, and stars—each revolved on its own perfect sphere about the earth. Since comets were such vagabonds of the sky, they could not possibly be a part of this framework of perfectly uniform circular motion.

Aristotle concluded that comets were a strange phenomenon of the upper atmosphere, well within the orbit of the moon. In 1577, the Danish observational astronomer Tycho Brahe shattered Aristotle's theory (without the aid of a telescope) by measuring the parallax (or motion against the background stars) of a comet and deduced that the object was at least 230 earth radii away—placing it well beyond lunar orbit. His methodical observations of the motions of planets and comets led Johannes Kepler to formulate laws of planetary motion. Kepler was also the first to understand that a comet's tail always orients itself away from the sun.

Isaac Newton believed that the sun was powered by gravitational potential energy turned into kinetic energy and resultant heat as infalling comets continually fueled the star. Newton's laws of motion and universal gravitation also helped Edmond Halley to realize that the comets of 1531, 1607, and 1682 were one and the same and to predict its return in 1758. In 1819, Johann Franz Encke became the second astronomer to deduce the orbital elements of a comet and to have it named for him rather than for the observational discoverer. Encke found that the comets of 1786, 1795, 1805, and 1818 were one and the same, with a period of about three and one-third years. Encke also found that the comet appeared two and one-half hours early each return.

To explain the early return of comets like Encke and the late arrival of Halley (which is around four and a half days tardy each trip around the sun), scientists theorized that comets had a composition similar to a "flying sandbank" of individual grains traveling together through space. The model was based on the observation that annual meteor showers coincided with the orbits of known comets. Spectral observations, however, showed that comets were composed mostly of water ices, along with some carbonaceous compounds. By the mid-twentieth century, a more complete picture of comets emerged. In 1950, Fred L. Whipple of Harvard University proposed that comets were in essence "dirty snowballs" coming from the outer solar system. According to the modern model, a comet's nucleus is composed of water ice along with an aggregate of volatile and organic compounds.

Whipple's dirty snowball model was essentially confirmed in 1986, when the European Space Agency's Giotto spacecraft (using navigational data obtained from twin Soviet Vega probes) passed only 500 kilometers from Comet Halley. Giotto imaged Halley's nucleus and monitored the electromagnetic environment around the comet to try sampling the comet's complex interactions with the solar wind. Giotto found Halley's reflective power (albedo) among the lowest in the solar system, as carbonaceous materials make the reflectivity very low, and the nucleus appears jet black except in the bright regions where jets were erupting. Halley's nucleus measured 16×8×8 kilometers, resembling a lumpy potato or peanut. Observations of Halley helped to develop an updated version of the dirty snowball. It seems that comets are volatile ices as originally thought, covered with a thin crust of nonconducting carbonaceous material that serves to protect the internal reservoir of ice from the intense heating experienced during perihelion. Based on analysis from its 1986 appearance, scientists believe that the density of Halley's nucleus is about one-quarter the density of water.

Halley rotates on its axis once every fifty-three hours and undergoes a nutation (wobbling) period about once every seven and one-half days. The nutation is caused by the explosive eruption of gas jets punching through the thin crust as the internal ices are heated during solar approach. The gas jetting accounts for the so-called rocket effect that distinguishes comets as capable of jet propulsion through the solar system. Up to eight active jets were observed on Halley, with vents covering about 10 percent of the surface. Giotto and the Soviet Vegas were unable to get an accurate measurement of the mass of Halley using gravitational perturbation information because of the buffeting effect of the jets. The jet propulsion power of the jets also explains the early arrival of some comets and the late arrival of others. Depending on the direction of rotation, the cometary jets either increase or decrease the size of the orbit, which in turn changes the arrival time.

Radiation pressure, which pushes the dust tail about 120 degrees away from the Sun, could not account for the 180-degree orientation of the gas tail. In 1951, German astronomer Ludwig Biermann correctly proposed that the charged particles or solar wind streaming from the sun could account for the positioning of the plasma tail. When a comet passes through the sun's magnetic field sector boundaries, the tail disconnects, usually re-forming on the other side of the boundary.

In 1985, Comet Giacobini-Zinner became the first comet visited by spacecraft when the National Aeronautics and Space Administration's (NASA's) International Cometary Explorer (ICE) crossed the tail about 7,800 kilometers from the nucleus. The spacecraft measured the magnetic field strength in the tail and showed that the interaction produces ions, which are in turn picked up by the solar wind and drag the plasma tail away from the sun with respect to the nucleus.

To answer some of the questions remaining after the spacecraft flybys of Giacobini-Zinner and Halley, NASA proposed an ambitious mission to explore three comets and two asteroids during the 1990's and into the twenty-first century. The spacecraft, called the Comet Rendezvous and Asteroid Flyby (CRAF) spacecraft, would give planetary astronomers a bonanza of information on small solar system bodies. Visiting Comet Tempel 1, the CRAF spacecraft would get the first truly accurate mass determinations (good to within one-tenth of 1 percent) of a nucleus. In a parking orbit alongside the comet, the spacecraft would fire into the nucleus a penetrating probe, containing a gas chromatograph, to survey the comet's chemistry within the nucleus and to monitor the comet's temperature profile.

Possible cometary impact with the earth has led to some highly controversial theories. In the late 1970's, a team of scientists led by Nobel physics laureate Luis Alvarez found the element iridium, abundant in comets and meteoroids, in sedimentary clays at the geologic boundary marking mass extinctions ending the age of dinosaurs. At the close of the Cretaceous period, 65 million years ago, it is possible that a shower of comets descended upon the inner solar system, with one or more large bodies striking the earth. Although a comet shower is one possible mechanism, it is also possible that the bombarding object was an earth-crossing asteroid.

Proponents of the comet-shower hypothesis believe that the sun has a dark, orbiting companion star called Nemesis that passes through the Oort cloud, sending a rain of comets into the inner solar system at intervals of about 30 million years. Some iridium has been found at other geologic boundaries coinciding with mass extinctions, but none has as conclusive evidence as the Cretaceous-Tertiary boundary, which displays shocked quartz grains and pure carbon soot from fires ignited by the impact.

In the late 1970's, Sir Fred Hoyle of the University of Cambridge proposed that comets are actually harbors for life, with tiny pools of organic soup inside the nucleus that contain bacterial and viral colonies. Hoyle argued that comets are perhaps the original seeders of life on earth, depositing organic compounds and even pathogenic organisms that caused outbreaks of illness on the planet. Although no one has ever sampled a comet directly, the theory has not found acceptance in the scientific community.

In the 1980's, Louis Frank of the University of Iowa proposed a revolutionary and controversial idea. Using data from the earth-monitoring Dynamics Explorer Satellite, Frank reported that he had detected ultraviolet holes in the spectrum of oxygen. Frank concluded that the holes are caused by "minicomets" about a meter across, striking the earth's upper atmosphere. At their apparent rate of twenty per minute, if the minicomets exist, they could provide a continuous replenishing of water for the earth. The mass of one atmosphere of water would be added every 5 million years, and an ocean of water would accumulate in 1.5 billion years. Like the Nemesis theory, Frank's minicomets are highly controversial and ironically reminiscent of Newton's comet.

### Context

For centuries, comets were associated with a number of misfortunes, from plagues and wars to the fall of kings and empires. Science has dispelled superstitious notions about comets, but much of the mystery surrounding them remains. These tiny objects, the oldest in the planetary system, offer a tremendous challenge to modern scientists. Although comets no longer inspire quite the reaction that they did in earlier times, they are still objects of wonder that may play greater roles in shaping the earth than was once thought. If funding is garnered, an American-built spacecraft may be able to park alongside an incoming comet and watch it "turn on" as energy from the sun begins to activate the nucleus. Visual and infrared pictures of this phenomenon would be truly spectacular.

Scientists have learned much about other planets and moons in the solar system, but despite visits to two comets by a flotilla of international spacecraft, the objects remain cloaked in mystery. One of the greatest puzzles surrounding the comets is their origin with respect to the rest of the solar system. Based on their composition (mostly water ice), comets should have formed somewhere near Jupiter and Saturn. Instead, they are found at the fringes of the sun's gravitational control, nearly one light-year away, in the Oort cloud.

The most ancient solar system bodies, comets existed even before earth formed. When one examines the surface of the moon or other solar system bodies, the multitude of craters pay mute testimony to a period of intense bombardment early in the history of the solar system. Some of the impact craters were caused by asteroids, but most were caused by comets, especially craters found on the outer solar system satellites. Comets have shattered worlds and seeded others with volatile elements such as water, methane, and ammonia. Tiny vagabonds hurtling through space, comets have left mementos of their existence throughout the solar system.

## Bibliography

Brandt, J. C., and Robert D. Chapman. *Introduction to Comets*. Cambridge, England: Cambridge University Press, 1981. Geared toward the advanced-level reader, this work contains technical information on comets. An extensive annotated bibliography serves as a guide to the technical literature on comets through 1981.

Burke, John G. *Cosmic Debris: Meteorites in History*. Berkeley: University of California Press, 1986. An excellent compilation of the history of meteoritic objects, from Aristotle to the late twentieth century. Of special interest is chapter 5, "Late Nineteenth-Century Meteorite Theories," on the cometary origin of meteors and meteor showers. Extensively referenced with notes. Written for a college-level audience.

Chapman, Robert D., and J. C. Brandt. *The Comet Book*. Boston: Jones and Bartlett, 1984. Another of a plethora of books celebrating the return of Halley, this one is well written by two scientists from NASA's Goddard Space Flight Center. A good popular work on the subject, it is not referenced and has a scant bibliography. Suitable for high school and college-level readers.

Morrison, David, and Tobias Owen. *The Planetary System*. Reading, Mass.: Addison-Wesley, 1988. Chapter 4, "Small Bodies: The Asteroids and Comets," is a summary of comets, asteroids, and meteoroids by two eminent American planetary scientists. Richly illustrated and carefully indexed with color plates. Suitable for a nontechnical, college-level audience.

Robinson, Leif J., ed. *Sky and Telescope* 77 (March, 1987). This special issue on the anatomy of a comet is probably the best source for post-Halley information on the cometary nucleus, Oort cloud, gas and dust composition, and interactions with the solar wind, along with a preview of the Comet Rendezvous and Asteroid Flyby mission planned for the 1990's. Most of the articles are suitable for a popular, nontechnical audience.

Sagan, Carl, and Ann Druyan. *Comet*. New York: Random House, 1985. Lavishly illustrated with photographs and drawings by leading space artists, this work was written primarily to celebrate the 1986 appearance of Halley's comet. Although the famous comet is the focal point of the book, all aspects of comets are thoroughly discussed, including the mass extinction theories. Written much in the style of Sagan's popular *Cosmos*, the book is well referenced and suitable for anyone interested in comets.

Whipple, Fred L. *The Mystery of Comets*. Washington, D.C.: Smithsonian Institution Press, 1985. Affectionately known as "Dr. Comet," Whipple is the world's leading authority on comets and is the author of the "dirty snowball" model of cometary nuclei. Black-and-white photographs and figures supplement the text, which is written in a nontechnical style suitable for a popular audience.

*David M. Schlom*

## Cross-References

Asteroids, 98; The Evolution of Earth's Composition, 496; Lunar Craters, 1393; Mass Extinctions, 1514; Meteorites: Carbonaceous Chondrites, 1638; Meteors and Meteor Showers, 1666; Phase Changes, 2042; Elemental Distribution in the Solar System, 2434; The Origin of the Solar System, 2442.

# CONTINENTAL CRUST

*Type of earth science:* Geology
*Field of study:* Tectonics

*Continental crust underlies the continents, their margins, and isolated regions of the oceans. Continental crust is distinguished from its counterpart oceanic crust by its physical properties, chemical composition, topography, and age. The creation and eventual modification of continental crust is a direct function of plate tectonics.*

### Principal terms

ASTHENOSPHERE: a layer of the earth's mantle at the base of the lithosphere
CRUST: the outermost shell of the lithosphere
LITHOSPHERE: the outer, rigid shell of the earth, overlying the asthenosphere
MANTLE: the region of the earth's interior between the crust and the outer core
MOHOROVIČIĆ (MOHO) DISCONTINUITY: the seismic discontinuity, or physical interface, between the earth's crust and mantle
OROGENESIS: the process of mountain-range formation
PLUTON: a deep-seated igneous intrusion
TECTONICS: the study of the assembling, deformation, and structure of the earth's crust

## Summary of the Phenomenon

The earth's crust exists in two distinct forms: continental crust, or sial, and oceanic crust, or sima. Oceanic crust is characterized by the dense, basic, igneous rock basalt, while continental crust is an assemblage of sedimentary, metamorphic, and less dense, silicon-rich igneous (granitic) rocks. Oceanic crust makes up the floors of the earth's ocean basins. Continental crust underlies the continents and their margins and also small, isolated regions within the oceans. The total area of all existing continental crust is $150 \times 10^6$ square kilometers. In total, continental crust covers about 43 percent of the earth's surface and makes up about 0.3 percent of its mass.

Continental crust is distinguished from its counterpart, oceanic crust, and from underlying mantle by its physical properties and chemical composition. In addition, the continental crust and oceanic crust contrast in topography. The earth's major topographic features range from the highest mountain on the continental crust (Everest: 8,848 meters) to the deepest ocean trench (Marianas: 10,912 meters). The difference in average elevation between the two crustal forms is quite pronounced. Continental crust varies in thickness from 10 kilometers along the Atlantic margin to more than 90 kilometers beneath the Himalaya mountain system. On average, continental crust is about 35 kilometers thick. Seismic studies of the Mohorovičić (Moho) discontinuity indicate that oceanic crust is on average 5-8 kilometers thick. Continental crust averages a height of 0.9 kilometer above mean sea level, while oceanic crust averages a depth of 3.8 kilometers below that datum. This difference in levels is attributed to the fact that despite being thin, oceanic crust comprises the majority of the earth's crust and has a density (3.0-3.1 grams per cubic centimeter) greater than that of continental crust. While continental crust is thicker than oceanic crust, it is less dense (2.7-2.8 grams per cubic centimeter) and comprises less crustal surface area. For the most part, continental crust lies near sea level or above it. It is thickest where it underlies places of great elevation, such as mountain ranges. It is thinnest where it lies below sea level, such as along continental shelves. There are exceptions to this pattern of thickening and thinning. The relatively flat basins of the oceans are transversed by 2-kilometer-high ridge systems, and areas of continents where intraplate volcanism is active often display thinning where the crust is stretched by rising hot mantle material. Rising hot material also makes for more buoyancy and raises the surface elevation yet maintains a thin crust. The Basin and Range province of the western United States is a good example; the crust beneath the mountains is of relatively normal thickness, yet the elevation is high.

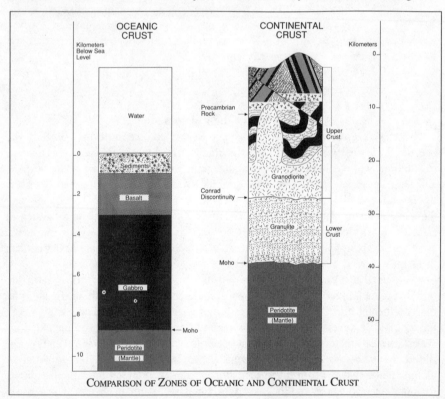

COMPARISON OF ZONES OF OCEANIC AND CONTINENTAL CRUST

Differences in the vertical structure and rock composition between oceanic and continental crust are pronounced. The structure of oceanic crust has a prominent layered effect that seismic waves can readily detect. The layers are attributed to petrologic differences between basalt, gabbro, and peridotites that comprise the layers. Continental crust has a more complex layered structure, and the contacts between layers are not well defined. Continental crust is separated into upper and lower zones (see figure). The upper zone is usually highly variable in composition, with the top few kilometers of material being any combination of unmetamorphosed volcanic or sedimentary rocks, to medium-grade metamorphics such as quartzites and greenschists. Below this immediate layer, the upper zone of continental crust is typically regarded as either granodiorite or quartz diorite. This assumption is based on seismic wave travel times. The upper zone of the crust is separated from the lower zone by a change in seismic velocity similar to that which separates the asthenosphere from the crust itself. This intracrustal boundary is called the Conrad discontinuity. The composition of the lower continental crust is less well known because of the relatively few places where outcrops are available for study. Observations made on rocks in the most deeply eroded regions of Precambrian shields lead researchers to believe that the lower zone is composed of granulite. Granulite is a rock of intermediate-to-basic composition, containing mainly pyroxene and calcium feldspars. The velocities of seismic waves through granulite compare favorably with seismic velocities observed passing through rocks of the lower zone. Such circumstantial evidence favors granulite as the composition of the lower continental crust.

When taken on average, the overall chemical composition of continental crust corresponds to that of an intermediate igneous rock with a composition between andesite (tonalite) and dacite (granodiorite). Because igneous rocks of this type are added to continental crust from the mantle at convergent (destructive) plate boundaries, igneous activity of this kind is thought to be responsible for the majority of growth to the continental crust. The accretion rate for new continental crust forming at destructive margins is estimated at 0.5 cubic kilometer per year. Based on calculation of existing continental crust surface areas, ages, and thicknesses, an accretion rate of 0.5 cubic kilometer per year can account for only about half of the existing continental crust. It is concluded that while the formation of continental crust has happened throughout geological time, the accretion rates for new continental crust must have occurred at higher rates at different times during the past.

Rocks of the continental crust formed throughout nearly the complete 4.6-billion-year history of the earth. These rocks can be grouped into three main components: orogenic belts, Precambrian shields, and continental platforms. Orogenic belts (orogens) are long, broad, linear-to-arcuate (curved) areas of deformed rocks. The deformation occurs to the crust during uplift and usually includes faulting and sometimes the formation of plutons and volcanoes. The result of the deformation is the creation of a mountain system. The deformations affect thick sections through the crust and leave permanent scars that can be recognized long after the uplifted mountains are eroded away. Precambrian shields consist of deformed crystalline igneous and high-grade metamorphic rocks more than 570 million years old. These shields are the eroded roots of ancient orogens. Continental platforms are regions of relatively underformed, younger sedimentary or volcanic rocks overlying Precambrian basement. These platforms, while nestled within the continental interior and isolated from internal strain, still typically warp into broad regional structures, usually basins or domes. Shields and platforms can form a stable nucleus to continental masses. These stable regions are called cratons. Examples of a shield and sedimentary platforms forming stable craton regions are the Canadian Shield, the Michigan Basin, and the Ozark Uplift.

The earth's crust is a solid, rigid layer of mobile plates that comprise the uppermost part of the lithosphere. There are seven major plates, several minor plates, and numerous microplates. These plates appear to float on the plastic upper mantle of the earth, called the asthenosphere. The vertical boundary between the asthenosphere and the crust is called the Mohorovičić discontinuity, or the Moho. The Moho is a zone less than 1 kilometer thick in some places but several kilometers thick in others, where the velocity of seismic waves changes from about 7 kilometers per second in the crust to about 8 kilometers per second in the mantle. This change in seismic velocity is caused largely by a change in composition between the crust and mantle. Rocks of the mantle are rich in iron and magnesium but poor in silicon, making them denser than the silicon-enriched overlying crust.

The movement of crustal plates upon the denser asthenosphere is believed to be caused by complex convection currents deep within the mantle. The upper zone of the earth's crust, in which plate movement takes place, is called the tectonosphere. As the plates move about the tectonosphere, they interact with one another. The plates tear apart (rift), collide, slide under (subduct), or slide against each other (transform fault). The active edges of the plates are called plate boundaries. The interaction of crustal plates at plate boundaries, in addition to the cyclic phenomena of sedimentation, metamorphism, and igneous activity, makes the crust the most complex region of the earth. These activities process and reprocess crustal material and lead to the diversity of physical and chemical properties observed in crustal rocks. The rocks of the crust indicate that these processes have taken place throughout geological time and further suggest that the crust has grown in bulk at the expense of the upper mantle.

The oceanic and continental crusts interact along their margins. The margin may be passive, in that stresses are no longer deforming it, or the margin may be active, in which case it is a zone of seismic and tectonic activity. Along passive margins, the transition between continental and oceanic crust is gradual; a good example is the Atlantic shelf along the eastern coast of North America. The best example of an active margin between continental and oceanic crustal plates is the Pacific basin. Around the margin of the Pacific basin, relatively dense oceanic crust is being actively subducted beneath the lighter continental crust. On the continental side, mountain ranges rise (the Andes) and island arcs are formed (the Aleutians), both dominated by active volcanism. Active margins also exist where two continental plates collide. When continents come together, there is little subduction because both plates are of low density. While igneous activity is less prominent than along convergent plate boundaries, the degree of deformation along the margins can be extreme; there is often considerable uplift involved. The contacting continental plates can either slide past each other along a transform fault (such as the San Andreas fault) or act like two cars in a head-on collision. As the plates collide, the crust shortens and the intervening sea floor is uplifted, folded, faulted, and over-thrust. The most dramatic example of such an interaction of continental masses is the Himalaya mountain system.

Regions such as the Himalaya of Asia and the Alps of Europe are known as suture zones. They mark the boundaries where two plates of continental crust have collided. At suture zones, oceanic crust is subducted until the ocean basin separating the two continents disappears, and a violent collision takes place. Moving only centimeters per year, the two continents ram into each other. The deformation to the plates during such a collision can be quite dramatic. The two continental plate margins that collide already have thick, mountainous continental margins along their active subduction zones. As the collision takes place, mountain range meets mountain range, and a new, higher, and more complex set of mountains is created. The already thicker-than-average crusts beneath the two colliding continental edges combine to form an even thicker crust to support the newly uplifted mountains. This process is complicated by secondary magmatic activity that adds buoyancy and uplift. At such suture zones, the continental crust is at its thickest, and mountain peaks reach their most spectacular heights.

Continental crust thus forms convergent (subducting) boundaries with oceanic crust and can also collide or slide alongside other continental plates at transform boundaries. Continental crust can form one other tectonic boundary within its plate margin: It can split and form a spreading zone (rift) similar to the spreading ridges of oceanic crust. Plate interaction at a continental margin may influence the crust hundreds of kilometers inland. If forces within the plate work to stretch the crust, thinning it markedly, crustal faults may develop along the thinning zone. The crustal fault blocks that form will begin to subside as the crust continues to be stretched. Because the upper mantle is also being stretched, material from the lower mantle rises to take its place. This material is hotter and raises the temperature of the surrounding rock. The result is the formation of a magma zone beneath the thin crust of the rift zone. If the magma reaches the surface, volcanic activity similar to that seen at ocean ridge systems develops. Basaltic lava flows to the surface and begins to force the sides of the rift apart. Sometimes the divergence ends as a result of a shift in the overall dynamics of the plate. If that happens, the rift may leave a scar only a few tens of kilometers wide. Some examples are the Midcontinental rift system of North America, the Rhine Valley of Europe, and the East African rift valley. If the rift continues to expand, a new ocean basin/plate is formed. The Atlanic basin is an example of continued rifting of a continental plate to form an active oceanic plate. In some instances, rifting of two continental bodies occurs near the margin of an older continental margin, and fragments are rifted away from the main continental body. When that happens, small plateaus of continental crust (microplates) become partially submerged in the ocean or become surrounded by oceanic crust. One example is the Lord Howe Rise of the South Pacific. The highest part of the Lord Howe microplate surfaces above the ocean as New Zealand.

## Methods of Study

Earth scientists have used studies of seismic velocity waves to define the boundaries and limits of continental crust and, through exhaustive field investigations and geophysical analysis, have made reliable estimates of the crust's composition. The processes responsible for the formation and dynamic nature of continental crust, however, have remained elusive. To explain their observations, earth scientists have come to rely on their present understanding of plate tectonics and the related processes of volcanism and orogenesis.

The Andesite Model is a tectonics-based explanation for the formation and growth of continental crust. The model can be stated as follows: The growth of continental crust results from the emplacement or extrusion of largely mantle-derived magmas formed at destructive plate margins. The process begins at the ocean ridges, where melted mantle peridotite rises to the surface as basaltic lava, forming new oceanic crust. The oceanic crust moves away from the ridge by way of sea-floor spreading. The spreading is caused by the constant extrusion of more basaltic lava at the ridge. Eventually, the oceanic plate encounters a continental plate and, because of the oceanic crust's greater density, descends below the continental plate. The oceanic crust descends at an angle of 30-60 degrees, forming deep trenches along the continental margin. The descending plate eventually reaches a seismically active region of the mantle known as the Benioff zone. At the Benioff zone, the subducting plate melts, producing a chemically complex, destructive margin magma (andesitic). This lighter, less dense andesitic melt rises through the mantle and into the overriding continental crust. The rising melt creates large plutons within the crust or breaks through to the surface to form andesitic volcanoes. Many large andesitic stratovolcanoes surround the Pacific basin and form the Ring of Fire. Around the Ring of Fire, andesitic lava is erupted and added to the surface of the continents. The volcanoes of the Andes, Cascades, Indonesian Arc, Japan, and Alaska, having such familiar names as Krakatoa, Rainier, and Fujiyama, are the birthplaces of new continental crust.

## Context

The study of continental crust and its related processes is important to earth scientists because the development of continental crust appears to be a terrestrial phenomenon, that is, one not observed on other planets in the solar system. Furthermore, the continental crust of the earth provided a platform on which the later stages of the evolution of animal and plant life occurred. Without it, life would have been restricted to ocean basins and isolated volcanic islands, and evolution would have taken a drastically different course.

The memory of early earth history can only be found in the continental crust. Since oceanic crust records an age no older than 200 million years, the continental crust is scientists' only link with the 4.1-billion-year-old geological record of the earth. Studies of the continental crust also allow scientists to venture educated speculations as to the beginnings of the solar system some 4.6 billion years ago.

Although the mass of continental crust is small compared to the overall mass of the earth, it contains substantial amounts of all minerals and elements that are necessary for life to continue on earth. Additionally, continued investigations into the dynamic processes that form continental crust aid scientists in understanding many of the geological hazards that plague humans. Earthquakes and volcanoes, two of the earth's most destructive forces, are directly related to the processes that form and shape continental crust. By establishing a more complete understanding of the nature and functions of continental crust, scientists can better prepare and warn citizens of impending geological hazards.

## Bibliography

Brown, G. C., and A. E. Mussett. *The Inaccessible Earth.* Winchester, Mass.: Allen & Unwin, 1981. An excellent source of general information about continental crust and crustal processes. For the undergraduate student.

Foster, R. J. *Geology.* 2d ed. Westerville, Ohio: Charles E. Merrill, 1971. Excellent general reference on continental crust and crustal processes. Written specifically for the undergraduate nonscience major.

Meissner, R. *The Continental Crust: A Geophysical Approach.* San Diego, Calif.: Academic Press, 1986. Highly technical approach to the study of continental crust. Graduate student reading level.

Taylor, S. R., and S. M. McLennan. *The Continental Crust: Its Composition and Evolution.* Oxford, England: Blackwell Scientific, 1985. Highly technical, more advanced text about the continental crust. For the graduate-level geology student.

Windley, B. F. *The Evolving Continents.* New York: John Wiley & Sons, 1977. A good reference on plate tectonics, crustal processes, and crustal evolution. Written for the college-level reader.

*Randall L. Milstein*

## Cross-References

Continental Growth, 268; Continental Rift Zones, 275; Continental Structures, 290; Earth's Core-Mantle Boundary, 511; Earth's Crust, 518; Earth's Mantle, 555 Earth's Structure, 589; Island Arcs, 1261; Isostasy, 1269; The Lithosphere, 1380; Lithospheric Plates, 1387; Plate Margins, 2063; Plate Motions, 2071; Plate Tectonics, 2079; Subduction and Orogeny, 2497.

# CONTINENTAL GROWTH

*Type of earth science:* Geology
*Field of study:* Tectonics

*Continents are believed to have increased in size during earth history by accretion of additional crustal material along their margins. This process has played a significant role in the formation of valuable mineral deposits such as gold, silver, copper, gas, and oil.*

*Principal terms*

FAULT: a fracture in rock strata with relative displacement of the two sides

FOLD: an upward or downward bend in layered rock strata

GEOSYNCLINE: an elongate subsiding trough in which great thicknesses of sedimentary and volcanic rocks accumulate

GRANITE: a light-colored crustal rock produced by the underground cooling of molten rock

LATERAL ACCRETION: the process by which crustal material is welded to a shield by horizontal compression

MANTLE: the earth's 2,900-kilometer-thick intermediate layer, which is found beneath the crust

PLATE TECTONICS: a theory that describes the earth's outer shell as consisting of individual moving plates

SHIELD: a continental block of the earth's crust that has been stable over a long period of time

SUBDUCTION: the process by which one crustal plate slides beneath another as a result of horizontal compression

## Summary of the Phenomenon

Geologists believe that the continents have increased in size during geologic time by the accretion of additional material along their margins. This additional material usually consists of younger rocks deposited in a deeply subsiding belt (known as a geosyncline), which is then welded to the continent by compressive forces. In some cases, the additional material may represent portions of a preexisting continent—or even an entire continent itself—that has been "drifted in" by the mechanism known as plate tectonics.

The idea of geosynclines dates back to the work of two nineteenth century American geologists. In the 1850's, James Hall pointed out that the crumpled strata of mountain ranges along the continental margins were thicker than the equivalent strata in the continental interiors, and in 1873 J. D. Dana suggested the term "geosyncline" (literally, "great earth downfold") for elongated belts of thick sedimentary rocks deposited along the continental margins. Further geologic fieldwork, primarily in the Alps and in the Appalachians, showed that the sedimentary rocks of the geosynclines had been deformed by compressive forces emanating from the ocean basins. By the 1950's, the generally accepted picture of continental growth was that of a stable continental interior, called the shield or craton, surrounded by increasingly younger belts of deformed rock. Each belt was believed to represent a geosynclinal sequence that was deposited in a bordering trough and then welded to the shield by lateral accretion. Yet, no satisfactory mechanism for the source of the compressive forces from the ocean could be discovered.

In North America, the central shield is called the Canadian Shield. Its exposed portion occupies the eastern two-thirds of Canada, the U.S. margins of Lake Superior, and most of Greenland. The Canadian Shield is the largest exposure of Precambrian rocks in the world, consisting predominantly of igneous and metamorphic rocks. There is also a buried portion of the Canadian Shield extending westward to the Rocky Mountains and southward to the Appalachian Mountains, the Arbuckle Mountains in Oklahoma, and into Mexico. This buried portion of the shield has a thin cover of largely Paleozoic sedimentary rocks deposited in shallow transgressing seas. These Paleozoic rocks are still flat-lying except where they have been gently warped into broad domes and basins. Along the margins of the Canadian Shield, four belts of deformed sedimentary rocks represent the former geosynclines. Geologists named the deformed belt on the eastern side of the shield the Appalachian geosyncline, the belt on the south side the Ouachita geosyncline, the belt on the west side the Cordilleran geosyncline, and the belt on the north side the Franklin geosyncline. Because of compressive forces emanating from the ocean basins, overturned folds and thrust faults are present in all four geosynclinal belts.

Similar patterns of continental growth are found elsewhere in the world. Each continent has at least one shield. These include shields in South America, Africa, northern Europe, Siberia, eastern Asia, India, Australia, and Antarctica. The remnants of geosynclinal belts are located adjacent to these shields. The most famous of these geosynclinal belts is the Tethyan geosyncline, found along the southern margin of Europe and Asia. The present-day Alps and Himalaya have risen out of this geosynclinal belt.

During the 1960's, the concept of plate tectonics gradually emerged as the result of the work of oceanographers trying to explain the origin of the planet's major seafloor features. These features include mid-ocean ridges rivaling the largest mountain ranges on earth and volcanic island chains with associated deep oceanic trenches that rim the Pacific. The plate tectonics theory has revolutionized not only the field of oceanography but also the field of geology. According to the plate tectonics theory, the surface of the earth is covered by a series of rigid slabs or plates that are capable of moving slowly over the earth's interior. Geologists recognize six or seven major plates, each one usually containing a continent. The plates are presumed to behave as separate units, and where plates jostle each other, intense geologic activity occurs along their boundaries.

Three different types of activity are believed to take place at plate boundaries.

Divergence occurs where two plates are moving apart from each other. The result of the divergence of two continental plates is believed to be the formation of a new ocean basin, a process referred to by geologists as sea-floor spreading. When two plates are moving toward each other, the result is convergence. In this case, three possibilities arise, depending on the nature of the plate boundary. If two continental plates converge, the intervening oceanic sediments are believed to be compressed into a new mountain range, such as the Himalaya. If a continental plate runs into an oceanic plate, the oceanic plate is believed to slide beneath the overriding continental plate, producing a deep oceanic trench. Geologists refer to this process as subduction. Finally, one oceanic plate may override another oceanic plate, producing a trench and adjoining volcanic island arc. The third type of movement found along plate boundaries occurs when two plates slide past each other horizontally, just as trains pass each other in opposite directions on adjacent tracks. Such movement may proceed continuously or in a series of abrupt jerks, depending upon the amount of friction encountered along the plate boundary. The abrupt jerks result in the type of earth movement known as earthquakes, and these are particularly associated with the famous San Andreas fault in California.

The underlying causes for plate movements are not well understood. Geologists speculate that convection cells of rising and sinking material in the mantle (the earth's intermediate layer) may carry the plates slowly along. Nor is the mechanism by which rigid plates are able to slide across the earth's interior well known either. Presumably there is a "plastic" layer in the upper mantle that provides the necessary lubrication for the crustal plates to move.

The significance of plate tectonics for the concept of continental growth has been recognized by scientists. Because most of the jostling takes place at plate boundaries, that is where they find the downwarped geosynclinal belts, earthquakes, volcanic activity, and recently formed mountains. On the other hand, the stable plate interiors are places where little jostling takes place and thus where the quiescent continental shields are located.

An example of a present-day geosynclinal belt that is being squeezed between two converging shields is the Tethyan geosyncline. This geosyncline is believed to have originated between the Eurasian and African shields during the Mesozoic era. It must have resembled a broad tropical seaway extending from the Caribbean eastward through the Mediterranean and the Himalaya to Indonesia on the borders of the Pacific. Thick marine sediments accumulated on the floor of this seaway, and they are preserved today as richly fossiliferous limestone sedimentary rocks. During Cenozoic time, geologists believe, the convergence of several continental plates initiated the destruction of this seaway. The Indian subcontinent, for example, is believed to have drifted northward until it collided with Asia, producing the Himalaya, the highest mountain chain on earth. A second collision occurred as the Arabian plate (a minor subplate) drifted north to collide with Asia Minor, forming the Zagros and other mountains. Finally, Africa is believed to have drifted northward, resulting in the compressive forces that have produced the Alps. The result of these collisions is the near obliteration of the old Tethyan seaway. The only relics of it that survive are the Caspian Sea, the Black Sea, and the Mediterranean Sea. In addition, the sedimentary rocks that accumulated in the geosyncline have been folded and thrust northward against the Eurasian continental platform. Scientists have a clear picture, therefore, of continental growth taking place as a result of crustal plates moving toward each other, with the intervening sediments being welded to the shields by lateral accretion.

As indicated earlier, continental growth can also result when a portion of a preexisting continent, or even an entire continent, collides with another continent. An example of such a collision is believed to be provided by the formation of the Soviet Union's Ural Mountains at the end of the Paleozoic era. Geologists now believe that these north-south trending mountains, which have been eroded down to their roots, were formed by the compression of sediments deposited in a seaway lying between Europe and Asia. In other words, the present-day continent of Eurasia, which is twice as large as any other continent, was once two separate continents.

In the cases of the destruction of the Tethyan geosyncline and the formation of the Ural Mountains, the role of plate tectonics seems clear because the plates that did the moving can be identified. Sometimes, however, relationships are not so apparent—for example, in the case of the deformation of North America's Appalachian geosyncline and the thrusting of its Paleozoic sediments against the shield. No continental plate lies along the east coast of North America that might account for the compression. As a result, students of plate tectonics have postulated an elaborate scenario that involves two stages. They assume, first, the closing of the Atlantic Ocean at the end of the Paleozoic era as a result of the collision of Europe with North America, and then, that Europe moved eastward again, resulting in the reopening of the Atlantic because of sea-floor spreading.

The deformation of the Cordilleran geosyncline along the west coast of North America offers no such problems. It can be explained by the collision of the North American plate with the Pacific Ocean plate. According to plate tectonics, the Pacific Ocean is a separate plate even though it lacks a continent. Thus, the deformation of the Cordilleran geosyncline has resulted from the sliding of the Pacific Ocean floor beneath the North American continent in the process known as subduction.

## Methods of Study

Scientists have studied the subject of continental growth in many ways. Foremost among them has been field investigations in the rock strata found along the margins of the shields. Using the fossils contained within these rocks, as well as radioactive dating, geologists have pieced together a detailed history of geosynclinal accretion. By analyzing the geometry of the folds and faults, scientists have also been able to infer the direction from which the compressive forces came.

An example of such geologic field investigations is seen in the deciphering of the rocks of the Canadian Shield. These rocks constitute the largest outcrop of Precambrian strata exposed anywhere in the world today, and to early workers they appeared to be a hopeless tangle of similar-looking igneous and metamorphic rocks. After years of painstaking research, however, scientists have been able to identify an orderly sequence of mappable rock units within the Canadian Shield, so that at least four distinct cycles of deposition and mountain making during Precambrian time are recognized.

Another way in which scientists have approached the subject of continental growth is by examining the rock types that compose the shields and ocean floors. They have found that the continental rocks are largely granitic and are rich in silica, aluminum, and potassium. These rocks also have a slightly lower average density than do the rocks underlying the ocean basins, and they stand higher, as if both were floating on interior layers of the earth. By contrast, the rocks of the ocean floors consist of slightly heavier basalt lava and related volcanic rocks.

To everyone's surprise, the granitic rocks of the continents have not proved to be the oldest rocks on earth. Radioactive dating indicates that slivers of sea-floor rocks incorporated in the granites claim this distinction. Thus, scientists have concluded that the shields do not represent parts of the earth's original crust but have been built up through time by a process of lateral accretion. Their granites may have come from the reworking of sea-floor rocks.

A third way in which scientists are investigating the subject of continental growth is through detailed study of the sea floor itself. This study began with the Deep Sea Drilling Project in 1968, using the *Glomar Challenger*, a drillship that was retired in 1984. Subsequently the program continued under the name Ocean Drilling Project, utilizing the *JOIDES Resolution*, a 143-meter drillship which is capable of recovering samples of rock and sediments from depths of 9,000 meters under water. The findings of these ships have been of great significance for plate tectonics.

All evidence seems to point to a very young age for the ocean basins—less than 200 million years old, which is less than one-twentieth the earth's presumed age of 4.7-5.0 billion years. Furthermore, it appears that the Atlantic and Indian oceans are widening, while the Pacific is shrinking, which, if true, means that the crustal plates will eventually collide, thus providing the mechanism for further continental growth.

## Context

The same processes that have thrust former geosynclinal belts against the shields have also produced rich mineral deposits in the resulting mountain chains. These mineral deposits fall into three categories: metals, such as gold, silver, and copper; nonmetallic deposits, such as certain abrasives, gemstones, and the building stones granite, marble, and slate; and the important energy resources petroleum, natural gas, and anthracite coal.

A good example of a metal deposit found in the deformed rocks of a former geosyncline is California's famous Mother Lode. This zone of gold veins, which is more than 200 kilometers long but barely a kilometer wide, can be traced along the western slopes of the Sierra Nevada, a mountain range that has risen out of the former Cordilleran geosyncline. The gold discoveries—which attracted the "forty-niners" to California and led to the rapid growth of San Francisco and neighboring cities—were nuggets and flakes of gold derived from these veins and washed down into the sand and gravel deposits of rivers at the foot of the mountains. The early settlers realized the gold was from a source upstream, and they called this source the Mother Lode (literally, "parent vein"). Eventually, the settlers traced the streams up to their headwaters in the Sierra Nevada and discovered the Mother Lode itself.

The fabulously rich oil deposits of the Middle East are another example of an economic resource related to continental growth. The Tethyan seaway, which stretched from the Caribbean to the Pacific during Mesozoic time, was the site of extensive deposits of thick limestone sedimentary rocks. These limestones are now oil-bearing and have been caught in the closing vise between the northward-moving Arabian plate and the portion of the Eurasian continent known as Asia Minor. Because of this compression, the limestones have been shaped into a series of gently undulating folds. Migrating oil has been trapped in the crests of the upfolds (technically known as anticlines), where it is obtained by drilling wells down into the anticlinal structures.

In 1988, more than 40 percent of the world's oil imports came from the Middle Eastern oil fields, a situation that has enabled the Arab nations to wield a political and economic influence far out of proportion to their geographic size or number of inhabitants. A dramatic example of this influence was provided in the 1970's, when these nations paralyzed the free world's economic system with an oil embargo. Even though the major consumers of Middle Eastern oil were Western Europe and Japan, the dislocation in world oil supplies had severe consequences in the United States as well. Americans were asked to turn down their thermostats, the nation-wide speed limit was reduced to 55 miles per hour, and automobile companies were told to improve the gas mileage of their cars. As the ripple effects of the oil shortage spread through the United States' economy, a recession was triggered that cost people their jobs and set off a major stock market decline.

## Bibliography

Cloud, Preston. *Oasis in Space: Earth History from the Beginning*. New York: W. W. Norton, 1988. A definitive, one-volume synthesis of earth history by a distinguished geologist and gifted writer. Illustrated with more than three hundred maps, photographs, and diagrams. Continental growth is a major theme, with heavy emphasis on the Precambrian era. Suitable for college-level readers and laypersons with some technical background.

Dott, Robert H., and Roger L. Batten. *Evolution of the Earth*. 4th ed. New York: McGraw-Hill, 1988. A well-written and well-illustrated text. Presents an up-to-date account of earth history from the viewpoint of plate tectonics and explains the analytical methods used for obtaining this knowledge. The emphasis is on world synthesis, with coverage of all the continents. The Tethyan seaway is also documented. Suitable for college-level readers.

King, P. B. *The Evolution of North America*. Rev. ed. Princeton, N.J.: Princeton University Press, 1977. The leading work on the overall geology of the North American continent. Originally written in the 1950's, it reflects the ideas then prevalent but has been revised to incorporate the concepts of plate tectonics. Suitable for college-level readers and interested laypersons.

Scientific American. *The Dynamic Earth*. New York: W. H. Freeman, 1983. A collection of eight outstanding articles written by leading scientists who have been involved in the development of the plate tectonics theory as well as the unified view of the earth. Excellent color photographs, maps, and line drawings. Suitable for college-level readers and the interested layperson.

Sullivan, Walter. *Continents in Motion: The New Earth Debate*. New York: McGraw-Hill, 1974. As science editor of *The New York Times*, the author has the ability to make this introduction to plate tectonics understandable and exciting for the average reader. He uses the historical approach, which gives the reader the feeling of participating in the various discoveries. Well written although photographs are sparse.

Windley, Brian F. *The Evolving Continents*. New York: Wiley, 1977. A good source book for the serious student of continental growth. Data are provided for selected shields and fold belts throughout the world, with major emphasis on the Precambrian, Europe, the Alps, and areas outside North America. Photographs, however, are lacking. Suitable for college-level readers with some technical background.

Wyllie, Peter J. *The Way the Earth Works: An Introduction to the New Global Geology and Its Revolutionary Development*. New York: Wiley, 1976. A concise introduction to plate tectonics, suitable for high-school-level readers and the interested layperson. The supporting evidence for plate tectonics is explained in more detail than is customary in most textbooks. Many excellent diagrams have been especially prepared for this text in order to illustrate the basic concepts.

*Donald W. Lovejoy*

## Cross-References

The Alps, 37; The Appalachians, 62; Continental Crust, 261; Continental Rift Zones, 275; Displaced Terranes, 377; Fold Belts, 734; Geosynclines, 898; Gold and Silver, 975; The Himalaya, 1073; Mountain Belts, 1725; The Worldwide Distribution of Oil and Gas, 1923; Plate Tectonics, 2079; Earth Resources, 2175; Subduction and Orogeny, 2497; Thrust Belts, 2519.

# CONTINENTAL RIFT ZONES

*Type of earth science:* Geology
*Field of study:* Tectonics

*Continental rift zones are places where the continental crust is stretched and thinned. Distinctive features include active volcanoes and long, straight valley systems formed by normal faults. Continental rifting in some cases has evolved into the breaking apart of a continent by sea-floor spreading to form a new ocean.*

*Principal terms*

ASTHENOSPHERE: a layer in the upper mantle beneath the lithosphere that behaves as a fluid, permitting the overlying plates to move

CRUST: the outer layer of the earth, composed of silica-rich, low-density rock, which in continental areas ranges from about 25 to 70 kilometers in thickness

FAULT: a large fracture or system of fractures across which relative movement of rock bodies has occurred

FAULT SLIP: the direction and amount of relative movement between the two blocks of rock separated by a fault

FOOTWALL: the rock body located below a nonvertical fault

GRABEN: a roughly symmetrical crustal depression formed by the lowering of a crustal block between two normal faults that slope toward each other

HALF-GRABEN: an asymmetrical structural depression formed along a single normal fault as the downthrown block tilted toward the fault

HANGING WALL: the rock body located above a nonvertical fault

LITHOSPHERE: the outer shell of the earth, including both the crust and the upper mantle, which behaves rigidly over time periods of thousands to millions of years

LITHOSPHERIC PLATES: segments of the lithosphere that are similar in size to continents; these plates form a mosaic that covers the earth's surface

MANTLE: the iron- and magnesium-rich, silica-poor part of the earth beneath the crust

NORMAL FAULT: a fault across which slip caused the hanging wall to move downward relative to the footwall

## Summary of the Phenomenon

Continental rift zones are areas where the continental crust has been stretched and thinned. They are characterized by long valleys bounded by faults (rift valleys), by active volcanoes both within and adjacent to the rift valleys, by earthquakes, and by hot springs and other manifestations of unusually high temperatures near the earth's surface. Rift zones are sometimes regions of high elevation, so that the margins of the rift valleys are high mountain ranges. Continental rifts are considered to be an expression at the surface of hot, partially molten rock in the mantle buoyantly rising beneath a continent.

Continental rifts are commonly roughly linear valley systems that trend at a high angle to the direction the crust has been stretched. Examples of linear rifts are the Rio Grande rift in New Mexico and Colorado, the Rhine Valley in northern Europe, and the East African rift system in Ethiopia, Kenya, and Tanzania. Other continental rift zones are broad areas of alternating linear valleys and mountain ranges such as the Basin and Range province of western North America.

The basic architectural unit in the upper crust of continental rift zones is the half-graben. Half-graben valleys collect sediment eroded from the adjacent, relatively uplifted fault block. The resulting sedimentary accumulations are wedge-shaped, thicker at the place of greatest subsidence adjacent to the bounding fault and gradually thinner away from the fault. Some rift valleys are bounded by normal faults on both sides to form grabens, not half-grabens. In most cases, however, the amount of slip is much larger across one of the two bounding faults, and the smaller fault is generally interpreted to represent minor modification of the basic half-graben form. The size of a half-graben basin is determined by the length and amount of slip across the main normal fault that formed the basin. Sizes vary, but a typical major half-graben basin in a continental rift zone is 50-200 kilometers in length and 20-50 kilometers across. Slip across the bounding fault of a large half-graben is typically several kilometers and may exceed 10 kilometers.

Linear continental rift zones are chains of half-grabens, linked end to end, with from one to three half-grabens occurring side-by-side across the rift. The linked half-grabens define a major valley system along which a large river system commonly develops, such as the Rio Grande and the Rhine River. The bounding normal faults of the end-linked half-grabens commonly alternate in dip direction, so that the asymmetry of the half-graben basins reverses from one half-graben to the next down the rift valley. Broad rift zones such as the Basin and Range province are also composed of half-grabens. In these areas, however, the half-grabens are arrayed side-to-side, such that the rift zone may be ten or more half-graben units wide, as well as being linked at the end. In contrast to the reversing asymmetry of end-linked half-grabens, laterally adjacent half-grabens commonly have the same asymmetry.

Normal slip along faults stretches the crust horizontally. Estimates of the amount of stretching across continental rifts vary from a few kilometers across linear rifts such as the Rhine Valley to hundreds of kilometers across broad rift zones such as the Basin and Range. The higher estimates of extension predict extreme thinning of the crust if the crust does not change volume in the process. Although the crust in rift zones is thinner than normal (usually about 25-30 kilometers), it generally is too thick to be consistent with constant-volume stretching of the amount indicated by surface observations.

The discrepancy in crustal thickness is probably explained by addition of new rock to the crust during rifting, resulting from intrusion and extrusion of magma derived from the upwelling mantle below. A significant fraction of rift-zone volcanism is basalt, which represents new crustal rock extracted from the mantle by partial melting. The amount of mantle-derived magma trapped within the crust to form intrusions probably greatly exceeds the amount erupted at the surface, so that although the amount of new crust formed during rifting may be quite large, the precise amount is not yet known.

Basaltic volcanism commonly occurs together with eruptions of more silica-rich rocks, particularly rhyolite. The silica-rich rocks are believed to have formed from the melting of the continental crust by the heat carried into it by the mantle-derived basalt. This "bimodal" association of basalt and rhyolite has been considered to be a distinctive characteristic of continental rifts; however, studies have documented important exceptions. For example, much of the volcanism during rifting in the Basin and Range province formed rocks of intermediate composition (specifically dacite) rather than a bimodal suite. The intermediate volcanic rocks formed mainly by mixing of basaltic and rhyolitic magmas. Therefore, the appearance of bimodal and intermediate volcanism seems to depend on whether the basaltic magmas and rhyolitic magmas remain separate or are mixed together. This mixing and what causes (or prevents) it are a focus of modern research.

Although it has been established that a close relationship exists between crustal stretching and volcanism, the nature of the relationship is controversial. Two main possibilities have been presented, the "active rift" model and the "passive rift" model. It is uncertain if one or the other of these models, or a combination of them, is most correct. In the active rift model, upwelling in the asthenosphere causes rifting of the lithosphere. Hot, partially molten mantle rock rises buoyantly beneath a continental plate, releasing basaltic magma, which in turn rises into and through the plate. Heat from the basaltic magma warms the lithosphere, causing it to expand, resulting in uplift of the earth's surface in that area. Over geologic time, the heated lithosphere behaves roughly like a fluid, spreading out from the elevated area. In the upper crust, this spreading occurs by normal faulting.

In the passive rift model, stretching of the lithosphere causes the upwelling of the mantle and the basaltic volcanism. The lithosphere thins as it is stretched, allowing the underlying asthenosphere to well up passively beneath. The upwelling reduces the pressure in the asthenosphere, because the weight of the overlying thinned lithosphere is less than that of lithosphere of normal thickness. Because melting temperatures decrease as pressure decreases, the pressure decrease induces melting of the asthenosphere and basaltic volcanism.

Continental rifts are commonly thought of as features that lie within a lithospheric plate. In some instances, however, continental rifting evolves into sea-floor spreading, breaking the plate in two and forming a new ocean basin at the site of the rift. Therefore, continental rifting might be viewed as the beginning of continental drift. In other cases, however, rifts cease activity without causing continental breakup; these are sometimes called "failed rifts." It appears that there is a critical threshold at which a change occurs from continental rifting to sea-floor spreading, but the nature of this threshold is still obscure.

The North Atlantic Ocean and its margins form a classic example of the results of this rift-to-drift process. At the beginning of the Triassic period, about 245 million years ago, there was no North Atlantic Ocean; the continents of North America, Europe, and Africa were joined together to form a part of the supercontinent Pangaea. During the Triassic, a broad continental rift zone formed that was similar to the modern Basin and Range province of western North America. After 20 or 30 million years of rifting, the continent began to break apart, and sea-floor spreading began, first between Africa and North America and later between Europe and North America. The record of continental rifting before the North Atlantic Ocean formed is left in the continental margins that surround the ocean. The continental shelf areas that surround the Atlantic are underlain by continental crust that contains numerous half-graben rift basins of the Triassic period.

## Methods of Study

Continental rifts and the processes that form them have been studied by virtually every geological, geochemical, and geophysical technique available. Applications of these techniques fall into three main categories: field studies of surface geology, laboratory analysis of samples collected in the field, and geophysical field studies. Study of any natural phenomenon starts with basic fieldwork, in this case making maps of the rock bodies and their interrelationships as exposed at the surface. These data allow the geologist to draw inferences about the three-dimensional arrangement of rock bodies and the geologic history that led to that arrangement.

Field geologists' ability to formulate detailed and predictive interpretations from surface observations has been expanded greatly by new and improved laboratory measurement techniques. Potentially applicable techniques span all earth science, because tectonic analysis of a region involves synthesizing all pertinent observations in a single integrated framework. Of particular importance are paleontology and isotopic geochronology, which provide information about timing of geological events and involve petrological and geochemical techniques that are used to infer the depth, rock type, and pressure and temperature at the source regions of rift-related volcanic rocks.

Most geophysical field techniques used in the study of continental rifts utilize seismology, the study of the way sound waves pass through the earth. Earthquake seismologists analyze the spatial distribution of earthquakes to find what areas are tectonically active at present. Seismic refraction studies, using both earthquakes and artificial explosions as sound sources, are used to determine the thickness of the crust and its large-scale structure. Seismic reflection studies use artificial sound sources such as explosions or specially designed vibrator trucks to provide more detailed information about the internal structure of the crust.

The best approach in tectonic research, in studying continental rifts or any other type of feature, is to blend all these sources of information into an integrated scheme. For example, the three-dimensional structure of the crust can be inferred best by combining seismic reflection and refraction data with data regarding variations in the strength of the earth's gravity field (which reflects variations in rock density at depth) and with surface geologic mapping.

## Context

Modern continental rift zones present significant seismic and volcanic hazards. The largest earthquakes along continental rift zones generally measure from 7 to 7.5 on the Richter scale. They are therefore smaller than the magnitude 8 or greater earthquakes that occur along large strike-slip faults, such as the 1906 San Francisco earthquake along the San Andreas fault, or the magnitude 9 or greater earthquakes that occur along subduction zones, such as the 1960 earthquake in Peru. A large rift-zone earthquake is nevertheless capable of great destruction in areas near the epicenter, especially if buildings are not built to withstand earthquake stresses. Recent damaging earthquakes in Greece, for example, reflect continental rifting in the area of the Aegean Sea.

Continental rifts have been the sites of some of earth's largest explosive volcanic eruptions. Major eruptions from large rift-related volcanic centers can be literally thousands of times larger than the May, 1980, eruption of Mount St. Helens. Because no historic eruption of this size has occurred anywhere on the earth, it is hard to estimate how much damage would result from such an eruption. At least three, and perhaps more, such large explosive volcanic centers in the western United States were the sources of huge explosive eruptions within the last million years and are still volcanically active (Yellowstone National Park, Long Valley in California, and the Valle Grande in northern New Mexico). Similar active centers are present on other continents.

Ancient continental rift zones are important sites of metallic mineral deposits, mainly formed at or near the explosive volcanic centers just mentioned. A large portion of the gold, silver, copper, lead, and zinc deposits in the Basin and Range province of the western United States formed beneath or adjacent to rift-related volcanic centers. Petroleum accumulations are found in some half-graben basins in continental rift zones, such as the Great Basin, the Rhine Valley in Germany, and the Pannonian Basin in Hungary and Romania.

## Bibliography

Courtillot, Vincent, and Gregory Vink. "How Continents Break Up." *Scientific American* 249 (July, 1983): 42. This is a brief, nontechnical account of the authors' ideas about the transition from continental rifting to sea-floor spreading. It focuses almost exclusively on large-scale patterns related to lithospheric plate movement rather than on processes and products of crustal rocks formed in continental rifts.

Holmes, Arthur. *Principles of Physical Geology.* 2d ed. New York: Ronald Press, 1965. This introductory college text was written by one of the great creative minds of twentieth century geology. Originally published in the 1930's and revised late in Holmes's career just before the plate tectonics revolution, it is somewhat dated but well written and illustrated. Chapter 29, "Plateaus and Rift Valleys," emphasizes the vertical movements related to these features, whereas horizontal movements currently receive more emphasis. Descriptions and illustrations pertaining to the Rhine graben and the African rift valleys are especially useful.

Quennell, A. M. *Rift Valleys: Afro-Arabian.* Stroudsburg, Pa.: Hutchinson, Ross, 1982. This volume reprints selected articles from professional journals to provide overviews of the geology and geophysics of the East African-Arabian continental rift and of the development of thought regarding its origins. Although the reproduction quality of the articles is fair to poor and the selection of papers is somewhat uneven, the book makes some articles originally published in obscure places more accessible. Suitable for college students.

Rieker, Robert E., ed. *Rio Grande Rift: Tectonics and Magmatism.* Washington, D.C.: American Geophysical Union, 1979. This symposium volume contains twenty-six papers concerning the geological and geophysical characteristics of a well-known young continental rift. Although somewhat dated, it is unusually complete and uniform in its coverage of types of features and methods of study. Recommended for college students.

Rosendahl, B. R. "Architecture of Continental Rifts with Special Reference to East Africa." *Annual Review of Earth and Planetary Sciences* 15 (1987): 445. This paper discusses the crustal architecture of the East African rift as an illustrative example for continental rifts in general. The main foci are geometries of faults in continental rifts and what insight into such faults is derived from the seismic reflection data that Rosendahl and his students have collected in the East African rift. It is written at an advanced college level, but the illustrations are clear and informative for the general reader.

Smith, David G., ed. *The Cambridge Encyclopedia of Earth Sciences.* New York: Crown, 1981. This book provides an excellent overview of the earth sciences. Includes clear discussions of continental volcanism (chapter 12), continental rift valleys (chapter 15), and continental rifting (chapter 16). Accompanying photographs and drawings are also helpful.

*John M. Bartley*

## Cross-References

The Basin and Range Province, 157; Earthquake Distribution, 421; Earth's Crust, 518; Earth's Mantle, 555; Normal Faults, 676; Gondwanaland and Pangaea, 982; Heat Sources and Heat Flow, 1065; The Lithosphere, 1380; Lithospheric Plates, 1387; Plate Margins, 2063; Plate Tectonics, 2079; Volcanic Hazards, 2601; Volcanoes: Eruption Forecasting, 2622; Yellowstone National Park, 2757.

# CONTINENTAL SHELF AND SLOPE

*Type of earth science:* Oceanography

*The continental shelf and slope mark the continental margins in the ocean. They are repositories for much of the weathered rock material eroded and transported by rivers and wind. In addition, they serve as major reservoirs for petroleum and a variety of other mineral resources.*

### Principal terms

MANGANESE NODULES: lumps of minerals, mostly iron, manganese, nickel, and copper, that form on deeper parts of continental shelves

SEDIMENT: solid matter either inorganic or organic in origin that settles on a surface; sediments may be transported by wind, water, and glaciers

SHELF DAMS: geologic formations that hold back sediments on the continental shelf

SONAR (SOUND NAVIGATION AND RANGING): subsonic sound systems for measuring ocean depth and mapping the sea floor

SUBMARINE CANYONS: channels cut deep in the sediments by rivers or submarine currents

SUBMERSIBLES: miniature submarines capable of carrying two or three persons and descending to great depths in the ocean, as deep as 11,000 meters

TERRIGENOUS: sediments that originate from the weathering and erosion of mountains and other land formations

TRENCH: a long, narrow, and very deep depression in the ocean floor; usually has steep sides and is often adjacent to island arc systems and continental landmasses

TURBIDITY CURRENTS: fast-moving submarine avalanches of inorganic sediment

### Summary of the Phenomenon

The continental shelf of the ocean has been called the submerged shoulders of the great landmasses. The shelf, together with the adjacent, seaward continental slope, separates the land from the great depths of the sea. Thus, the shelf is part of a dynamic transition zone, a zone that has changed markedly over the millennia; as well, it is a zone that has been contested by a number of nations eager to maintain what are considered Rights of the Sea. These rights include the free passage of ships, access to valuable submerged minerals, fishing rights, and military intelligence gathering. The shelf is a nearly flat area that marks the submerged edges of continents. It slopes very gently toward the ocean basins, but the slope is so slight that it is not discernible. The width of the shelf varies, usually wide off the east coasts and narrow off the west coasts. The width may range from 30 meters in some locations to more than 100 kilometers in others, with the average width being 65 kilometers. The nature of the adjacent landmass often dictates the shelf width— broad next to low-lying land and narrow next to rugged, mountainous land.

The massive continental glaciers that covered the earth some 2 million years ago during the Pleistocene epoch helped to shape the continental shelf. Wide, deep shelf areas with rugged topography are found in those parts of the world that were covered by ice sheets during the Pleistocene. As the glacial fronts advanced over the face of the land, they bulldozed vast amounts of the regolith, the earth's surface, to be deposited many hundreds of kilometers away. The glaciers ground huge boulders into gravel, gravel into sand, and sand into a fine, dustlike "glacial flour." This debris was deposited on the surface of the continental shelf. The shelf itself was dry land during these glacial excursions. The ice sheets, some 3 kilometers high at their maximum, had stored so much of the oceans' waters that sea level was lowered nearly 150 meters below the present level. The immediate impact on the coastal zone was rough, turbulent surf with great waves crashing on the exposed shore. As a result, the beach sediments of these shores were coarse, with an abundance of gravel, cobbles, and boulders.

The broad expanse of the exposed coastal lowlands encouraged the development of wetlands and ponds. Vegetation that accumulated in the wet areas formed peat, which is dredged occasionally from depths of 50 meters, and sometimes depths of 50 to 100 kilometers, off the present coast. In addition to the wetlands, the exposed shelf zone supported forests of spruce, fir, pine, and later, oak. Humans lived and hunted a variety of game in these forests some 15,000 to 20,000 years ago. Then the glaciers began to melt, and the sea level reached its present extent some 5,000 years ago. Fish now swim through marine waters where birds once flew among the towering trees. The nearshore deposits on the present-day continental shelf also contain the fossilized remains of giant mastodons, woolly mammoths, and other huge land mammals that once grazed over the coastal plains in vast numbers. In addition to biological deposits, old sand dunes and the rounded pebbles of ancient beaches have been found on the shelf.

The continental shelf is covered with a veneer of sediments that vary greatly in depth. The submerged shelf areas receive most of the weathered rock debris from the erosion of the continents. Indeed, deep exploration has revealed thousands of meters of sediments that have accumulated on the sedimentary rock forming the edges of the continents. Most of the sediments of the shelf are classified as relict; that is, they are not representative of the environment of today but were laid down thousands and perhaps millions of years ago. About 70 percent of continental shelf sediment was deposited during the past 15,000 years. During the million-year extent of the Pleistocene epoch, there were four major lowerings of sea level, followed by flooding, as the glaciers waxed and waned. The flooding from the last major stage led to the accumulation of the sediments found on the continental shelf today.

Marine sediments are classified by a number of criteria. These include origin, particle size, density and shape, mineral composition, and color. Sediments that originate from the erosion of land formations are termed terrigenous. These include sand, gravel, silt, and clay. Sediments that are formed by the accumulation of the shells and skeletons of animals are termed biogenous; those that are formed directly from chemicals in seawater are termed hydrogenous, or authigenic. Most of the sediments on the continental shelf are terrigenous; a few are biogenous or mixtures of the two.

At one time, it was believed that sediments on the continental shelf showed size gradations—coarse sands and gravels close to shore, with finer particles farther from shore. The finest particles, the silts and clays, formed a "mud line" along the seaward edge of the shelf. Research conducted during World War II, however, revealed that this progression from coarse to fine is rarely found. Samples of the sediments retrieved from the continental shelf reveal that they consist mostly of coarse sand. The sediment particles are stained red by iron deposits. Frequently, the shelf sediments also contain the empty shells of clams, whelks, and other marine animals that live close to the shallow waters of the coastal region. Occasionally, masses of broken shells accumulate along the outer edge of the continental shelf. Fields of cobble and boulders dot some of the shelf areas. These massive structures represent rocks transported by glaciers and deposited when the glaciers melted.

Sediments are deepest on those shelf areas that received masses of sand and gravel deposited during glacial meltback. Georges Bank, off Massachusetts, and the shallow North Sea between the British Isles and northeastern Europe feature much glacially deposited debris. The varied topography of these glaciated shelf areas includes banks, channels, and deep basins. An example of a broad but unglaciated shelf, however, is found off the coasts of New York and New Jersey. The deep shelf sediments there are generally smoother, although they may be sculpted by strong currents to form low relief ridges and, occasionally, deep submarine canyons. The west coast of the United States, in contrast, is relatively clear of sediment on the shelves. There is only a thin veneer of materials, and the shelves show little evidence of glaciation. Strong ocean currents can also sweep shelves clear of sediments. These currents contribute as well to the formation of narrow, or even absent, continental shelf areas. The east coast of southern Florida is a good example of this. There, the Gulf Stream, often flowing at 11 kilometers per hour, sweeps close to the mainland. This strong current has prevented normal shelf development. The Gulf Stream is credited with sweeping sediments from the Blake Plateau, located several hundred meters below the sea surface.

The sediments that carpet most of the continental shelf are kept in place by a variety of dams along the shelf break. The break marks the boundary between the gently sloping continental shelf and the steeper continental slope. The dams thus trap the sediments and hold them against the continents, preventing them from spilling downslope into the deep-sea basins. Continental shelf dams may be formed by volcanoes, coral reefs, or salt domes. Often, the dams result when massive blocks of basement rock are thrust up by powerful forces in the earth's interior. The dams and the sediments behind them are often eroded by waves, glacial ice, or powerful local currents. The waves and currents ridge the sediments in a series of terraces that are parallel to the shore. Cutting across the terraces are channels that were eroded by streams during the glacial periods, when the shelves were exposed. Major modern river systems, including the Hudson River and the Congo River, cut deep channels in the exposed shelf sediments. These channels are easily traced across the continental shelf off the east coast of North America and the west coast of Africa. The Hudson River channel, for example, is so large that it has not yet filled with sediment, despite the active rate of erosion by the riverine system. The great scar of the canyon extends across the broad continental shelf, cuts through the dam at the shelf edge, and plunges down the continental slope. This canyon is a major feature of both the shelf and the adjacent slope.

The continental slope is a well-delineated geologic separation between the flat shelf and the moderate grade of the continental rise. Of the three features, the slope is the steepest. It has an average angle of 4 degrees (with a range of between 3 degrees and 20 degrees), and in many oceans, this steep boundary extends all the way to the floor of the deep ocean basin. It is one of the largest topographic features of the earth's surface and may extend nearly 4,000 meters from the depths of the seabed to the shelf edge. Perhaps the most dramatic continental slope area is below the narrow continental shelf off the west coast of South America. There, the slope wall drops precipitously for 8,000 meters into the Peru-Chile trench. This slope is similar to others in that it features craggy outcroppings and is relatively bare of sediments because of the steepness.

The continental slope is steepest in the Pacific Ocean basin. There, it averages more than 5 degrees, while in the Atlantic and Indian ocean basins it averages about 3 degrees. The Pacific Ocean continental slope is associated with the geologic processes that form the coastal mountain ranges and the deep ocean trenches. The word "slope" does not adequately describe the great and varied topography of these oceanographic regions. Underwater landslides, submarine earthquakes, and the processes of subsurface erosion have produced a variety of topographic features. The continental slope is incised by numerous valleys and canyons, some rivaling the Grand Canyon in size. They are long and short, straight and branched, and may be cut through solid rock as well as through the sediments that may carpet the slope. Many of the canyon walls are cut by side canyons in a variety of sizes.

Most of the canyons that cut across and down the slope are continuations of the canyons of the continental shelf. These are easily traceable to continental landforms and are believed to have been eroded by rivers or glaciers during the Pleistocene epoch, when the shelves were exposed. Many canyons on the slope, however, are nowhere connected to shelf canyons and may, in fact, be far removed. It is believed that these canyons may have been (and continue to be) eroded by fast-moving, powerful turbidity currents. The currents may be triggered by earthquakes or by an excessive buildup of sediment on steep areas of the slope. Moving rapidly downslope, the currents—fast-moving submarine avalanches of mud, sand, fine gravel, and water—erode the walls of the slope and carve out the submarine canyons. In 1929, an earthquake caused a turbidity current on the shelf and slope off Newfoundland that was estimated to have moved 700 kilometers at speeds of 40 to 55 kilometers per hour. The millions of tons of abrasive sediments that periodically sweep through existing canyons effectively erode the walls and floors. As the currents move downslope, the velocity decreases and the sediments spread out to be deposited at the base of the slope as deep-sea fans.

## Methods of Study

Early mariners' curiosity about the sea floor was limited to practical matters— for example, finding the channel for entering a harbor. The earliest instrument that yielded any information about the sea floor was the sounding lead. This club-shaped device, about 20-30 centimeters long, was attached to a long hemp or cotton line marked in fathoms. (One fathom is approximately 2 meters long.) The base of the lead, the part that touched the ocean floor, had a shallow, cup-shaped indentation that was packed with lard or tallow. When the lead was dropped over the side of the vessel and touched bottom, markers on the retrieving line indicated the depth of water. When it was hauled back on deck, the fat in the cup usually brought back a small sample of the sea-floor sediment. With no other information available to them, mariners (and even the first curious scientists) believed the ocean basin to be a smooth, unrelieved depression whose bottom dropped off to unmeasurable and unimaginable depths.

The early research was limited to mapping the coast and making soundings in water less than 200 meters. The principal concern was safe navigation. Toward the end of the nineteenth century, however, the laying of transoceanic telegraphic cables, including those from North America to Europe, spurred greater interest in making more accurate and detailed surveys. The pioneering global voyage of the British research vessel, *Challenger*, from 1873 to 1876, included many soundings in areas previously not studied, but research methods were tedious and progress was slow. The soundings were made with hemp rope, which frequently broke under the strain of its own weight. The line and its weight—often a cannonball—were laboriously hauled up with a capstan turned by the crew. Later, twisted wire rope and single-strand wire, often graduated in diameter, reduced the time required for lowering and reeling in the line and weight. An innovation that involved releasing the weight after it had touched bottom, lessening the load, further reduced the retrieval time. By the beginning of the twentieth century, there were still less than ten thousand soundings in waters deeper than 2,000 meters and only about five hundred in waters deeper than 5,500 meters. Such data provided information about the depths involved but gave no indication of the submarine topography.

In the 1920's, the introduction of sonic devices for making depth soundings revolutionized the procedure. These devices, variously called sound navigation and ranging (SONAR), or simply depth sounders, transmitted a sound impulse from the ship to the ocean floor. The impulse "bounced" off the sea floor and was received by an instrument that translated the round-trip time to depth. Later refinements of the device provided paper traces with near-photographic representation of the ocean floor over the entire span of the basins. For the first time, the grandeur of the sea-floor topography was revealed. It showed that the land beneath the sea surface is nearly as rugged and sculpted as any part of the dry land. The sonic devices could also penetrate the surface sediments to reveal their depth and complexity. Further refinements make it possible to probe the basement rock beneath the veneering sediments.

As valuable as the sonic data are, nothing is more revealing than samples of the ocean floor over the continental margins. The earliest specimens were collected with rugged iron dredges dragged over the bottom. As with the early hemp sounding lines, the dredges took hours to drop, tow, and retrieve. All too often, the dredge closed up before it reached the bottom. At other times, powerful underwater currents twisted the line into an impossible tangle, and again, the dredge failed to gather bottom samples. Despite these hazards, dredges did collect much valuable material and are still widely used. A variety of grabs lowered from vessels are used to collect bottom samples in specific locations. As with the dredges, the grabs often retrieve biological specimens with the bottom sediments. Corers also collect bottom sediments. These devices are dropped or thrust into the bottom sediment to collect a cylinder of sample sediment.

Perhaps the most dramatic sampling utilizes deep-drilling equipment. Special vessels drill into the bottom sediments, penetrating to depths of more than 2,000 meters. The vessel *Glomar Challenger* has successfully drilled into the continental slope in water depths of nearly 3,000 meters. Manned submersibles, minisubmarines such as *Alvin*, are fitted with maneuverable arms and collecting baskets, still and video cameras, and viewing ports. Thus, the observations of scientists aboard the submersibles are supplemented by photographs and specimens of the ocean floor.

## Context

Anyone who has ever been swimming or at least wading at the seashore has entered the realm of the continental shelf. The sandy bathing beach is the shoreside portion of the broad, gently sloping shelf. In contrast, the continental slope is well beyond the reach of the average person. Both the shelf and the slope, however, play major, if indirect, roles in the lives of most people. The continental shelf is an important avenue for navigation of a variety of vessels. The shifting shoals of sand require frequent dredging to ensure safe passage of both pleasure and commercial vessels. Dangerous reefs are marked by buoys, with their lights, bells, and whistles. The military, too, has found a knowledge of the sediments of the continental shelf to be an advantage. While SONAR has aided in mapping the sediments, it has also helped to reveal the movements of enemy submarines. The sound impulses, however, are altered by the variations in sediment texture and depth. Rocks and coral reefs produce confusing echoes. Sandy sediments on the sea floor favor long-range acoustical detection; muddy sediments absorb some of the impulses, allowing for only short-range detection.

Many valuable charts of the sea floor were made by naval vessels of a number of nations eager to gain the advantage in possible future submarine combat. The charts serve a more utilitarian purpose in delineating favored habitats for commercial marine organisms. As habitat for fish and crustaceans such as crabs, shrimp, and lobsters, the continental shelf supports many valuable fisheries. Because of their proximity to the land, the shelf and slope zones receive the benefit of nutrient-rich sediments eroded by rivers and streams. The shelf areas are mostly shallow, 200 meters deep or less, and are the most productive marine zones in the world. Although these areas form only 7.5 percent of the total area of the oceans, they produce 79.5 percent of the world's edible marine harvest. The rest of the ocean waters are virtually a biological desert.

When coupled with information about the nature of the sediments on the shelf and slope, charts of the sea floor also serve as bases for exploitation of marine minerals. While marine organisms are a renewable resource, the nonrenewable mineral resources are the most valuable. Chief among these are the hydrocarbons, petroleum and natural gas, which are extracted from wells drilled deep into the shelf sediments and rock. The first offshore petroleum production took place in 1897 off the coast of Santa Barbara, California, but these wells were simply drilled from wooden piers that extended only a few tens of meters from the shore. By 1937, a completely offshore well was drilled, but this too was quite close to the shore. By the end of the 1940's, wells were drilled and began producing in locations approximately 25 kilometers from shore, beyond the sight of land. Modern wells have been drilled in water 1.6 kilometers into the sea-floor sediments.

Curiously, the second most valuable mineral resource from the continental shelf zone is sand and gravel. Demand by the construction industry for sand and gravel is great, especially near large cities, and as the deposits on land become more difficult to mine, builders look to the offshore deposits. Another factor favoring use of offshore sand and gravel is the relative low cost of transportation by barge compared to over-the-road trucking. Large coastal cities are particularly good prospects for using the submarine mineral deposits.

Other shelf and slope zone mineral resources include phosphorite, placer deposits of gold and diamonds, and ferromanganese deposits. Phosphorite is found most often as irregularly shaped nodules. It is used as an agricultural fertilizer, and demand is increasing with the United States as a major producer and exporter of phosphorite. It is obtained primarily by surface strip-mining on the land. As the land supplies run out, producers will turn to the continental shelf sources. Some gold has been obtained on the shelf off Alaska, and diamonds have been collected from the offing of the west coast of South Africa; however, these sources are limited. Other placer minerals from the shelf include tin, chrome, and titanium. The most intriguing and potentially valuable submarine minerals are those bound up in ferromanganese deposits. These deposits are sometimes called, simply, manganese nodules, but this term is misleading. The nodules are formed by the accretion, or layered growth, of iron, manganese, nickel, copper, cobalt, and platinum around a nucleus. The nucleus is often a hard pebble but sometimes is a fossilized shark tooth. The cost of recovering minerals from the continental shelf and slope is high. The value of the minerals, however, more than offsets the recovery costs.

## Bibliography

Backus, Richard H., and D. W. Bourne, eds. *Georges Bank*. Cambridge, Mass.: MIT Press, 1987. This is a detailed and informative book about one of the most extensively studied continental shelf areas in the world. Well illustrated with photographs, drawings, and maps that supplement fifty-seven articles written by experts. The chapters on marine geology and physical oceanography are particularly well prepared and explain complex ocean basin processes to the nonspecialist.

Borgese, E. M. *The Mines of Neptune: Minerals and Metals from the Sea*. New York: Harry N. Abrams, 1985. Recommended for anyone with an interest in seabed mineral resources, this volume discusses the recovery of mineral resources from the sea floor. Includes color and black-and-white photographs and drawings that show mineral samples and the equipment used to collect them.

Champ, Michael A., William P. Dillon, and David G. Howell. "Non-living EEZ Resources: Minerals, Oil, and Gas." *Oceanus* 27 (Winter, 1984/1985): 28-34. This article describes the seabed's mineral resources in an easy-to-understand style. It also discusses the exclusive economic zone (EEZ) and American possession of sand and gravel, phosphorite, ferromanganese nodules, and oil and gas on the continental shelf and abyssal plains.

Hunt, John M. "Offshore Oil and Gas: Past, Present, and Future." *Oceanus* 26 (Fall, 1983): 3-8. This entire issue is devoted to petroleum resources from the continental shelf. It describes the early history of exploration and exploitation of the resource, techniques for deep ocean research, naturally occurring submarine petroleum seeps, and the estimation of undiscovered oil reserves.

Leet, L. D., Sheldon Judson, and M. E. Kaufman. *Physical Geology*. 7th ed. Englewood Cliffs, N.J.: Prentice-Hall, 1987. This textbook covers such marine geology-related subjects as sea-floor topography, plate tectonics, seamounts, and the effects of waves and currents on ocean-floor sediments. A useful reference volume for the general reader.

Maury, M. F. *The Physical Geography of the Sea, and Its Meteorology*. Cambridge, Mass.: Harvard University Press, 1963. This classic oceanographic textbook, first published in 1855, is considered to be the first real textbook on the subject. It discusses the depths of the ocean, the basin and bed of the Atlantic Ocean, sediments, and how samples and data are collected. Although the style is sometimes archaic, the reader can gain useful insight into the history of ocean-floor science.

Milliman, J. B., and W. R. Wright, eds. *Environment of the U.S. Atlantic Conti-

*nental Slope and Rise*. Boston, Mass.: Jones & Bartlett, 1987. This book discusses the topography and geology of the region. It contains an extensive bibliography and will serve as a useful reference for students of earth science.

Rabinowitz, Phillip, Sylvia Herrig, and Karen Riedel. "Ocean Drilling Program Altering Our Perception of Earth." *Oceanus* 29 (Fall, 1986): 36-40. Useful for those interested in the methodology of research in the ocean basins, this article discusses studies that used ocean-floor drilling and a deep-water camera able to photograph a volcano nearly 3 kilometers below the ocean surface in order to gain a better understanding of the nature of ocean-floor sediment. Suitable for high school readers.

Scientific American. *Ocean Science: Readings from Scientific American*. San Francisco: W. H. Freeman, 1977. A collection of detailed articles about the continental shelf, deep ocean floor, plate tectonics, and mineral resources. The text is well illustrated with photographs, drawings, charts, and maps.

Wertenbecker, W. "Land Below, Sea Above." In *Mysteries of the Deep*, edited by Joseph J. Thorndike. New York: American Heritage, 1980. This discussion of sea-floor processes is very understandable and informative. Covered are the history of ocean-floor research, the impact of volcanism and deep-sea currents in shaping the benthic zone, seamounts and other submarine topography, and methods for mapping the ocean floor. Excellent photographs and drawings are included.

*Albert C. Jensen*

## Cross-References

The Abyssal Sea Floor, 1; Deep-Sea Sedimentation, 325; Continental Glaciers, 967; Manganese Nodules, 1459; Ocean Basins, 1785; Ocean-Floor Drilling Programs, 1805; Ocean-Floor Exploration, 1813; Oil and Gas Exploration, 1878; Oil and Gas: Offshore Wells, 1886; Oil and Gas: Petroleum Reservoirs, 1909; Earth Resources, 2175; Sand, 2253; Sediment Transport and Deposition, 2290; Sedimentary Mineral Deposits, 2296; Turbidity Currents and Submarine Fans, 2555.

# CONTINENTAL STRUCTURES

*Type of earth science:* Geophysics
*Field of study:* Exploration geophysics

*The continental crust is layered on a large scale and in most places can be divided into upper granitic and lower gabbroic layers. A variety of rock types and structures are superimposed on this compositional layering. The crust thus is a mosaic of geological terranes that have been assembled to form the present continents.*

*Principal terms*
  BASEMENT: a term that refers to the crystalline, usually Precambrian, igneous and metamorphic rocks that occur beneath the sedimentary rock on the continents
  CONTINENTAL SHIELD: the oldest exposed Precambrian rocks that form the nuclei of the continents
  CRATON: the part of the continent that is covered with a variable thickness of sedimentary rock but that has not been affected by mountain building
  CRUSTAL DISCONTINUITY: a boundary within the crust that is detected by a change in the velocity of seismic waves and that results from the different densities of crustal layers
  GEOLOGIC TERRANE: a crustal block with a distinct group of rocks and structures resulting from a particular geologic history; assemblages of terranes form the continents
  MOHOROVIČIĆ DISCONTINUITY: the boundary between the crust and the upper mantle that was first defined by a rapid change in seismic velocities; it separates low-density crust from the denser mantle
  RIFTING: a process of crustal extension or separation that is accomplished by a series of faults involving down-dropped blocks in the central portion, forming a large valley

## Summary of the Phenomenon

The continental crust contains rocks of many different ages that are complexly related to one another. These rocks were formed and emplaced by a wide range of geological processes operating from the earliest Precambrian (approximately 4.0 billion years ago) to the present. As such, the continental crust preserves the most complete history of the development of the earth. Most of what can be seen of the continents is limited to the surface outcrops and to information from some deep mines and drill holes. These observations have shown that the continents consist of a veneer of sediments and sedimentary rocks overlying a complex basement of igneous and metamorphic rocks. The character of the deep crust, however, remained unknown before a variety of geophysical techniques were brought to bear upon the problem. The nature and history of the continental crust is beginning to be understood from studies involving gravity, magnetics, heat flow, and seismic refraction and reflection surveys.

On a large scale, the continental crust appears to be a horizontally layered mass of variable thickness. The base of the crust is defined by the Mohorovičić discontinuity, the boundary where the rapid increase in seismic wave velocity marks the beginning of the mantle. The depth to the Mohorovičić discontinuity, and therefore the continental crustal thickness, varies between 15 and 80 kilometers. The continents are thickest under the great mountain systems and appear thinnest where the crust is submerged beneath sea level along continental margins or where it has been subjected to rifting. Over much of the interior of the continents, the Mohorovičić discontinuity appears to undulate gently, yielding crustal thicknesses between 25 and 45 kilometers.

In most places, seismic refraction studies have shown that below the sedimentary veneer, the continental crust is divided into two, three, or four layers defined by crustal discontinuities. In general, the lower crust has a higher seismic wave velocity and has a composition that is more mafic than the upper crust. Comparisons of seismic velocities suggest that the lower crust is gabbroic. On the other hand, the upper crust has the composition of granite or granodiorite. While the terms used for the crustal layers are igneous names, scientists think that most of these rocks have been metamorphosed. The existence of this layering is confirmed by two kinds of observations. First, in some mountain ranges, more than 10 kilometers of uplift of early Precambrian rocks has occurred. The rocks exposed in these eroded mountains are granodioritic to dioritic gneisses similar to those deduced from the seismic studies. Second, independent geophysical studies, including seismic refraction, gravity and magnetic anomalies, and heat-flow measurements, confirm the trend to more basic rocks in the deep crust.

The origin of this layering has been speculated upon for many years. The occurrence of denser (gabbroic) material at the base and lighter (granitic) rock at the top of the crust is consistent with what is expected based on segregation of materials by gravity. While the mechanism by which this gravitational segregation developed is not certain, major possibilities that have been considered include remobilization, partial melting, and upward migration of magmas throughout much of geologic time. The low melting fractions form magmas, which migrate upward and crystallize, resulting in rocks that are usually lighter. Thus, igneous processes may lead to the concentration of the less dense granitic fraction to the top of the crust, which is consistent with the distribution of radioactive elements that has been deduced from heat flow and from measures of natural radioactivity. The second idea proposes that the crust has gradually thickened with time as a result of subcrustal deposition of basic material out of the mantle. The last materials to come from the mantle might be denser and more gabbroic than the first, more granitic, upper layers. Whatever the cause, some horizontal layering occurs in all areas of the continental crust. In places, three layers will change gradually into two or into four over distances of a hundred kilometers. In other cases, more sudden lateral changes occur.

Considerable detail on the structure of continental layering has been derived from deep seismic reflection studies. These studies have shown the existence of thick sections of layered rock within the Precambrian crust. These layered rocks have been interpreted as piles of volcanic and sedimentary rock that have been metamorphosed and preserved within the crust. Elsewhere, major reflectors appear to represent thrust faults within the upper or middle sections of the crust, attesting the ability of tectonic events to affect more than the uppermost crustal layers.

The continental crust is a mosaic of subcontinental, geologic terranes with different ages, different rock types and structures, and different geologic histories. For many years, this mosaic was recognized in the continental shields, where age determinations on the outcropping rocks allowed the division of the exposed Precambrian rocks into provinces. Within the Canadian Shield of North America, the structures of the younger provinces crosscut earlier structures, and the igneous and metamorphic processes associated with the development of the younger province rework the rocks in older provinces. A classic example occurs in Quebec and in eastern Ontario, where there is a juxtaposition between the early Superior Province, dating from 2.8 to 2.5 billion years before the present, and the linear, northeast-trending Grenville Province, dating from 1.2 to 0.9 billion years before the present. While studies of the shields had demonstrated the existence of crustal provinces, much of the crustal mosaic on the craton was hidden beneath sedimentary rocks of Paleozoic and younger ages. Currently, scientists aided by geophysical surveying recognize many provinces within the continental interiors, based on the character of gravity and magnetic anomalies and on observed crustal layering.

Along the margins of continents or within modern mountain ranges, continental structures have been studied extensively. These regions have been most affected by the most recent cycle of sea-floor spreading and plate motions. Thus, geologists have found structures within the continents related to divergent plate motions, involving normal faulting and volcanic activity; to convergent motions, leading to thrust faulting, volcanic activity, metamorphism, and batholith formation; and to transform boundaries such as that found along the San Andreas fault in California.

A large number of "foreign" or "suspect" geologic terranes have been found within the younger mountain belts. These foreign terranes are often geologically and structurally distinct from adjacent terranes. These terranes are similar to the Precambrian provinces of the continental crust in that they have been assembled with other crustal components to form the continents as they are today. The boundaries between the foreign terranes or between crustal provinces are similar in that they often involve thrust faults that may affect a significant thickness of the crust and that may even displace the Mohorovičić discontinuity and involve the mantle.

Continental structures indicate that continents have been assembled over a long period of time and that the process is an ongoing one. The latest cycle of plate motions tells scientists, however, that continents are subject to forces and processes that tend to disassemble them as well. While these forces often lead to continental breakup, in many cases they are only partially successful. In these cases, scars are left on the continental crust that record the event. In general, the disruption of the continent is marked by thinning or rifting of the crust and by injection of material from the mantle. Where the continental breakup is incomplete or stalled, the rift zone and injected igneous rocks are preserved as bodies of dense, highly magnetic rock that cut across the layering of the continental crust. One such zone, which extends within the midcontinent of the United States from Lake Superior through Minnesota and Iowa on into Kansas, is the largest continuous section of a Precambrian rift system that has been largely disrupted by later tectonic events. Other failed rift systems include faults and intrusions in the lower Mississippi River valley and in Kentucky.

In summary, the continental crust is an assemblage of sections or crustal provinces with different geologic ages, histories, rocks, and structures. Most important, these provinces have different physical properties including different densities, thicknesses, and zones of weakness. The provinces of the crust, with their Precambrian rocks and structures, may behave differently under the same set of forces and may guide or even control later geological events. A zone of weakness formed by a set of Precambrian forces may become an active fault zone and earthquake belt under a completely different set of forces.

## Methods of Study

The structure of continents has been defined by geologic mapping, by radiometric age determinations, by remote-sensing techniques, and by geophysical methods. By far the most important in characterizing the deep crust or areas covered with sedimentary rocks are the geophysical methods. These include all the methods described in general geophysics textbooks, but the most important are probably gravity and magnetic anomalies and seismic refraction and reflection profiles.

Gravity anomalies allow the scientist to investigate the mass distribution in the subsurface. Observations are made with a gravimeter, which measures values as small as 0.00001 centimeter per second squared (0.01 milligal), which is approximately one part in one hundred million of the earth's total gravity. Surveys are done where elevation and locations are well known, and the data are evaluated by standard equations. The gravity data allow one to model the densities, depths, sizes, and shapes of rock bodies in the subsurface.

Magnetic surveys may involve measurement of the total magnetic field or simply the strength of the field in the vertical direction. The magnetometer commonly measures values of the magnetic field of one part in fifty thousand of the earth's field. The magnetic anomaly allows investigation of the magnetic susceptibility of rock in the subsurface. The susceptibility is the property of a material that causes it to reinforce or to move into a magnetic field the way a nail will move toward a magnet. The permanent magnetic effect of the rocks, termed the remanence, can also be evaluated as is done for the rocks created at the crests of the mid-ocean ridges. Data are corrected for the natural variation of the earth's field as a function of location and are evaluated by a standard set of equations which allow the scientist to characterize bodies at depth. The magnetic method is especially good for the study of the crust because the mantle has very low values of the magnetic properties and does not influence the data much.

Gravity and magnetic data are often analyzed together for a region. The combination of the physical properties of density and the magnetic susceptibility restrict the possible rock types rather well. The patterns, or "fabrics," of magnetic and gravity anomalies have been used to define different crustal provinces. The coincidence of large gravity and magnetic anomalies has been one of the best ways to locate and evaluate dense mafic volcanic rocks and intrusions associated with the crustal rift zones.

Seismic investigations have provided the most detailed information about the structure of the continental crust. Two methods have been used, and both involve the use of a seismometer with a number of sensors (or phones) and a seismic energy source. The first involves measuring the arrival times of seismic wave energy from a distant source. By this method, a series of phones that will detect ground vibrations is laid out in a straight array. The seismic energy may come from an earthquake or a man-made source, but in either case, it travels through the earth at a velocity characteristic of the rocks through which it passes. The time that it takes the seismic wave to reach the individual phones on the array is analyzed graphically or by a simple set of equations. The velocity structure and layering of the subsurface is then determined. These layer velocities may be interpreted in terms of specific rock types that have been measured in the laboratory.

The second seismic method involves reflection of the seismic waves off of surfaces at depth. Seismic reflection profiling is done with a shorter array of seismic phones and usually uses an artificial energy source. The times for waves to reflect back to the surface are measured and are translated into depths using the rock velocities. In general, more detail can be seen in layered regions by using the reflection method. On the other hand, in areas with few layers, refraction may give sufficient information.

An additional method for the study of crustal structure uses remote sensing. Remote sensing is the use of electromagnetic radiation from ultraviolet to infrared and of radar wavelengths to survey the surface. Observations are taken from satellites or from aircraft and may be processed by computer. The resulting photographs or computer images are studied to characterize the earth's surface. One of the primary discoveries of this method has been the existence of long linear features, called lineaments, on the earth's surface. Some lineaments are only vaguely seen, while others are very obvious. The lineaments often cut across rocks of different ages and types and often truncate major topographic features. Comparison of lineament maps with magnetic and gravity maps show good correlations in many areas. The lineaments appear to be related to deep basement structures, or zones of weakness. Throughout geologic time, the reactivation of these old zones may have affected the overlying rocks and geologic processes, whatever their types or ages. These basement structures have also served as conduits for ore-forming solutions through time, and thus lineament analysis is used by many in the exploration for natural resources.

## Context

Although the upper sections of the continental crust can be studied through standard geologic mapping and borehole analysis, the largest part of the crust is understood through several geophysical techniques. Primary among them are studies based on heat-flow, seismic, gravity, and magnetic observations. These studies have demonstrated that the continental crust is strongly layered, with the lighter and lowest melting components toward the top of the crust. This chemical separation tells scientists that most of the economically valuable elements, such as the precious and base metals as well as the energy-related resources, have already been concentrated upward.

Geophysical studies have also allowed scientists to locate lines of weakness within the mosaic structure of the continents. Basement structures include large vertical fault systems that cut through much of the continental crust. Occasionally, these structures may be reactivated by modern-day geologic conditions, causing seismic activity far from the margins of the major plates. The historic earthquakes in the Mississippi Valley are of this type. In addition, the existence of the deep basement faults may be important in the localization of ore deposits. Economic geologists have found that many large ore districts or metal provinces are related to lineaments apparently caused by basement structures.

While the continental masses on earth were formed by the assembly of smaller blocks, they are also subject to disruptive forces that cause continental rifting and separation. Geophysical evidence has identified a number of rift zones that partially disrupted the crust and then were healed. These failed rift systems usually involve the intrusion into the crust of large volumes of mafic igneous rock. Such dense intrusive masses may have considerable influence on later geologic events, such as the formation of depositional basins and the location of inland seas.

## Bibliography

Barazangi, M., and Larry Brown. *Reflection Seismology: The Continental Crust.* Washington, D.C.: American Geophysical Union, 1986. This book contains a number of advanced articles by specialists in the field of crustal studies. Of great value to the nonspecialist are the many reproductions of seismic reflection profiles and the excellent illustrations showing the nature of the continental crust and crustal structure in selected areas throughout the world.

Bott, M. H. P. *The Interior of the Earth.* 2d ed. London: Edward Arnold, 1982. This textbook gives an excellent nonmathematical introduction to seismic refraction and reflection profiling and to other geophysical methods as they relate to continental structures and composition.

Brown, G. C., and A. E. Mussett. *The Inaccessible Earth*. London: Allen & Unwin, 1981. This book contains clearly written chapters on the continental crust and its evolution throughout time. Excellent diagrams and photos allow the reader to evaluate the complexity of the continental crust.

Dawson, J. B., D. A. Carswell, J. Hall, and K. H. Wedepohl. *The Nature of the Lower Continental Crust*. Palo Alto, Calif.: Blackwell Scientific Publications, 1986. This volume is a collection of advanced articles on the character of the lower crust with regard to seismic profiling, electrical surveying, heat-flow data, and geochemical and petrologic studies.

Dennis, J. G. *Structural Geology: An Introduction*. Dubuque, Iowa: Wm. C. Brown, 1987. This basic text in structural geology discusses a wide variety of structures important in crustal studies. Excellent photographs and diagrams show the complexity of structures within the upper crust and in mountain ranges.

Robinson, Edwin S., and Cahit Coruh. *Basic Exploration Geophysics*. New York: John Wiley & Sons, 1988. This intermediate-level text describes exploration methods. Good treatments of the geophysical methods by which continental structures have been detailed are provided throughout.

Suppe, John. *Principles of Structural Geology*. Englewood Cliffs, N.J.: Prentice-Hall, 1985. This book contains an excellent presentation of stress and strain important in crustal studies. The concept of isostatic adjustments is handled clearly, and the explanation of the effects of loading of the continental crust are treated with examples and calculations. The regional stress patterns in the continental crust are also described. Two chapters on the structures of the mountain ranges of North America are very useful.

Verhoogen, J., et al. *The Earth: An Introduction to Physical Geology*. New York: Holt, Rinehart and Winston, 1970. This beginning geology textbook has several chapters dealing with the earth's interior, the thermal and structural evolution of continents, and the chemical evolution of the earth. Principles of investigation are discussed. Especially good for an advanced high school student or a beginning college student.

*Donald F. Palmer*

## Cross-References

Continental Crust, 261; Continental Growth, 268; Continental Rift Zones, 275; Displaced Terranes, 377; Earthquake Distribution, 421; Earth's Crust, 518; Earth's Mantle, 555; Earth's Oldest Rocks, 561; Plate Margins, 2063; Plate Tectonics, 2079; Rock Magnetism, 2217; Seismic Reflection Profiling, 2333.

# CREEP

*Type of earth science:* Geophysics
*Field of study:* Seismology

*Creep involves small deformations under small stresses acting over long periods of time. The effect of time on rock properties is important in understanding geologic processes as well as deformation and failure. In general, creep results in a decrease in strength and an increase in ductile or plastic flow.*

### Principal terms

CREEP TESTS: experiments that are conducted to assess the effects of time on rock properties, in which environmental conditions (surrounding pressure, temperature) and the deforming stress are held constant

DISLOCATION: a linear defect or imperfection in the atomic structure (arrangement) of rock-forming minerals; virtually all minerals and crystals contain dislocations

DUCTILITY: the rock property that expresses total percent deformation prior to rupture; the maximum strain a rock can endure before it finally fails by fracturing or faulting

ELASTIC DEFORMATION: a nonpermanent deformation that disappears when the deforming stress is removed

PLASTIC DEFORMATION: a nonrecoverable deformation that does not disappear when the deforming stress is removed

STRAIN: the deformation resulting from the stress, calculated from displacements; it may involve change in volume, shape, or both

STRAIN RATE: the rate at which deformation occurs, expressed as percent strain per unit time

STRESS: the force per unit area acting at any point within a solid body such as rock, calculated from a knowledge of force and area

STRESS-STRAIN TEST: a common laboratory test utilized in the study of rock and soil deformation; stress is plotted versus strain throughout the test along the vertical and horizontal axes

ULTIMATE STRENGTH: the peak or maximum stress recorded in a stress-strain test

## Summary of the Phenomenon

Creep is an important geologic process related to rock deformation. It involves small displacements that occur under the influence of small but steady stresses that act over long periods of time. Understanding the deformation mechanisms that define creep is important to the structural geologist studying rock mechanics as well as to the engineering geologist concerned with landslide prediction and control or with the stability of earth retaining structures.

Scientists and engineers involved in experimental rock and soil deformation and the assessment of creep commonly perform stress-strain tests. These experiments are designed to deform earth materials in the laboratory under controlled conditions. The effect of environmental factors such as surrounding (confining) pressure, temperature, pore-fluid pressure, and strain rate (or time) have been documented through the years based on countless tests. In essence, these factors dictate whether rocks will fracture as brittle substances or considerable ductile flow and creep strain will occur prior to rupture. The effect of increasing confining pressure on dry rocks (containing no appreciable amounts of liquid pore fluid) at room temperature is to increase both the ultimate strength and the ductility. Rocks tested under constant confining pressures tend to weaken and become more ductile as temperature increases. An increase in confining pressure on rocks saturated with pore fluids generally results in a decrease in both ultimate strength and ductility. This result is caused by the fact that part of the load (or stress) is carried by the pore fluid and less by grain-to-grain contacts. Decreasing the strain rate (or increasing the time during which the stress is applied) lowers ultimate strength and increases ductility—which basically defines the influence of creep strain on rock properties.

The mechanism of creep may be expressed as follows: Rocks subjected to the steady action of small stresses first undergo elastic deformation. After a given period of time, the elastic limit is exceeded. (The elastic limit is the point of no return beyond which deformation is permanent or nonrecoverable.) Following elastic deformation, rocks undergo strain hardening, a phenomenon characterized by a continuous rise in stress with increasing strain because of dislocations moving within individual mineral grains, interfering with one another and causing a literal "traffic jam" at the interatomic level. This initial stage of deformation comprising elastic behavior and strain hardening is termed transient creep; following the transient creep stage, steady-state creep is achieved. During this stage, rocks deform by plastic or ductile flow under a constant strain rate. Deformation mechanisms are characterized by gliding flow (intracrystalline movements) and by recrystallization. Gliding flow may take the form of translation or twin gliding. In translation gliding, layers of atoms slide one interatomic distance or a multiple thereof relative to adjacent layers. The overall mineral grain changes shape, but the interatomic lattice (arrangement) remains unchanged. In twin gliding layers, atoms slide a fraction of an interatomic distance relative to adjacent layers, distorting the interatomic lattice. Recrystallization involves rearrangements of the deforming minerals at the molecular scale through solution and redeposition by local melting or by solid diffusion. A common type of recrystallization occurs by local melting at those grain contacts experiencing the greatest stress and by precipitation (or redeposition) along grain contacts subjected to low stress. Recrystallization can also occur through mixing and rearrangement of the atoms and molecules in mineral grains by "spreading" into each other, analogous to the mixing of gases and liquids through the process of diffusion. Beyond steady-state creep, the final stage, known as accelerated creep, is reached. During accelerated creep, strain rate increases rapidly, ending in rock failure by fracturing or faulting. Deformation mechanisms during this final stage are characterized by cataclasis and formation of voids or pores. Cataclasis involves mechanical crushing, granulation, fracturing, and rotation of mineral grains. It results in intergranular movements.

Creep strain is equal to the sum of all of the stages of deformation, starting with elastic strain, followed by the transient stage, and culminating with steady-state and accelerated flows prior to failure by rupture. The rate at which creep strain occurs is very sensitive to temperature, with creep rates increasing rapidly as temperature rises. In fact, increasing temperature has been used as an alternative to experiments involving low strain rates or deformations over long periods of time. Increasing temperature or lowering strain rates affects rocks in a similar fashion by decreasing the ultimate strength and increasing the overall ductility.

## Methods of Study

The study of creep is conducted in the laboratory in special experiments under controlled conditions. Environmental factors such as confining pressure, temperature, pore pressure, and strain rate are closely monitored and regulated. Among the methods that have been used to study creep are tension, bending, uniaxial compression, and triaxial compression. Pure tension has been utilized mainly to study creep in metals but has not been common in testing rocks. Bending is a simple method that has been used in creep studies of coal. By far, however, uniaxial and triaxial compression experiments have been utilized most often in testing creep behavior in rocks. In uniaxial compression, rock samples are loaded with the stress directed vertically. The sample itself is generally unconfined laterally. The vertical or axial load is maintained constant, and percent strain is plotted as a function of time. In triaxial compression, a rock sample is loaded in a pressure chamber, and an all-around confining pressure is applied. The magnitude of the confining pressure can be significant, simulating pressure conditions expected several kilometers below the earth's surface. An axial or vertical load is then applied and maintained constant. The total stress along the vertical axis of the specimen is the sum of the axial load plus the confining pressure. The deforming stress therefore equates to the axial load. The latter is often referred to as differential stress or deviatoric stress because it is the stress that deviates from the all-around confining (or hydrostatic) pressure. The deviatoric stress is maintained constant until failure occurs. Some pressure vessels are equipped with heating elements in order to increase the surrounding or ambient temperature; others have the additional capability of recording the increase in fluid pressure for samples saturated with pore fluids. Some of the recent designs have the capacity to subject samples to confining pressures of 20 kilobars (20,000 atmospheres), temperatures of 1,000 degrees Celsius, and strain rates as low as $10^{-10}$ per second.

Creep tests are not easy to run from a purely mechanical point of view. For example, the choice of magnitude of the deviatoric stress is a matter of difficulty and importance because each experiment may occupy an apparatus for a considerable time. (It is not unusual for creep tests to last for a period of one year.) In addition, if the stress is too low, little effect is produced; if too high, failure may occur too quickly. Temperature effects must be closely controlled because they can accelerate creep rates. Also, with many rocks, absorption of water produces effects similar to creep, so that humidity must be monitored and regulated.

Mechanisms common to creep (such as translation and twin gliding, recrystallization, and cataclastic flow) are routinely documented by studying thin sections of deformed rock specimens using the petrographic (polarizing) microscope and the universal stage. The petrographic microscope differs from a conventional model in that it is equipped with two polarizing elements and other accessories. When both polarizers (or nicols) are engaged, a ray of light transversing a mineral grain is generally refracted into two rays that vibrate in planes at right angles to each other. In contrast, when the lower polarizer is the only one engaged, the light impinging on the mineral grain is plane-polarized. The universal stage allows the rock-forming minerals in the thin sections to be studied at different inclinations from vertical and horizontal axes.

Earth and soil creep that may eventually result in landsliding or damage to foundations and retaining structures can be studied in the field and laboratory. Evidence of creep strain along slopes may be detected by direct observation; bent or distorted tree trunks are common indicators. The rate of creep strain is recorded through installation and monitoring, or strain (displacement), gauges. The magnitude of pressures exerted on man-made structures resulting from creep flow can be predicted through laboratory experiments designed to record shear strength and shrink-swell (potential volume change) of soils and argillaceous (clay-rich) rocks. Specialized laboratory experiments simulating pressure-temperature conditions expected in the earth's mantle have been designed to study the effects of creep as a mechanism for releasing stored strain energy resulting in earthquakes.

## Context

Understanding creep, or the effect of time on rock properties, is of utmost importance in the fields of both structural and engineering geology. Deformation of earth materials may occur as brittle failures or after considerable ductile or plastic strain has resulted. Intuitively, it is easy to understand rock failure through fracturing or cracking, since one tends to think of rocks as brittle substances. Under the influence of high confining pressures, elevated temperatures, and stresses acting over long periods of time, however, rocks can and do undergo considerable ductile or plastic deformation. Entire mountain chains of visibly folded rock are common throughout the planet.

Studying the process of folding, creep, and rock flowage has a number of practical applications. For example, it is common to find commercial quantities of oil and gas in folded structures known as anticlines. Therefore, understanding how and where rocks fold and which rock types are likely to develop the best porosity and permeability during the process is of critical significance in the search for new petroleum reserves. Similarly, quantifying creep strain and rates is very important in predicting, preventing, and correcting earth hazards such as landslides and in the proper design of foundations and retaining walls. On the subject of slope instability, creep can play a key role. Earth creep, or the slow, imperceptible downslope movement of soil and argillaceous rocks is the main cause of a specific type of landslide recognized worldwide. In this form of creep, considerable volumes of earth move as the sum of a very large number of minute displacements of individual particles and grains that do not necessarily strain at the same rate. This motion may be caused by expansion and contraction of clay-rich rocks in response to fluctuations in moisture content, which is especially critical in earth materials containing minerals from the smectite or montmorillonite family that expand considerably when wet and contract when dry. The end result of this creep strain is mass flow or landsliding. Similarly, soil creep can exert enormous stresses on retaining walls and foundations. Pressures exceeding 207,000 kilopascals or 2.1 kilobars (where one bar is basically equivalent to one atmosphere of pressure) have been recorded in north-central Texas.

Finally, creep is important in understanding earthquake mechanisms. Earthquakes are classified as shallow, intermediate, and deep based on their focal depth. Shallow earthquakes have focal depths not exceeding 70 kilometers. Intermediate earthquakes occur within a range of 70-300 kilometers. Deep earthquakes occur between 300 and 700 kilometers. The elastic rebound theory and the brittle failure of rock are accepted as the main mechanism giving rise to earthquakes—but only of the shallower types, because at depths where intermediate and deep earthquakes occur, the environmental conditions are conducive to ductile behavior. Convection currents in the earth's mantle and the thermal instability of creep have been proposed as the major mechanism responsible for the deeper earthquakes.

## Bibliography

Dennen, William H., and Bruce R. Moore. *Geology and Engineering*. Dubuque, Iowa: Wm. C. Brown, 1986. A complete reference dealing with the subject of engineering geology, this text is well illustrated and readable. Chapter 13 includes a discussion of slope stability and creep flow.

Font, Robert G. *Engineering Geology of the Slope Instability of Two Overconsolidated North-Central Texas Shales*. Vol. 3, *Reviews in Engineering Geology*. Washington, D.C.: Geological Society of America, 1977. A review of three distinct types of landslides, their causes, occurrence, and prevention along north-central Texas; one type is a classical example of creep strain and ductile flow. Although technical, the article is well illustrated and should be relatively easy for the nonscientist to follow.

Griggs, David T. "Creep of Rocks." *The Journal of Geology* 47 (April/May, 1939): 225-251. A classic reference on the subject of creep, this article is thorough and well illustrated. Covers the most important aspects of the subject as related to rock mechanics and structural geology. Although technical, it should not be too difficult for the nonscientist.

Heard, Hugh C. "Effect of Large Changes in Strain Rate in the Experimental Deformation of Yule Marble." *The Journal of Geology* 71 (March, 1963): 162-195. A very thorough and well-written article on the effects of time on rock properties. Technical, but definitely readable material for the nonscientist.

Hobbs, Bruce E., Winthrop D. Means, and Paul F. Williams. *An Outline of Structural Geology.* New York: John Wiley & Sons, 1976. Chapter 1 is a good review of mechanical properties of rocks, the concepts of stress and strain, and the response of rocks to stress. A fine discussion of ductile flow and creep strain is presented in the chapter, which is well illustrated.

Spencer, Edgar W. *Introduction to the Structure of the Earth.* New York: McGraw-Hill, 1977. Chapter 4 is a good review of experimental study of rock deformation and is well illustrated. The effects of time on rock properties and the subject of creep are reviewed.

*Robert G. Font*

## Cross-References

# THE CRETACEOUS-TERTIARY BOUNDARY

*Type of earth science:* Geology
*Field of study:* Structural geology

*The Cretaceous-Tertiary boundary, 66 million years ago, is the junction between the Mesozoic and Cenozoic eras. This boundary coincides with a major extinction of marine and terrestrial organisms, the most conspicuous of which were the ammonoid cephalopods in the sea and the dinosaurs on the land. A 10-kilometer-diameter bolide that collided with earth at this time has been invoked by some as the cause of these extinctions.*

### Principal terms

BOLIDE: a meteorite or comet that explodes upon striking the earth

CENOZOIC ERA: the youngest of the three Phanerozoic eras, from 66 million years ago to the present; it encompasses two geologic periods, the Tertiary (older) and the Quaternary

CRETACEOUS PERIOD: the third, last, and longest period of the Mesozoic era, 144 to 66 million years ago

ERA: a large division of geologic time, composed of more than one geologic period

EXTINCTION: the disappearance of a species or large group of animals or plants

FAMILY: a grouping of types of organisms above the level of a genus

MESOZOIC ERA: the middle of the three eras that constitute the Phanerozoic eon (the last 570 million years), which encompasses three geologic periods—the Triassic, the Jurassic, and the Cretaceous—and represents earth history between about 250 and 66 million years ago

STRATUM (pl. STRATA): a single bed or layer of sedimentary rock

TERTIARY PERIOD: the earlier and much longer of the two geologic periods encompassed by the Cenozoic era, from 66 to 1.6 million years ago

## Summary of the Phenomenon

The Cretaceous-Tertiary boundary is a point in geological time located 66 million years before the present. It corresponds to the junction between the geological eras known as the Mesozoic, of which Cretaceous is the youngest subdivision, and the Cenozoic, of which Tertiary is the oldest subdivision. This boundary coincides with (and, using fossils, is recognized by) a major extinction of marine and terrestrial organisms. This extinction is not the most massive extinction in the history of life; the Paleozoic-Mesozoic extinction, 250 million years ago, holds that honor. The extinction at the end of the Cretaceous is, however, the most talked about extinction in earth history, because it was during this time that the dinosaurs disappeared.

When British paleontologist John Phillips coined the terms Mesozoic and Cenozoic in 1840, he already knew that they represented time intervals in earth history characterized by very different types of organisms. It was not until the beginning of the twentieth century, however, that paleontologists recognized the full significance of the boundary between the Mesozoic and Cenozoic eras. By 1900, about a century of scientific collecting and study of fossils demonstrated that many types of organisms had become extinct at or just before the Cretaceous-Tertiary boundary. This extinction thus ended what is popularly termed "the age of reptiles," setting the stage for the appearance and proliferation of the types of organisms that have inhabited earth for the last 66 million years, or what is popularly called "the age of mammals."

In examining the extinctions that took place in the seas at the end of the Cretaceous, scientists have learned that about 15 percent of the families (or approximately one hundred families) of shelled invertebrates became extinct. Particularly hard-hit groups were the ammonoid cephalopods, relatives of living squids and octopi, who suffered total extinction; clams and gastropods (snails), who endured significant losses; and the marine reptiles, the mosasaurs (giant marine lizards) and plesiosaurs (long-necked reptiles), who vanished altogether. Major changes also occurred in the marine plankton, and the foraminiferans (microscopic shelled protozoans) also suffered heavy losses. On land, the flying reptiles (pterosaurs) and the dinosaurs became extinct; many types of marsupial mammals disappeared; and a few types of flowering plants, especially broad-leafed forms and those living in low latitudes, died out.

After the extinction, the land surface was populated by many placental mammals, which rapidly diversified during the early Tertiary; by turtles, crocodiles, lizards and snakes, and reptiles little affected by the extinction; and by birds and flowering plants, groups not seriously impaired by the extinctions. In the sea, the most conspicuous Mesozoic denizens—ammonoids, mosasaurs, and plesiosaurs—were gone, as were some types of clams, especially the reef-building rudists and the platelike inoceramids. However, many other clams survived, as did representatives of the other hard-hit invertebrate groups. The plankton and bony fishes recovered, and sharks remained unscathed by the extinctions.

The Cretaceous-Tertiary boundary is almost always identified by the extinctions that took place at that time. Thus, in the sequence of strata, certain fossil groups (for example, dinosaurs) are present in Cretaceous rocks but are absent in Tertiary rocks. Using the criterion of extinction, however, to identify the Cretaceous-Tertiary boundary, produces two significant problems.

The first of these problems stems from the inherent diachrony of extinction—in other words, the fact that an extinction almost always does not occur simultaneously across the geographic range of an organism. Thus, hippopotamuses have been undergoing extinction for thousands of years and disappeared from Europe and Asia a few thousand years ago. They are now restricted to small areas in Africa, where they will probably suffer extinction within the next few thousand years unless human intervention saves them. With the exception of a possible pervasive global catastrophe at the Cretaceous-Tertiary boundary, why should not the extinction of many Cretaceous organisms have taken place in the same diachronous fashion as the ongoing extinction of the hippopotamus? Indeed, some paleontologists believe that there is evidence that dinosaurs became extinct in South America after their extinction in North America. If this is correct, then what is identified as the Cretaceous-Tertiary boundary in North America is older than what is identified as the boundary in South America. This presents a serious problem for placing the Cretaceous-Tertiary boundary which, ideally, should represent the same point in time everywhere.

The second problem faced when using extinctions to identify the Cretaceous-Tertiary boundary is the circularity of reasoning that can result; that is, if one identifies the Cretaceous-Tertiary boundary by the extinction of dinosaurs, one must be careful in saying that dinosaurs became extinct at the Cretaceous-Tertiary boundary. What if, as some believe, dinosaurs survived longer in some parts of the world than in others? To determine if this was the case, another criterion (usually another group of fossils) must be used to determine the age of the youngest dinosaur fossils.

Without question, the most intriguing aspect of the Cretaceous-Tertiary boundary is what caused all of the extinctions. In order to answer this question, the timing of these extinctions must be determined. Did they occur simultaneously and suddenly? If so, then a major catastrophe of global proportions apparently was their cause. If, however, the extinctions were not simultaneous, and if some groups of organisms were already in decline prior to the Cretaceous-Tertiary boundary, then a single catastrophe alone cannot explain the extinctions.

In 1979, Nobel physics laureate Luis Alvarez, his geologist son Walter Alvarez, and two nuclear chemists, Frank Asaro and Helen Michel, proposed that a bolide (a comet or meteorite) the size of a mountain (10 kilometers in diameter) collided with earth 66 million years ago and caused the extinction of the dinosaurs and other groups of organisms that died out at the end of the Cretaceous. They initially based this proposition on chemical analysis of a clay layer at Gubbio in northern Italy. This clay layer was deposited at the bottom of the sea 66 million years ago, and the chemical analysis revealed that it contains an unusually large concentration of the platinum-group metal iridium. Such a high concentration of iridium, reasoned Alvarez and his colleagues, could not be produced by known terrestrial mechanisms and thus must have settled in the dust produced by a huge bolide impact.

Geological studies at other localities worldwide where 66-million-year-old rocks are preserved have confirmed the Alvarez team's proposition of a bolide collision with earth 66 million years ago. Their claim that the bolide impact is linked directly to the Cretaceous-Tertiary-boundary extinctions has not fared as well. Indeed, the fossil evidence indicates that many groups of organisms in the sea (for example, the ammonoids and inoceramid clams) and on the land (dinosaurs) were declining millions of years before the Cretaceous-Tertiary boundary. Furthermore, some groups of organisms (rudist clams are an example) became extinct a million or more years before the boundary. Also, there is some evidence, hotly debated, that a few types of dinosaurs may have survived into the earliest Tertiary. Nevertheless, the fossil evidence is not without its detractors, since many fossils remain to be discovered and the suddenness and synchrony or diachrony of some extinctions still is subject to debate.

A dispassionate reading of the existing fossil evidence does not support a single, mass extinction at the Cretaceous-Tertiary boundary. Instead, it suggests that, as a result of changing climates and sea levels, a period of extinction beginning three to five million years before the Cretaceous-Tertiary boundary was culminated by the final disappearance of several groups of organisms at (or perhaps just after) the end of the Cretaceous. Perhaps the bolide impact at the Cretaceous-Tertiary boundary is best interpreted as the last piece of bad luck encountered by a Mesozoic biota already doomed to extinction.

## Methods of Study

Research on the Cretaceous-Tertiary boundary first must focus on locating the boundary in strata of a given region. To facilitate this, there are two places—Stevns Klint in Denmark and Gubbio in Italy—where by international agreement the position of the Cretaceous-Tertiary boundary is fixed in the strata. Identifying the boundary elsewhere on earth has thus been reduced to a problem of stratigraphic correlation, the method by which the equivalence in age or position of strata in disparate areas is determined. The goal of the fieldworker then has to be identifying criteria (usually fossils) by which correlation with the Cretaceous-Tertiary boundary in Denmark and/or Italy can be demonstrated.

Since the Cretaceous-Tertiary-boundary rocks in Denmark and Italy were deposited at the bottom of the sea 66 million years ago, it is sometimes difficult to identify good criteria for stratigraphic correlation in 66-million-year-old rocks that were deposited on land. In these rocks, the youngest dinosaur fossils usually are believed to mark the Cretaceous-Tertiary boundary until other evidence demonstrates otherwise. This other evidence sometimes comes from fossil pollen grains, numerical ages, or other geophysical techniques, such as studying the magnetic properties of the rocks in order to determine their age.

Once the boundary has been placed with confidence, other aspects of studying the Cretaceous-Tertiary boundary are even more complex. They focus on the extinctions themselves and their potential causes. Data and techniques from many fields are brought to bear here, including paleontology (the study of fossils), sedimentology (the study of how sediment is transported and deposited), and geochemistry (the study of rock chemistry). At its simplest, in a given sequence of strata that encompasses the Cretaceous-Tertiary boundary, the goal of research is to collect and document the vertical ranges of all fossils, their relative abundances, and how their ranges and abundances correspond to environmental changes indicated by the sediments and rock chemistry.

One of the problems these studies face is the incompleteness of the fossil record. For example, when paleontologists think that they have found the youngest dinosaur fossil in a local sequence of strata, how can they be sure? Maybe younger dinosaurs lived in the area and their fossils were not preserved, or, if they were preserved, the fossils may not have yet been found. This caveat makes it difficult, especially in rocks deposited on land, where fossil occurrence often is very spotty, not only to be certain of the position of the Cretaceous-Tertiary boundary but also to be confident of the correspondence between fossil range, fossil abundance, and environmental changes indicated by sediments and rock chemistry. The potential for new fossil discoveries always exists. This is only one reason that research on the Cretaceous-Tertiary boundary continues at a fast pace, and that the cause of the extinctions at and around this boundary remains a subject of heated debate.

## Context

One of the most interesting aspects of the extinctions at the Cretaceous-Tertiary boundary is the disappearance of the dinosaurs. Dinosaurs included the largest land animals of all time and dominated earth's surface for 150 million years. Why such large and seemingly successful reptiles died out has captured the imagination of scientist and layperson alike for more than a century. More important, understanding extinctions in the past, such as those that took place at the Cretaceous-Tertiary boundary, may allow humankind to understand the causes and effects of massive extinctions. This understanding may, in turn, help us to avoid extinction in the future. Insight into these past extinctions would also provide some basis for understanding the potential effects of the ongoing extinction of species in the tropical regions of the globe.

Finally, there is seemingly incontrovertible evidence that a large bolide impacted the earth 66 million years ago. The effects of this impact have been likened to the "nuclear winter" that might result from a global thermonuclear war. Such a nuclear winter would be a period of intense cold when all incoming sunlight is blocked out by the smoke accumulated in the atmosphere from continent-wide forest fires. Analogous conditions may have existed on earth during the first ten to one hundred years that followed the bolide impact at the Cretaceous-Tertiary boundary. Studying the effects of this impact thus provides insight into a global disaster of horrific proportions and, if nothing else, is an inducement to the human species to avoid such a cataclysm.

## Bibliography

Alvarez, Luis W. "Mass Extinctions Caused by Large Bolide Impacts." *Physics Today* 40 (July, 1987): 24-33. This very polemical article presents a strong argument for the bolide impact at the Cretaceous-Tertiary boundary having caused sudden and simultaneous mass extinctions. It also relates a very readable chronology of the Alvarez team's work on the iridium-rich clay layer and the other lines of evidence and arguments that ensued. This is the late Luis Alvarez's last written word on the subject. Well illustrated and referenced.

Archibald, J. D., and W. A. Clemens. "Late Cretaceous Extinctions." *American Scientist* 70 (July/August, 1982): 377-385. This article examines the Cretaceous-Tertiary-boundary extinctions on land in eastern Montana, where an outstanding fossil record of these extinctions is preserved. It argues that a complex pattern of extinctions is evident here, not a sudden and simultaneous extinction at the end of the Cretaceous, and thus represents a good contretemps to Alvarez's article. Well illustrated and referenced.

Hsü, Kenneth J. *The Great Dying: A Cosmic Catastrophe Demolishes the Dinosaurs and Rocks the Theory of Evolution.* New York: Harcourt Brace Jovanovich, 1986. Hsü extensively reviews and accepts the ideas of the Alvarez team. He then argues against typical notions of Darwinian evolution to support the idea that major crises (extinctions) are the driving force of evolution. Some very debatable ideas are wrapped up in this well-written, novel-like book. Indexed but lacks illustrations and references.

Russell, Dale A. "The Mass Extinctions of the Late Mesozoic." *Scientific American* 246 (January, 1982): 58-65. In this well-illustrated article, Russell presents evidence for a sudden and simultaneous extinction of life on land (including dinosaurs) at the end of the Cretaceous. His evidence has subsequently been picked apart by other scientists, but this article articulates well the viewpoint of one of the few paleontologists to have readily accepted the Alvarez team's propositions. Lacks references.

Stanley, S. M. *Extinction.* New York: Scientific American Books, 1987. A very readable, extensive treatment of the subject of extinction. Chapter 7 reviews the extinctions at the end of the Cretaceous and elegantly reduces the welter of data and viewpoints to explain why the fossil record does not support a single, massive extinction at the Cretaceous-Tertiary boundary. Well illustrated and indexed.

Ward, Peter. "The Extinction of the Ammonites." *Scientific American* 249 (October, 1983): 136-141. A very readable and extensively illustrated article that presents the evidence that ammonoids were declining well before the end of the Cretaceous. Ward sees this decline as a losing battle against more mobile, shell-crushing predators. No references.

*Spencer G. Lucas*

## Cross-References

# DAMS AND FLOOD CONTROL

*Type of earth science:* Engineering geology

*Dams have provided a means of substantially reducing the risk of catastrophic floods, as well as saving lives and dollars. As added benefits—which help to offset environmental costs—dams generate pollution-free hydroelectric power and provide a reliable water supply for drinking, irrigation, industrial use, and recreation.*

### Principal terms

CHANNELIZATION: the practice of deliberately rerouting a stream or artificially modifying its channel by straightening, deepening, widening, clearing, or lining it

FLOODPLAIN: a wide, flat, low-lying area, adjacent to a river, that is generally inundated by floodwaters

FLOOD ZONING: passing laws that restrict the development and land use of flood-prone areas

LEVEE: a dike-like structure, usually made of compacted earth and reinforced with other materials, that is designed to contain the stream flow in its natural channel

OUTLET WORKS: gates or conduits in a dam that are generally kept open so as to discharge the normal stream flow at low water

SPILLWAY: generally, a broad reinforced channel near the top of the dam, designed to allow rising waters to escape the reservoir without overtopping the dam

## Summary of the Methodology

Humans and rivers have competed for the use of floodplains for centuries. The floodplain, a wide, flat, low-lying area adjacent to the river, is built by natural sedimentation as the river carries its load of sand, silt, and clay to the sea. During times of excess flow, the river spills over its banks and covers the floodplain with muddy water. When the water retreats, a new layer of fertile soil is left behind. Humans have long exploited floodplains for these rich soils in order to grow crops. Floodplains are also attractive places to settle because the nearby river provides an accessible source of water, transport, and sewage disposal. In some rugged terrains, the development of communities in any area other than floodplains is almost impossible.

Unfortunately, floodplain development has often proceeded without an awareness of the risks involved, and the result has been disaster. In the United States, a few flood-related deaths occur almost every year; sometimes one flood kills many. For every death that occurs, many more are left homeless or experience property damage, hardship, or suffering. Heavy rains in the winter of 1926-1927 caused disastrous floods on the Mississippi River that killed several hundred people and left up to 650,000 homeless.

Because of this conflict, humans have sought to control floods by the use of dams. This attempt goes at least as far back as ancient Egypt, where about 2700 B.C., a dam was built at Sadd-el-Karfara. The basic principle of dam flood control is to store floodwaters in the reservoir instead of allowing them to spread over the natural floodplain, which contains valuable man-made structures. After the smaller tributary streams below the dam have passed their floodwaters safely, the main reservoir is drained in a controlled fashion. The overall effect is to lengthen the time of passage of the flood, while drastically reducing the peak flow.

Dams are constructed of three basic materials: earth, rocks, and concrete. Eighty percent of all dams in the United States, Canada, and the Soviet Union are earth dams. In these, sand and soil are compacted into a broad triangular embankment surrounding a watertight clay core. The upstream face must be reinforced with rock or concrete to prevent wave erosion. Earth dams are the most practical in broad valleys and are relatively inexpensive to construct. Rockfill dams are similar to earth dams, but the heavy weight of the rock requires a more solid natural foundation. The upstream side must be covered with a watertight material to prevent water from leaking through the dam.

Concrete dams require narrow valleys with hard bedrock floors to anchor and support them. A concrete gravity dam uses its great bulk and weight to resist the water pressure. These dams can generally remain stable when floodwaters overtop them, but they are costly (Washington State's Grand Coulee Dam, which is of this type, required 8.1 million cubic meters of concrete). A concrete buttress dam relies both on its weight and structural elements to support it: The watertight upstream face slopes underneath the reservoir, which helps to distribute the water pressure to the foundation. Buttresses on the downstream face of the dam both counteract the force of the water and help the dam to withstand minor foundation movements—a distinct advantage in earthquake-prone areas. Concrete arch dams have a convex upstream face that spans the steep valley walls. The water pressure transmits the force along the arch to the side abutments and foundation, bonding the dam to the canyon. These dams are less expensive to construct than are gravity dams, but also are more likely to fail in the event of a small rupture.

All dams must contain properly designed outlet works, which are gates or conduits near the base of the dam kept open to discharge the normal low-water flow of the stream. These gates can be operated manually or automatically, but they must be carefully regulated to control the reservoir flood storage in an optimum manner and to prevent overwhelming of the spillway or overtopping of the dam. This means that the engineers of the outlet works must have an intimate knowledge of the design flood (the statistical probability and approximate return period of the maximum flood for which the dam was designed), the reservoir capacity, characteristics of past flood behavior, downstream flood hazards, accurate meteorological forecasts, and a good dose of intuition.

Finally, all dams must be constructed with a spillway. A spillway is generally a broad reinforced channel near the top or around the side of the dam that acts as a safety valve because it allows rising waters, which might otherwise overtop the dam and cause its collapse, to escape harmlessly. Outlet works cannot be depended on to relieve the rising waters because they may become either blocked with debris or inoperative during a flood. The spillway must be large enough to convey the maximum probable flood.

An additional benefit of dams is that they not only provide flood control, but also the reservoir can be used as a water supply for irrigational, industrial, and municipal purposes. When the water falls from the top of the reservoir to the dam base through turbines, it generates inexpensive and pollution-free electricity. The reservoir also can be used for fishing, boating, and swimming and can become a haven for certain kinds of wildlife.

Unfortunately, a multiple-purpose reservoir contains built-in conflicts of interest. Because a reservoir used to control floods must have storage space for the floodwaters, ideally the water level should be kept low, or the reservoir kept nearly empty. Conserving water for irrigation or domestic use, however, requires holding floodwaters in storage, sometimes for years. For hydropower generation, the reservoir must be kept as full as possible and certainly never emptied. The area's fish and wildlife are best served by maintaining a stable reservoir level, as are recreational uses. Thus, the management of a multipurpose reservoir for flood control is a very complicated enterprise. The goal is to derive the maximum dollar value from the water while keeping the threat of flood damage to a minimum. All forecasts of possible and probable floods must be carefully weighed against the need for keeping the reservoir full for other purposes.

Flood protection is rarely implemented by the construction of a single dam. An integrated flood-control program also involves the construction of levees, floodways, and channel modifications. Levees are dikes or structures that attempt to confine the stream flow to its natural channel and prevent it from spreading over the floodplain. They have the advantage of increasing the flow velocity in the channel, which diminishes the deposition of sediment in it. The increased velocity, however, also tends to undercut and erode the levee. Levees block off the floodplain, but the increased volume of water in the channel raises the level to which the waters will flood. When levees are breached, the floodwaters spill out over the floodplain suddenly, catching residents by surprise. A breached levee may also trap floodwaters downstream by preventing their return to the channel, thereby increasing the damage. A way to prevent the breaching of levees is to install emergency outlets (like dam spillways) to specially constructed floodways, or flood-diversion channels. These are a means for safely returning the river to its natural floodplain.

Channelization, or modifications to the stream channel, is also used in conjunction with flood-control dams. This generally involves straightening, deepening, widening, clearing, or lining the channel in such a way that the stream flows faster. In this way, potential floodwaters are removed from the area more quickly. The lower Mississippi River was shortened by 13 percent between 1933 and 1936 (by short-cutting meander bends), which reduced the flood levels 61-366 centimeters for equal rates of flow. Channelization may also have deleterious effects. Erosion of the channel from faster flows may drain adjacent wildlife habitats and may undermine levees and bridges. The rapid passage of floodwaters also increases the hazard to places downstream of the channelized area.

Flood protection by means of dams and their attendant structures has some other disadvantages. The term "flood control" is often misinterpreted by the general public to mean absolute and permanent protection from all floods under all conditions. This leads to a false sense of security and promotes further economic development of the floodplain. Every levee and every dam has a limit to its effectiveness. To compound the danger, there is always the possibility that the dam could fail entirely. The main causes of dam failure are overflowing because of inadequate spillway capacity, internal structural failure of earth dams, and failure of the dam foundation material. During the twentieth century, more than 8,000 people have perished in more than 200 dam breaks. An earth dam across the Little Conemaugh River above Johnstown, Pennsylvania, was overtopped and failed on May 31, 1889, killing 2,209. To prevent such failures, geologists and engineers must cooperate closely to design the safest possible structure matching the geology of the dam's foundation.

Dams can also cause undesirable sedimentation on and erosion of a riverbed. As the river enters the reservoir, it is forced to slow and drop its sediment load, which decreases the water-holding capacity of the reservoir and limits its usable lifetime. The resulting delta can grow upstream and engulf adjacent properties and structures. The opposite effect results from the discharge of the reservoir water, now deprived of its sediment load, back into the natural channel below the dam. Here, the water can rapidly erode the bed. At Yuma, Arizona, for example, 560 kilometers downstream of the Hoover Dam, the riverbed has been lowered by 2.7 meters. If a river formerly supplied sediments to beaches, the deprivation of this material could result in coastal erosion. The loss of top soil deposition as a result of flood control on the Nile (the river is protected by the Aswan Dam) has required farmers to add expensive fertilizers to their crops.

Other harmful effects of the construction of dams and flood-control projects include an increase in the water's temperature, salinity, and nutrient content (from the strong solar heating and evaporation in reservoirs and the return flow of irrigation waters). This decrease in water quality can result in undesirable weed growth in reservoirs and in fish kills. Fish that migrate up rivers to spawn, such as trout and salmon, are physically prevented from doing so by dams. Fish ladders around dams are expensive and have proven to be only partially effective. The loss of wet floodplain habitat to reservoir inundation has been detrimental to many water birds, some of which are already endangered species. Unfortunately, the reservoir itself does not usually substitute for this loss because its elevation must fluctuate. Finally, dams are expensive to build and maintain, and they cause the loss of valuable farmland because of reservoir inundation and sometimes force the relocation of entire communities.

One of the best methods to avoid the economic, social, and environmental disadvantages of dams is to prevent floodplain misuse. This is often effectively done through the use of flood zoning laws, which restrict or prohibit certain types of development in flood hazard areas. (Appropriate uses of flood hazard zones include parkland, pastureland, forest, or farmland.) Flood insurance laws, building codes, and tax incentives can have the same effect. If necessary, existing buildings can be flood-proofed (raised higher, reinforced, or both) or relocated. Land-treatment procedures can improve the ability of the natural ground surface to retain water and release it slowly to streams. These techniques include reforestation, terracing, and building contour ditches and small check dams. In urban areas, rooftop or underground floodwater retention tanks and porous pavements can be installed to reduce the risk of flooding.

## Applications of the Method

The Mississippi River is an example of a massive flood-control project. Levees were first constructed on it in 1727 to protect New Orleans, and they continued to be constructed (privately and haphazardly) into the 1830's. Major funds were granted in 1849 and 1850 by Congress to the U.S. Army Corps of Engineers for a flood-control study. After the Civil War, the entire 1,130-kilometer lower Mississippi Valley was organized into levee districts. In spite of the levees, major floods struck the Mississippi River in 1881, 1882, 1883, 1884, 1886, 1890, 1903, 1912, 1913, and 1927. The worst of these came in the spring of 1927 after a long winter of heavy rains, when the levees failed in more than 120 places. Many people were killed or left homeless. This inspired Congress to pass the Flood Control Act of May 15, 1928, which provided for levee expansion and improvement, dams and reservoirs, bank stabilization coverings (revetments), floodway diversion channels, artificial meander cutoffs, and emplacement and operation of river gauging stations (to monitor the water level continuously). The first test of the system came in 1937. Although the potential for another 1927 flood was just as great, the damages caused in 1937 were far less severe.

Work has continued on the Mississippi. A major contribution was the 1944 project on the Missouri River, a tributary of the Mississippi. On the Missouri, six huge dams and a 1,500-kilometer chain of reservoirs and levees have been built. From 1950 to 1973, the combined effect of natural events and man-made structures produced a lull in the floods. The calm was broken when a massive flood in 1973 moved down the Mississippi, a flood that was a significant test of the control projects. The maximum flow was approximately 56,800 cubic meters per second, enough to supply New Orleans with its daily water needs in less than 10 seconds.

Despite the flood-control facilities, losses were great. Thirty-nine levees were breached or overtopped. Property losses were estimated at $1 billion. In spite of this, the river crested 21 centimeters lower than it had in 1927 in Cairo, Illinois, and

207 centimeters lower than it had the same year in Vicksburg, Mississippi. Engineers estimated that flood-control works had reduced damages from a possible $15 billion. Still, the flood left 23 dead and another 69,000 homeless.

Where humans have been short-sighted in settling and building cities on floodplains, wisely built and well-managed dams and their attendant structures are an excellent way to reduce (but not eliminate) the flood hazard. The lives and dollars saved have been great. The environmental losses, which are harder to measure, also have been great. Wild, natural rivers are rapidly becoming one of the nation's rarest possessions. As the demands for electric power generation and water resources continue to increase, managing the rivers wisely is in the nation's best long-term interest.

## Context

In some geographic regions, more than half the population lives on a floodplain—that broad, flat area adjacent to the river. The land is fertile, there is room for construction, and the water supply is ample. On the other hand, the floodplain exists because of the river, and when the river is swollen with extra rain or snowmelt, it needs the floodplain to store temporarily all that extra water. Humans find this phenomenon inconvenient, so they build dams, levees, floodways, and channel modification structures to keep the river off the floodplain and themselves out of harm's way.

As flood protection, these structures work fairly well. Historically they have reduced suffering and saved both lives and dollars. The reservoirs have the added blessings of generating inexpensive, pollution-free electricity; supplying irrigation, industrial, and municipal water; and providing areas for swimming, boating, and fishing. Those who live near a dam may have lower electric bills than others do, and they may be able to drink or irrigate crops with the water stored in the reservoir during dry periods. They may even be able to water ski or own waterfront property on a man-made lake surrounded by desert. They may feel safe from nature's wrath on the floodplain because human engineering has finally tamed the river—but it has not. The flood hazard has been reduced, but it has not been eliminated. Every dam and every levee has a limit to its effectiveness.

Dams have other hidden costs. They can cause undesirable and unpredictable erosion or siltation—resulting in levee undermining, bridge collapse, draining of wetlands, or even floods in other areas. A decrease in water quality is often the result of the thermal stratification of reservoirs, and addition of pollutants and heat from irrigation return flows to the river, which drastically affects fish. The inundation, which results from the filling of the reservoir, of large areas of land can cause habitat loss for wildlife and agriculture and even displacement of entire communities. A poorly designed or maintained dam can collapse, killing many. Still, the benefits of dams and flood-control projects are enormous, and they are a very necessary commodity in major cities of the United States, especially on the lower Mississippi.

## Bibliography

Barrows, Harold Kilbrith. *Floods: Their Hydrology and Control*. New York: McGraw-Hill, 1948. A somewhat technical yet practical discussion of flood control projects in the United States, including their costs and problems. Also included are sections on basic flood hydrology and some notable great floods. Suitable for the college-level reader. Appendices, index.

Berkman, Richard L., and W. Kip Viscusi. *Damming the West: Ralph Nader's Study Group Report on the Bureau of Reclamation*. New York: Grossman, 1973. A thorough scrutiny of the politics of water-resource projects in the western United States involving dams financed by the Bureau of Reclamation. Cost-benefit studies are reevaluated in terms of the environmental impact of dams, who really benefits from the projects, and Indian water rights. Suitable for the college-level reader. Index.

Chadwick, Wallace L., ed. *Environmental Effects of Large Dams*. New York: American Society of Civil Engineers, 1978. A collection of short articles concerning various environmental effects of large dams and reservoirs. Topics include harmful temperature effects, fish, algae, and aquatic weed problems, loss of wildlife habitat, erosion, and seismic activity. This latter article contains an extensive list of dams in the United States that have experienced some earthquake difficulties. Suitable for the college-level reader. Index.

Clark, Champ. *Flood*. Planet Earth Series. Alexandria, Va.: Time-Life Books, 1982. One of a popular series of books that are nontechnical and abundantly illustrated with full-scale color photography. Chapter 3 describes the history of flood control on the Mississippi River. Chapter 5 contains a short discussion of dam construction and several examples of floods caused by dam failure. Bibliography and index.

Committee on the Safety of Existing Dams, Water Science and Technology Board, Commission on Engineering and Technical Systems, and the National Research Council. *Safety of Existing Dams: Evaluation and Improvement*. Washington, D.C.: National Academy Press, 1983. A practical and not overly technical consideration of dam safety problems intended for the college-level reader. Considers hydrologic, geologic, and seismologic factors, foundation, outlet works, reservoir problems, and available instrumentation. For each problem additional technical references are included. Index.

Hoyt, William G., and Walter B. Langbein. *Floods*. Princeton, N.J.: Princeton University Press, 1955. A thorough and comprehensive treatment of all aspects of floods that is so well-written as to be a classic reference. Chapters 5 and 6 cover flood damage and flood-control measures. Numerous examples of flood-control projects are described. Also contains a comprehensive list and description of historic floods from 1543-1952 by date and stream. Suitable for the college reader. Bibliography and index.

Leopold, Luna B., and Thomas Maddock, Jr. *The Flood Control Policy: Big Dams, Little Dams, and Land Management*. New York: Ronald Press, 1954. A close examination of the conflict between the advantages of the construction of one large dam and having many small tributary dams to control floods. Also contains chapters on the technical and political difficulties of flood control. Intended for those professionally concerned with water resources as well as for the general public. Bibliography and index.

Leuchtenburg, William Edward. *Flood Control Politics*. Cambridge, Mass.: Harvard University Press, 1953. A detailed history and assessment of the Connecticut River valley flood-control problems from 1927 to 1950, with emphasis on the political and economic issues. Well written and suitable for college-level readers. Extensive bibliography, index.

Smith, Norman. *A History of Dams*. London: P. Davies, 1971. Well written and interesting historical discussion of dam-building through the ages beginning with the Egyptians and continuing to the end of the nineteenth century, but not including India or the Far East. Suitable for the high school-level reader. Photographic plates, glossary, and index.

Tennessee Valley Authority. *Floods and Flood Control*. Technical Report 26. Knoxville, Tenn.: Author, 1961. A comprehensive discussion of the development, costs, operation, and benefits of the Tennessee River system based on the integrated multiple-purpose system of reservoirs. No discussion of environmental impacts. Suitable for a college reader with some technical background. Appendices, index.

Walters, R. C. S. *Dam Geology*. London: Butterworth, 1962. A short general discussion of the influence of geologic structures on dam construction and failure is followed by a lengthy compendium of dams from all over the world that have experienced typical geological difficulties. Suitable for the college-level reader. Well-illustrated, with a bibliography, an index, and appendices with civil engineering data.

*Sara A. Heller*

## Cross-References

Earthquake Engineering, 430; Earthquake Hazards, 437; Environmental Health, 615; Floodplains, 712; Floods, 719; Hydroelectric Power, 1095; Land-Use Planning, 1335; River Valleys, 2210; Surface Water, 2504.

# DEEP-EARTH DRILLING PROJECTS

*Type of earth science:* Geophysics
*Field of study:* Exploration geophysics

*Deep-earth drilling projects represent the newest and most ambitious attempts by earth scientists to investigate the origins, structure, and nature of planet Earth. The projects already under way and those proposed for the future promise to reveal information concerning the planet unobtainable by other methods.*

### Principal terms

CORE DRILLING: a method of extracting samples of the materials being drilled through in a deep-drilling project

CRUST: the outer layer of the earth, averaging 35 kilometers in thickness on land and 5 kilometers on the ocean bottoms

MANTLE: the area of basaltic rocks separating the earth's crust from its core; it is estimated to be about 2,900 kilometers thick

MOHOROVIČIĆ (MOHO) DISCONTINUITY: an area of undetermined composition and depth between the earth's crust and mantle

ROTARY DRILLING: a method of drilling holes to great depths using a rotating drill bit

## Summary of the Methodology

The idea of drilling deep holes in the earth's crust in order to determine its nature and history originated with nineteenth century geologists and naturalists. Charles Darwin was among the first scientists to call for a deep drilling project for purely scientific purposes. In 1881, Darwin proposed that a shaft be sunk to a depth of 150-180 meters on a Pacific atoll to test his theory concerning the origins and growth of coral islands. Eighteen years later, the Royal Society of London financed the drilling of a 348-meter-deep hole on one of the Ellice Islands (Tuvalu) in the South Pacific to test Darwin's theories. That was perhaps the first deep-earth drilling project for purely scientific purposes ever undertaken.

Since Darwin's time, many earth scientists have proposed deep-earth drilling projects to advance scientific knowledge of the earth's interior; those proposals have usually met with indifferent success because of the great expense and the technological problems involved. In the 1950's, a number of well-known geologists, geophysicists, and oceanographers from several countries began corresponding with one another. A major topic of their correspondence was a deep-drilling project that might capture the imagination of the public (which they perceived to be over-focused on space research) and consequently allow earth scientists to claim a larger share of research funds from government agencies. The correspondents eventually formed an unofficial organization they called the American Miscellaneous Society (AMSOC), which held informal meetings during official scientific conferences at which they discussed the desirability of a deep-drilling project that would penetrate the Mohorovičić (Moho) discontinuity into earth's mantle. Ideally, they agreed, there would be two deep-drilling projects, one on land, the other on the ocean bottom. In 1958, the members of AMSOC became the Deep Drilling Committee (DDC) of the National Academy of Sciences (NAS), a private organization chartered by then-President of the United States Abraham Lincoln in 1865 to act as an adviser to the federal government on scientific matters.

NAS, on the recommendation of the DDC, proposed in 1958 that the federal government of the United States fund a deep-drilling project to penetrate the Moho. The catalyst for NAS's recommendation seems to have been rumors circulating at the time that the Soviet Union had already begun such a project and was about to "beat" the United States in learning the secrets of the earth's interior as they had recently beaten the Americans into outer space. The original proposal envisioned a hole to be drilled on land to a depth of perhaps 10,500 meters as a training project to develop the technology necessary to penetrate the Moho at the ocean's bottom, where the crust is thinner. The DDC subsequently scrapped the ground-hole idea when it received a grant of $15,000 for a feasibility study of the deep-sea drilling project. A DDC member summarized the result of the feasibility study in an article in *Scientific American* (April, 1959) entitled "The Mohole," which stirred immediate industrial and public interest. The interest thus generated resulted in a much-publicized government-sponsored deep-sea drilling project that failed to meet most of its objectives, cost considerably more than originally estimated, and discredited the idea of deep drilling in the minds of many members of Congress and the public. The Mohole project became a source of considerable international embarrassment for American science and may have delayed a sound deep-drilling project by two decades. It was not until 1968 that oceanographers were able to convince Congress to finance another deep-sea drilling project. A further decade passed before federal funds were forthcoming for continental deep-drilling projects.

The rumors concerning a Soviet deep-drilling project were at least partially responsible for the urgency with which the U.S. scientific community and government embraced the ill-fated Mohole project. The rumors were unfounded. Scientists in the Soviet Union did not begin such an effort for twelve years after Mohole. In 1970, Soviet geophysicists launched a deep-drilling project on Kola peninsula near Murmansk, 240 kilometers north of the Arctic Circle; the project has reached a depth of more than 12,000 meters, almost twice the depth of any preceding hole. Under the direction of a Soviet government agency called The Interdepartmental Council for the Study of the Earth's Interior and Superdeep Drilling (formed in 1962), the Kola project is the first of several proposed deep holes meant to explore the structure of the earth's crust and mantle.

The Kola drillers penetrated through almost 3 billion years of earth's geologic history, into rock from the Archean eon. Along the way, they discovered hot, highly mineralized water in larger quantities and at greater depths than geophysicists and geologists had previously thought possible. Scientists at the Kola project have concluded from this and other unexpected findings that enormous mineral deposits may be located at great depths, waiting for humankind to discover a way to reach them. Soviet scientists expect that as they develop a better understanding of the deeper layers of the earth's crust from the Kola project, they will concurrently find ways to discover and exploit petroleum, gas, and minerals at great depths.

Spurred in large part by Soviet successes in deep continental drilling and the propaganda reaped therefrom by the Soviet government, scientists and government agencies in several Western nations began developing similar programs in the 1970's. The U.S. Geodynamics Committee of NAS held a workshop on deep continental drilling for scientific purposes near Los Alamos, New Mexico, in 1978. The members of the workshop convinced NAS to form its own permanent Continental Drilling Committee (CDC) that same year. The members of the CDC identified a number of geophysical problems that could be resolved through deep-earth drilling projects. The CDC also solicited proposals from U.S. geologists and geophysicists for specific projects that would address those problems. After examining the many proposals received, the CDC assigned highest priority to two of them: a project to drill a hole 3.7 kilometers deep through the highly mineralized area near Creede, Colorado, and a core hole in the southern Appalachian region 8-10 kilometers deep.

At its 1983 meeting, the CDC unanimously endorsed the Appalachian project as the most promising for America's first deep continental drilling project. At the same time, it endorsed drilling projects at a future time in two other areas, including Creede and Cajon Pass in California. The following year, the CDC convened a workshop in New York to consider exactly how the project should be approached. After the workshop, the committee organized the Continental Scientific Drilling Program, established with the aid of a grant from the National Science Foundation (NSF). NSF gave the grant to a management group called Direct Observation and Sampling of the Earth's Continental Crust (DOSECC). DOSECC, coordinating its activities with the U.S. Geological Survey and the Department of Energy, prioritizes deep-drilling projects and issues contracts for drilling deep continental holes for scientific purposes. In 1985, the White House's Office of Science and Technology Policy (OSTP) recommended to the NSF that it appropriate $2 million for preliminary studies of the Appalachian project. OSTP also recommended that by 1990 the various deep-earth drilling projects be funded at a level of $20 million per year. In 1988, the Cajon Pass project, overseen by DOSECC, got under way and, within two years, reached its targeted depth of 4,875 meters. DOSECC began the Appalachian project in the northwest corner of South Carolina in 1989. Its goal is a continuously cored hole 15,250 meters deep drilled over a period of ten years.

Other nations also have ambitious plans for deep-earth drilling projects either planned or already under way. West Germany has initiated a $250 million project near Windischeschenbach in Bavaria near the Czechoslovakian border. The German hole will eventually reach almost 14,650 meters and will be continuously cored. German scientists estimate that the project will require ten years to complete.

Swedish scientists plan to deepen an existing hole of 6,700 meters in the Siljan impact crater. The Belgians are drilling a deep research hole near their western border that has a projected depth of more than 5 kilometers. The French government has approved funds for two deep-drilling projects in central France.

The most ambitious deep-drilling projects, however, are those of the Soviet Union, which seems intent on maintaining its lead in the field. In addition to continuing the Kola project, which is already the deepest hole in the world at almost 15,250 meters, Soviet scientists will drill three superdeep holes (more than 6,000 meters deep) and 6 deep holes (deeper than 3,500 meters) during the next decade in widely separated regions of the Soviet Union. In addition to gaining local geological information at the new sites, the Soviet system of deep holes will also be part of seismic experiments from which an understanding of the entire crustal structure underlying the Soviet Union may be gained.

## Applications of the Method

The technology employed in deep-earth drilling projects derives directly from the petroleum industry. The modern origins of that industry date back to the middle of the nineteenth century, when petroleum fields were discovered and exploited in widely separated regions of the world, including Romania, Burma, Sumatra, Iran, the Caucasus, and the United States. The oil wells in those areas were initially shallow, drilled with tools designed to drill water wells.

As the petroleum industry grew in importance, the search for petroleum went deeper and deeper into the earth and required ever more sophisticated drilling machinery. In addition, oil companies began to employ geologists and geophysicists in their quest to meet the skyrocketing demand for petroleum of an increasingly industrialized society. These earth scientists, in part to become more efficient in their effort to locate significant quantities of petroleum, in part as a by-product of that endeavor, began to learn more and more about the nature and history of the earth's crust from the drilling process itself. This new knowledge led to the modern deep-earth drilling projects that seek to drill deep and superdeep holes, not necessarily to locate mineral resources (although that may well be an important spinoff of the projects) but to learn still more about the earth.

The quest for petroleum in the twentieth century penetrated ever deeper into the earth's crust. By the latter part of the century, wells in the United States were producing oil from depths of more than 6,000 meters (the record being a well in Louisiana, producing oil at a depth of 6,527 meters). There are two basic methods of drilling deep wells: cable-tool and rotary. Cable-tool drilling utilizes a heavy drill bit and drill that are suspended by a cable and raised about a meter above the bottom of the hole, then dropped. Workers add mud and water to the hole to hold the rock chips produced by the concussion in suspension. Periodically, drilling crews extract the tools from the hole and pump out the mud, water, and rock chips. The method is slow and has been largely superseded by the rotary drill, which is much more effective in deep-earth drilling.

Rotary drilling, though much faster than the cable-tool method, is also more expensive. The rotary drilling method requires hundreds to thousands of meters of drill pipe and well casing, a derrick, drill bits of several kinds (depending on the type of rock being drilled through), drilling muds and chemicals, a power source (usually one or more diesel engines), and a sizable crew of workers. In rotary drilling, the workers attach the drill bit to a string of drill pipe that has at its top a square cross section called the kelly. The kelly passes through a square hole in a powered turntable, which rotates the drill pipe and bit. The workers add new sections of drill pipe just below the kelly as the bit progresses downward. The rock cut by the rotating drill bit is removed by pumping chemically treated mud down the drill pipe through the drill bit, then back up through the space outside the pipe (the pipe being somewhat smaller in circumference than the hole in which it rests) to a settling pit on the surface.

One drill bit developed for the rotary process, the hollow or core bit, is of particular importance for current deep-earth drilling projects. Because petroleum is often found in readily identified geological formations, companies exploring for oil found it expedient to bring to the surface intact samples of the rock being drilled through for examination by geologists. To extract the samples, technicians developed a hollow bit that would allow a cylindrical section of the rock, called a core, to be extracted from the hole without otherwise damaging it. The cores thus derived allow geologists to determine not only the petroleum potential of the rock but also the geological history of the earth in the area of the hole. Core drilling has become an integral part of all deep-earth drilling projects.

The deep-earth drilling projects have required considerable modification of the methods developed for petroleum drilling. Soviet scientists at the Kola project learned that at depths exceeding 9,000 meters, conventional rotary drilling encounters virtually insurmountable problems. The conventional rotary method uses a power source to turn the drill bit by rotating the entire string of pipe connected to it and to the kelly. At 9,000 meters, the pipe weighs in excess of 800 metric tons, the rotation of which creates enormous stress at the kelly-power source interface and multiplies the friction resistance of the rock through which the scientists are drilling. The Soviets overcame this problem by developing a bottom-hole turbine to rotate the drilling bit, driven by the flow of the drilling mud being injected into the hole. The necessity of rotating the pipe is thus completely eliminated.

To reduce the weight of the huge lengths of drill pipe necessary for deep-earth drilling, Soviet scientists at Kola have begun to utilize a high-strength aluminum alloy pipe, which weighs only about half as much as conventional drill pipe. This innovation considerably reduces the burden on the derrick and the power required to lift the pipe periodically to replace the drill bits and remove the core samples.

Core sampling has also undergone modification at Kola. In conventional wells, core samples several inches in diameter enter the hollow drill tube as the bit cuts a ring of rock at the bottom of the hole. The core remains in the tube until it is brought to the surface and removed. At depths of more than 2,100 meters, however, the rock is under such tremendous pressure that it literally bursts when the drill bit relieves the compression of overlying rock strata. Soviet drillers have developed a new core sampling device that diverts some of the mud into the core tube and catches the pieces of burst rock, then carries them to the surface in a special chamber. This technique also offers the advantage of clearing the tube for new core samples without the necessity of bringing the tube to the surface.

Undoubtedly, other modifications of present drilling technology will be necessary as continental deep-drilling projects proceed. Given the progress of such technology in the twentieth century, it may confidently be expected that innovations will solve the problems that will certainly be encountered, provided that funding for the projects is adequate.

## Context

The mineral and fossil fuel resources of the earth are finite and nonreplaceable commodities. As industrialization continues to spread to the so-called Third World countries and to intensify in the regions where it already exists, the demand for those irreplaceable and limited commodities can only increase. Sometime in the twenty-first century, the presently known reserves of fossil fuels may be exhausted. If current life-styles are to be maintained in industrialized regions of the world and living standards raised for a burgeoning population in the Third World, new reserves of fossil fuels and sources of minerals must be discovered and exploited, and/or new sources of energy must be developed. Deep-earth drilling projects offer one approach to both these necessities.

Strong evidence exists that significant quantities of fossil fuels, both petroleum and natural gas, may be found at depths that are currently unreachable or economically unprofitable. Technology developed in the deep-earth drilling program will almost certainly put those resources at the disposal of humankind. In addition, the Soviet Kola project has demonstrated that enormous mineral resources lie buried at great depths beneath the Soviet Union. When continental drilling projects reveal that the same is true in the United States and Western Europe, can it be doubted that enterprising individuals and companies will rapidly find ways to exploit the wealth beneath their feet?

Deep-earth drilling projects already under way in the United States and elsewhere are exploring the possibility of exploiting on a large scale a relatively new way of producing energy by utilizing the earth's internal heat. The temperature of the earth increases by about 1 degree Celsius per hundred meters to a depth of 3 kilometers and, as shown at Kola, by 2.5 degrees Celsius thereafter. At 15 kilometers beneath the surface, the earth's temperature is more than 300 degrees Celsius. The U.S. Department of Energy is currently funding several deep-drilling projects to investigate the possibility of commercially exploiting this source of virtually inexhaustible energy.

Some scientists suggest that deep-earth drilling might offer a solution to the problem of toxic waste disposal. Safe disposal of the wastes produced by modern industry and by the production of atomic energy ranks as a major concern of contemporary scientists. Before industries and atomic energy plants inject these materials into the deep crust of the planet, however, extensive studies must be conducted into the potential ecological consequences of such an action. Nevertheless, deep-earth drilling may help to solve the problem of toxic waste disposal.

## Bibliography

Anderson, Ian. "Drilling Deep for Geothermal Power and Science." *New Scientist* 111 (July 24, 1986): 22-23. This brief article presents a nontechnical overview of current deep-drilling projects exploring the possibility of exploiting the earth's own heat to produce energy. The author is optimistic that many of the energy needs of the future may be met if governments are willing to make the necessary expenditures for research.

Bascom, Willard. "Deep Hole Story." *Modern Machine Shop* 54 (March, 1982): 92-111. A thorough review of the technology of deep drilling, including Soviet innovations. Assumes considerable technical knowledge on the part of the reader but very informative for those wanting to know more about the technology involved in deep-drilling projects.

_____. "Drilling the World's Deepest Hole." *Engineering Digest* 34 (June, 1988): 16-24. This article is primarily concerned with technical drilling problems. Readers should have strong technical background. Will be of interest only to those readers wanting to know more about the actual mechanics of deep-earth drilling.

_____. "Geothermal Boreholes Make Drilling History." *Machine Design* 53 (October 22, 1981): 8. This article contains a rather technical discussion of the problems encountered in deep drilling for geothermal purposes and their often ingenious solutions. The reader should have a dictionary handy.

_____. *A Hole in the Bottom of the Sea: The Story of the Mohole Project*. Garden City, N.Y.: Doubleday, 1961. Although the main topic of Bascom's book is the ill-fated Mohole project, it contains a considerable amount of information about early proposals for scientific drilling projects and deep continental drilling projects. Also contains fascinating insights into the workings of the "scientific establishment" in the United States and the ways in which it interacts with the federal bureaucracy. Written for a nontechnical audience.

Heath, Michael J. "Deep Digging for Nuclear Waste Disposal." *New Scientist* 108 (October 31, 1985): 30. This article briefly explores the possibilities of using deep-drilling technology to solve the perplexing problem of disposing nuclear wastes. The ideas presented are interesting but not entirely convincing, as they do not address the environmental problems that might be created by such a program.

Kerr, Richard A. "Continental Drilling Heads Deeper." *Science* 224 (June 29, 1984): 1418-1420. An excellent account of the then-current status of United States deep-earth drilling projects and proposals. Offers considerable information about the organizations and individuals who are forming the policies for the United

States continental drilling program.

Kozlovsky, Yephrim A. "The World's Deepest Well." *Scientific American* 251 (December, 1984): 98-104. The best and most complete account in English of the Kola deep-drilling project in the Soviet Union. The reader should keep a geological dictionary nearby but will find a wealth of information about the origins, purpose, scientific findings, and future of the Soviet continental drilling program.

*Paul Madden*

## Cross-References

# DEEP-SEA SEDIMENTATION

*Type of earth science:* Geology
*Field of study:* Sedimentology

*Deep-sea sedimentation occurs by the settling of particles to the ocean floor and by the transport of material from deep to shallow water. Knowledge of the distribution of sediments and the processes of sedimentation will help to evaluate the potential of the world's oceans for the mining of natural resources and the storage of waste.*

*Principal terms*

CALCAREOUS OOZE: sediment in which more than 30 percent of the particles are the remains of plants and animals whose skeletons are composed of calcium carbonate

CARBONATE COMPENSATION DEPTH (CCD): the depth in the oceans at which the rate of supply of calcium carbonate equals the rate of dissolution of calcium carbonate

CLAY: a particle whose size is less than one-tenth of a millimeter

CLAY MINERALS: a group of minerals that have abundant water and are characterized by layers of atoms that form thin sheets that are held together loosely

PELAGIC: meaning "of the open sea"; it refers to sediments that are fine-grained and are deposited very slowly at great distances from continents

SILICEOUS OOZE: sediment in which more than 30 percent of the particles are the remains of plants and animals whose skeletons are composed of silica

TURBIDITY CURRENT: a mass of water and sediment that flows downhill along the bottom of a body of water because it is denser than the surrounding water; common on continental slopes

UPWELLING: an ocean phenomenon in which warm surface waters are pushed away from the coasts by the rotation of the earth; cold waters that carry more nutrients are brought up from depth to replace the warm waters

## Summary of the Phenomenon

Sedimentation in the deep sea differs substantially from that in any other environment. Deep-sea sedimentation is pelagic. It occurs at great distances from continents at depths in excess of 1,000 meters primarily by the settling of particles through the overlying water. One gram of extremely small particles is in every 100,000 liters of seawater. Settling is extremely slow, and sediments accumulate at rates on the order of a few millimeters per thousand years. Transport of material by turbidity currents along the bottom of the ocean from shallow to deep regions is also a mechanism by which deep-sea sediments are deposited, but this is far less important than settling of particles from the surface. In contrast, current transport dominates sedimentation in all other environments where sedimentation rates typically exceed several centimeters per year.

The oceans cover 70 percent of the earth, and, as a result, deep-sea sedimentation may be the most common sedimentary process. Early investigations of the seas were limited, however, to coastal processes and oceanic circulation because of the lack of techniques available to study the deep ocean bottom. Knowledge of deep-sea sedimentation was profoundly increased by the voyage of HMS *Challenger* from 1872 to 1876, which made the first systematic study of the ocean floor. Prior to the *Challenger* expedition, practical investigations of the oceans concentrated on winds, tides, and water depths in harbors to provide information for commercial navigation and for the laying of submarine telegraph cables. The *Challenger* crew collected data on the temperature and depth of the oceans, marine plants and animals, and sediments on the ocean bottom. Deep-sea sediments were described by John Murray, naturalist to the expedition. It was noted that sediments in the deepest parts of the ocean are fine-grained and are composed of particles that settled from the surface. Comparison of rocks exposed on land with those dredged from the ocean led to the assertion that only a few questionable exceptions existed to prove that deep-sea sediments could not be found on land. This conclusion caused great debate, and the interpretation of some rocks as deep-sea deposits by a few scientists persisted despite general agreement within the scientific community against the interpretation.

Investigation of deep-sea sedimentation flourished again during and immediately after World War II. Despite the voluminous amount of data available by 1950, the prevailing doctrine in the first half of the twentieth century was similar to that in the previous century: The continents and oceans were permanent features of the earth's surface that developed close to their present form near the beginning of geologic time. Thus, the ocean basins were billions of years old; ocean-bottom sediments were tens of kilometers thick, having accumulated from early in the history of the earth to the present, and deep-sea sediments were not exposed on land, a point that was still severely contested. Then, during the 1950's, two discoveries shocked the oceanographic community. First, fossils taken from seamounts (submarine mountains) in the Pacific Ocean at depths of 2 kilometers were only a hundred million years old, suggesting that subsidence of the ocean floor was recent. Second, deep-sea sediments were found to be less than 200 meters thick. The advent of the theory of plate tectonics in the 1960's profoundly changed ideas about the ocean basins by providing both an explanation for the two observations of the previous decade and a mechanism for the emplacement of deep-sea sediments onto continents. In addition, the motion and cooling of the oceanic plates predicted by plate tectonics explain the global distribution of deep-sea deposits.

Pelagic sediments are characterized by their fine grain size. Few particles are larger than 0.025 millimeter, and most are smaller than 0.001 millimeter. Particles include terrigenous debris (derived from the continents), such as clay minerals, quartz, and feldspar; volcanogenic grains (derived from volcanoes), such as volcanic glass, pumice, and ash; biogenic material (derived from living organisms), such as fecal pellets (waste produced by organisms inhabiting the surface waters) and skeletons of planktonic plants and animals; and cosmogenic matter (derived from space or the cosmos), such as pieces of meteorites. Pelagic sediments that contain more than 30 percent biogenic material are oozes. If the biogenic debris is composed of calcium carbonate, the sediment is a calcareous ooze. If the biogenic debris is composed of silica, the sediment is a siliceous ooze. Most calcareous oozes consist of foraminiferans, which are single-celled animals that secrete calcium carbonate and live in the surface waters. In contrast, siliceous oozes contain diatoms (green, unicellular algae) in cold water and radiolarians (silica-secreting single-celled animals) in warm water. Pelagic clays are sediments that contain less than 30 percent biogenic debris.

The two major controls on pelagic sedimentation are the calcium compensation depth (CCD) and the fertility of the surface waters. The CCD reflects the interplay between the release of carbon dioxide during the decay of a surface organism and the dissolution of its calcium carbonate skeleton as it descends through the ocean. Above the CCD, calcareous oozes are dominant, whereas below the CCD, siliceous oozes and pelagic clays are common. For example, in one region of the ocean, sediments decreased from 90 percent calcium carbonate at a depth of 1,000 meters to 20 percent calcium carbonate at a depth of 5,000. Oozes accumulate below areas of high fertility where upwelling brings nutrient-rich bottom water to the surface. Because upwelling creates increased productivity of both calcareous and siliceous organisms, siliceous oozes form only where the water depth exceeds the CCD. Calcareous oozes, the most abundant biogenic sediments in the ocean, cover only 15 percent of the Pacific Ocean bottom but blanket 60 percent of the Atlantic Ocean floor. This difference reflects the combination of a shallower CCD and greater water depth in the Pacific Ocean than in the Atlantic Ocean. Siliceous oozes are in areas of elevated CCDs such as the equatorial regions, the subarctic and subantarctic zones, and the continental margins of northwestern South America and eastern Africa.

Sedimentation of pelagic clays is restricted to the central portions of the oceans where the fertility is low. This reflects the difference in settling rates between nonbiogenic particles and fecal pellets. Because of its small size, a particle may take many years to sink through the ocean. The concentration of many particles into fecal pellets by organisms feeding at the surface, therefore, is thought to be an important mechanism by which debris settles to the bottom. The greater size of the pellets allows them to fall much faster than other particles. It is only in areas of low productivity, therefore, where biogenic material does not overwhelm the sediment. Wind is the primary means by which nonbiogenic particles reach the sea. Dust occurs in the atmosphere at great distances from continents and constitutes as much as 10 percent of pelagic sediment.

Additional processes in deep-sea sedimentation include the rafting of glacial debris by ice, the transport of terrigenous and shallow-water material by turbidity currents along the ocean floor, and the precipitation of nodules on the ocean bottom. Pieces of ice calve off glaciers in the polar regions and float toward warmer waters where they eventually melt, releasing glacial sediment into the ocean. Although this process is most common in the south polar region today, glacial sediments greater than ten thousand years old elsewhere on the ocean floor suggest the process extended over a much greater area in the past. Turbidity currents generated along continental slopes may traverse hundreds of kilometers of ocean basin where ridges and depressions do not occur. Far away from continents, the currents commonly contain only silt but may deposit the grains over great distances. These currents also may locally erode the sea floor, creating breaks in the continuity of the sediment pile by removing the most recent sediments and exposing older sediments at the surface. Chemical reactions of seawater with the surface of the sediment cause the precipitation of ferromanganese (composed of iron and manganese) nodules in areas where sediments accumulate slowly. The nodules initiate by nucleating around manganese in the sediment and by accreting minerals from the seawater. Nodules may cover more than 40 percent of the sea floor.

Sedimentation in the deep sea is a complex interaction between water depth, fertility of the surface waters, and current transport. To illustrate how the depth dependence of sedimentation affects the global distribution of sediments, one must understand the relationship between plate tectonics and the topography of the ocean floor. At a mid-ocean ridge, which rises a few thouand meters above the surrounding ocean basin, molten rock is extruded to form a new piece of sea floor. Calcareous oozes accumulate on the new sea floor because of its depth above the CCD. As another piece of sea floor forms, the older piece moves away from the mid-ocean ridge toward the deep ocean basin (sea-floor spreading), cools, and sinks. The old sea floor gradually descends below the CCD, where siliceous oozes accumulate above the calcareous oozes. Eventually the piece of sea floor passes below a region of low surface productivity such that pelagic clays are deposited above the siliceous oozes. This vertical sequence has been documented in several localities throughout the world's oceans.

## Methods of Study

Techniques used to study sedimentation in the deep ocean are diverse and include piston coring, seismic reflection profiling, the use of deep-diving submarines, and experiments performed both at sea and in the laboratory. Piston coring is the most important technique because it enables scientists to sample the ocean floor directly. It uses the same kind of rotary-drilling equipment that is standard in petroleum exploration on land to drill into the top few hundred meters of the sea floor. The cores are 7 centimeters in diameter and provide samples that are large enough to preserve features that yield insight into the process by which the sediment accumulated. For example, current-produced features in some samples were the first direct evidence of currents in the deep seas. In addition, piston coring confirmed the vertical sequence of sediments predicted by plate tectonics.

To map the ocean floor using a 7-centimeter drill core is time-consuming and inefficient. Seismic reflection profiling has the advantage of providing information about the thickness and distribution of layers in the sediments on the sea floor relatively quickly. The two major disadvantages are that it cannot determine the composition of the sediment and that it only identifies layers that are tens of meters thick. In seismic reflection profiling, a low-frequency sound source is towed over the bottom. The sound waves are reflected by the sea floor and by layers several kilometers below the boundary between the sediment and the water. The returning signals are displayed on strip charts that reveal the water depth and the thickness and pattern of layers in the sediments. One of the most significant early contributions of seismic reflection profiling was the evidence that sediments on the ocean floor were too thin to have been accumulating since early in the history of the earth, an observation explained by plate tectonics.

The use of deep-diving submarines has allowed scientists to observe the ocean floor directly. Previously the ocean floor was only photographed; deep-diving submarines allowed scientists to confirm or reject hypotheses based on other indirect techniques. The ranges and endurance times of the submersible vessels, however, are limited. In addition, they frequently cannot be used in areas where current velocities are greater than 1 meter per second.

Simple experiments either at sea or in the laboratory also can be illuminating. For example, the existence of the CCD was verified by lowering spheres of calcium carbonate to various water depths in the Pacific Ocean. When the spheres were examined, it was discovered that the sphere in the deepest water had dissolved the most. Scientists in the laboratory conduct experiments on settling rates by dropping particles of various sizes in large beakers and measuring the time necessary for the particles to reach the bottom. Thus, the amount of time represented by the thickness of sediment on the ocean floor was estimated at a few hundred million years.

One of the most important developments in deep-sea sedimentation was the creation in 1965 of the Deep Sea Drilling Project (DSDP), now known as the Ocean Drilling Project (ODP), to drill and investigate the ocean floor. The project began in earnest in 1968 with the maiden voyage of the American ship the *Glomar Challenger*, which was outfitted with state-of-the-art navigational, positioning, and drilling equipment. International teams of scientists board the ship in ports all over the world and remain at sea for two months. Since its inception, ODP has undertaken more than sixty-five voyages and contributed significantly to scientists' understanding of the ocean.

## Context

The oceans cover nearly three-quarters of the surface of earth. To study deep-sea sedimentation, therefore, is to understand one of the most globally prevalent processes. Understanding deep-sea sedimentation, however, is important for several other reasons. First, sediments on the ocean floor yield insight into bottom currents and water depths, which affect the navigation of submarines and the installation of underwater communications cables. Second, the sediments preserve the climatic record of the past few hundred thousands of years. For example, glacial deposits approximately ten thousand years old are found over a much greater area of the bottom of the ocean than recent glacial deposits, suggesting that transport of glacial debris by ice was very common ten thousand years ago. This implies that the temperature of the earth was colder in the past, to allow the formation of significant quantities of ice. Scientists can use this information to gauge present-day and predict future fluctuations in the global climate. Third, the seas receive a significant amount of the garbage produced by modern society. Knowledge of sedimentation rates and currents in the deep sea helps to establish the length of time necessary to bury the waste, the direction the waste will travel prior to its burial, and the effect of dumping waste on the overall health of the ocean.

Fourth, and most important, understanding deep-sea sedimentation and the global distribution of deep-sea sediments provides a framework within which one can estimate the economic potential of the deep sea and minimize the damage of ocean exploitation. As the reserve of natural resources on the continents dwindles because of expanding demand from high-technology industries, exploding population growth, and increasing consumer appetite, attention focuses on the oceans as a possible source of raw materials. Important resources that may be found locally in the deep sea are oil and gas. The decay and accumulation of plants and animals are essential to the generation of hydrocarbons and are processes that occur over a large area of the sea floor. Emphasis also is placed on mining the deep sea for important materials such as manganese, gold, cadmium, copper, and nickel. Similar to most new industries, large-scale exploitation of the natural resources of the deep sea is limited at present by the current state of technology. The incentive to mine the oceans, however, will grow as cheaper and more sophisticated technologies are created. Eventually, the cost of extracting the materials will be far less than the price people are willing to pay for the resources.

## Bibliography

Andel, Tjeerd Hendrik van. *Tales of an Old Ocean*. New York: W. W. Norton, 1978. A descriptive story of the evolution of thought on the oceans. Chapters discuss deep-sea sedimentation in general terms. Additional material covers the topography of the sea floor and the theory of plate tectonics. Highly enjoyable for anyone interested in the oceans.

Blatt, Harvey, Gerard Middleton, and R. Murray. *Origin of Sedimentary Rocks*. 2d ed. Englewood Cliffs, N.J.: Prentice-Hall, 1980. This textbook describes sedimentary rocks and processes. An excellent introduction to mechanics of sedimentation, classification of sediments, features of sediments that form under different conditions of water flow, environments of sedimentation, and transformation of sediments into rocks. Most of the discussion is purely descriptive. Some chapters assume some quantitative knowledge. Suitable for the college-level student and for the layperson who is technically inclined.

Murray, John, and Alphonse J. Renard. *Deep Sea Deposits*. Edinburgh: Neill, 1891. The original volume written by two members of the crew of the *Challenger*, which made the pioneering voyage in deep-sea studies. The classification scheme for deep-sea sediments is still used. An excellent source for the historical framework of deep-sea investigations, the book dramatically emphasizes the importance of observation in science.

*Ocean Science: Readings from "Scientific American."* San Francisco: W. H. Freeman, 1977. A collection of articles previously printed in *Scientific American*. Articles include discussions of all aspects of the ocean, including circulation, composition of seawater, topography of the oceans, plate tectonics, and deep-sea sedimentation. A good source of information on natural resource exploitation and waste disposal in the world's oceans. Well illustrated.

Press, Frank, and Raymond Siever. *The Earth*. 4th ed. New York: W. H. Freeman, 1986. An introductory text on the evolution of the earth, designed to accompany a beginning class on geology. Several chapters discuss sedimentary rocks, the oceans, plate tectonics, and deep-sea sediments. Especially suited for high school students.

Reading, H. G., ed. *Sedimentary Environments and Facies*. New York: Elsevier, 1979. Discusses sediments in terms of the environment (beach, pelagic) in which they occur instead of by type (sand, mud). The chapter on pelagic environments is very detailed and is an excellent text for the comparison of modern and ancient deep-sea sediments. Exceptionally well illustrated; the reference list is thorough. Suitable for college-level students.

Shephard, F. P. *Submarine Geology*. 3d ed. New York: Harper & Row, 1973. A complete description of sediments and the physiographic provinces of the oceans, including sections on continental margins and mid-ocean ridges Also discusses methods used by geologists to investigate the oceans and the relationship between plate tectonics and deep-sea sedimentation. A good historical treatment of the study of the oceans. Suitable for college-level students.

*Pamela Jansma*

**Cross-References**

The Abyssal Sea Floor, 1; Clays, 210; Continental Shelf and Slope, 281; Ocean Basins, 1785; Deep Ocean Currents, 1792; Surface Ocean Currents, 1798; Ocean-Floor Drilling Programs, 1805; The Ocean Ridge System, 1826; Oceans: Carbonate Compensation Depths, 1855; Plate Tectonics, 2079; Seamounts, 2274; Seawater Composition, 2282; Sediment Transport and Deposition, 2290; Sedimentary Rocks: Biogenic, 2312; Turbidity Currents and Submarine Fans, 2555.

# DELTAS

*Type of earth science:* Geology
*Field of study:* Sedimentology

*Deltas are dynamic sedimentary environments which undergo rapid changes over very short periods. Found in lakes and shallow ocean waters, they are rich in fossil fuels and provide food and shelter for fish and wildlife.*

### Principal terms

CREVASSE: a break in the bank of a distributary channel causing a partial diversion of flow and sediment into an interdistributary bay

DELTA: a deposit of sediment, often triangular, formed at a river mouth where the wave action of the sea is low

DISTRIBUTARY CHANNEL: a river which is divided into several smaller channels, thus distributing its flow and sediment load

GEOARCHAEOLOGY: the technique of using ancient human habitation sites to determine the age of landforms and when changes occurred

INTERDISTRIBUTARY BAY: a shallow, triangular bay between two distributary channels; over time, the bay is filled with sediment and colonized with marsh plants or trees

NATURAL LEVEE: a low ridge deposited on the flanks of a river during a flood stage

PRODELTA: a sedimentary layer composed of silt and clay deposited under water; it is the foundation on which a delta is deposited

SEDIMENT: fragmented rock material composed of gravel, sand, silt, or clay which is deposited by a river to form a delta

WAVE ENERGY: the capacity of a wave to erode and deposit; as wave energy increases, erosion increases

## Summary of the Phenomenon

Deltas contain many valuable resources. Government agencies such as the U.S. Fish and Wildlife Service study the surface properties of deltas because of the enormous wetlands and abundant wildlife that occupy these landforms. Geologists study deltas because they are favored places for the accumulation of oil and gas resources. This low topographical feature serves society in many ways, and that is why it has been the object of intense study.

Deltas are deposits of sediments, such as sand or silt, which are carried by rivers and deposited at the shoreline of a lake, estuary, or sea. As the river meets the water body, its velocity is greatly decreased, causing the river sediment to be deposited. If the accumulated sediment is not removed by waves or currents, a delta will accumulate and continue to extend itself into the lake or ocean. The term "delta" is used to describe this depositional landform because it is often triangular. It is believed that the Greek historian Herodotus coined the term with the shape of the Greek letter *delta* in mind. Herodotus visited Egypt, where the Nile delta is located, and he correctly defined the shape of that delta; not all deltas, however, are triangular.

The Ganges delta, the Colorado River delta, and many other deltas have different shapes. The shape postulated by Herodotus is, in fact, somewhat unusual, but it is applicable to the Nile and the Mississippi river deltas. The Nile delta has a smooth but curved shoreline—it is an "arcuate" delta—whereas the Mississippi delta has spreading channels and resembles the digits of a bird's foot. Occasionally, current and wave action at the shoreline causes sediment to be distributed to the left and right of a river channel, forming smooth beaches on either side. Such a delta is shaped like a cone, the point of which projects toward the sea, and is called a "cuspate" delta. The Tiber River, which empties into the Mediterranean Sea, is a classic example of this type of delta. Rivers like the Seine, in France, may deposit sediment in elongated estuaries, forming shoals and tidal flats.

Earth scientists have noted that the shapes of deltas are associated with several conditions, such as the character of river flow, the magnitude of wave energy and tides, and the geologic setting. The bird-foot delta of the Mississippi River has extended itself well into the Gulf of Mexico, because the river carries and deposits a high volume of sediment on a shallow sea floor or continental shelf. The wave and tidal forces are low, and the delta deposit is not redistributed along the shoreline or swept away. Conversely, a cuspate delta, such as that of the Tiber, is a product of strong waves moving over a steep continental shelf. The persistent high wave energy redistributes the sediment often, forming beaches and sand dunes along the delta shoreline. The Nile delta is an arcuate delta characterized by moderately high wave energy and a modest tide range. Occasional high wave conditions deposit beaches and sand dunes along the arc-shaped delta front at the Mediterranean Sea. Tides also play a direct role in the creation of deltas. Deltas in estuaries are formed because of a high tidal range coupled with low wave conditions. The Seine estuary, with its distinctive mud flats exposed at low tide, provides a good example.

Although deltas have different shapes which reflect differences in the intensity of river, wave, current, and tidal processes, certain landforms may be identified as characteristic of delta formation. Submarine features are deposited below sea level, and subaerial features form at or just above sea level. As a river empties into the sea, the finest sediments, usually very fine silt or clay, are deposited offshore on the sea floor. This submarine deposit forms the foundation on which the delta sits and is appropriately referred to as a "prodelta deposit." The deposit can often be detected on navigation maps as a relatively shallow, semicircular deposit under the water.

As deposition continues, the prodelta deposit is covered with the extending subaerial delta, which is composed of coarser sediments. Deltaic extension occurs along the distributary channels. During higher river flow, the distributary channels overflow, depositing natural levees along their sides. The digitate distributary pattern of the Mississippi delta illustrates this process very well. As the distributaries extend to deeper water, the shallow areas between the distributaries are better developed. These areas, known as interdistributary bays, are shallow landforms colonized by aquatic plant life. Over time, deposition occurs in the interdistributary bays through breaches in the natural levees. As the river mouth distributaries enter a flood stage, the lower regions of a natural levee are broken and fine suspended sediments introduced into the interdistributary bay area. Such overbank splays, or crevasse splays, are primarily responsible for the infilling of a delta. The crevassing is usually a very rapid but short-lived process, occurring during a high river stage and operating over a ten- to fifteen-year period. With the passage of time, the open-water interdistributary bays are silted and colonized. Eventually, however, the marshy bays may subside, because of the compaction of the sediment, creating water areas once again.

Although the geologic history of large deltas such as the Mississippi is complex, the succession and behavior of shifting deltas have been determined in some detail. Over the past twenty thousand years, the large continental glaciers that occupied much of the upper Midwestern United States began to melt. As the climate of the earth continued to warm, the melting ice was returned to the oceans and the seas rose some 100 meters, inundating valleys that had previously been cut by streams. The oceans reached their present approximate level about five thousand years ago. The Mississippi and similar valleys were flooded and became elongated bays. Over time, the shallow water bays were choked with sediments which formed broad floodplains extending down the valleys. Once a depositing river extended beyond the confines of its valley, a delta was deposited in deeper water. Because the river was no longer confined, it was free to shift over great distances. The Mississippi River delta is actually composed of seven distinct delta lobes extending over an approximate distance of 315 kilometers. The oldest delta, Salé Cypremort, was deposited some 4,600 years ago; the most modern delta was deposited within the past 550 years. Older Mississippi delta lobes, such as the Teche delta, have subsided since they were deposited, giving an opportunity for a more recent delta (in this case, the Lafourche) to be deposited on top and more seaward of the older feature. The different delta lobes making up the enormous deltaic plain have resulted from a shifting of the Mississippi River well upstream in its valley. This process is analogous to a hand movement's occurring because of a shoulder movement.

Because of significant changes in the shoreline environments, many deltas in marine coastal zones are eroding. The Mississippi River is at the edge of the continental shelf and cannot build out into deep water. Also, subsidence and a slight rise in sea level are causing the delta to erode. The Nile delta is eroding as well. With the construction of the High Aswan Dam upstream, there has been a decrease in the sediment supplied to the Nile delta. This lack of sediment, along with a slight rise in sea level, has led to erosion. Some earth scientists have suggested that the wave action in coastal Egypt is cutting back the Nile delta at a rate of 15 to 3 meters per year in some areas.

## Methods of Study

In some ways deltas are difficult to study, because most of the features are very flat, marshy, or under water. Since deltas change rapidly over only a few decades, however, maps are an important tool with which to determine changes. Navigation maps and maps that illustrate the topography of coastal areas around the world have been made for generations. By comparing the size and location of a delta on old maps and new maps, changes can be analyzed. Also, aerial photographs and pictures taken from satellites aid in identifying the erosion and deposition of delta landforms.

Often, older delta lobes were settled by ancient peoples. Through the science of geoarchaeology, it can be determined when changes occurred. As deltas, such as the Mississippi, shift from side to side over time, the human population follows the deltas from place to place. By examining the location or archaeological sites over the past fifteen hundred years, scientists have determined the minimum age of the several deltas forming the Mississippi deltaic plain. The Indian pottery found there reveals that the delta framework was deposited very recently. Cultural remains indicate other changes—in salinity, subsidence, and delta deterioration.

By boring holes into the soft sediments of a delta, geologists can decipher its subsurface aspects. Because oil and natural gas are often associated with deltas, oil companies have bored holes in many delta landforms. Information derived from this method of study reveals the composition of the thick delta sediments and the rate of delta accumulation. In fact, boreholes in some deltas have indicated that older deltas once existed and are now buried beneath younger deltas.

Finally, deltas can be created in the laboratory. In nature, deltas are often very large and complex. To make the study of deltas less difficult, scientists use tanks filled with water and sediments. Experiments can be performed which, for example, control the amount of sediment used to build deltas. Relationships between sediments and current velocities may be studied to gather information on such properties as the rate of delta growth. By controlling the phenomena that cause deltas to form, geologists can gain an overview of the behavior and processes of delta development.

## Context

Deltas, with their marshes and bogs, are not aesthetically pleasing; however, depositional landforms have been useful to prehistoric and historic populations in many ways. Deltas, along with estuaries, are perhaps the most biologically productive areas on the earth's surface. Most deltas are colonized with wetland swamps or marshes, which are breeding areas for wildlife. In the United States, for example, duck hunting is a popular sport which is associated with wetlands. In marine deltas, where there is tidal influence, freshwater and saltwater mix. The river brings oxygen and nutritive substances into the delta, and the result is an enormous production of sea life. High biological productivity attracted humans to this land feature. Deltas have often been centers of civilization; the deltas of the Nile, in Egypt, and the

Tigris-Euphrates, at the head of the Persian Gulf, have supported important societies. Soils in delta regions are nourished through seasonal flooding, and water
tables are high, guaranteeing adequate water with which to irrigate crops, even in
the dry season. Food and crop production from tropical deltas is significant because
most tropical soils are not very productive. Deltas such as those of the Mekong and
the Ganges are outstanding examples.

Deltas are transition zones between the land and the sea, between river and
marine processes. Their rivers are also links between ocean and continent. Cities
such as New Orleans, Venice, Amsterdam, and Rotterdam owe their prosperity to
their delta geography. Such cities, known as *entrepôts*, thrive on marine traffic
entering a country or on overland traffic exiting the country.

Since deltas are areas of vast accumulations of sediments, they generate building
material for future mountains. The young mountains of the world, such as the Alps
and the Himalaya, parallel coastal areas and are composed of sedimentary rocks.
Marine fossils frequently found in such rocks reveal that they not only are composed
of sediment but also were once deposited under water, later to be thrusted to great
heights.

## Bibliography

Bird, Eric. *Coasts: An Introduction to Coastal Geomorphology.* 3d ed. New York:
Basil Blackwell, 1984. An introductory text on coastal zones and processes. Most
examples are taken from Australia. The chapter on deltas is well illustrated with
maps and diagrams. The text is nontechnical and comprehensible to readers with
little scientific background.

Coleman, J. M. *Deltas: Process of Deposition and Models for Exploration.* Boston:
International Human Resources Development Corporation, 1982. A detailed review of deltaic processes, including an overview of the Mississippi River delta
and discussions of other deltas and their variability. Numerous maps and diagrams illustrate specific points. For readers with some background in the subject,
this text can be a useful supplement.

Davis, R. A., Jr. *Coastal Sedimentary Environments.* 2d rev. ed. New York:
Springer-Verlag, 1985. A book on deposition in coastal areas. Topics include
deltas, beaches, marshes, and estuaries. The treatment of deltas is generally
narrative, and equations are sparingly used. A comparative presentation of deltas
is instructive and not difficult to understand; some background in physical geology is useful but not necessary.

LaBlanc, R. J., ed. *Modern Deltas.* Tulsa, Okla.: American Association of Petroleum Geologists, 1976. A college-level text describing some of the world's deltas. The treatment is generally nonmathematical and descriptive, but it will be
most useful to those who have had a course in geology. Well illustrated with
diagrams, maps, and pictures.

Morgan, J. P. "Deltas: A Resume." *Journal of Geologic Education* 18 (1970): 107-117.
An excellent introductory article on deltas. The emphasis is on the Mississippi

River delta, which the author studied for many years. Different processes and their influence on delta development are covered. An excellent and not overly technical paper. Includes maps and tables.

_____, ed. *Deltaic Sedimentation Modern and Ancient.* Tulsa, Okla.: American Association of Petroleum Geologists, 1970. An old but not outdated series of chapters by different authors on deltas around the world. Thorough in its treatment but not overly technical, the book emphasizes sedimentary differences and the biological and physical character of deltas. Well illustrated with maps and aerial photographs. Some knowledge of geology or earth science would be useful.

Peterson, J. F. "Using Miniature Landforms in Teaching Geomorphology." *Journal of Geography* 85 (November/December, 1986): 256-258. This paper discusses small-scale landforms and their advantages in the classroom. Deltas and related features, such as alluvial fans, are highlighted. The nontechnical text is supplemented with photographs. A good article for those interested in reconstructing a delta on a small scale. Suitable for high school students.

Raphael, C. N., and E. Jaworski. "The St. Clair River Delta: A Unique Lake Delta." *The Geographical Bulletin* 21 (April, 1982): 7-28. A delta in the Great Lakes is described and compared with the Mississippi River delta. The paper suggests that although many deltas look the same, different processes are at work in them. Good aerial photographs, maps, and cross sections. A nontechnical treatment of delta processes, forms, and vegetation.

Thornbury, W. D. *Principles of Geomorphology.* 2d ed. New York: John Wiley & Sons, 1969. A well-written introductory textbook on landforms. The various landforms of deltas and related river features are discussed in detail. The book emphasizes form rather than process and is nontechnical in its presentation. Suitable for those who want a rapid, nonmathematical introduction to deltas and related features, such as floodplains and coasts.

*C. Nicholas Raphael*

## Cross-References

Alluvial Systems, 31; Archaeological Geology, 86; Biostratigraphy, 173; Coal, 232; Continental Shelf and Slope, 281; Dams and Flood Control, 309; Drainage Basins, 384; Floodplains, 712; Floods, 719; Oil and Gas: Petroleum Reservoirs, 1909; River Flow, 2203; River Valleys, 2210; Sea Level, 2267; Sediment Transport and Deposition, 2290; Turbidity Currents and Submarine Fans, 2555; Weathering and Erosion, 2723.

# DESERT PAVEMENT

*Type of earth science:* Geology
*Field of study:* Sedimentology

*Desert pavements are concentrations of stones on the land surface of arid areas, produced by wind and running water erosion and upward movement of stones through the soil. Stone pavements may signal serious soil erosion that must be addressed before the land can be irrigated for agriculture.*

### Principal terms

CREEP: the slow, gradual downslope movement of soil materials under gravitational stress

DEFLATION: the sorting out, lifting, and removal of loose, dry, silt- and clay-sized soil particles by a turbulent eddy action of the wind

DIRT CRACKING: a process in which clays accumulate in rock cracks, take on water, and expand to rupture the rock

EXPANSION-CONTRACTION CYCLES: processes of wetting-drying, heating-cooling, or freezing-thawing, which affect soil particles differently according to their size

SALT WEATHERING: the granular disintegration or fragmentation of rock material affected by saline solutions or by salt-crystal growth

THERMAL FRACTURE: the formation of a fracture or crack in a rock as a result of temperature changes

VENTIFACT: any stone or pebble that is shaped, worn, faceted, cut, or polished by the abrasive action of windblown sand, generally under desert conditions

## Summary of the Phenomenon

Desert pavements are extensive stony surfaces in arid areas that occur not only on slopes but also on a range of lowland surfaces, including water-eroded and deposited areas. The stones tend to be closely packed on flat or moderately inclined plane surfaces. Stone pavements are rendered prominent by their lack of vegetation but, in any case, they form most readily by processes typical of arid regions where plant roots do not bind the soil very much. The pavements are most striking in areas of low relief, where it is the largely flat, stony surface itself that impresses the observer, rather than the contours of the land.

Desert stone pavements range from rocky or boulder-strewn surfaces to smooth plains of the finest gravel. Terminology for different types commonly derives from Arabic, as one might expect, given the prevailing aridity across North Africa and the Middle East, where that language is spoken. Thus the term "hamada" (Arabic for "unfruitful") describes a bouldery terrain, and "reg" (meaning "becoming smaller") indicates a finer pavement of small stones. The term "serir" is a synonym for "reg" in the central Sahara.

Most hamada pavements are residual, consisting of stones derived from the bedrock beneath, or constitute boulders transported only short distances. Most regs consist of transported stones. These distinctions of size and transport distance become rather blurred over time, as the larger rock fragments are progressively weathered to finer sizes and transported farther by wind and water. Nevertheless, a residual origin of many hamada pavements is clearly evident in a number of places by the angularity and lack of sorting of the rock fragments and by the similarity to the bedrock beneath. The water-deposited nature of a reg pavement can be indicated by sorted and rounded gravels of mixed composition and distant origin and also by the pavement's occurrence close to dry stream channels. Residual regs, which are usually closely associated with hamadas, commonly consist of angular flakes of local bedrock or of a less weatherable residue. Reg pavements can be composed of two elements in varying proportions: a compact mosaic of small stones embedded in soil and a more uneven component of larger fragments lying loose on that surface or protruding through it.

Desert pavements are polygenetic; that is, there is more than one process by which they can be produced. The most traditional explanation, however, is that the stones are concentrated by means of wind erosion or deflation of the fine particles. Deflation may eventually settle the pebbles into such stable positions that they fit together almost like the blocks of a cobblestone street.

The effectiveness of deflation on desert pavements is less, however, than is commonly claimed. Under natural conditions, soils that have been tested by scientists can resist wind erosion, because they are silty and cohesive and tend to form crusts as a result of repeated wetting and drying. A large grain size of the soil makes it resistant to wind erosion; soil cohesiveness, too, is an important factor. Even where particles are spherical, the magnitude of the cohesive forces between particles less than 0.1 millimeter in diameter is greater than the weight of the particle. Small particles, however, are usually more irregular in shape, or even platy, a factor that increases their cohesion. Since cohesion is so important between small particles, silts and clays should be quite resistant to wind erosion. That is true, however, only where the surfaces are smooth, the clays and silts are uniformly fine, and no other material is blown onto them. Otherwise, large grains can be dislodged from fine soils as aggregates of particles or knocked loose by the impact of other large sand grains. In any case, the amount of lowering and stone concentration by the wind is limited; the efficacy of deflation diminishes markedly as the protective stone cover increases, and deflation becomes virtually ineffective when stones cover 50 percent of the surface. Undisturbed stone pavements are among the most wind-stable of desert surfaces.

Rain and water flow appear to be more effective than wind in eroding fine-textured soils on sloping desert pavements. In test plots cleared of stones in one experiment on 5-degree slopes, water wash accounted for most of the 5- to 50-centimeter surface lowering that occurred in a period of five years. During this time, the stone pavement was renewed with stones from below this differential erosion.

Where subsoils are clay-rich so that they do not erode easily by either wind or water and the subsoils are also largely stone-free, the formation of stone pavements by deflation of such soils is more difficult to understand. In these situations, the mechanism of formation seems to have been forces of expansion and contraction within the soil that cause upward displacement and concentration of stones on the surface. Soils that exhibit this phenomenon contain expansive clays in alkaline chemical conditions and are subject to swelling and heaving upon wetting and to shrinkage and cracking upon drying. Periods of heating followed by cooling and of freezing followed by thawing also contribute to the expansion-contraction cycles, which cause stones to move upward and concentrate on the surface.

The exact mechanism for upward stone movement in deserts is not precisely known, although by analogy to known stone movement in areas of intense freeze and thaw, some details are understood. It is possible, for example, that the stones shift upward as the underlying soils swell in wet periods and that as the soil shrinks in dry periods, fine particles fall into cracks beneath the stones and prevent the return of the rock fragments. Stones may also induce differential swelling in the soil by speeding the downward advance of a wetting front around and over them. The stones are then likely to be displaced upward, away from the dry zone beneath them, and held tightly by the wet and sticky soil above. Soil may squeeze into the space left and thus prevent a return movement of the stones. These processes also resemble those postulated for certain types of sorted, patterned ground, where stones become arranged in polygons or striped zones. In these cases, it is clear that no process other than upward movement along certain zones could produce such patterns.

Stone pavements of the upward-movement type occur on and in the topsoils of weakly salty soils on the stony tablelands of arid Australia, where the subsoils are almost stone-free. The pavement stones are silica-rich gibber stones, which were originally precipitated within the soils by mobilization and concentration of silica in unusual chemical reactions. For those stone pavements to have originated as a residue from erosion would have required a stripping of more than 1.5 meters of erosion-resistant, clay-rich soil. Such a process is not viewed as likely; an upward movement is far more probable, given the swelling and cracking potential of salty clays. Similar forms have been noted in deserts in Nevada and California as well as in the great Atacama desert of Peru.

An alternative form of displacement is possible where the soil material has been transported, particularly by the wind. For example, in South Australia, a stone pavement occurs on a layer of clay rich in gypsum (calcium sulfate), which is thought to have been blown into place by the wind. The stone pavement on the surface resembles a buried pavement. It is possible that the original pavement first trapped a small amount of windborne dust among the stones. Some of the rock fragments were then displaced upward, little by little, through wetting and swelling of the eolian (wind-deposited) clays during the course of their accumulation, and thus the stones were never deeply buried.

Concentration of a stone pavement through winnowing by wind or wash can be relatively rapid, but the contribution by movement through the soil may take longer. Once formed, a pavement is relatively stable. The closely spaced stones act as a drag on the surface wind, restrict the entrainment of finer intervening materials, and so limit deflation. On moderate slopes, runoff water is spread over the surface by the stone mantle and thus does not tend to cut a deep gully. Selective erosion is countered further as the stone concentration increases. Whether residual or transported, pavements naturally consist of materials resistant to weathering and therefore serve as "armor" for deserts.

Another manner in which stone pavements can be generated is by relative concentration through surface weathering. Rock fragments in the relatively moist environment of a desert soil are more susceptible to weathering than those on the arid surface, particularly where the soil is impregnated with salt or gypsum. Consequently, a stone pavement may survive above a soil that itself has few stones because they disintegrate at depth over time. The phenomenon is pronounced in granitic gravels; for example, some terrace sediments are known to have larger-sized stone pavements above horizons of small granite fragments formed by the weathering breakdown of boulders beneath the surface. These subsurface zones of fine particles are deepest and most free of subsurface stones on the highest and oldest terraces, where they may be more than 50 centimeters thick. In such cases, it is thought that stone pavements first formed from the abundant rock fragments in the area, but as subsurface weathering progressed all the buried stones were destroyed, while those on the surface remained relatively unweathered.

In spite of their status as a protective armor on desert surfaces, stone pavements are subject to further evolution over thousands of years as the stones weather and their secondary products are redistributed. This evolution is generally toward an increasingly even surface of small grain size and greater compaction. Also common is progressive darkening by surface weathering and the formation of rock or desert varnishes of manganese and iron stains, precipitated on the stone surfaces by microbial and weathering action.

Weathering of pavement stones occurs not only beneath the stones, where they are in contact with the protected soil layers, but also on their exposed surfaces. Pavement stones can be wetted frequently by dew, which also contributes salts to both surface and subsurface in the weathering process. Because pavements are generally unchanneled and provide little runoff, the features are particularly subject to episodic or seasonal cycles of shallow wetting by rainfall and evaporative drying, through which weathering is activated. Bare and generally dark-colored pavement, among the most strongly heated surfaces of the desert, are areas of considerable evaporation, as (mostly saline) moisture is drawn upward through narrow cracks. As a result, thin salt crusts are widespread, the soil itself is impregnated with chlorides and sulfates of calcium and sodium, and salt weathering is significant. In this process, the growth of various salt crystals in the pores of the stones causes forces sufficient to disrupt the rocks.

Pavement stones also trap windborne dust in fissures and cracks, and dirt cracking can result from expansion of the dust particles when they are wetted. Lichens and algae also exploit the shaded and somewhat more moist environments under the stones, adding an organic element of chemical decomposition to the weathering process.

In the breakdown of pavement stones, there tends to be a further selective concentration of resistant fine-grained material—for example, siliceous flint or chert pebbles that accumulate on the surface as soft limestones are weathered. Such stones can eventually break down by incorporation of water into their microcrystalline atomic structures, by spalling (chipping), by blocky fracturing (crazing), or by complete cleavage and radial splitting. Coarser-grained stones undergo granular disintegration and pitting. Fracturing of pavement stones also has been attributed to differential expansion and contraction caused by solar heating, but the idea is controversial. Such thermal fracturing may be only a partial cause; much of the broken stone is superficially altered chemically, and dirt-cracking expansion may be more important. In some cases, stones below the surface, where solar heating is not a possibility, can be seen to have been pried apart in this fashion.

Wind abrasion is a form of natural sandblasting. Its effectiveness is related to wind velocity, the hardness of the sand and dust carried by the wind, and the hardness of the rock fragments being eroded. It is probably most effective in certain polar areas where cold, dense air can carry large particles at very high velocities and where, at winter temperatures, even ice has a hardness of some minerals. The "dry valleys" of Antarctica, for example, have extensive stone pavements that have been affected in this way.

Boulders and pebbles in stone pavements may be fluted, scalloped, and faceted by wind abrasion. Flute and scallop forms vary in length from a few millimeters to several meters, but large flutes are not common in hard rocks. It is thought that they are produced by turbulent helical (helix-shaped) flows carrying dust and sand and that the scallops grow downwind. Where they are cut on large, immobile boulders, they are clear indicators of the strongest (dominant) wind directions. For this reason, they are most commonly reported from places where wind directions have remained largely unchanged for thousands to hundreds of thousands of years.

Some of the best-known wind-eroded stones in pavements are ventifacts (a general term for wind-faceted pebbles and boulders). A rock face abraded by wind may be pitted if there is a range of hardness in the minerals of the face, or it may be smooth where the rock is fine-grained or composed of only one mineral. Thus, rocks such as coarse-grained granite have pitted surfaces, but fine-grained quartzite generally produces only smooth, polished surfaces. Ventifacts have a great range of surface shapes, with plane and curved faces and two or more facets. The German term "dreikanter" is used for ventifacts with three facets, and "einkanter" is used for two-faceted stones. Multiple facets indicate either that there was more than one wind direction or that the stones have been turned over through time. As the sizes of the stone pavements' fragments are progressively reduced, a matrix of increasingly fine particles is supplied to the pavement. The proportion of such secondary material reveals the maturity of development of a desert stone pavement, although in practice it may be difficult without sophisticated analysis to distinguish between a new pavement in the process of being formed and an old one being degraded.

The fine particles in a degraded pavement are redistributed by wash and rain, a process that contributes to the smoothing and compaction of the pavement. Any exposed soil is puddled and sealed by heavy rainfall or runoff water so that a saturated layer flows into hollows between the stones. Bare soil interspersed through a pavement is generally crusted above a bubbly or vesicular horizon, 1-3 centimeters thick, that also extends around and beneath the pavement stones. The bubbles result from the escape of entrapped air. Equally important in compaction is the gravitational settling of the stones during the expansion and contraction of the surface upon heating and cooling and (especially in saline and expansive clay soils) upon wetting and drying. Pavements of this type are generally soft and puffy after rain, but, upon drying, the stones become ever more firmly embedded in a tight mosaic.

The slow downhill creep of water-saturated surface materials can also assist in either the smoothing or the roughening of a sloping stone pavement, particularly where dispersal of the matrix is accentuated by salinity. Microrelief on a stone pavement can be reduced by the differential flow of the fine sediments, and the pavement stones can thereby become more evenly distributed and further embedded. In some cases the stone pavements can move into a series of rough steps, aligned along the contours of the slope.

## Methods of Study

Among the first ways that geologists studied desert pavements was by clearing an existing pavement of stones and observing the rate and manner of reestablishment of stones on the surface. These analyses were combined with basic geologic and topographic mapping that showed how the wind could erode closed depressions in the ground, in some places below sea level, and concentrate stones on the surface. Wind-tunnel experiments in the laboratory also demonstrated the process. In recent years, closely spaced horizontal and vertical natural wind velocity readings, combined with portable wind-tunnel experiments in the field, have further elucidated deflation and wind-erosion production of desert pavements.

## Context

Desert pavements on earth are directly relevant to people who are attempting agriculture in highly arid areas. In such cases, the ground may have to be cleared of stones and precautions taken to retard the formation of new stone surfaces. In addition, travel over desert pavements is difficult for people, for beasts of burden, and for machines.

It has been discovered that desert pavements cover much of the surface of the planet Mars. When humans finally succeed in landing on the red planet and perhaps even colonize the surface, travel over the rocky terrain there will be a difficult problem. Study of desert pavements here will facilitate such activity there.

Deflation on a large scale happens only where there is little or no vegetation and where loose rock particles are fine enough to be picked up by the wind. Where fine-grained sediments are particularly prone to deflation, basins can reach more than 50 meters. Big Hollow, near Laramie, Wyoming, is about 5 kilometers wide, 15 kilometers long, and 100 meters deep. It was developed under more rigorous and windy climatic conditions, and its desert pavement is now somewhat degraded and covered with grass. In any deflation basin, however, the depth to which wind erosion can reach is limited either by the water table or by the growing concentration of stones in a deflation armor that cannot be further penetrated by wind erosion. In some cases, desert pavements can be created by deflation of as little as 4-5 centimeters of sediment.

In one unusual occurrence of reg desert pavement in southwestern Afghanistan, intense wind erosion of the finer sediments in ancient graveyards has produced a carpet of human bones interspersed with rock fragments. Aside from the life-threatening winds and intense aridity of the area, the local name for the region, Dasht-i-Margo (desert of death), derives in part from this strange pavement of bones.

## Bibliography

Cooke, Ronald U. "Stone Pavements in Deserts." *Annals of the Association of American Geographers* 60 (1970): 560-577. One of the most comprehensive non-technical journal articles available on desert pavements. The emphasis is on polygenesis, with examples mainly from California and Chile. The author notes that deflation may be a relatively unimportant process of pavement formation, a view decidedly in contrast with the ideas of many workers. He does note that the relative importance of the different processes may vary greatly between sites.

Cooke, Ronald U., and Andrew Warren. *Geomorphology in Deserts*. Berkeley: University of California Press, 1973. One of the chief English-language sources on dry climate geomorphology. The text has a long section on the formation of desert pavements as well as on the many other collateral processes and landforms that occur with or around such features.

Mabbutt, J. A. *Desert Landforms*. Cambridge, Mass.: MIT Press, 1977. This book has a chapter on stony deserts that is a superb exposition on desert pavements. Their polygenetic origin is well explained, and numerous examples and illustrations aid the discussion. The remainder of the book is replete with material on other arid landforms and processes that occur in the same context as do desert pavements.

McGinnies, William G., B J. Goldman, and P. Paylore, eds. *Deserts of the World*. Tucson: University of Arizona Press, 1968. This survey of research into the physical and biological environments of the world's deserts is one of the most comprehensive studies of arid regions ever attempted. Gives valuable information specific to many particular deserts and has an extensive reference list. The section on desert pavements is short but useful and contains many references not generally cited elsewhere.

Twidale, C. R. *Geomorphology, with Special Reference to Australia.* Melbourne, Australia: Thomas Nelson, 1968. A book on general geomorphology that has a short section on desert pavements, known as "gibber" in Australia, where such features are most common. Twidale's extensive experience with Australian desert landforms makes this a useful text for one seeking to understand the context of desert pavements.

*John F. Shroder, Jr.*

## Cross-References

Desertification, 346; The Geomorphology of Dry Climate Areas, 882; Mars' Valleys, 1494; Sand Dunes, 2259; Sediment Transport and Deposition, 2290; Soil Erosion, 2387.

# DESERTIFICATION

*Field of study:* Soil science

*Desertification comprises a variety of natural and human processes that cause the impoverishment of ecosystems, manifested in reduced biological productivity, rapid deterioration of soil quality, and associated declines in the condition of regional human economic and social systems.*

### Principal terms

ALBEDO: the fraction of visible light of electromagnetic radiation that is reflected by the properties of a given type of surface

AQUIFER: a water-bearing bed of rock, sand, or gravel capable of yielding substantial quantities of water to wells or springs

DESALINIZATION: the process of removing salt and minerals from seawater or from saline water occurring in aquifers beneath the land surface to render it fit for agriculture or other human use

MOVING DUNES: collections of coarse soil materials that result from wind erosion and threaten marginal vegetation and settlements as they move across deserts

PHOTOSYNTHESIS: the process of fixing atmospheric carbon in organic compounds in plants with production of free oxygen as a by-product

## Summary of the Phenomenon

Desertification—or, as some authorities prefer, desertization—as a process represents a complex set of interactions between natural and cultural forces and most often occurs in the borderlands of large, natural desert environments. The broadest conventional definition of desert conditions refers to precipitation levels: Regions which receive less than 100 millimeters of precipitation per year, for example, usually exhibit commonly recognized surface features such as flat, gravelly or pebbly tables and accumulations of sand dunes. The long-term absence of concentrated vegetation cycles and water erosion features results in only thin, marginally fertile soils, although in places along internal drainage systems these soils may be quite productive in the short run.

The term "desert" inevitably evokes references to land and soil, but in terms of precipitation levels and their consequences, the term can also be applied to surface regimes such as glacier fields and ice caps. Annual precipitation in Antarctica, for example, is well below 100 millimeters. Both ocean surfaces, in the sense of annual precipitation input, and various ocean levels and seabed, in terms of the presence of nutrients analogous to soil on land, may be classified as desert or as undergoing forms of the desertification process, resulting from both natural and human-induced causes. Land deserts typically feature dispersed, perennial vegetation, some of which may be in a dormant state much of the time. Vegetation may be somewhat denser in regions where groundwater aquifers are near the surface or may be absent entirely, as in major dune fields.

Human activities along the desert fringe, at least until recent times, were also remarkably accurate indicators of the boundaries of desert conditions. The 100-millimeter line of annual precipitation marks the effective limit of economical agriculture without the use of systematic irrigation. The presence of irrigation, therefore, is frequently a danger signal that human exploitation has ignored the limiting factors of arid environments.

Desertification is primarily the result of wind and water erosion. The first step is usually the loss of diffuse, arid zone vegetation that normally is sufficient to protect the soil surface from dramatic erosion or to impede the wind transport of a sufficient amount of airborne sand and dust from other areas to balance the loss of local soil matter. This vegetation loss may occur from natural or human causes. The former may include long-term climatic shifts resulting in reductions in annual precipitation or in shorter-term climatic or meteorological phenomena such as abnormally long drought or erratic cloudbursts.

Once protective vegetation is lost, wind erosion can remove even the coarser materials in a soil layer in a matter of a few years. Much of this material will accumulate in moving dunes that become a threat to surviving marginal vegetation. Finer materials may be carried thousands of miles, even to other continents. Dust from the Sahara, for example, may be carried deep into Europe or even across the Atlantic Ocean to Florida and the Caribbean littoral.

Erosion of soil matter exposes a surface of pebbles and gravels extremely sensitive to further damage, particularly that resulting from human actions. In parts of the North African Sahara, vast areas that were scenes of armored engagements in World War II still exhibited ruts and surface disturbance from heavy-tracked vehicles nearly half a century later. Mass motorcycle races in the Mojave Desert of California have caused extensive, and most likely permanent, surface damage.

Assessment of the desert environment in terms of average conditions often obscures the potential of water erosion to accelerate desertification. Hard stone or clay desert surfaces can become impermeable to water absorption by the action of raindrops on the finer soil materials, which seal the surface to the point where nearly all precipitation is lost by runoff. This condition not only destroys remnant vegetation beneath the surface by depriving it of water but also vastly increases the volume of water passing through internal drainage systems in periodic flash floods, which wreak havoc on surviving vegetation clinging to the banks of usually dry riverbeds.

Still another cause of desertification is accumulation of salts and alkaline substances in the soil. Although this process may develop naturally along interior drainage systems, the most extreme cases result from prolonged irrigation. Virtually all water sources contain some level of dissolved minerals. In regions of poor drainage, an endemic characteristic of many arid and semiarid zones, these minerals accumulate over the years and eventually render the soil useless for agriculture, encouraging its abandonment to the forces of wind erosion. Thousands of square kilometers have been lost to productive agriculture through salinization in ancient agricultural centers such as the Near East and Pakistan as well as in more recently exploited regions in California and Australia.

In traditional or premodern societies, human exploitation of desert environments relied upon pastoral economies, wherein grazing livestock converted plant matter for human consumption in the form of dairy products. Herders moved their animals from region to region in a form of transhumance. Social mechanisms that discourage intensive environmental exploitation and continually redistribute wealth were common in these societies.

The introduction of alien social values and exotic animal species into arid environments has greatly accelerated the desertification process. Destruction of social controls on human population growth results in unprecedented numbers of people making demands on the land. Conversion of a pastoral economy from dependence on a species such as the dromedary, which is a solitary and desultory grazer, to social herders and voracious grass-eaters such as sheep or goats, together with expanding human numbers, can destroy the equilibrium in a marginal zone in a few seasons. Sheep, for example, have been known to stimulate erosion simply because entire herds repeatedly follow the same path to a water source and destroy the vegetation and soil cover along the way.

In the last quarter of the twentieth century, as fossil fuel prices have soared, peasant populations have opened a new assault on marginal lands by cutting down the few available woody plants for firewood. Ecologists estimate that an average-sized family living in the arid borderlands of the Afro-Asian desert belt consumes the wood production of 1-3 hectares of land each year and that more than 25 million hectares per year may be denuded of trees and woody growth to provide fuel for burgeoning peasant societies.

## Methods of Study

The study of desertification is an interdisciplinary pursuit inasmuch as the phenomenon derives from both natural processes and human activities. The research contains a strong applied component in that its major objective is the discovery of procedures that may slow, or even reverse, what specialists in all fields agree is a relentless advance of desert frontiers in the twentieth century.

Remote sensing techniques, using special films in aerial photography and various optical sensors in satellite observations, now provide a season-by-season record of conditions in deserts and borderlands. Infrared-sensitive films are capable of recording early germination of plant life, concentrations of various substances in the soil composition, and the presence of certain contaminants. Landforms and topographic configurations not readily apparent on the ground, and which may have a bearing on the presence of water or the beginnings of vegetation deterioration, or which may make certain areas particularly vulnerable to erosion, frequently reveal themselves through remote sensing. Small-scale mapping of vast areas and careful monitoring of conditions are keys to identifying desertification in its early stage, when reversal may still be possible.

Conditions in sandy deserts with moving dunes have received particular attention in applied research because of the danger they present to settlements and installations. Careful analysis of the mineral and chemical composition as well as the physical sizes of particles, all of which may vary widely, are crucial in determining the most appropriate measures for possible fixation. Some dunes may be anchored by carefully chosen plant cover. Liquid binders and emulsions have also been tried with some success. Ironically, since intensive human exploitation is responsible for much contemporary desertification, applied research is frequently directed toward new dimensions of human adaptation to desert conditions. Results have included attempts to exploit desert plant species, inexpensive means of desalinization to utilize often plentiful sources of water in desert aquifers, and more efficient solar energy technologies.

The central problem in desertification research is to determine to what degree expansion of deserts results from long-term, natural fluctuations in the global environment and to what extent the phenomenon is a result of human intervention, and to distinguish the two. All the techniques that may be applied to reconstruction of climatic history and tracking of meteorological patterns therefore pertain to desertification studies.

Because of the generally brief period covered by modern meteorological records and an imperfect knowledge of the broader patterns of global climatic change, many theories have emerged that accord varying importance to natural and human-induced factors in desertification. Some climatologists propose that during the twentieth century a global swing toward greater aridity is apparent. Northern Hemisphere records suggest an expansion of polar air masses into lower latitudes with a consequent depression of moist equatorial air masses closer to the equator, so that the convergence between these systems—which roughly marks the northernmost penetration of tropical monsoons into North Africa and the Middle East—does not come as far north as it once did.

Conversely, the input of solar energy into tropical ecosystems, which drives the monsoons, could be decreasing. The Global Atmospheric Tropical Experiment (GATE), a massive, international research effort conducted in the mid-1970's to learn more about tropical environments and weather patterns, provided a knowledge base from which alarming conclusions may be drawn concerning the rapid deforestation of the tropics because of human exploitation, the consequent decrease in photosynthesis activity and increases in the albedo of the tropics, and the overall decrease in solar energy entering tropical ecosystems that results from these changes. Appreciation of the enormous importance of the tropics, as opposed to high latitudes, in understanding middle-latitude desertification was a major outcome of GATE.

Research on desertification in the last quarter of the twentieth century has concentrated on the Sahel, the fragile zone on the southern margins of the Sahara where true desert conditions become transitional to the grassland environments of tropical Africa. Beginning in the 1970's, a series of calamitous droughts struck the Sahel, bringing death and misery to huge numbers of people and animals and destroying entire pastoral societies. The impact of drought in the Sahel is magnified tremendously by the fact that the greatest breadth of the African continent is precisely in this zone, so that changes in northernmost penetration of the tropical monsoons of only a few minutes of latitude can spell catastrophe over thousands of square kilometers.

Research in the Sahel demonstrates the difficulty of separating natural from human causes of desertification. In the Republic of Sudan, for example, there is well-documented evidence, even in the recent colonial period, for retreat of the boundary zone between grassland and desert in some areas several hundred miles to the south and concomitant decreases in rainfall. Yet there is also a much broader picture, derived from archaeological studies, suggesting that this pattern may extend many centuries into the past and that modern socioeconomic and demographic change, therefore, cannot be entirely responsible.

Despite evidence that desertification processes have been at work for many centuries, the pressure of recent population increase on the Sahel and other marginal areas has created an atmosphere of crisis around applied research programs, so that most are directed toward fundamental changes in local practices in agriculture and animal husbandry or toward climate modification and desert reclamation. Both strategies often have the characteristic of uncontrolled experiments. Socioeconomic intervention tends to stress traditional or small-scale economic practices, often on the partly subjective conviction that they are better adapted to local conditions.

Schemes for climate and weather modification frequently require drastic environmental change. Among the more moderate proposals for the Sahel are construction of tree shelter belts, local vegetation modification, and cloud seeding designed to force the monsoon effect northward. Other schemes demand fundamental intervention in the patterns of atmospheric circulation that broadly determine the location of major desert systems. Most of these require gross changes in surface features. The creation of huge lakes in the natural drainage basins of the Sahara, through dams, evaporation control, and exploitation of groundwater aquifers, might increase precipitation levels. One research team has proposed paving large strips or "islands" of the Sahara with asphalt. The surface albedo of these areas would be much lower than sand or even vegetation, and their higher temperatures presumably would heat the air above them, promoting cloud formation and precipitation. Others have proposed periodic releases of carbon dust into the atmosphere over the Sahara to increase heat absorption and cloud formation. None of these schemes has been attempted, and all of them are likely to generate scientific controversy because of their impact on environment and their unknown potential.

## Context

Desertification in the broadest sense, including the degradation of all classes of land by human exploitation, ranks among the most serious and potentially devastating forms of environmental change. When linked with other human-induced changes that seriously affect albedo values, such as tropical deforestation and atmospheric and surface pollution of major ice fields, the threat of desertification becomes the focal point of concern for the future productive capacity of a world ecosystem that must support unprecedented human population levels.

Desertification is not confined merely to marginal lands bordering on true deserts. Careless agriculture or animal husbandry can create near-desert conditions in vast areas of grassland, as in the case of poorly planned development schemes in Soviet Central Asia or the Dust Bowl phenomenon of the 1930's on the central plains of the United States. Enormous amounts of top-quality soil are lost each year to water and wind erosion encouraged by unwise farming practices.

Much of the land most vulnerable to desertification, however, lies in lower or tropical latitudes, where soil regimes and microenvironments are not nearly as resilient as they are in Europe or North America. In many of these areas, moreover, the human issues arising from desertification involve not so much a lowering of living standards as the very survival of local populations. They call for massive intervention schemes with multiple economic and social dimensions, usually on the assumption that the indigenous social fabric or capacity to respond to emergencies of this magnitude is nonexistent or has broken down.

What can be done to halt or reverse the process of desertification is a complex and pressing issue. Knowledge of the physical processes involved in desertification and related long-term environmental and climatic change as well as an understanding of the dynamics of human interaction with this process are both far from perfect. The problem of desertification presents a challenge to the critical judgment of everyone concerned with environmental degradation and the inescapable realities of population growth and rising human expectations. It is an excellent illustration of the need for educated citizens and public servants to possess a scientific background as a basis for making public policy decisions.

## Bibliography

Allan, J. A., ed. *The Sahara: Ecological Change and Early Economic History.* Outwell, England: Middle East and North American Studies Press, 1981. A review of ecological changes in this great desert region and human utilization of the desert margins in preclassical times. This careful reconstruction of historical environmental conditions is useful as a comparison to modern desert limits and the impact of long-term settlement.

Brooks, George E. "A Provisional Historical Schema for Western Africa Based on Seven Climate Periods, ca. 9000 B.C. to the Nineteenth Century." *Cahiers d'études africaines* 16 (1986): 46-62. This is a summary of the historical evidence for climatic change in the Sahel, including maps projecting fluctuations of desert limits in various periods.

Bryson, Reid A., and Thomas J. Murray. *Climates of Hunger: Mankind and the*

*World's Changing Weather.* Madison: University of Wisconsin Press, 1977. An excellent general work on climatic change and the possible extent of human-induced factors, with emphasis on deforestation and desertification around the world.

Crawford, Clifford S., and James R. Gosz. "Desert Ecosystems: Their Resources in Space and Time." *Environmental Conservation* 9 (1982): 181-195. This article discusses the tensions between continuous exploitation of desert environments and the intermittent character of vital resources such as water and vegetation in a given location.

Eckholm, Erik, and Lester R. Brown. *Spreading Deserts: The Hand of Man.* New York: Worldwatch Institute, 1971. A brief, useful summary of world desertification patterns, emphasizing careless human exploitation and the interruption of natural processes that limit the spread of deserts.

Evenari, Michael, Leslie Shanan, and Nephtali Tadmor. *The Negev: The Challenge of a Desert.* Cambridge, Mass.: Harvard University Press, 1982. The best comprehensive study of attempts to develop settlement styles suitable to desert resources, based on a combination of archaeological research on ancient settlement patterns and the most recent findings in the earth sciences.

Glantz, Michael H., ed. *Desertification: Environmental Degradation in and Around Arid Lands.* Boulder, Colo.: Westview Press, 1977. An excellent discussion of a broad selection of related phenomena, including nature and causes of desertification, theories of natural versus human-induced environmental change, case studies of desertification, experiments in weather modification, and efforts of international agencies to treat desertification as a unified, global problem. Includes an extensive bibliography.

Oliver, F. W. "Dust-Storms in Egypt and Their Relation to the War Period, as Noted in Maryut, 1939-1945." *Geographical Journal* 106-108 (1945-1946): 26-49, 221-226. An early study of the extent to which intensive and extensive human movement and occupation of the desert may result in short-term deterioration of arid environments.

United Nations Conference on Desertification, Nairobi, Kenya. *Desertification: Its Causes and Consequences.* Elmsford, N.Y.: Pergamon Press, 1977. Includes four in-depth studies on the relationship between desertification and climate, ecological change, population, and technology, each with an extensive bibliography.

Walls, James. *Land, Man, and Sand: Desertification and Its Solution.* New York: Macmillan, 1980. An extensive collection of case studies from around the world, each illustrating facets of desertification and pragmatic, localized solutions. Contains numerous examples of how physical, biological, and social science approaches may be combined in comprehending and controlling deterioration.

*Ronald W. Davis*

**Cross-References**

Aerial Photography, 17; Alluvial Systems, 31; Aquifers, 71; The Atmosphere's Global Circulation, 121; Climate, 217; Desert Pavement, 338; Drainage Basins, 384; Land Management, 1327; Paleoclimatology, 1993; Precipitation, 2108; Remote Sensing and the Electromagnetic Spectrum, 2166; Future Resources, 2182; Sand Dunes, 2259; Soil Erosion, 2387.

# DIAGENESIS

*Type of earth science:* Geology
*Field of study:* Petrology, sedimentary

*Diagenesis refers to the physical, chemical, and biological changes that sediment undergoes after it is deposited. These processes change loose sediment into sedimentary rock and occur in the upper several hundred meters of the earth's crust.*

### Principal terms

BAR: a unit of pressure equal to 1 million dynes per square centimeter

CARBONATE: a mineral with $CO_3$ in its chemical formula, such as calcite ($CaCO_3$)

LITHIFICATION: the hardening of sediment into a rock through compaction, cementation, recrystallization, or other processes

PORE FLUIDS: fluids, such as water (usually carrying dissolved minerals, gases, and hydrocarbons), in pore spaces in a rock

POROSITY: the amount of space between the sedimentary grains in a rock or sediment

SEDIMENT: loose grains of solid, particulate matter resulting from the weathering and breakdown of rocks, chemical precipitation, or secretion by organisms

SEDIMENTARY ROCK: a rock resulting from the consolidation of loose sediment that has accumulated in flat-lying layers on the earth's surface

## Summary of the Phenomenon

Diagenesis refers to the physical, chemical, and biological processes that occur in sediment after deposition as it is buried and transformed into sedimentary rock. These processes alter the texture, porosity, fabric, structure, and mineralogy of the sediment. Through diagenesis, sand is changed into sandstone, mud is changed into shale, and carbonate sediments are changed into limestone and dolomite. The processes and degree of alteration depend in part on the initial sediment composition and the depth of burial.

As sediment is buried to increasing depths, the temperatures and pressures increase, and diagenesis becomes metamorphism. The increase in temperature with depth is referred to as the geothermal gradient. Although the exact limits separating diagenesis and metamorphism are not strictly defined, diagenesis can be considered to occur under temperatures ranging from those at the earth's surface up to nearly 300 degrees Celsius and under pressures ranging from atmospheric pressure to at least 1 kilobar (1,000 bars). These conditions occur at depths of about 10 kilometers. Some classifications restrict the zone of diagenesis to about 0 to 1 kilometer, grading down into the zones of catagenesis (several kilometers deep, with temperatures of 50 to 150 degrees and pressures of 300 to 1,000 or 1,500 bars), meta-genesis (up to about 10 kilometers deep), and metamorphism. Temperature is an important control on many diagenetic processes, because it influences chemical reactions such as the dissolution and precipitation of minerals, recrystallization, and authigenesis.

The primary physical diagenetic process is compaction. Compaction presses sedimentary grains closer together under the load of overlying sediment, causing pore space to be decreased or eliminated and squeezing out pore fluids. In sandstones, compaction occurs by the rotation and slippage of sand grains, the breakage of brittle grains, and the bending and mashing of ductile (soft, easily deformed) grains. Brittle grains include thin shells, skeletal fragments, and feldspar grains. Ductile grains include clay or shale chips, fecal pellets, and some metamorphic rock fragments, such as slate. Compaction also causes some mineral grains to interpenetrate, producing irregular stylolitic contacts. In general, sands compact much less than muds. That is true since the average sandstone has a high percentage of hard grains, such as quartz; muds typically have a high initial water content, and water is squeezed out during compaction. The compaction of sands, however, is influenced by the nature of the sand grains present; sands with a large percentage of ductile grains are more susceptible to compaction.

Chemical diagenetic processes include cementation, the growth of new minerals (authigenesis), replacement, neomorphism (recrystallization and inversion), and dissolution. Cementation is the precipitation of minerals from pore fluids. These minerals glue the grains of sediment together, forming a rock. The most common cements are quartz (silica), calcite, and hematite, but other cements occur, including clays, aragonite, dolomite, siderite, limonite, pyrite, feldspar, gypsum, anhydrite, barite, and zeolite minerals. The type of cement is controlled by the composition of the pore fluids.

Authigenesis refers to the growth of new minerals in the sediment and the transformation of one mineral into another. Some of the most common authigenic minerals in sandstones are calcite, quartz, and clay cements. Other than cements, authigenic minerals include glauconite, micas, and clay minerals. Glauconite is a green mineral which forms on the sea floor when sedimentation rates are low. Authigenic micas and clays typically form in the subsurface at higher temperatures and pressures. Often, one clay mineral is transformed into another as a result of dehydration (water loss) or chemical alteration by migrating fluids. Clays may also be formed from the alteration of feldspars or volcanic ash and rock fragments. Authigenesis also includes the alteration of iron-bearing minerals (such as biotite, amphibole, or pyroxene) to pyrite, under reducing conditions, or to iron oxide (limonite, goethite, or hematite), under oxidizing conditions.

Replacement is the molecule-by-molecule or volume-for-volume substitution of one mineral for another. Replacement generally involves the simultaneous dissolution of an original mineral and precipitation of a new mineral in its place. Fossils which were originally calcium carbonate may be replaced by different minerals, such as quartz, pyrite, or hematite. Many minerals are known as replacement minerals, including calcite, chert, dolomite, hematite, limonite, siderite, anhydrite, and glauconite. Factors controlling replacement include pH, temperature, pressure, and the chemistry of the pore fluids.

Neomorphism is a term meaning "new form"; it refers to minerals changing in size, shape, or crystal structure during diagenesis. The chemical composition of the minerals, however, remains the same. Neomorphism includes the processes of recrystallization and inversion. Recrystallization alters the size or shape of mineral grains without changing their chemical composition or crystal structure. Recrystallization can occur in any type of sedimentary rock, but it is most common among the carbonates. Limestones are commonly recrystallized during diagenesis, producing a coarsely crystalline rock in which original sedimentary textures and structures may be fully or partially obliterated. The reason that minerals recrystallize is not well understood, but it may be related to energy stored in strained crystals or to a force arising from the surface tension of curved crystal boundaries. Inversion is a process in which one mineral is changed into another with the same chemical composition but a different crystal structure. The two minerals involved are called polymorphs, meaning "multiple forms." Aragonite and calcite are polymorphs. Both have the same chemical composition, but each has a different crystal structure: Aragonite is orthorhombic and calcite is rhombohedral. Aragonite, with time, will become calcite by inversion. Inversion may occur along a migrating film of liquid, causing the simultaneous dissolution of one mineral and precipitation of its polymorph, or by solid-state transformation (switching of the positions of ions in the crystal lattice).

Dissolution refers to the dissolving and total removal of a mineral, leaving an open cavity or pore space in the rock. This pore space may persist, or it may become filled by another mineral at a later time. Some of the more soluble minerals are the carbonates and the evaporites, such as halite and gypsum. Large-scale dissolution of limestone leads to the formation of caves and caverns. Pressure solution is the dissolution of minerals under the pressure of overlying sediment. Stylolites are a common result of pressure solution, and they commonly occur in carbonate rocks. Stylolites are thin, dark, irregular seams with a zigzag pattern that separate mutually interpenetrating rocks. The dark material along the seam is a concentration of insoluble material such as clay, carbon, or iron oxides. Pressure solution can result in a 35 to 40 percent reduction in the thickness of carbonate rocks. The carbonate removed by pressure solution is frequently a source of carbonate cements.

Biological diagenetic processes occur soon after sediment is deposited and consist of the activities of organisms in and on the sediment. Bacteria are particularly important to the chemical diagenetic processes. Bacteria living in the sediment control many chemical reactions involving mineral precipitation or dissolution; they are involved in the breakdown or decomposition of organic matter (one of the steps in the formation of oil and gas), and can cause the pH of the pore fluids to increase or to decrease, depending on the kinds of microorganism, type of organic matter, decomposition products, and availability of oxygen. For example, in aerobic environments (those where oxygen is present), decay of organic matter generally causes decreasing pH—increasing acidity—which may lead to the dissolution of carbonate minerals such as calcite. Under anaerobic conditions, organic decay generally raises the pH and may lead to the precipitation of calcite cement. The formation of pyrite is also influenced by the activity of bacteria. Sulfate-reducing bacteria in anoxic environments change sulfate into hydrogen sulfide. If iron is present, it reacts with the hydrogen sulfide to form iron sulfides, such as pyrite.

Bioturbation is the disturbance of the sediment by burrowing (excavation into soft sediment), boring (drilling into hard sediment), the ingestion of sediment and production of fecal pellets, root penetration, and other activities of organisms. Bioturbation generally occurs shortly after deposition and causes mixing of sediment that was originally deposited as separate layers, destruction of primary sedimentary structures and fabrics, and breakdown or clumping of grains. In some cases, chemical alteration of the sediment accompanies bioturbation. For example, light-colored halos may form around burrows or roots, particularly in red or brown sediments, because of the reduction of iron.

Diagenesis may decrease or increase the porosity and permeability of the sediment. Porosity is decreased by compaction, the precipitation of cements in pore spaces, and bioturbation. Porosity is increased by dissolution. Zones of increased porosity are particularly favorable for oil and gas accumulations.

## Methods of Study

Diagenesis is primarily studied using sedimentary petrography, which is the microscopic examination of thin sections of sedimentary rocks. Thin sections are slices of rock, typically 30 micrometers thick, bonded to glass slides, which are examined with a petrographic microscope. In this way, minerals can be identified based on their optical properties, and textural relationships can be studied, such as the size, shape, and arrangement of grains; the geometry of cements and pore spaces; the character of contacts between grains; the presence of dissolution features; and mashing or fracturing of grains. Thin sections may be enhanced, to allow easier identification of minerals, with various staining and acid etching techniques. In addition, acetate peels may be prepared of etched and stained rock surfaces for examination with the microscope.

There are a number of other techniques which can be used in conjunction with petrography to obtain more specific diagenetic data, including cathodoluminescence, X-ray diffraction, scanning electron microscopy, and fluid inclusion studies. Cathodoluminescence microscopy can provide information about the spatial distribution of trace elements in rocks. Luminescence is the emission of light from a material which has been activated or excited by some form of energy. Cathodoluminescence works by activating various parts of a polished thin section with a beam of electrons. The electron beam excites certain ions, producing luminescence.

This technique can reveal small-scale textures and inhomogeneities of particles and cements through differences in their luminescence, which is related to differing concentrations of trace element ions. Cathodoluminescence is commonly used to study cements in carbonate rocks.

X-ray diffraction is used to determine the mineralogy of sedimentary rocks, particularly fine-grained rocks such as shales. The technique is based on reflections of X rays from planes in the crystal structure of minerals. Each mineral has a characteristic crystal structure and produces a distinctive X-ray diffraction pattern consisting of peaks of different position and intensity, which are plotted on chart paper by the X-ray diffractometer. Minerals are identified by comparing peak positions and intensities with well-established standards.

Scanning electron microscopy can be used to examine small-scale textural features of sedimentary rocks. The technique can magnify seventy thousand times or more, permitting detailed study of extremely small particles that cannot be adequately examined using a petrographic microscope. Scanning electron microscopy involves reflections of an electron beam from a rock or mineral surface. Fine details of cements and grains may be readily observed and photographed. When used in conjunction with an energy dispersive analyzer, the technique can provide semiquantitative chemical analyses of selected particles.

Fluid inclusions are extremely small droplets of fluid encased within crystals or mineral grains. The fluids are a small sample of the original pore fluids from which the mineral was precipitated. By examining fluid inclusions using heating and freezing devices attached to a microscope, the geologist can determine the composition of the original pore fluids and the temperature at which the mineral was precipitated. This technique reveals that many minerals and cements were precipitated from hot, saline pore fluids.

Stable isotopes of oxygen and carbon are commonly used to determine the chemistry of the pore fluids and the temperatures under which precipitation of cements or authigenic minerals occurred. Studies of the stable isotopes of microfossils have also provided information on past climatic changes. Isotopes are different forms of elements which vary in the number of neutrons present in the nucleus; hence, the various isotopes of an element have different atomic weights. The term "stable" is used to indicate that these isotopes are not radioactive. By comparing the ratios of oxygen 16 and oxygen 18 or carbon 12 and carbon 13 in minerals such as calcite, it is possible to determine whether the minerals precipitated from fresh water or marine water, or to determine the temperature of the fluid from which the mineral precipitated. Stable isotope ratios of other elements, such as sulfur, are also studied.

## Context

As the process that causes lithification, or the production of sedimentary rocks from loose sediment, diagenesis is responsible for the transformation of sand into sandstone, clay and mud into shale, and carbonate sediments (lime sands and muds) into limestone and dolostone. Chemical diagenetic processes include the precipitation of minerals as cements in the pore spaces between grains, the growth of new minerals in the sediment, the replacement of one mineral by another, changes in the size, shape, or crystal structure of a mineral, and the removal of minerals by dissolution. Biological processes which affect sediment after deposition include the activities of burrowing, boring, or sediment-injesting organisms and the activity of bacteria living in the sediment.

Aside from adding to the general understanding of the history and development of the earth, the study of these diagenetic processes is important to the exploration and discovery of oil and gas: Petroleum may accumulate in porous rocks, so determining porosity may help the geologist to identify potential hydrocarbon reservoirs.

Diagenesis is also responsible for creating some interesting geologic features, including geodes and "thunder eggs," concretions, septarian nodules (or "turtle backs"), sand crystals and barite roses, dendrites, and liesegang banding. Geodes are subspherical hollow rocks lined with crystals, which formed by precipitation of cements in cavities in the rock. Many geodes form in dissolution cavities in limestone or in large gas bubbles in basalt. Thunder eggs are similar to geodes; however, the cavity in the rock is completely filled with mineral precipitates, typically chalcedony, opal, or agate. Concretions are the product of localized precipitation of cement (commonly calcite or iron oxide) in the pore spaces of sediment and are generally spherical or disk-shaped but may have diverse forms. Septarian nodules are spherical bodies with a series of irregular, radiating, and concentric cracks inside. The cracks are typically filled with several generations of cement (commonly calcite). The outside of some septarian nodules is so weathered and eroded that the interior calcite veins can be seen, forming a polygonal pattern resembling the plates on a turtle's shell and hence named "turtle backs." These nodules are believed to form as a result of cementation and hardening of the exterior, followed by desiccation and shrinkage of the interior, forming cracks, which are later filled with cement. Sand crystals and barite roses result from the precipitation of large, well-formed crystals (or clusters of crystals) of cement in sediment. Dendrites are flat, gray to black, branching structures, resembling plant fossils. They consist of deposits of manganese oxide minerals (such as the mineral pyrolusite) from solution along planar surfaces in the rock. Liesegang banding (also called diffusion banding) is a pattern of brown, curving, parallel lines or rings on rock surfaces. They result from the rhythmic precipitation of iron oxides within fluid-saturate rock, commonly sandstone.

## Bibliography

Boggs, Sam, Jr. *Principles of Sedimentology and Stratigraphy.* Columbus, Ohio: Merrill, 1987. A textbook designed for undergraduate geology majors. It is clearly written, comprehensive, and well illustrated, with a long chapter on the topic of diagenesis. The chapter discusses the major diagenetic processes, the diagenetic environment (temperatures and pressures, as well as the chemical composition of subsurface waters), major controls on diagenesis, and the major effects of diagenesis (physical, mineralogic, and chemical changes). Contains background information on other aspects of sedimentary rocks.

Jonas, E. C., and E. McBride. *Diagenesis of Sandstone and Shale: Application to Exploration for Hydrocarbons*. Austin: Department of Geological Sciences, University of Texas, Continuing Education Program, 1977. This book provides clear coverage of the diagenesis of sandstones and shales. It is well illustrated, with photomicrographs of thin sections showing the evidence for various diagenetic processes. It also has graphs and line drawings, which make the processes easier to envision. It is written for persons with a basic background in sedimentology, but it can be understood by the nonspecialist.

Larsen, Gunnar, and George V. Chilingar, eds. *Diagenesis in Sediments and Sedimentary Rocks*. New York: Elsevier, 1979. A two-volume book which is number 25 in the Developments in Sedimentology series. The series covers a number of aspects of sedimentary geology in depth, and each volume contains papers written by and for specialists in the field. The first chapter of volume 1 is an introduction to the diagenesis of sediments and rocks; subsequent chapters deal with more specialized subjects, such as the diagenesis of sandstones, coal, and carbonate rocks. In volume 2, there are specialized chapters on the various phases of diagenesis, low-grade metamorphism, and the diagenesis of shales, deep-sea carbonates, and iron-rich rocks. The book is suitable for advanced college students. The first chapter is probably the most useful for the nonspecialist.

McDonald, D. A., and R. C. Surdam, eds. *Clastic Diagenesis*. Memoir 37. Tulsa, Okla.: American Association of Petroleum Geologists, 1984. This book is divided into three parts: basic concepts and principles of diagenesis, changes in porosity, and applications of diagenesis in the exploration and production of hydrocarbons. Most of the articles are case histories of the diagenesis of particular rock units. Most are technical in content, but there are some which provide general overviews of specialized aspects of diagenesis. Suitable for advanced college students.

Pettijohn, F. J. *Sedimentary Rocks*. 3d ed. New York: Harper & Row, 1975. This textbook provides an introduction to the basic types of sedimentary rock and touches on various aspects of diagenesis. Of particular interest is a chapter on concretions, nodules, and other diagenetic segregations. The chapter explains more about secondary sedimentary structures than most other textbooks on sedimentology, and it is a useful guide for persons curious about the origin of geologic oddities and those who would like a better background on the formation of sedimentary rocks. Suitable for college and advanced high school students.

Scholle, Peter A. *A Color Illustrated Guide to Carbonate Constituents, Rock Textures, Cements, and Porosities*. Memoir 27. Tulsa, Okla.: American Association of Petroleum Geologists, 1978. A superbly illustrated book on various types of carbonate rock as seen in thin section. It illustrates the major carbonate grains, along with dolomite, evaporite, silica, iron, phosphate, and glauconite minerals. Cements and carbonate rock textures are also covered. It provides background information on porosity and techniques for studying carbonate rocks. There is a brief explanatory caption and geologic locality data for each photograph.

_____. *A Color Illustrated Guide to Constituents, Textures, Cements, and Porosities of Sandstones and Associated Rocks*. Memoir 28. Tulsa, Okla.: American Association of Petroleum Geologists, 1979. A color picturebook of various types of sandstone as seen in thin section, this source illustrates all the major detrital sand grains, textures, cements, replacement or displacement fabrics, compaction and deformation fabrics, and porosity. Clays and shales, chert, and other types of sediment are also included. There is a brief explanatory caption and geologic locality data for each photograph. Basic information on sandstone classification and various techniques for studying sedimentary rocks is offered.

Scholle, P. A., and P. R. Schluger, eds. *Aspects of Diagenesis*. Special Publication 26. Tulsa, Okla.: Society of Economic Paleontologists and Mineralogists, 1979. This book is divided into two major sections. The first covers the determination of diagenetic paleotemperatures; the second, the diagenesis of sandstones (in particular, hydrocarbon reservoirs). The papers are the result of symposia that were held on these topics. They include both general review articles and specific examples. Suitable for advanced college-level readers.

Tucker, M., ed. *Techniques in Sedimentology*. Boston: Blackwell Scientific Publications, 1988. This volume covers techniques used by sedimentologists to study diagenesis and other areas of sedimentology. Chapters are included on the collection and analysis of field data, grain-size data and interpretation, microscopical techniques, cathodoluminescence microscopy, X-ray powder diffraction, scanning electron microscopy, and chemical analysis. The book explains the techniques used to study diagenesis and also discusses diagenetic fabrics produced by compaction, cementation, dissolution, alteration, and replacement. It is well indexed and profusely illustrated. Includes a number of excellent photomicrographs of rock thin sections illustrating diagenetic textures. For college-level students.

*Pamela J. W. Gore*

### Cross-References

Carbonates, 190; Clays, 210; Fluid Inclusions, 726; Geothermometry and Geobarometry, 922; Metamorphic Rock Classification, 1553; Contact Metamorphism, 1594; Regional Metamorphism, 1606; Micropaleontology: Microfossils, 1674; The Structure of Minerals, 1693; The Origin of Oil and Gas, 1901; Physical Properties of Rocks, 2225; Sedimentary Mineral Deposits, 2296; Sedimentary Rock Classification, 2304; Sedimentary Rocks: Biogenic, 2312; Sedimentary Rocks: Chemical Precipitates, 2318; Sedimentary Rocks: Siliciclastic, 2324; Stress and Strain, 2490; Weathering and Erosion, 2723.

# DIAMONDS

*Type of earth science:* Economic geology

 *Diamond is an important industrial mineral as well as the most valued of gemstones. Natural diamonds crystallize only at very high pressures and are brought to the earth's surface in kimberlite, an unusual type of igneous rock that forms in the upper mantle. Kimberlite also contains "gems" of another sort: rare pieces of the earth's deep crust and mantle.*

### Principal terms

BORT: a general term for diamonds that are suitable only for industrial purposes; these diamonds are black, dark gray, brown, or green in color and usually contain many inclusions of other minerals

COESITE: a mineral with the same composition as quartz (silicon dioxide), but with a dense crystal structure that forms only under very high pressures

CRYSTAL: a solid that possesses a definite orderly arrangement of its atoms; it differs from an amorphous solid such as glass, and all true minerals are crystalline solids

DIAMOND: a crystalline variety of the element carbon, characterized by its extreme hardness; the carbon atoms are bonded into a dense, three-dimensional network that is very strong

GRAPHITE: a crystalline variety of the element carbon, characterized by its softness and ability to cleave into flakes; the carbon atoms are arranged in sheets that are weakly bonded together

KIMBERLITE: an unusual, fine-grained variety of peridotite that is believed to be congealed magma from the deep mantle; it contains not only olivine—which is commonly altered to serpentine—and pyroxenes but also calcite, mica, and trace amounts of diamond

METASTABLE: crystalline solids are said to be metastable if they exist outside the temperature and pressure conditions under which they formed; thus, diamond forms at very high pressures within the earth but is metastable at the earth's surface

PERIDOTITE: a dense, dark-green rock that is composed mainly of the silicate mineral olivine ("peridot" is an ancient word for olivine) and other magnesium- and iron-rich silicates such as pyroxenes; the earth's mantle and the ultramafic nodules derived from it are composed of peridotite

ULTRAMAFIC: rocks such as peridotite that contain abundant magnesium- and iron-rich minerals

## Summary of the Phenomenon

In the eighteenth century, virtually all the world's diamonds came from India and were hoarded by royalty; few people had ever seen a diamond, let alone possessed one. Brazil became an important producer in the late 1700's, but diamonds were still unavailable to most people. In 1866, a farm boy discovered a bright pebble on the banks of the Orange River in South Africa and unknowingly started a chain of economic, social, and political upheavals that continue to this day; the stone was later determined to be a 21-carat diamond (one carat equals 200 milligrams). Within a decade, South Africa's mines would be producing 3 million carats a year to a world market; by the turn of the century, diamonds would become an important industrial commodity. Today, several South American countries and the Soviet Union also export diamonds, but South Africa remains the world's foremost diamond producer. North America has no major diamond deposits.

Early diggings were concentrated along the Orange and Vaal rivers of South Africa, where prospectors staked small claims and shoveled into the diamondiferous gravel deposits. Fines were washed away in a rudimentary method known as wet digging, and the remaining gravel was spread out to be examined, pebble by pebble. Around 1870, a diamond was found approximately 100 kilometers from the nearest river, and prospectors began to speculate that the stones along the riverbanks did not originate there but were washed in from elsewhere. Increasing numbers of miners went into the bush to pursue diamonds, finding them in local patches of weathered rock known as yellow ground. As geologists would soon understand, the yellow ground was merely the uppermost layer of deep, funnel-shaped pipes of diamond-bearing igneous rock that had been injected into the earth's crust by ancient volcanoes. The bluish-gray rock was named kimberlite for a nearby South African town.

At present, more than 90 percent of the world's diamonds are found in river gravels, beach sands, and glacial deposits of many geological ages. Only in kimberlite pipes are diamonds found in the original rock in which they were formed. Kimberlite pipes are rather insignificant features, seldom having diameters greater than 1 kilometer. Mining has shown them to be carrotlike bodies whose vertical dimensions far exceed the sizes of their surface outcrops. Mine shafts have penetrated about 1.5 kilometers into kimberlite pipes, but minerals contained in the kimberlite, including the coveted diamonds, suggest that the pipes extend all the way through the crust and into the earth's upper mantle to a total depth of about 250 kilometers. This is deeper than any other variety of igneous rock.

Beneath the weathered yellow ground, fresh kimberlite is a hard, dark bluish-gray rock that miners call blue ground. Its texture gives strong evidence of an igneous origin, indicating that kimberlite was injected into the earth's crust as a molten liquid and then quickly solidified against cooler rocks surrounding the pipe. The major constituents of kimberlite are silicate minerals: compounds of silicon and oxygen with other metal ions. Kimberlite is a variety of peridotite ("peridot" is an ancient word for olivine), and hence its major constituent is the mineral olivine, a magnesium-iron silicate. The olivine is usually altered to the mineral serpentine, giving the rock its characteristic blue-gray color. Other minerals present are calcite (calcium carbonate, not a silicate mineral) and phlogopite, a variety of mica that is rich in potassium and magnesium.

Exotic rocks contained within the kimberlite matrix are perhaps more interesting than the kimberlite itself. Diamonds are one such inclusion, although they comprise a minuscule proportion of the total rock. Typical diamond contents in minable kimberlite range from about 0.1 to 0.35 carat per ton; even the famous Premier Mine in South Africa has produced only about 5.5 tons of diamonds from 100 million tons of rock, which is about 0.000005 percent. Much more common than diamonds, if economically less interesting, are inclusions of rocks torn loose from the walls of the volcanic pipe. Known as xenoliths (from the Greek for "foreign rocks"), these inclusions are of great interest to geologists because they are the deepest known samples of the earth's continental crust and upper mantle. Many of the xenoliths come from the same rock strata that occur in the surrounding terrain, but of greatest interest are those believed to originate in the earth's mantle. These rocks are called ultramafic nodules. Like diamonds, they are rare, but in kimberlite they are far more common than in other types of igneous rock. Many of the xenoliths are centimeter- to decimeter-sized; in order to carry such large, heavy inclusions, the kimberlite must either have been explosively injected or have had an unusually high strength for a magma. Geologists believe that the xenoliths were abraded from the walls of the pipe and were rapidly carried upward in the kimberlite during violent expansion of its dissolved gases, mainly carbon dioxide and water vapor. Geological information from numerous kimberlite pipes that have been eroded to different levels, together with their demonstrated ability to carry large pieces of the earth's mantle, suggests that kimberlite magma rises through the earth much faster than do other types of magma, perhaps as a gas-charged explosion. The gas-particle mixture apparently bores through the upper mantle and crust, injecting its high-pressure cargo of kimberlite, crustal xenoliths, ultramafic nodules, and diamonds into shallow levels of the crust before eventually erupting onto the surface as broad volcanic cones.

Kimberlite pipes are found only in the interiors of the earth's ancient continental landmasses. The rate at which temperature increases with depth beneath continents (the continental geotherm; near the surface it is about 20-25 degrees Celsius per kilometer) is fairly well known from geophysical calculations and from measurements of the earth's heat output in deep mines. The rate at which pressure increases with depth (lithostatic pressure, or pressure resulting from the weight of overlying rocks) is similarly known; pressure increases by about 1,000 atmospheres per kilometer of depth. The influence of temperature and pressure on the compositions of minerals is also known from laboratory experiments and theoretical calculations. When suitable minerals are present in igneous rock, the minerals can be used to calculate the temperature and depth of origin of the rock.

Three independent lines of evidence indicate that kimberlite is formed in the upper mantle, at depths and pressures far greater than for any other type of igneous rock. To calculate pressures of formation, it is usually necessary to know or assume the temperature of formation. The continental geotherm supplies the needed temperature information. At temperatures along the continental geotherm, diamond is stable only at depths greater than about 100 kilometers; at lower pressures, graphite forms instead. Diamond exists at low pressures only because it is metastable (otherwise there could be no diamonds on the earth's surface), but diamond does not form naturally at low pressures. A second line of evidence for great pressure involves the minerals that have been trapped inside the diamonds during their growth. Diamonds sometimes contain inclusions of coesite, a mineral with the same chemical composition as quartz (silicon dioxide) but with a more compact structure that forms only at very high pressures. At temperatures along the continental geotherm, laboratory studies have shown that coesite, in turn, gives way to the silica mineral stishovite at depths greater than about 300 kilometers. Because stishovite has never been found in diamonds, the diamonds must have formed at depths less than about 300 kilometers. Hence, diamonds seem to have formed at depths between about 100 and 300 kilometers in the earth's upper mantle. The pressures and temperatures that have been calculated from minerals in the ultramafic nodules are in agreement with this depth range: Most of the nodules seem to have formed at depths of 100-250 kilometers in the upper mantle and at temperatures of about 1,100-1,500 degrees Celsius.

The unusual physical properties of diamond are a reflection of its crystalline structure. Diamond is a three-dimensional network of elemental carbon, with each carbon atom linked to four equidistant neighbors by strong covalent bonds. The dense, strongly bonded crystal structure gives diamond its extreme hardness. Another mineral made of pure carbon is graphite, the writing material in lead pencils. In graphite, sheets of carbon atoms are weakly bonded and are separated by relatively large distances. Thus, graphite has a lamellar structure and is very soft.

The physical properties of diamond are remarkable in comparison to virtually all other materials. It is the hardest substance known. With a hardness of 10, it tops the Mohs scale of relative hardness and is actually about forty-two times as hard as corundum, its nearest neighbor, with a hardness of 9. Its luster is adamantine to greasy, and it cannot be wetted by water—a property that is of great practical benefit in separating diamonds from waste rock. Diamonds vary in color from water-clear (most valuable) to pale blue to yellow to deep yellow or brown; industrial varieties are brown or grayish-black. Raw diamonds occur most often as octahedra (eight-sided polygons) or as cubes but are also found as tetrahedra (four-sided polygons) and dodecahedra (twelve-sided polygons) as well as in slender, irregular shapes. Diamond can be cleaved in four directions, parallel to its octahedral faces. Its refractive index of 2.42 is the highest of all gems, producing strong reflections in cut stones, and its very high dispersion (ability to separate white light into the colors of the spectrum) gives cut diamonds their "fire." Diamond is also triboelectric (becomes electrically charged when rubbed) and fluorescent (emits visible light when struck by ultraviolet rays).

Diamonds are separated from waste rock by first crushing the kimberlite, wetting it, then passing it over a series of greased bronze tables. Diamond cannot be wetted by water and is the only mineral that sticks to the grease, which is later scraped off as the diamonds are extracted. Another way of separating diamonds takes advantage of their fluorescent property. As the crushed rock is passed beneath ultraviolet lamps, the diamonds are spotted by photosensors, which trigger jets of compressed air that eject the diamonds into bins. The diamonds are then graded by size, shape, and color. Gem-quality stones of less than 1 carat are called melee. Less than 5 percent of all diamonds are suitable for cut stones of 1 carat or larger.

Diamonds have been fashioned into precious jewels for several millennia, but diamond cutting has become a major industry only during the past century, in response to worldwide demand and to the abundant supply of South African diamonds. Five basic steps are involved in diamond cutting: marking, cleaving, sawing, girdling, and faceting. The diamond is first carefully studied, sometimes for months, in order to identify its cleavage planes and to map out any inclusion-rich areas that will affect how it is to be cut. Large diamonds are usually irregular in shape and are seldom left whole. A central, master stone is commonly envisioned within the mass, and the "satellite" offcuts become fine gems in their own right. Lines for cleaving or sawing are marked in black ink, and the diamond is then sent to the cutter. If the diamond is to be cleaved, a thin groove is first established using a saw charged with diamond dust. The diamond is mounted in a dop or clamp, and a steel wedge is inserted into the groove and is struck sharply with a mallet. A misdirected blow can shatter the stone: It is said that Joseph Asscher, after successfully cleaving the 3,100-carat Cullinan diamond in 1908, swooned into the arms of an attending physician. Sawing is a slower, if not safer, alternative to cleaving; it uses a thin, circular bronze blade that is charged with diamond dust. Next, the diamond is girdled by placing it in a lathe and grinding it against another diamond to make it round; the "girdle" is where the upper and lower sets of facets meet. Finally, the diamond is faceted: The facets are cut and polished by clamping the stone in a holder and placing it against rotating laps that are charged with diamond dust. The most popular cut is the "brilliant"—a round stone with fifty-eight facets. Other cuts include the marquise (oval), emerald (rectangular), and pear.

Cut stones are graded under strict rules, using an elaborate system of four criteria: cut, color, clarity, and carat. Cut refers to the skill with which the gem has been shaped—its symmetry and reflective brilliance. Color refers to the tint of the stone: The most valuable gems are water-clear, but many fine stones are pale yellow, blue, or pink; colored diamonds are called "fancies." Clarity refers to the size, number, and locations of any inclusions that may be present. Inclusions do not necessarily degrade a stone if they are small or are located in inconspicuous places. Carat refers to the weight of the stone. The largest known diamond was the Cullinan, which weighed 0.6 kilogram before it was cleaved and fashioned into an assemblage of stones that are now part of the British crown jewels.

All stones not suitable for use as gems are destined for industrial use. "Bort" refers to dense, hard, industrial diamonds, and carbonado is diamond that has a lower specific gravity than does a normal diamond. Such diamonds vary in color from off-white to black. Most industrial diamonds are used as abrasives. Crushed into various sizes, they are used for grinding wheels, grinding powders, polishing disks, drill bits, and saws. Diamond is indispensable for grinding the tungsten-carbide cutting tools that have been in use since the 1930's. Industrial diamonds are also sorted for shape: Blocky stones are suited for more severe grinding operations such as rock-drill bits, and more splintery ones are reserved for grinding tungsten-carbide.

## Methods of Study

Diamonds have been studied using the same analytical methods that are applied to other crystalline solids, notably X-ray diffraction to identify their crystalline structure. Mineral inclusions in diamond (mostly coesite and garnet) have been examined with the electron microprobe, a device that employs a tiny electron beam to measure the percentages of elements that are present in a mineral. The compositions of coexisting minerals in kimberlite and in ultramafic nodules have similarly been analyzed.

Igneous petrology is a subdiscipline of geology concerned with the description and origin of igneous rocks. Petrologists use all the methods listed above for individual minerals, plus larger-scale observations of entire rock masses. Minerals are assemblages of atoms, and rocks are assemblages of minerals; hence, understanding the origins of minerals, including diamond, involves an understanding of how the enclosing rock was formed. Individual rock masses such as kimberlite, ultramafic nodules, and xenoliths of the crust are glued onto glass slides, ground into thin slices, and studied under the microscope. In addition to the minerals they contain, the textures of rocks also reveal much about their origins. The results of mineralogical and textural observations are then interpreted in the light of even larger-scale observations, involving geological mapping on the surface and underground. Finally, all mineralogical, petrological, and geological observations must be interpreted within the constraints of geophysical data on the internal constitution of the earth.

## Context

The quest for diamonds has fostered much inquiry of the rock in which diamonds are found. Kimberlite is a very unusual type of igneous rock that forms deep in the earth's mantle, at depths up to 250 kilometers. The ultimate source of diamonds, kimberlite also contains "gems" of a different sort: pieces of the earth's deep continental crust and upper mantle that would be inaccessible by any other means. Volcanic pipes of kimberlite are therefore windows into the earth's interior, and the rock and its inclusions are avidly studied in order to learn more about the internal constitution of the earth. Diamonds contain trapped inclusions of liquids, mineral solids, and gases, mostly carbon dioxide. Analyses of these inclusions have led to a better understanding of the conditions under which diamond is formed and of the volatiles that are present in the earth's mantle.

The hardness, brilliance, and fire of diamonds have made them unsurpassed as gems; the use of diamonds as industrial materials is perhaps less well known. With the discovery of South Africa's enormously rich diamond fields in the late 1800's, industrial diamonds became readily available. Simultaneously, the use of harder metals and the need for closer machine tolerances led to demands for high-quality abrasives. Diamonds revolutionized the machine-tool industry. In the twentieth century, very hard synthetic abrasive compounds such as silicon carbide, boron carbide, and aluminum oxide came into use, replacing diamond in some applications. Tungsten carbide machine tools were in wide use by 1940, however, and this extremely hard synthetic material can be ground and polished only by diamond. In 1955, the General Electric Company succeeded in manufacturing synthetic diamonds at low pressure. Initially more expensive than natural stones, synthetic diamonds are now widely used in grinding wheels to sharpen tungsten carbide. Synthetic diamonds are smaller but have rougher surfaces than natural stones and are now manufactured in a variety of shapes and sizes for specialized abrasive applications.

Diamonds are also used as dies for drawing out the fine tungsten filaments of incandescent light bulbs, as scalpels for eye surgery, and as stereo phonograph needles. Unrivaled as a heat conductor, diamond is an important component in the miniature diodes that are used in telecommunications. Diamond has even served as a tiny instrument window on the Pioneer space probe to Venus, as it tolerates the extremes of heat and cold in outer space.

## Bibliography

Cox, K. G. "Kimberlite Pipes." In *Volcanoes and the Earth's Interior*, edited by Robert Decker and Barbara Decker. San Francisco: W. H. Freeman, 1982. This article is reprinted from *Scientific American* (April, 1978). Its main points can probably be understood by the high school student with a strong science background. An excellent summary of the origin of kimberlite and its inclusions, including diamonds. Mostly covers the geological aspects of kimberlite and diamond.

Decker, Robert, and Barbara Decker. *Volcanoes*. New York: W. H. Freeman, 1981. This 240-page paperback is geared to the general public and contains much useful and interesting information. A few pages focus on diamonds and kimberlite pipes, described within the context of volcanoes. Includes a glossary, selected references for each chapter, and an index.

Hurlbut, C. S., Jr., and G. S. Switzer. *Gemology*. New York: John Wiley & Sons, 1979. A well-illustrated and complete introduction to gemstones, describing the methods of gem study. Includes a section with descriptions of minerals and other materials prized as gems. A good introduction to mineralogy for the nonscientist.

Kluge, P. F. "The Man Who Is Diamond's Best Friend." *Smithsonian* 19 (May,

1988): 72. This very interesting article follows the strategy and execution of cutting a 900-carat diamond into one large stone and ten smaller ones. Color photographs document the procedure from start to finish. Readable for all.

O'Neil, Paul. *Gemstones*. Alexandria, Va.: Time-Life Books, 1983. Readable by everyone, this superbly written and thoroughly entertaining book is a treasure trove of color photographs. Contains much historical and geological information about many important gemstones; the chapters on diamonds are outstanding. Bibliography and index.

Smith, D. G., ed. *The Cambridge Encyclopedia of Earth Sciences*. New York: Crown, 1981. Although there is little mention of diamonds, the section on physics and chemistry of the earth provides a good foundation for understanding the earth's interior and hence the origin of diamonds and kimberlite. This well-illustrated and carefully indexed volume is suitable for college-level readers.

*William R. Hackett*

## Cross-References

Gem Minerals, 802; Igneous and Contact Metamorphic Mineral Deposits, 1124; Igneous Rock Classification, 1138; Igneous Rocks: Carbonatites, 1173; Igneous Rocks: Ultramafic, 1207; The Origin of Magmas, 1428; Physical Properties of Minerals, 1681; The Structure of Minerals, 1693; Non-Silicates Other Than Oxides and Carbonates, 1741; Earth Resources, 2175; Strategic Resources, 2188.

# DINOSAURS

*Type of earth science:* Paleontology and earth history

*Dinosaurs were one of the most successful early life forms, thriving for more than 150 million years before becoming extinct by the Cretaceous period. The reasons behind their longevity and their sudden extinction hold important implications for humankind's own survival.*

### Principal terms

ANKYLOSAURS: a group of later ornithischians characterized by heavy armor

CEROTOPSIANS: a group of later ornithischians characterized by a beaked snout and a bony frill on the back

ORNITHISCHIANS: one of the two orders of dinosaurs; it comprises the "bird-hipped" dinosaurs

ORNITHOPODS: the early, bipedal ornithischians

SAURISCHIANS: one of the two orders of dinosaurs; it comprises the "reptile-hipped" dinosaurs

SAUROPODS: the herbivorous, quadrupedal saurischians

STEGOSAURS: a group of later ornithischians characterized by a row of plates down the back

THECODONTS: an order of Triassic reptiles that were the ancestors of dinosaurs, birds, and crocodiles

THEROPODS: the carnivorous, primarily bipedal saurischians

## Summary of the Phenomenon

"Dinosaur," which is derived from the Greek term for "terrible lizard," is the popular name for a group of extinct land-dwelling reptiles. They were the dominant vertebrate animals during most of the Mesozoic era, which began 225 million years ago and ended 65 million years ago. Among the dinosaurs were the largest animals that ever walked the earth, although some of the earliest dinosaurs were very small.

The Mesozoic era is divided into three periods—Triassic, Jurassic, and Cretaceous—of approximately equal length. Dinosaurs first appeared in the later third of the Triassic period. Experts believe that a group of reptiles called *Eosuchia*, which are also known as dawn crocodiles, were the ancestors of dinosaurs. The thecodonts descended from the dawn crocodiles. A typical example of the thecodont group was *Saltoposuchus*, a slender reptile 1.2 meters long with long hind legs and short front legs. Because it walked only on its hind legs and used its front claws for grasping things, *Saltoposuchus* looked very different from all the animals preceding it.

Scientists divide all descendants of the thecodonts into two separate orders, depending on the arrangement and shape of the hipbones, which determine the way an animal walks and holds its body. The saurischians, or "reptile hips," as they are commonly called, arose about the middle of the Triassic period; the ornithischians, or "bird hips," arose toward the end of the Triassic period.

The pelvis of the saurischians so closely resembles that of the thecodonts that a direct descent could have occurred. The order *Saurischia* may be divided into two major suborders: the theropods, or "beast-footed dinosaurs," and the sauropods, or "reptile-footed dinosaurs." The theropods, which were more primitive than the sauropods, were primarily bipedal, although many of them probably used all four feet when walking or resting. The hind legs were strong and bore birdlike feet, while the forelimbs bore sharp, curved claws for seizing and holding prey. All theropods had long tails that functioned as stabilizers. The head was large, and the jaws of most of the theropods contained sharp teeth.

The theropods are subdivided into two categories: the long-necked, lightly built *Coelurosauria* and the short-necked, large-headed *Carnosauria*, both of which appeared in the Late Triassic. The coelurosaurs, like the chicken-sized *Compsognathus*, had long, narrow, pointed skulls, long necks, short forelimbs, and strong but slender legs that were made for running. The carnosaurs were larger and more predatory than the coelurosaurs. They also differed from the coelurosaurs in having larger skulls, short necks, very small forelimbs, and more massive hind legs to support their great weight. *Allosaurus*, from the Late Jurassic period of North America, was nearly eleven meters long and had only three fingers. The largest of all the theropods—*Tyrannosaurus Rex*, from the Late Cretaceous period of North America—grew to a weight of 4,500 kilograms, a height of 6 meters, and a length of 15 meters.

The sauropods, which appeared earlier in the Triassic than the theropods, have come to stand as a symbol of gigantism in land animals. They were all quadrupeds and vegetarians. They had small skulls, long necks and tails, large barrel-shaped bodies, padded feet, and large claws on the innermost toe of the forefoot and the innermost toe of the hind foot. The ancestral stock of the sauropods were the prosauropods, which were much smaller than the sauropods. Like most prosauropods, *Plateosaurus* had blunt, spatulate teeth, was a herbivore, and was quadrupedal, although it was capable of bipedal posture and gait.

The later sauropods had longer necks, and their skulls were relatively small. The limb bones became solid and pillarlike to support their great weight. This category contained the largest of the dinosaurs, *Brachiosaurus*, which is estimated to have weighed 73,000 kilograms. The best known sauropods are *Brontosaurus* and *Diplodocus*, from the Late Jurassic period of North America. Although it was once assumed that these huge beasts had to live in swamps where the water could support their great weight, this thinking has been revised in recent years.

The sauropods reached their zenith in the Late Jurassic; the ornithischians replaced them as the dominant herbivores in the Cretaceous period. The expansion of this group was associated with the advent of the flowering plants during the Cretaceous period. A horny beak was developed at the front of the mouth. The toes ended in rounded or blunt hooves instead of claws.

The earliest ornithischians were the ornithopods. A typical example is *Hyp-*

*silophodon*, a small, swift dinosaur with a long, slender tail and long, flexible toes. The most specialized of the ornithopods were the "duck-billed dinosaurs," also known as trachodonts or hadrosaurs. Although they had flat beaks and no anterior teeth, the cheek region had rows of grinding teeth. The various types of duck-billed dinosaur can be distinguished by modifications of the bones associated with the nostrils. Some were molded into hollow, domelike crests, bizarre swellings of the nasal region, or long, projecting tubular structures that were used to warm the air or to produce sounds. The remaining three groups of ornithischians presumably evolved from the primitive ornithopods.

The earliest of these three groups of highly specialized quadrupeds was the "plated dinosaurs," or stegosaurs, which first appeared early in the Jurassic period. This large dinosaur was more than 6 meters long. In comparison to its body size, its head was extremely small. *Stegosaurus* had an average of twenty plates arranged down the back in a line. The plates were originally thought to have been used for protection, but scientists now believe that the plates could have been used as cooling structures. *Stegosaurus* died out in the Early Cretaceous period.

The "armored dinosaurs," or ankylosaurs, are not very well known, even though their remains have been found over much of the world. Their armor consisted of a mosaic of studs over the body, spikes that protected the legs, and, in some cases, spikes on the tail. They protected themselves by crouching and drawing in their head and legs.

The last dinosaurs to develop were the "horned dinosaurs," or ceratopsians. The skull was characterized by a beaked snout and a bony frill that extend along the back. The ceratopsians were also distinguished from others by various patterns of horns. The skull of *Triceratops*, for example, had three sharp horns, one on the snout and one above each eye. The best known of the small ceratopsians was *Protoceratops*, which walked on all fours and had a neck frill that could have been used to protect the neck area, although it could also have been used to control body temperature. The dinosaurs became extinct with the demise of the ceratopsians at the end of the Mesozoic era.

Several theories regarding the dinosaurs' extinction were first proposed in the late nineteenth and the early twentieth centuries. According to one popular theory, dinosaurs were wiped out because early mammals of the Cretaceous period ate their eggs. Yet the eggs of many modern reptiles have faced the same threat and have survived, primarily because reptiles lay so many eggs. Another theory suggested that the same animals ate the plants on which the dinosaurs depended. Although that is possible, virtual plagues of mammals would have been required to eradicate the dinosaurs. Some early scientists also believed that the dinosaurs became too big for their environment; that is unlikely, however, because gigantic dinosaurs had been successful for millions of years. Changes in the physical environment also occurred in the Late Mesozoic. Evidence indicates that the sea levels fell. Geologic evidence shows, though, that drastic environmental changes had occurred many times during the dinosaurs' reign without any detrimental effect.

A theory proposed in the early 1980's by Luis and Walter Alvarez suggests that the iridium that has been found in several samples of sedimentary layers between the rock of the Cretaceous and Tertiary periods came from an asteroid that struck the earth at that time. Such a catastrophic event could have caused an enormous cloud of dust to circle the earth and cut off the sunlight, destroying the plants and the dinosaurs that depended on them. This theory, however, fails to explain why so many other animals, such as the mammals, managed to survive.

Another modern theory places the blame on the greenhouse effect. It has been argued that the reduction of the seas that occurred during the Cretaceous period caused a reduction of marine plants. As a result, the amount of carbon dioxide in the air increased, trapping heat from the earth's surface. A similar theory suggests that the eruption of a tremendous volcano produced a fatal amount of carbon dioxide. Neither theory, however, explains why other animals, especially heat-sensitive reptiles, survived.

Other theories include the reversal of the earth's magnetic field, a supernova explosion, racial senescence, and the spread of disease from animals that crossed the land bridge. Unfortunately, there is not enough evidence to prove any of these hypotheses true. So far, no one theory seems to be able to account satisfactorily for both the extinction of the dinosaurs and the survival of crocodiles and other reptiles. It is more likely that some combination of changes in land and sea rendered the world unsuitable for dinosaurs.

## Methods of Study

Scientists study dinosaurs by examining their fossil remains, which are the remains of animals that have turned to stone. If a dinosaur died near a river or in a swamp, it stood an excellent chance of being preserved. Its body might sink into the mud, or flood waters might float it downstream, where it would end up on a sandbar, on the bottom of a lake, or even in the sea. After the flesh decayed, the bones would be covered by sediments, such as mud or sand. The weight of accumulated layers of sediment would compress the remains and turn them into rock: mud into shale, sand into sandstone, limy oozes into limestone or chalk.

The way a fossil is studied is determined by the category to which it belongs. The first category is petrified fossils. They may be preserved in two ways. In replacement, minerals replace the original substance of the animal after water has dissolved the soft body parts. In permineralization, minerals fill in the small air spaces in bones or shells, thereby preserving the original bone or shell. The second group of fossils is composed of natural molds which form when the bodies dissolve. Scientists make artificial casts of these molds by filling them with wax, plastic, or plaster. The third type is prints, which are molds of thin objects, such as feathers or tracks. Sometimes, even skin is preserved. Prints are formed when the soft mud in which they are made turns to stone. Scientists can determine the length and weight of the dinosaur that made a set of footprints by studying the depth, size, and distance between them.

Most fossils are found in sedentary rocks, which lie beneath three-fourths of the earth. The best collecting areas are places where the soil has worn away from the rocks. Areas in Colorado, Montana, Wyoming, and Alberta, Canada, have been especially rich in fossils. Most of the finds consist of no more than scraps of limb bones, odd vertebrae, loose teeth, or weathered lumps of rock with broken bone showing on the surface. Once a scientist has discovered a few fossilized fragments, he or she combs the area to find the rest of the animal. If the skeleton is embedded, it is extracted with the help of a wide variety of tools, ranging from picks and shovels to pneumatic drills. Loose fragments are glued back into place, and parts which are too soft or breakable are hardened by means of a special resin solution which is sprayed or painted on.

As the fossil is uncovered, it is encased in a block of plaster of paris. (A more modern method uses polyurethane foam instead of plaster.) After the entire surface is covered, the fossil is rolled over, and another layer of plaster is added. After the fossil has been transported to the museum, the plaster is removed. The "development" stage involves the removal of the rock around the bones. The oldest way is by hand, using tools such as hammers and chisels; a more modern technique uses electrically powered drills similar to dentists' drills. Sandblasting and chemicals may also be employed. After the fossil is cleaned, it is ready for mounting. The bones are fastened to a steel framework that makes the skeleton appear to stand by itself.

## Context

From the dinosaurs, scientists are learning new lessons about the physiology of such beasts, their relationship to the world in which they lived, their distribution and the bearing of that distribution on the past arrangements of the continents, various aspects of evolution, and the reasons that they became extinct. The dinosaurs played a major part in the shaping of the natural world. Birds, for example, are probably their descendants, as evidenced by the intermediary species *Archaeopteryx*, a primitive bird that lived during the Late Jurassic period; although its beak contained teeth, *Archaeopteryx* also had feathers and could fly. It seems certain that, without dinosaurs, the course of evolution would have been entirely different and humans would never have originated.

The disappearance of a species that seemed to rule the world for more than 100 million years brings into question the notion of a "dominant" species. Most people believe that mammals are now the dominant form of life; however, dinosaurs did not "rule," and neither do mammals. If one were to list the biological organisms whose influence on the planet is such that their removal would produce chaos, then that list would be headed by microorganisms so small that they can be seen only through powerful microscopes. The list would also include the green plants and the fungi.

The extinction of the dinosaurs also brings into question humans' ability to destroy the world. All species, from the simplest microorganism to the largest plant or animal, modify their immediate surroundings. They cannot avoid doing so. The success of one group, however, does not imply the failure of the groups it exploits. The complexity of individual organisms may increase, but the simpler forms do not necessarily disappear. Life continued after the demise of the dinosaurs and would probably continue to do so if humankind were destroyed.

## Bibliography

Allaby, Michael, and James Lovelock. *The Great Extinction*. London: Secker and Warburg, 1983. This book posits that the dinosaurs died as the result of some sort of catastrophic occurrence, such as the collision of an asteroid with the earth. The authors support their contention by examining the effects that modern catastrophes, such as the eruption of Mount St. Helens, have had on wildlife. The conclusion discusses the implications that the extinction of the dinosaurs has for humankind's possible extinction. It is well written and well indexed. Suitable for college students.

Bakker, Robert T. *The Dinosaur Heresies*. New York: William Morrow, 1986. Bakker's book paints a revolutionary picture of dinosaurs as dynamic, intelligent, hot-blooded creatures that dominated the earth for more than 150 million years. Bakker suggests, for example, that *Brontosaurus* was not a sluggish, swamp-bound creature but rather a nimble land-dweller. He also theorizes that the dinosaurs died as the result of diseases transmitted across the land bridge by foreign species. This highly personal account is interesting throughout and written with both the general reader and the college student in mind.

Charig, Alan. *A New Look at the Dinosaurs*. New York: Avon, 1983. Charig begins by answering the question "What were the dinosaurs?" and then proceeds to answer other intriguing questions, such as "Were dinosaurs warm-blooded?" "Did birds evolve from dinosaurs?" "Were dinosaurs too heavy to walk on land?" and "Why did dinosaurs suddenly die out 65 million years ago?" Charig explains all the known facts and theories with the aid of black-and-white drawings, maps, charts, photographs, and several beautiful watercolor plates.

Colbert, Edwin H. *Dinosaurs: An Illustrated History*. Maplewood, N.J.: Hammond, 1983. This volume, beautifully illustrated with more than one hundred color photographs and paintings, is essentially a condensed version of the following source, although Colbert discusses all the theories regarding the extinction of the dinosaurs in the conclusion. A fascinating book written for the general reader.

——————. *Dinosaurs and Their World*. New York: E. P. Dutton, 1961. One of the finest and most comprehensive books on dinosaurs available. Colbert begins with the discovery of the first dinosaur fossils and then discusses the brains, nervous systems, and temperatures of the dinosaurs; their environments; and their reactions to terrain, climate, and food conditions. The book also classifies dinosaurs according to geologic time and includes a list of museums and pertinent books. Written for the general public and useful for students, teachers, and researchers.

De Camp, L. Sprague, and Catherine Crook de Camp. *The Day of the Dinosaur.* New York: Bonanza Books, 1968. The authors begin by classifying the various types of dinosaur and end with a discussion of the history of paleontology. The content reflects the authors' belief that the simpler forms of life evolved into the more complex forms. Its extensive bibliography and index and numerous illustrations make it an excellent reference work for high school or college students.

Desmond, Adrian. *The Hot-Blooded Dinosaurs.* New York: Dial Press, 1976. Drawing upon recent discoveries, Desmond rejects the Victorian view of dinosaurs being sluggish, small-brained, titanic lizards. He argues that dinosaurs kept mammals in their place for 130 million years. Before they vanished, they developed bigger brains and were indeed the "crown of creation." For college-level students and scientists.

Lambert, David. *A Field Guide to Dinosaurs.* New York: Avon, 1983. This book discusses the physical characteristics, behavior, and evolution of all known dinosaur genera, one in five of which has been named since 1970. Also covers the various theories regarding the extinction of dinosaurs, the process of fossilization, and the discovery and display of fossils. Richly illustrated and nontechnical enough for junior high and high school students.

Swinton, W. E. *The Dinosaurs.* New York: John Wiley & Sons, 1971. Swinton's original book, on which this volume is based, is among the first general accounts of dinosaurs and became a standard work. This newer book incorporates many advances that were been made since then. A general section on the discovery, environment, and physiology of dinosaurs is followed by more specialized chapters on their classification and main orders. The final part deals with their homes and eventual extinction. Contains more than sixty diagrams. For the general reader.

Witford, John Noble. *The Riddle of the Dinosaurs.* New York: Alfred A. Knopf, 1985. Although Witford relates the history of paleontology in the beginning of this book, his primary purpose is to demonstrate how discoveries made since the 1960's have revolutionized dinosaur theory. He proposes, for example, that some dinosaurs were warm-blooded, quick moving, and good parents. He also discusses the most radical change in dinosaur theory: the idea that they disappeared because of a massive catastrophe, such as global floods, asteroid collisions, or exploding stars. Filled with photographs and color drawings, the book is accessible to the general reader but technical enough for the researcher.

*Alan Brown*

## Cross-References

Biostratigraphy, 173; The Evolution of Flight, 648; The Evolution of Life, 655; The Fossil Record, 760; Fossilization and Taphonomy, 768; Mammals, 1453; Mass Extinctions, 1514; The Mesozoic Era, 1535; Paleobiogeography, 1984.

# DISPLACED TERRANES

*Type of earth science:* Geology
*Field of study:* Tectonics

*The development of the concept of displaced or exotic terranes within the branch of geology known as plate tectonics is an important one, as it explains how hitherto inexplicable regions of crust arrived at their present locations. It also provides an approach to a more detailed understanding of how continents grow by accretion of their crust through collision with smaller tectonic bodies.*

*Principal terms*

ACCRETION: in tectonics, a term used to describe the process of growth of a larger crustal unit, such as a continent, by collision with smaller tectonic terranes, such as volcanic arcs or microcontinents

COLLAGE TECTONICS: a complex patchwork of different types of terranes thought to represent a region in which accretion has joined together suspect terranes

CRATON: a large, geologically old, relatively stable core of a continental lithospheric plate, sometimes termed a continental shield

LITHOSPHERIC PLATE: one of a number of crustal plates of various sizes that comprise the earth's outer crust; their borders are outlined by major zones of earthquake activity

MICROCONTINENT: an independent lithospheric plate that is smaller in size than a continent but that possesses continental-type crust; for example, Cuba or Japan

OBDUCTION: a tectonic collisional process, opposite in effect to subduction, in which heavier oceanic crust is thrust up over lighter continental crust

PLATE TECTONICS: the branch of geology that describes many crustal phenomena, such as volcanism, in terms of movements and interactions of large and small crustal units called lithospheric plates

SUBDUCTION: the process by which one lithospheric plate, usually a continental one, collides with another, typically oceanic, plate overriding it, causing it to dive below the continent

SUTURE ZONE: a narrowly definable region of the earth's crust thought to represent a place where two lithospheric plates have collided and subsequently been joined together

TERRANE: any sizable, more or less discrete region of the earth's surface crust that is the product of tectonic forces; for example, island or volcanic terranes

## Summary of the Phenomenon

The concept of displaced terranes was developed by geologists to explain how anomalous regions of continental crust may have originated. Such areas were discovered to possess indications that their sites of origination differed from their present locations. Most were found to have one or more of a distinctive suite of features, such as a fossil record, mineralogy, stratigraphy, or structural pattern that was basically foreign to the surrounding or adjacent continental rock units. As an additional clue that such regions may have been added to a continental landmass at a later date, they were usually found to have boundaries that displayed structural deformation, similarly suggestive of subsequent emplacement. Thus, every indication pointed to a starting point remote from their present geographic location. To complicate matters, geologists differentiate the term "terrain" from "terrane." The former term is used to describe an area of surface topography, while the latter is reserved usually for description of a region's subsurface. Whatever the precise terminology employed, the concept remains the same: Regions of questionable lineage are variously termed terranes of suspect, exotic, or displaced nature. Earth scientists, working within the plate tectonic theoretical system, consider such terranes as products of the collision of a continental lithospheric plate with lesser plate bodies or other entities such as island arcs. From various lines of physical evidence, researchers have concluded that such terranes have undergone a process called accretion.

In the crust of the earth, according to plate tectonic theory, all the member units, called lithospheric plates, are in some type of interaction with one another. They are either spreading apart from some common center, as in the case of a mid-ocean ridge system (presently, in the mid-Atlantic Ocean), colliding with another unit with various end products and effects, or sliding alongside of one another along transform faults, such as in the San Andreas fault zone system. Slow, convection cells within the earth are considered the propelling force behind the global tectonic system, driving the plates apart at one point in the heat exchange cycle, together at another, and alongside in still others. In a scenario involving direct collision and not translational or separating motion, a plate, depending on its particular material composition, and thus its relative density and thickness, will behave in various ways. If it is of about the same density and thickness, it may ram up into a linear, folded mountain range, as in the case of the Himalaya. If of a different relative density and thickness, it may be jammed below the forward end of the oncoming plate, termed the leading edge, in which case it experiences a process called subduction. It also may be jammed above the leading edge, in which case it experiences a process termed obduction. Continental crust, because of the general composition of its basement rocks, is somewhat lighter than oceanic crust. This difference is also described as one in the specific gravities of the two types of rock compositions. Thus, in a typical interaction between the two types, oceanic crust is subducted beneath continental material. That is not always the case, however, and exceptions apparently exist, the mechanics of which are still poorly understood. Accretion is believed to occur when a leading edge of a continent for some reason either obducts heavier oceanic crust, adds other nonoceanic and noncontinental material, such as volcanic island arcs, or encounters smaller units of generally similar continental material termed microcontinents. In all the above cases, the encountered terrane becomes incorporated into the forward-moving portion of the continental lithospheric plate. In this manner, for example, North America and other continents have added many thousands of square kilometers of area. Recent evidence indicates that in the case of North America itself, at least 25 percent of its surface landmass is constituted of exotic terranes. An extreme case is the Alaskan region. Alaska is believed to be composed of about fifty distinct displaced terranes, which added together make up almost half of its area.

Orogenic belts, or deformed mountain belts, are sometimes listed as another example of suspect terrane accretion onto the edge of a continental, lithospheric superstructure. The superstructure itself is termed a continental craton or shield and is believed to have a great age in relation to microcontinents and other relatively transitory phenomena. The age disparity is along the order of billions of years for cratons as compared to less than 100 million years for a microcontinent—probably the smaller units, from creation to destruction or accretion, last on average only tens of millions of years. Various past orogenies, or mountain-building episodes, are interpreted as evidence for microcontinent collision and accretion with regard to different cratons.

One example is a scenario devised to explain the evolution of the southern Appalachian orogenic belt in the United States. This area is very complex structurally, and, prior to the acceptance of plate tectonic interpretations generally defied any satisfactory hypothesis that explained what its geologic history might have been. According to the scenario involving accretionary tectonics, the Cambrian period (about 570-505 million years ago) of the early Paleozoic era witnessed, among other things, a tectonic rifting event that resulted in the proto-Atlantic Ocean and production of various microcontinents, among them one termed the Piedmont. As time passed, the Ordovician period (about 505-438 million years ago) saw the onset of crustal subduction and the closure of the marginal sea. The Ordovician period gave way to the Silurian period (about 438-408 million years ago), during which the Piedmont microcontinent collided with and accreted to North America, resulting in the Taconian orogeny. Further subduction resulted in another collision during the Late Devonian period (about 380-360 million years ago), which involved North America with another microcontinent termed Avalonia. This accretionary episode resulted in the Acadian orogeny. Further subduction continued on into the Late Paleozoic era (about 360-245 million years ago), resulting, at its close, in the Permian period collision of a large continent called Gondwanaland with North America and the generation of extensive overthrust faulting. This event is known as the Appalachian, or Alleghenian, orogeny. Subsequent to these events, the Mesozoic era (about 245-66 million years ago) witnessed still more large-scale changes, such as the rifting action that caused the present Atlantic Ocean to appear and widen, a phenomenon still in evidence. Because of the compounding of all these large-sale tectonic events, the geology of Appalachia is an intricate and confusing affair, with a number of exotic terranes of different ages in close proximity to one another.

This patchwork of accreted terranes has been described by the term "collage tectonics." Such a collage includes not only jammed-together microcontinents and volcanic arcs but also narrow units termed suture zones, which are thought to be actual relic lines of collision. The presence of suture zones is an additional line of evidence used to substantiate the existence of an accretionary event. Suture zones are easily identified because they display a narrow area of intensely metamorphosed and deformed basalts and ultramafic rocks. The rocks, such as ophiolites, and structures of such zones are interpreted as representing the remains of the last vestiges of unsubducted oceanic plate material that once separated a microcontinent and the continent proper. The vestigial, dense, ocean rocks have been jammed up onto the lighter, less dense, continental rock.

Other areas of the world in which collage tectonics is prominently expressed are in the regions of the northern North American Cordillera and eastern Siberia. This area is composed to a great extent of a number of named and as yet unnamed suspect terranes, including, as mentioned, a significant part of Alaska. One of the better understood terranes in this overall region is one that has been called Wrangellia, which is a long, narrow, sinuous terrane thousands of kilometers in length that stretches from south-central Alaska down to about the northern border of the state of Washington.

Evidence indicates that the anomalous terrane of Wrangellia has been displaced from 35 to 65 degrees of latitude northward from a presently unknown equatorial area. Wrangellian basement rocks are oceanic basalts overlain by a sequence of limestones of the Middle and Upper Triassic period (about 220-208 million years ago). These limestones are stratigraphically inconsistent with the rocks of the other suspect terranes surrounding or adjacent to Wrangellia, not to mention the actual continental rocks to the east. The exotic, displaced terrane of Wrangellia and its neighboring members of the tectonic collage attest the long accretionary history that North America, along with all other continents, has experienced probably throughout most of geologic time.

## Methods of Study

Geologists researching the problem of suspect or displaced terranes have recourse to a large array of techniques and methods to analyze collected, physical evidence. As in the other various branches of geology, as indeed in all the rest of the physical sciences, firsthand, on-site fieldwork or recording sites are the preferred methods of data acquisition. In the case of the terranes of North America, investigations into the geologic history of former or active continental margin areas where suspect terranes abound were at first economically motivated for mining or oil exploration purposes. Later, academic fieldwork increased the database upon which the theory of displaced terranes was developed. Finally, in recent decades the database was greatly expanded by new techniques involving seismic and other higher-technology approaches which were motivated by such public considerations as earthquake risk and the ever-increasing need for new mineral resources for expanding industries and populations.

Some of the more prominent techniques employed in the study of displaced terranes include those of biostratigraphy and the fossil records of terranes as compared to their host continents. Fossil floras and faunas, both microscopic and macroscopic, can be used to correlate rock layers and date them in relation to one another. This technique is one of the original dating methods used in geology and is termed relative dating. Fossil correlation and the comparison of the temporal and geographic distribution of certain particularly useful, key fossil species, called index fossils, were, until the development of radiometric or absolute dating, the cornerstone of all geologic dating and still are of great utility. A fossil line of evidence that has been a key factor in the establishment of the concept of suspect terranes is a direct consequence of biostratigraphy and the analysis of fossil assemblages. This factor has been the study of anomalous, extinct, marine faunas of microorganisms such as the fusulinids. Permian period fusulinids occur anomalously in a particular zone of limestones which can be traced from Alaska to California. The next nearest fossil matches to these faunas occur in Japan and southeastern Asia. Fossil assemblages such as the fusulinids and others have helped emphasize the exotic nature of the suspect terranes.

Following the development of radiometric techniques subsequent to World War II, another method was added to refine the dating of fossils and the strata or sediments in which they were found. Radiogenic isotopes are different nuclear species of an element that are unstable and very slowly change from one element to another, in the process producing radiation at a fixed, long-term rate. Using the natural decay rate of certain ones of these isotopes occurring in rocks and fossils as a kind of natural, internal clock, geologists have refined the results of relative dating; they have also been able to cross-check the results of both types of dating. Radiometric dating has proven to be of inestimable worth in the dating of most rocks and fossils and, consequently, in the analysis of accreted terranes.

Also by the end of the twentieth century, evidence from paleomagnetism grew increasingly in importance for the study of suspect terranes and the acceptance of the theory of plate tectonics in general. Paleomagnetism is based on the principle that certain minerals, such as iron oxides, are responsive to the earth's natural magnetic field. Many igneous rocks, such as basalts, possess these minerals and, once the molten mineral cools down to a certain point (for example, following an eruption where they are extruded or blasted free), the oxides will orient themselves with regard to the global field and remain in this orientation indefinitely unless, once again, further heated above the critical temperature. Thus, such minerals are natural indicators of past magnetic orientations and the parent rock's respective, past, relative geographic locations. Such fossil magnetism, referred to as remanent magnetism, is one of the primary proofs of sea-floor spreading and continental drift. The phenomenon, like radiometric dating, paleontology, and stratigraphy, has proven useful for tracing the possible paths and former locations of suspect terranes.

## Context

The theory of displaced terranes is important to the scientific community because it provides a reasonable explanation of how large areas of the earth's crust that were formerly viewed as puzzles or oddities—anomalous terranes—originated. The theory also ties in well with known aspects of plate tectonic theory and, indeed, is a refinement of that theory's plate collisional aspects. It provides a useful paradigm to elucidate long-range movements of crust that hitherto could not be satisfactorily explained. It also seems to offer a plausible explanation for the generation of a number of past orogenies that had not been explained very well by a strictly continent-against-continent type of collision, as in the case of some of the formative Appalachian region events.

As a working hypothesis to which further data can be applied profitably, the theory of displaced terranes can possibly generate practical applications in the long run by pointing the way toward a genuine understanding of how the border regions of continents are formed. As these regions are often orogenic belts, which are typically rich in minable minerals and other economically useful materials, the concept of exotic terranes may prove to be one of the more useful by-products of plate tectonics. Proper use of the theory as applied to particular, individual terranes may be instrumental in the efficient location and recovery of metals and fossil fuels. If that proves to be the case, then economic geologists, in industry and business, as well as the average nongeologist, will profit from the theory. What began as an academic abstraction may prove, like many other scientific discoveries, to help society as a whole by providing new resources for the development of economic wealth and thereby increasing the chances of social well-being.

## Bibliography

Batten, Roger Lyman, and Robert H. Dott, Jr. *Evolution of the Earth*. 4th ed. New York: McGraw-Hill, 1988. An excellent historical geology text. Emphasis is on the geological story of North America but always with a view to how the continent's evolution fits into the greater pattern of the evolution of all the continents and oceans. Includes good explanations, with examples of the concepts of displaced terranes, accretion, collage tectonics, and so on. A good book for those at a high school level and above who already are conversant with basic geologic principles and concepts.

McPhee, John. *In Suspect Terrain*. New York: Farrar, Straus & Giroux, 1982. McPhee's treatment of sometimes complex geological subjects in this book is identical to the light and easy-to-understand approach he uses in the other two popular books he has written on the earth sciences. This book would be a welcome addition to any reader's library who has a curiosity about or an enthusiasm for geology. Useful as well as a basic, good introduction to topics involving displaced terranes and associated concepts. A great book for readers at all levels of geologic knowledge.

Miller, Russell, and the editors of Time-Life Books. *Continents In Collision*. Alexandria, Va.: Time-Life Books, 1983. Part of a series of lavishly illustrated books dealing with atmospheric, geologic, and astronomic sciences for the general public. A useful book for those who wish to know more about the general subject of plate tectonics and how and what evidence influenced the majority of contemporary scientists to accept this theoretical system. Offers examples from around the world, with highly informative photographs and artwork. Featured are extensive chapters on the mechanics of tectonics, which include an explanation of suspect terranes and how they fit into current knowledge pertaining to continental growth. An appropriate reading choice for those with only a minimal science preparation, high school and above.

National Research Council. Geophysics Study Committee. *Continental Tectonics*. Washington, D.C.: National Academy of Sciences, 1980. An anthology of various thorough treatments of recent professional work on different aspects of plate tectonics. Contains a number of good explanations of displaced terrane-type topics substantiated with research findings from projects. Appropriate for advanced high school and college readers and above with a firm understanding of geology.

Redfern, Ron. *The Making of a Continent*. New York: Times Books, 1983. Treats a broad range of geological subjects concerned with the evolution of the North American continent. Good use of photographs, diagrams, and other illustrations to convey all the earth science theories and concepts involved. A substantial chapter on suspect terranes is featured. Assumes no prior exposure to geology.

Van Andel, Tjeerd H. *New Views on an Old Planet*. New York: Cambridge University Press, 1985. Approaches the history of the earth, including the evolution of the oceans, atmosphere, continents, and major groups of organisms, through the agency of the fossil record and various geological lines of evidence such as geochemistry. Plate tectonics is discussed, as well as displaced terranes, which the author refers to as "exotic terranes." Suitable for all readers at a high school or college level who possess some foundation in the physical sciences.

*Frederick M. Surowiec*

## Cross-References

Biostratigraphy, 173; Continental Growth, 268; Continental Structures, 290; Earth's Crust, 518; Gondwanaland and Pangaea, 982; Island Arcs, 1261; Lithospheric Plates, 1387; Mountain Belts, 1725; The Oceanic Crust, 1846; Ophiolites, 1954; Plate Margins, 2063; Plate Motions, 2071; Plate Tectonics, 2079; Stratigraphic Correlation, 2485; Subduction and Orogeny, 2497.

# DRAINAGE BASINS

*Type of earth science:* Geology
*Field of study:* Sedimentology

*Drainage basins reflect the operation of physical laws affecting water flow over the earth's surface and through rocks. They define natural units that concentrate flow into rivers, which, in turn, remove both water and sediment, the latter eroded from the surface of the basin. They become a focus for human activities whenever water is exploited as a resource.*

### Principal terms

ALTITUDE: the height (in meters or feet) above mean sea level

BASIN ORDER: an approximate measure of the size of a stream basin, based on a numbering scheme applied to river channels as they join together in their progress downstream

CHANNEL: a linear depression on the earth's surface caused and enlarged by the concentrated flow of water

EROSION: the removal of sediment (particles of various sizes) from the earth's surface

GROUNDWATER: water that sinks below the earth's surface and that slowly flows through the rock (ground) toward river channels; it keeps rivers flowing long after rainstorms

HYDROLOGICAL: relating to the systematic flow of water in accordance with physical laws at or close to the earth's surface

LIMESTONE: a rock composed primarily of the mineral calcium or dolomite, which can be dissolved by water that is acidic

## Summary of the Phenomenon

A drainage basin is an area of the earth's surface that collects water, which accumulates on the surface from rain or snow; its slopes deliver the water to either a channel or a lake. Normally, the channel that collects the water leads eventually to the ocean. In this case, the drainage basin is defined as the entire area upstream whose slopes deliver water to that channel or to other channels tributary to it. Thus, strictly speaking, drainage basins are defined as natural units only when streams enter bodies of water such as lakes or the ocean or when two streams join; one speaks of the Mississippi River drainage basin or the Ohio River drainage basin— this latter basin lying above the Ohio River's confluence with the Mississippi.

Less often there is no exit to the ocean: This type of basin is called a basin of inland or interior drainage. Notable examples are the basins containing the Great Salt Lake in Utah, the Dead Sea in Israel and Jordan, and the Caspian Sea in Asia. The Basin and Range province in the Rockies (an area of about 1 million square kilometers extending from southern Idaho and Oregon through most of Nevada, western Utah, eastern California, western and southern Arizona, southwestern New Mexico, and northern Mexico), has at least 141 basins of inland drainage. The center of these basins is usually marked by a playa—a level area of fine-grained sediments, often rich in salts left behind as inflowing waters evaporate. At certain times in the geological past, when the annual rainfall regime was wetter, some of these basins completely filled with water to the point of overflowing, at which point the drainage system may either connect to another interior basin or connect to a river system which drains to the sea. The basin now containing the Great Salt Lake (known to geologists as Lake Bonneville) overflowed at Red Rock Pass about 15,000 years ago. The overflowing waters discharged into the Snake River system, and thus to the Columbia River and the Pacific. It is clear, therefore, that drainage basins may change in character over relatively short periods of geological time. There is some evidence that the entire Mediterranean Sea was a basin of inland drainage for a period about 3-5 million years ago: Substantial salt deposits are found on its bed, and traces of meandering rivers have been seen in certain geological sections.

Although the term "drainage basin" is normally thought of as applying to the surface, a very important component of the basin as a hydrological unit is the rock beneath the surface. Much of the water that arrives on the surface sinks into the soil and the underlying rocks, where it is stored as soil water and as groundwater. Soil water either sinks farther to become groundwater, or it may flow through soil and back out onto the surface downslope when and where the soil is saturated. Groundwater moves very slowly through the rock (millimeters to centimeters per day), but it eventually seeps into stream channels and so keeps water flowing in rivers long after rain has finished falling.

This characteristic of groundwater can lead to a circumstance that alters the definition of a drainage basin when the rocks are primarily composed of limestone or any rocks susceptible to solution. Because limestone is soluble in acidic water (natural rain is slightly acid; acid rain accentuates the acidity), over long periods of time (thousand of years), percolating groundwater dissolves substantial volumes of rock and causes a system of underground channels to develop, which may sometimes be enlarged to caverns. Yugoslavia is famous for its underground cave systems; in the United States, Kentucky, Florida, and New Mexico (with its famous Carlsbad Caverns) are well known for their limestone terrain and underground drainage systems. In this case, the route of the water underground may bear little or no relation to the pattern of channels and slopes seen on the surface, some or all of which may have become completely inactive. The determination of the drainage basin is then very difficult as various types of tracer (colored dyes or tracer chemicals) have to be placed in the water in order to track it, and the pattern of water flow to any given site will also depend on the location of the storm waters causing the flow. The very slow solution of limestone to form underground river systems and caves emphasizes the fact that water moving through the basin removes solid rock. As the rivers dissolve their way downward, they leave some caves "high and dry" above the general level of the underground water (the water table), which points up the fact that rivers work down through the rock with the passage of time.

This aspect of drainage basins—that solid rock is slowly removed—is harder to observe in areas of less soluble rock, even though water flowing out of the drainage basin carried sediment (small particles of soil and rock) and has been doing so for long periods of geological time. Thus, in the long run, the surface of the earth is lowered, and even in the short run, enormous amounts of sediment may be removed from the basin every year. The Mississippi removes a total of about 296 million metric tons per year, or 91 tons per square kilometer, though this is small compared to the Ganges, which takes out 1,450 million metric tons per year, or 1,520 tons per square kilometer. If there were no corresponding uplift of the drainage basins or other interference, this removal would lead to the leveling of entire basins within 10 or 50 million years, depending on the lowering rate and the mean altitude of the basin. If the Ganges basin has a mean relief of 4,500 meters, it would be completely lowered in about 7 million years at present rates. If the Mississippi has an average relief of 1,000 meters, the time needed is on the order of 40 million years. These figures, however, are unrealistic because other processes cause compensating uplift, but they do indicate that drainage basins are being actively eroded within reasonable spans of geologic time.

The process of erosion proceeding at different rates in adjacent basins may cause the drainage divide (the line separating different flow directions for surface waters) to migrate toward the basin with the lower erosion rate. This is most common in geologically "new" terrain when stream systems are not deeply incised into the rocks. Drainage diversions may be simulated, as in the Snowy Mountain diversion in Australia, where waters are diverted across a divide by major engineering works in order to provide irrigation water for the Murray Darling river basin and also for hydroelectric power generation.

When winter snow melts (the late spring and early summer peak in Mississippi River flow is caused by melting snow in the Rocky Mountains) or severe storms bring heavy rain to large areas, the water which falls flows over the surface to channels and generates floods in the rivers. Floods are not abnormal; they are an expectable occurrence in drainage basins. It is easy to understand that when basin relief is high and slopes are steep (in the Rockies or the Appalachians), floods tend to generate higher flood peaks than when slopes are very gentle. A basin that is round in shape tends to concentrate floodwater quickly because the streams tend to converge in the middle, whereas a long, narrow stream has the effect of attenuating the flow peak, even when the total amount of water falling on the basin may be the same. Similarly, a forest tends to attenuate flood peaks and to promote higher river flows between flood peaks than does open farmland. With the latter, there is a tendency for water to flow very rapidly off the surface into channels, whereas with a forest much water is intercepted by the leaves of trees and the impact of rain on the surface is weaker, in part because leaf cover protects the soil. Because the soil is not so well protected, sediment loss from the surface into streams is greater from farmland than from forests and is higher again from land disturbed by major building projects.

## Methods of Study

Various methods have been devised to classify basins according to size, and the most common method depends on a numbering system applied to the streams that drain them. All the fingertip streams are labeled with 1. When two of these tributaries meet the channel, it is termed a second order channel and is labeled with 2. Subsequently, however, the order of a stream increases by one only when two streams of equal order join. Otherwise, if two streams of unequal order join, the order given to the downstream segment is that of the larger of the two orders. The order of the drainage basin is then the order of the stream in the basin. In this type of numbering system (called Horton/Strahler ordering), the Mississippi drainage basin is an eleventh or twelfth order basin; the exact number depends on the detail (map scale) with which the fingertip streams are defined. The larger orders are rare because if the Mississippi basin is twelfth order, it would take another river of roughly similar magnitude to join it to make a thirteenth order basin.

Basin order may be used as a relatively natural basis for the collection of other data about the basin (see table). The simplest measure is of the area in square kilometers. In addition, one may record the basin relief, the height difference between the lowest and the highest points, and the mean relief, or the average height of the basin above the outlet. The most precise method of recording basin relief is by computing the hypsometric (height) curve for the basin, which requires an

CHARACTERISTICS OF SELECTED MAJOR DRAINAGE BASINS

| River | Outflow | Length | Area | Average Annual Suspended Load |
|---|---|---|---|---|
| Amazon | 180.0 | 6,300 | 5,800 | 360 |
| Congo | 39.0 | 4,700 | 3,700 | — |
| Yangtze | 22.0 | 5,800 | 1,900 | 500 |
| Mississippi | 18.0 | 6,000 | 3,300 | 296 |
| Irawaddy | 14.0 | 2,300 | 430 | 300 |
| Brahmaputra | 12.0 | 2,900 | 670 | 730 |
| Ganges | 12.0 | 2,500 | 960 | 1,450 |
| Mekong | 11.0 | 4,200 | 800 | 170 |
| Nile | 2.8 | 6,700 | 3,000 | 110 |
| Colorado | 0.2 | 2,300 | 640 | 140 |
| Ching | 0.06 | 320 | 57 | 410 |

NOTE: Rivers are ordered by outflow; outflow is multiplied by 1,000 cumecs (a cumec is 1 cubic meter of water per second); length is measured in kilometers; area is measured in square kilometers multiplied by 1,000; average annual suspended load is measured in millions of metric tonnes.

accurate topographic map. When constructed, it shows, for any altitude, the proportion of the basin area above that particular altitude and, for comparative purposes, it may be produced in a dimensionless form by dividing both the height and the area measures by their maximum values or by the difference between the maximum and minimum heights if zero is not the minimum height.

Basin shape and basin dimensions (length and width) may also be recorded, although the notion of basin shape suffers from the problem that no completely unambiguous numerical measure exists that can be used to define the shape of an area in the plane (that is, on a map), and the problem is especially intractable if there are indentations in the edge of the basin. All measures are dependent to a considerable degree on the accuracy of source maps, and in mountainous terrain, such maps may often be much less than perfect, if they exist at all. Even with automated drafting aids and digitizers (which automatically record positions on maps and save them for a data file), the measurement of basin properties is a tedious and time-consuming process. Unless there are pressing reasons for a new analysis, it is common to rely on data tabulations made by hydrological or environmental agencies whenever possible.

Measurements are made of drainage basin properties because they are often used in statistical analyses together with the known flow of the few gauged rivers in order to predict flow characteristics for rivers that have not been metered. The direct measurement of stream flow, while straightforward in principle, is time-consuming, especially in the early stages, and a flow record is not very useful for predictive purposes until it has recorded at least twenty years of flow (preferably much more). Because of the high capital and maintenance costs involved in collecting river records, there has been an understandable emphasis on records for large rivers, the economic benefits from prediction (and eventual control) of the flow are more obvious, and measured flow records can sometimes be supplemented by anecdotal evidence of historic large floods—those flows which are often of most interest in land-use planning (for example, in the zonation of land for residential use). In recent years, it has been acknowledged that the hydrological behavior of low order basins is less well understood, and more information has been collected on them, especially for urban areas where the routing of the large quantities of water that run off from impermeable surfaces in the city (roofs and roadways) has been recognized as a serious planning problem, especially when the flow systems connect with urban sewage systems.

## Context

The control of water outflow from drainage basins is necessary in some regions in order to promote irrigation, to supply domestic and industrial water, to generate power, and to implement flood control. The Hoover Dam on the Colorado was originally conceived as a control dam, but hydroelectrical generators were also built in order to help defray costs by selling power. There are nineteen major dams in the Colorado basin. Difficulties (aside from the legal technicalities of water ownership and redistribution) arise from the fact that to control substantial amounts of water, large areas of the basin have to be regulated and, in addition, there are economies of scale in large projects, particularly in the construction of large dams and reservoirs. A single control dam strategically placed may regulate flow downstream for hundreds of miles, whereas it would require hundreds of small dams on first- and second-order streams to achieve the same effect.

Large control dams do generate problems. The reservoirs trap sediment coming from upstream (in addition to water), which will eventually fill them, at which point they will be useless, and small dams may fill within a few years. An original estimate for the Hoover Dam suggested that it would take only four hundred years to fill Lake Mead; after only fourteen years, surveys revealed that the water capacity had been reduced by 5 percent and that sediment in the lake bottom reached a maximum of 82 meters where the upstream river entered the still waters of the lake. Downstream of a dam, the reduced sediment content and the regulated water flow often seriously affect riparian environments, and there may be a variety of channel responses, often unpredictable, to the interference in the river regime caused by the dam. The stream may cut into its bed; it may change the dimensions of its channel; or it may even aggrade its bed. In the case of the Hoover Dam, the water downstream, deprived of its sediment by the dam, had an increased ability to remove fine sediment from the river bed but left coarser rocks behind because the flood peaks that would remove them normally were now controlled—that is, much reduced. The result is an "armouring" of the stream bed with coarse rocks, an effect that extends 100 kilometers downstream in the case of the Colorado River below the Hoover Dam. In the Colorado system as a whole, the net effect of controlling flood peaks has caused rapids to stabilize and to increase in size as sediment becomes trapped in them. A corollary of the "winnowing" of fine material has been the disappearance of river beaches and an increased propensity to pollution as sediment becomes much less mobile and more concentrated in space.

## Bibliography

Chorley, Richard J. "The Drainage Basin as the Fundamental Geomorphic Unit." In *Water, Earth, and Man*, edited by Richard J. Chorley. London: Methuen, 1969. Treats the modern geologic and geometric approaches to the measurement of the physical characteristics of the basin: stream numbering and ordering techniques, relief measures, and the relations of basin size, shape, and relief with stream flow behavior. Excellent bibliography.

Graf, William L. *The Colorado River: Instability and Basin Management*. Washington, D.C.: Association of American Geographers, 1985. An excellent, well-written study of the particular management problems and practices associated with this large and famous river. Focuses on the way the river has adjusted to a variety of changes caused by climatic change, rangeland management, the building of large dams, and the extraction of water for irrigation. Easily understood by the layperson; sound bibliography.

Gregory, K. J., and D. E. Walling. *Drainage Basin Form and Process: A Geomorphological Approach*. London: Edward Arnold, 1973. A comprehensive academic textbook aimed at the serious undergraduate or a well-prepared, scientifically minded layperson. Examples from around the world; well-illustrated with photographs, maps, and diagrams. Detailed information on instrumentation, and in chapters 5 and 6, the implications for socioeconomic management are carefully considered. Extensive bibliography.

More, Rosemary J. "The Basin Hydrological Cycle." In *Water, Earth, and Man*, edited by Richard J. Chorley. London: Methuen, 1969. Lays out in considerable diagrammatic detail how water circulates in and through the basin and the theoretical framework possible for modeling and studying it, particularly with a view to interfering with basin flows in an optimal manner. Excellent bibliography.

Smith, C. T. "The Drainage Basin as an Historical Basis for Human Activity." In *Water, Earth, and Man*, edited by Richard J. Chorley. London: Methuen, 1969. Explains how the drainage basin has long been a natural unit for the focus of human economic activity, with examples from China, Europe, and the Americas. The importance of the basin declined somewhat as the Industrial Revolution progressed, but the need for large-scale planning of water use may be reversing this trend. A helpful guide to the historical perspective.

*Keith J. Tinkler*

## Cross-References

Dams and Flood Control, 309; Groundwater Movement, 1020; The Hydrologic Cycle, 1102; Land-Use Planning, 1335; River Bed Forms, 2196; River Flow, 2203; Sediment Transport and Deposition, 2290.

# ELEMENTAL DISTRIBUTION IN THE EARTH

*Type of earth science:* Geochemistry

*Ocean floors are composed of a dark, fine-grained rock called basalt that is more depleted in silicon and potassium and is richer in magnesium and iron than are the abundant light-colored granitic rocks on the continents. Igneous rocks that form where one oceanic plate is being thrust below another are generally intermediate in composition. Certain ore deposits occur only where certain plate tectonic processes take place, thereby enabling a geologist to focus the search for these deposits.*

### Principal terms

ANDESITE: a volcanic rock that is lighter in color than basalt, containing plagioclase feldspar and often hornblende or biotite

BASALT: a dark-colored, volcanic rock containing the minerals plagioclase feldspar, pyroxene, and olivine

GRANITIC ROCK: a light-colored, intrusive rock containing large grains of quartz, plagioclase feldspar, and alkali feldspar

LIMESTONE: a sedimentary rock composed mostly of calcium carbonate formed from organisms or by chemical precipitation in oceans

P WAVES: the first waves from earthquakes to arrive at a seismic station; because they travel at different speeds through different types of rock, they may be used to deduce the rock types below the surface

PERIDOTITE: a dark-colored rock composing much of the earth below the crust; it usually contains olivine, pyroxene, and garnet

PLATE TECTONICS: the theory that assumes that the earth's crust is divided into large, moving plates that are formed and shifted by volcanic activity

SANDSTONE: a sedimentary rock composed of larger mineral grains than those forming shales, thus deposited from faster-moving waters

SEDIMENTARY ROCK: a flat-lying, layered rock formed by the accumulation of minerals from air or water

SHALE: the most abundant sedimentary rock, composed of very tiny minerals that settled out of slowly moving water to form a mud

## Summary of the Phenomenon

The surface of the earth may be broadly divided into the oceanic crust and the continental crust. The oceanic crust is on the average "heavier," or denser, than the continental crust. Both the continental and oceanic crusts are denser than the underlying rocks in the earth's mantle. The continental and oceanic crusts can thus be considered a lower-density "scum" floating on the denser mantle, somewhat analogous to an iceberg floating in water. Because the denser oceanic crust sinks lower into the mantle than the continental crust, much of the oceanic crust is covered by the oceans, but the less dense continental crust is mostly above the level of the oceans. Also, seismic waves from earthquakes indicate that the oceanic crust is much thinner (about 6 to 8 kilometers) than the continental crust (about 35 to 50 kilometers). The density difference between the oceanic and continental crusts is related to the kinds of minerals composing them. The oceanic crust contains more of the denser iron- and magnesium-rich minerals, olivine (iron and magnesium silicate) and pyroxene (calcium, iron, and magnesium silicate), than does the continental crust. The continental crust contains much more of the less dense minerals, quartz (silica) and alkali feldspar (potassium, sodium, and aluminum silicate), than does the oceanic crust. In addition, the oceanic crust contains much of the feldspar called calcium-rich plagioclase (calcium, sodium, and aluminum silicate) than does the continental crust.

This difference in mineralogy between the oceanic and continental crusts is reflected in their average elemental composition. The oceanic crust is enriched in elements concentrated in olivine, pyroxene, and calcium-rich plagioclase, and the continental crust is enriched in those elements concentrated in quartz and alkali feldspar. Thus, the continental crust contains larger concentrations of silicon dioxide (60 weight percent in the continental crust versus 49 weight percent in the oceanic crust) and potassium oxide (2.9 versus 0.4 weight percent) and lower concentrations of titanium dioxide (0.7 versus 1.4 weight percent), iron oxide (6.2 versus 8.5 weight percent), manganese oxide (0.1 versus 0.2 weight percent), magnesium oxide (3 versus 6.8 weight percent), and calcium oxide (5.5 versus 12.3 weight percent) than does the oceanic crust. The other major elements, aluminum and sodium, are fairly similar in concentration in both the oceanic and continental crusts. The mantle is even denser than the crust, since it contains the dense minerals olivine, pyroxene, and garnet (magnesium and aluminum silicate) in the rock called peridotite. It does not contain the less dense minerals, quartz and feldspar. Thus, the mantle is even more enriched in iron oxide and magnesium oxide and more depleted in potassium oxide, sodium oxide, and silicon dioxide than are the crustal rocks. (See the accompanying table for the typical elemental composition of rocks that form the mantle and continental crust.)

The above discussion summarizes the average characteristics of the oceanic and continental crusts, but they also vary substantially in composition. The continental crust is considerably more heterogeneous than is the oceanic crust. The oceanic crust consists of an upper sediment layer (about 0.3 kilometer thick), a middle basaltic layer (about 1.5 kilometers thick), and a lower gabbroic layer (about 4 to 6 kilometers thick). Basalts and gabbros both contain olivine, pyroxene, and calcium-rich plagioclase. They differ only in grain size; the basalts contain considerably finer minerals than do the gabbros. The basaltic and gabbroic layers are thus very similar in composition. They are also of fairly constant thickness across the oceanic floors. The gabbroic layers disappear over oceanic rises, or linear mountain chains on the oceanic floors. The basaltic rocks are believed to form at the rises by about 20 to 30 percent melting of the underlying peridotite in the upper mantle. The

TYPICAL COMPOSITION OF ROCKS THAT COMPOSE MUCH OF THE EARTH'S MANTLE OR CRUST

| Element Oxide | Unmelted Peridotite in the Mantle | Basalt Formed at Oceanic Ridges or Rises | Andesite Formed at Subduction Zones | Granitic Rock Along Continental Subduction Zones | Continental Rift Basalt | Shale | Sandstone Near the Source | Sandstone Far from the Source | Limestone |
|---|---|---|---|---|---|---|---|---|---|
| $SiO_2$ (silicon oxide) | 45.0 | 49.0 | 59.0 | 65.0 | 50.0 | 58.0 | 67.0 | 95.0 | 5.0 |
| $TiO_2$ (titanium oxide) | 0.4 | 1.8 | 0.7 | 0.6 | 3.0 | 0.7 | 0.6 | 0.2 | 0.1 |
| $Al_2O_3$ (aluminum oxide) | 8.7 | 15.0 | 17.0 | 16.0 | 14.0 | 16.0 | 14.0 | 1.0 | 0.8 |
| $Fe_2O_3$ (ferric iron oxide) | 1.4 | 2.4 | 3.0 | 1.3 | 2.0 | 4.0 | 1.5 | 0.4 | 0.2 |
| FeO (ferrous iron oxide) | 7.5 | 8.0 | 3.3 | 3.0 | 11.0 | 2.5 | 3.5 | 0.2 | 0.3 |
| MnO (manganese oxide) | 0.15 | 0.15 | 0.13 | 0.1 | 0.2 | 0.1 | 0.1 | — | 0.05 |
| MgO (magnesium oxide) | 28.0 | 8.0 | 3.5 | 2.0 | 6.0 | 2.5 | 2.0 | 0.1 | 8.0 |
| CaO (calcium oxide) | 7.0 | 11.0 | 6.4 | 4.0 | 9.0 | 3.0 | 2.5 | 1.5 | 43.0 |
| $Na_2O$ (sodium oxide) | 0.8 | 2.6 | 3.7 | 3.5 | 2.8 | 1.0 | 2.9 | 0.1 | 0.05 |
| $K_2O$ (potassium oxide) | 0.04 | 0.2 | 1.9 | 2.3 | 1.0 | 3.5 | 2.0 | 0.2 | 0.3 |
| Volatiles (water or carbon dioxide) | 1.0 | 1.0 | 1.0 | 2.0 | 1.0 | 8.0 | 2.0 | 1.0 | 42.0 |

NOTE: Compositions are given as weight percentages of the element oxide in the entire rock.

newly formed oceanic crust and part of the upper mantle are believed to be slowly transported across oceanic floors, at rates of about 5 to 10 centimeters per year, to where this material is eventually subducted or thrust underneath another plate.

The thickness of sediment on ocean floors varies considerably. It is nearly absent over the newly formed basalts at oceanic rises. It is thickest in basins adjacent to continents where weathering and transportation processes carry large amounts of weathered sediment into the basins. The composition of oceanic floor sediment varies considerably in composition. It contains varied amounts of calcite or aragonite (calcium carbonate minerals), silica (silicon dioxide), clay minerals (fine, aluminum silicate minerals derived from weathering), volcanic ash, volcanic rock fragments, and ferromagnesian nodules.

Finally, a few volcanoes composed of basalt form linear chains on the ocean floor, away from the rises or subduction zones such as the Hawaiian Islands. These ocean-floor basalts are similar in composition to those at oceanic rises, except that they contain greater amounts of potassium. The amount of basaltic rocks produced by these ocean-floor volcanoes is insignificant, however, compared to the vast amounts of basalt produced at oceanic rises.

In contrast to the oceanic crust, the continental crust is quite heterogeneous in mineralogy and chemical composition. About 75 percent of the surface of the continents is covered by great piles of layered rocks called sedimentary rocks. The average thickness of these sedimentary rocks on the continental crust is only about 1.8 kilometers, although they may locally range up to 20 kilometers in thickness. The main kinds of sedimentary rocks on the continents are the very fine-grained shales or mudrocks (about 60 percent of the total sedimentary rocks), the coarser-grained sandstones (about 20 percent of the total), and limestones or dolostones (about 20 percent of the total). The shales or mudrocks are composed of very small grains of mostly clay minerals and quartz. The resultant composition of the shales is often high in the immobile elements, aluminum and potassium, and low in the mobile elements, sodium and calcium. Sandstones vary in composition depending on which rocks weather to form the sandstone, the distance of the sandstone from the source, and the intensity of weathering. Sandstones formed close to a source of granitic rocks may have a composition similar to that of the granitic rock: high in silicon and potassium and low in magnesium, iron, and calcium compared to basaltic rocks. Sandstones formed a long distance from the source have more time to be weathered. Thus, these sandstones may have most of the unstable minerals weathered away to clays or soluble products in water (for example, sodium), and they may be enriched in silicon because of the abundance of the stable mineral quartz. Limestones typically form in warm, shallow seas by the action of organisms to produce most of the calcium carbonate in these rocks. Thus, limestones are enriched in calcium and depleted in most other elements. The dolostones are also enriched in magnesium as well as calcium. Some places, such as the Great Plains in the United States, consist mostly of alternating limestones and shales formed in ancient, shallow seas. (Thus, the average composition of the surface rocks in these areas may be considered an average of that of shale and limestone in whatever proportion they occur.) The average composition of sedimentary rocks on the continents is significantly different from that of the granitic rocks that weathered to form them. The average sedimentary rocks on continents are much more enriched in calcium (because of carbonate rocks), carbon dioxide (also because of carbonate rocks), and water (because of incorporation in clay minerals), and they are depleted in sodium (because of its solubility).

The thickness of these sedimentary rocks is still small compared to the 35- to 50-kilometer thickness of most of the continental crust. Only about 5 percent of the continental crust by volume is composed of sedimentary rocks. Most crustal rocks are igneous rocks or their metamorphic equivalents. Metamorphic rocks form in the solid state at high temperatures and pressures because of their deep burial in the earth. A substantial percentage of these igneous rocks of the upper continental crust are either granitic rocks (quartz and alkali feldspar rock) or andesitic rocks (plagioclase-rich rock). Basaltic rocks probably compose only about 15 percent of the upper continental crust.

Most of the granitic rocks and andesites originally formed along subduction zones, where oceanic crust is being thrust or subducted below either oceanic or continental crust. There also may be some basalts formed along these subducted plates. These basalts, andesites, and granitic rocks that formed along continental margins may eventually be plastered along the edges of the continents, resulting in the gradual growth of the continents. Other basalts are formed in portions of continents, called continental rifts, that are being stretched apart much like taffy. These basalts are considerably more enriched in potassium than basalts formed on ocean floors. For example, a large fraction of the states of Washington, Oregon, and Idaho is covered with these rift basalts extruded as lavas since about 20 million years ago. The total volume of about 180,000 cubic kilometers for these basalts is still comparatively insignificant; therefore, basalts make only a small contribution to the composition of the average upper continental crust.

The composition of the lower continental crust is much more difficult to determine than that of the upper continental crust because the rocks forming the lower crust are not exposed at the surface. Estimates of about 50 percent granitic and 50 percent gabbroic rocks in the lower crust have been reached. Thus, the lower continental crust is more enriched in the basaltic components, calcium, magnesium, iron, and titanium, and depleted in the granitic components, potassium and silicon, than is the upper continental crust.

## Methods of Study

The average composition of the surface rocks of the continental crust may be easily estimated from the distribution of the different crustal rocks and their composition. This estimate of the surface composition of crustal rocks will be dominated by sedimentary rocks, as 75 percent of the exposed area are sedimentary rocks. The composition of the surface of the oceanic crust may be more difficult to estimate, because basalts on the ocean floor are often covered by a thin layer of sediment. Therefore, the areal extent and composition of the oceanic sediment is now known as precisely as is that of the continental crust. The average compositions of the middle and lower oceanic and continental crusts are difficult to determine because they cannot be directly sampled. Much of the information about the nature of the crust below the surface comes from the behavior of seismic waves given off by earthquakes, from heat-flow measurements, and from the composition of rock fragments brought up by magma passing through much of the crust. In addition, there are places in the crust where rocks from the lower crust have been uplifted to the surface, so their composition can be examined in detail.

The speed of the earthquake waves through the oceanic crust is consistent with the crust being composed of a thin upper layer of sediment (indicated by P-wave velocities of 2 kilometers per second), a thicker middle layer of basalt (P-wave velocities of 5 kilometers per second), and a thick lower layer of mostly gabbro (P-wave velocities of 6.7 kilometers per second). The thicker continental crust, however, has P-wave velocities (6.1 kilometers per second) consistent with mostly granitic rocks below the overlying sedimentary rock veneer (2 to 4 kilometers per second). The lower continental crust has P-wave velocities (6.7 kilometers per second) similar to those expected for lower-silica rocks like gabbro, so there is probably more gabbro mixed with granitic rocks in the lower crust.

How fast heat flows out of the earth may also be used to limit the composition of crustal rocks. Variation in heat flow at the surface depends on how much heat is flowing out of the earth below the crust; the distribution of radioactive elements in the crust, such as uranium, thorium, and potassium, that give off heat; and how close magmas are to the surface. Oceanic ridges and continental rift zones, for example, have high heat flow, suggesting that magmas are close to the surface. In contrast, the heat loss from much of the ocean floor and over much of the continents with old Precambrian rocks (older than about 600 million years) is considerably lower because of the lack of magma close to the surface. It is surprising, however, that the oceanic floor and continents with old Precambrian rocks have similar low heat flow, as the abundant granitic rocks in the continents ought to be more enriched in the heat-producing radioactive elements than is the oceanic crust. That suggests that many of the granitic rocks at depth in these parts of the continental crust are depleted in radioactive elements, perhaps because of melting processes carrying away the radioactive elements in the magmas during the Precambrian. Also, that is consistent with the presence of abundant basaltic rocks depleted in radioactive elements in the lower crust.

There are places on the earth, such as the island of Cyprus in the Mediterranean Sea, that appear to be ruptured portions of the entire oceanic crust and part of the upper mantle. In Cyprus, the lower zone is composed of peridotite, olivine-rich rocks, or pyroxene-rich rocks, as are predicted to occur in the mantle. These rocks correspond to the P-wave seismic velocities of 8 kilometers per second. There is a rather abrupt change to the next overlying layer of mostly gabbros that correspond to the sharp decrease in P-wave velocities to about 6.7 kilometers per second. These rocks grade upward into basalt corresponding to the upper igneous rock layers of the oceanic crust with P-wave velocities of about 5 kilometers per second. The basalt and gabbros are also penetrated by a multitude of tabular igneous dikes that were feeders of magma to the overlying basalt at the surface. Finally, there are overlying sedimentary rocks corresponding to the upper oceanic layers with P-wave velocities of about 2 kilometers per second.

Finally, foreign rock fragments and drill cores give up some information about the crust. A number of peridotite fragments are brought up with magmas derived from the mantle of the earth. There may be a variety of crustal rocks also brought up with them that may confuse the picture, as their depth of origin is unknown. Drill cores provide mostly information about the sedimentary rocks that might contain oil; they also give some information about the first igneous rocks just below the sedimentary rocks. Generally, wells are never drilled deep enough to obtain samples from the intermediate and lower continental crust.

## Context

A knowledge of the overall distribution of rock types and the corresponding elemental compositions of these rocks over the earth can give geologists a guide to where to look for certain kinds of ore deposits, as certain ores occur in certain kinds of rocks. The most generalized pattern is the association of certain types of ores with certain tectonic environments. Both oceanic rises and subduction zones tend to heat waters and drive the resultant metal-rich waters toward the surface. Oceanic rises often contain sulfide-rich, copper and zinc hot-water deposits. These hot-water deposits at subduction zones are often enriched in copper, gold, silver, tin, lead, mercury, or molybdenum. One example of the subduction zones deposits are the copper porphyry deposits. These important ore deposits are formed in granitic rocks that crystallized at shallow depths below the surface in areas where an oceanic plate is being subducted, or thrust below, a second plate. They are especially abundant around the rim of the Pacific Ocean. The copper ores contain low copper concentrations (0.25 to 2 percent) and have some associated molybdenum and gold. These low-grade ores are often profitable to mine because of the large volume of ore (over a billion tons in some places) that can be rapidly extracted from the rock. A geologist looking for such ores designs an exploration campaign to search out only areas with active or inactive subduction zones. Also, the geologist looks for certain compositions of granitic rocks intruded at fairly shallow depths below the surface that have been exposed to erosion near the top of the intrusion, as these are the places where the copper porphyries form. Hundreds of these copper porphyry deposits have been discovered, accounting for about half of the copper ores of the world. Copper is used in wires to transmit electricity and in bronze and brass.

## Bibliography

Ahrens, L. H. *Distribution of the Elements in Our Planet*. New York: McGraw-Hill, 1965. This book provides a clear summary of the composition of the solar system and the earth. The elements are grouped in a geochemical classification. Directed to the nonspecialist.

Craig, J. R., D. J. Vaughan, and B. J. Skinner. *Resources of the Earth*. Englewood Cliffs, N.J.: Prentice-Hall, 1988. This is an excellent book describing the distribution of ore deposits on the earth. Information is provided on the history and use of the elements, geologic occurrence, and reserves. For a nonscience major in college or interested layperson. There is a glossary of technical terms.

Skinner, B. J., and S. C. Porter. *The Dynamic Earth*. New York: John Wiley & Sons, 1989. This one of many introductory geology textbooks for college students that has a chapter on mineral and energy resources in the earth. The interested reader with some understanding of geology can find information here about the major ore deposits and their distribution within the earth.

Smith, D. G., ed. *The Cambridge Encyclopedia of the Earth Sciences*. New York: Crown, 1981. This reference is written for the reader with some background in science who needs to locate information on a specific earth science topic. Chapters 4 ("Chemistry of the Earth"), 5 ("Earth Materials"), and 10 ("Crust of the Earth") might be most appropriate for further reading related to elemental distribution. There are also chapters on plate tectonics.

Utgard, R. O., and G. D. McKenzie. *Man's Finite Earth*. Minneapolis, Minn.: Burgess, 1974. This book is written as supplementary reading for college geology courses. A section on earth resources that gives some insight on ore distribution and how it relates to public policy is suitable for a layperson.

Wedepohl, Karl Hans. *Geochemistry*. Translated by Egon Althaus. New York: Holt, Rinehart and Winston, 1971. This book gives nontechnical descriptions of the elemental distributions within the solar system and the earth. Some knowledge of chemistry and geology is necessary for full use of the book. Chapter 7 gives specific information on the distribution of elements in the earth's crust.

*Robert L. Cullers*

## Cross-References

Continental Crust, 261; Continental Rift Zones, 275; Hydrothermal Mineralization, 1108; Igneous Rock Classification, 1138; Igneous Rocks: Andesitic, 1146; Igneous Rocks: Basaltic, 1158; Igneous Rocks: Granitic, 1180; Plate Margins, 2063; Plate Tectonics, 2079; Sedimentary Mineral Deposits, 2296; Sedimentary Rock Classification, 2304; Sedimentary Rocks: Chemical Precipitates, 2318; Sedimentary Rocks: Siliciclastic, 2324; Subduction and Orogeny, 2497.

# EARTH-SUN RELATIONS

*Field of study:* Atmospheric sciences and meteorology

*The relationship between the earth and the sun controls life on this planet. Earth's "heat budget" is a result of many factors, including the effects of the atmosphere and of the oceans, but the phenomena of earth rotation and revolution are primary. Earth motions also produce observable periodic changes in apparent sun paths, perhaps most visible in the directions of sunrise and sunset.*

> *Principal terms*
> AXIS TILT: a 23.5-degree tilt in the pole-to-pole line about which the earth rotates, relative to the plane of the ecliptic
> CIRCLE OF ILLUMINATION: the circle on the earth's surface that bisects the earth and separates the sunlit half from the shadowed half
> EARTH'S HEAT BUDGET: the balance between incoming short-wavelength solar radiation and outgoing long-wavelength infrared terrestrial radiation
> ELLIPSE: the shape of the earth's orbit; rather than a circle with one center, the ellipse has two foci with the sun located at one of the foci
> GREENHOUSE EFFECT: the ability of the earth's atmosphere to allow short-wavelength solar radiation to pass in to the earth's surface but to retard the escape of long-wavelength heat into space
> PATHS OF THE SUN: the apparent motions of the sun as it tracks across the sky
> PLANE OF THE ECLIPTIC: the plane in which the earth's orbit lies as it revolves around the sun
> SOLAR RADIATION: the energy given off by the sun
> SOLAR SYSTEM: the sun and all the bodies that orbit it, including the nine planets and their satellites, plus numerous comets, asteroids, and meteoroids
> SPECIFIC HEAT: the number of calories of heat required to raise the temperature of one gram of a substance 1 degree Celsius

## Summary of the Phenomenon

Earth-sun relations are the dominant controls of life on earth. The sun is a star, and its radiation warms the earth and supplies the energy that supports life on the planet. Earth-sun relations are the phenomena that determine the amount, duration, and distribution of solar radiation that is received by the earth. The earth motions of rotation and revolution cause day and night and the seasons, which serve to distribute solar radiation over the earth. The earth's atmosphere and oceans influence the reflection, absorption, and distribution of solar energy. The result of these interacting phenomena is an earth heat budget that is hospitable and constant. The earth motions also result in a pattern of periodic changes that are observable in the apparent paths of the sun.

The sun radiates energy from every part of its spherical surface. The earth, 150 million kilometers away, receives a minute portion of the star's radiation, no more than one two-hundred-billionth, and yet the earth cannot tolerate full exposure to even that amount of radiation. The greatest amount of solar radiation is, in effect, wasted as far as the earth is concerned, radiating outward in all directions. That small amount of the sun's energy that strikes the earth is the earth's energizer. It sustains life on the earth and drives the weather systems and the oceans' circulations. Solar radiation from the past has been preserved in the form of fossil fuels—coal, petroleum, and natural gas.

Perhaps the most remarkable aspects of the earth—remarkable because they are rare in the universe—are the moderate temperatures of the earth and the constancy of those temperatures. The adjectives "hot" and "cold" are frequently used in describing the weather. In relation to the temperatures that are found in the solar system, the earth is always moderate, and the words "hot" and "cold" better describe the other planets. The mean temperature of the earth is about 15 degrees Celsius; the absolute extremes recorded anywhere on earth are 58 degrees in North Africa and −89 degrees in Antarctica. Few inhabitants of earth will ever experience a temperature range of much over 55 degrees in a lifetime. Compare those temperatures with those of the earth's near neighbor, the moon, where temperatures range from 127 to −173 degrees. The earth's sister planet Venus has a surface temperature of about 480 degrees. The outer planets of the solar system experience a permanent deep freeze, below −200 degrees. All the planets' temperatures are extreme in comparison with the earth's.

The most convincing proof of the moderate nature of the earth's temperature is the presence of the world's oceans. Water in the liquid state is extremely fragile and will exist only in a narrow temperature band, 0-100 degrees at earth's atmospheric pressure. Water must be rare indeed in the universe; it is probably nonexistent elsewhere in the solar system, with the possible exception of trace amounts on Mars. Yet, the earth has 71 percent of its surface covered with this rare and fragile substance. Almost 98 percent of the earth's water is in the liquid state. The polar ice caps contain 2 percent, and a minute portion is water vapor in the atmosphere at any time.

The factors that cause the earth to experience such a moderate and unchanging temperature are complex and interrelated. The sun is the source of the energy. Yet being the right distance from the sun cannot be the sole cause of earth's moderate temperature; witness the moon. Rather, the explanation has to do with the earth's atmosphere, the oceans, and—in particular—earth-sun relations, determined by rotation and revolution. The atmosphere protects the earth during both daylight and darkness. During daylight, the atmosphere blocks excessive amounts of short-wave solar radiation from reaching the surface. During darkness, the atmosphere retards the escape of long-wave infrared heat energy back into space and thus prevents excessive overnight cooling. The result is a moderation of temperatures. The oceans, also, have a pronounced effect on the heat budget of the earth. Water has the highest specific heat of any common substance. More heat is needed to raise the temperature of water than to raise the temperature of other materials. Summers and daylight periods are kept cooler by the water's ability to absorb great amounts of solar energy without the water's temperature being raised significantly. During winter and during darkness, on the other hand, the water slowly gives up large amounts of heat without significant cooling of the water. Thus, the oceans act as a huge temperature buffer and, similar to the atmosphere, add a moderating effect to temperature extremes.

Even more significant in controlling the temperature of the earth, however, are the earth's rotation and revolution. Rotation is the earth's turning on its axis (counterclockwise, if one's vantage point were above the North Pole). Rotation causes places on the earth to be alternately turned toward and away from the sun. The effect is to prevent the earth from overheating or overcooling. If one side of the earth were continuously exposed to the sun, the illuminated side would heat to hundreds of degrees, and the dark side would cool hundreds of degrees. The rotation of Mercury is such that a given point on the planet's surface is exposed to the sun for eighty-eight earth days and then is on the dark side for eighty-eight days. The resultant temperature extremes range from about 450 to −170 degrees Celsius. The other planets have various rates of rotation. If the rate of earth rotation, once in twenty-four hours, were different, the earth's heat budget would be different. A slower rotation would result in greater extremes of daily temperatures.

One complete revolution, or orbit, of the earth around the sun defines the time unit of one year. During a single revolution, the earth rotates on its axis 365¼ times; therefore, there are 365 days in a year, with an extra day every fourth year—leap year. The earth orbits the sun in an elliptical path, or an ellipse, and the ellipse lies in a plane referred to as the plane of the ecliptic. The sun is located at one of the two foci of the ellipse; thus, the earth is nearer to the sun at one position in the orbit than at any other position. That position occurs on or about January 3 and is called perihelion, meaning "near the sun." The earth-sun distance at perihelion is about 147,000,000 kilometers. At the opposite position on the elliptical orbit, called aphelion, on or about July 4, the earth is farthest from the sun, 152,000,000 kilometers away.

This variation in the earth's distance from the sun does alter the amount of solar radiation that is received by the earth, but it is not the cause of the seasons. Perihelion, when the earth is nearest to the sun and seemingly when the earth would be the warmest, occurs during winter in the Northern Hemisphere, and aphelion occurs during the Northern Hemisphere's summer. The distance variations are out of phase with the Northern Hemisphere's seasons, then, but in phase with seasons in the Southern Hemisphere. In both cases, they modify the seasons but do not cause them. The cause of the seasons is the fact that the earth's axis of rotation is tilted 23.5 degrees from the vertical to the plane of the ecliptic. The figure shows

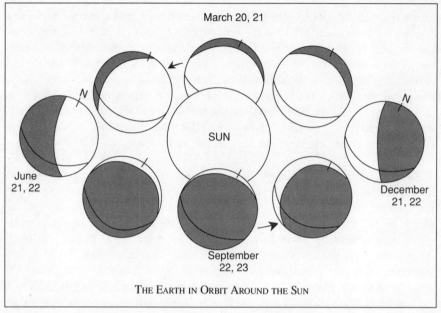

March 20, 21

SUN

June
21, 22

December
21, 22

September
22, 23

THE EARTH IN ORBIT AROUND THE SUN

how the axis is tilted. The tilt remains constant year-round in reference to space and the plane of the ecliptic, but because the earth revolves around the sun, the axis in the Northern Hemisphere alternately tilts toward and away from the sun. When the North Pole is tilted away from the sun, the Southern Hemisphere receives more solar radiation than does the Northern Hemisphere. At the position in orbit where the northern tip of the axis is tilted directly away from the sun, the sun is directly overhead at the Tropic of Capricorn (23.5 degrees south latitude), and the circle of illumination is tangent to the Arctic Circle (66.5 degrees north latitude). This position in orbit is referred to as the December solstice and occurs on December 21 or 22. For the Northern Hemisphere, it is the "winter solstice," but it is the "summer solstice" for the Southern Hemisphere. Six months later, when the northern tip of the axis is tilted directly toward the sun, the Northern Hemisphere in turn receives more solar radiation than does the Southern Hemisphere. This position in orbit, known as the June solstice, occurs on June 21 or 22. At this time, the sun is directly overhead at the Tropic of Cancer (23.5 degrees north latitude), and the entire area north of the Arctic Circle is experiencing continuous daylight. Approximately halfway in the orbit between the two solstices occur the two equinoxes. The March equinox, occuring on March 20 or 21, is the vernal or spring equinox for the Northern Hemisphere, but it is the autumnal or fall equinox for the Southern Hemisphere. The September equinox, September 22 or 23, is the fall equinox for the Northern Hemisphere but the spring equinox for the Southern Hemisphere. On the two equinoxes, the sun is directly overhead at the equator (0 degrees latitude), and the circle of illumination passes through both poles and bisects the parallels of all latitudes. Both hemispheres receive equal solar radiation on the equinoxes, but in March the sun is moving northward, whereas in September it is moving southward. It is on these two dates only that daylight and darkness are equal. It is also only on these dates that the sun rises due east and sets due west.

Between March and September, when the sun's vertical rays are north of the equator, sunrise is north of east and sunset is north of west. This is true for all locations that would experience sunrise and sunset on a particular date, both Northern and Southern Hemisphere locations. (The places that would not experience sunrise and sunset are those areas near the poles that would be experiencing either continuous daylight or continuous darkness on that date.) Sunrise would be farthest north of east on the June solstice, and sunset would be farthest north of west on that same day. After the June solstice, sunrise and sunset both migrate daily southward, being due east and due west on the September equinox. Between September and March, sunrise is south of east and sunset is south of west for all places that experience sunrise and sunset on a particular date, for both hemispheres. Sunrise is farthest south of east and sunset farthest south of west on the December solstice, after which they both begin a northward migration to repeat the pattern.

## Methods of Study

Astronomers and astrophysicists study the sun as they do any other star—that is, as having a life cycle that will eventually end in its death some 5 billion years hence, when it begins to exhaust its hydrogen fuel. Earth scientists, however, investigate the earth-sun system as though the sun were everlasting, which, from the perspective of earth-sun relations, it is. Earth scientists are concerned principally with the effects of the earth's rotation and revolution on the amount of solar energy the earth receives as well as with the effects of the atmosphere and of the ocean. Changes in the earth are considered more likely to alter the earth's heat budget than are changes in the sun. Nevertheless, earth scientists are interested in the study of such solar phenomena as sunspots, prominences, and flares in order to ascertain whether they have any effects on the earth's weather and climate patterns. The cycles of solar phenomena are compared to the records of tree growth rings. These solar phenomena are detected and photographed by filtering solar radiation so that light of a particular wavelength (color) can be viewed. Spectacular solar prominences have been captured on film.

Modern technology enables precise measurements over time of rotation and revolution in reference to the stars. Telescopic photography and the principle of parallax enable scientists to record the earth's position in space over time with great precision. Friction caused by tidal action, in turn caused by the moon's gravity, may have caused an eons-long slowdown in rotation. Perhaps, over time, precise measurements will shed light on such matters. It has been determined that there are wobbles and gyrations in the earth's axis tilt. At present, the axis orientation is slowly moving away from the star Polaris and toward Vega. It is hypothesized that the ellipticity of the orbit undergoes cyclic changes. The positions in orbit where the solstices and equinoxes occur have been ascertained to be slowly changing. A changing relationship between the solstices and perihelion will doubtless alter the distribution of solar radiation between the hemispheres. The analysis of orbit changes offers a possible explanation for the ice ages.

Several areas of research relate to possible earth-sun relations in the past. Fossils, sedimentation rates, and extinction of species offer insight into heat budgets that prevailed on the earth in former eras. Hypotheses of the causes of the ice ages make reference to such factors as changes in solar output, changes in earth output, changes in the earth's atmospheric makeup, a reconfiguration of ocean currents, and even the presence of volcanic dust. Satellite images of the oceans, on the various wavelengths of the electromagnetic spectrum, are analyzed to detect any slight temperature changes over time that may portend changes in the earth's environment. Sensitive instruments measure and record the intensity of sunlight in such areas as Antarctica. Satellite imagery also is providing an accurate record-base for areas of snow cover in polar regions. If the earth's heat budget should change, the areas and duration of snow cover will be among the earliest evidences to be detected. Intense research continues on changes in the composition of the atmosphere and their possible effects on the heat budget. One conclusion seems clear: The earth's heat budget is a product of many factors in earth-sun relations, not all of which are fully understood, and any changes in the budget are likely to be detrimental.

## Context

Life on earth is profoundly dependent upon the relationship between the earth and the sun. Fortunately, the sun is a long-lived and constant radiating star. Yet, it would blister the earth if the earth were exposed to it continuously. Rotation and revolution make the earth a rotisserie, slowly turning so as to expose all sides for a more even heat. The lengths of daylight and darkness and the changes of the seasons are phenomena that are beyond human control. It is to be hoped that they will not change, because life on earth can tolerate very little change.

While humans cannot alter basic earth-sun relations, they apparently can have effects on other factors in the earth's heat budget. The atmosphere protects the earth from overheating by day and from overcooling at night. The earth's "greenhouse effect" is a result of the atmosphere's ability to trap solar radiation as heat during the day and retard its escape back into space at night, when the sun is not above the horizon. A critical constituent gas that is responsible for the greenhouse effect is carbon dioxide. There is concern that a global warming resulting from an enhanced greenhouse effect may be under way because of additional carbon dioxide being added to the atmosphere through the burning of fossil fuels. This effect is exacerbated by deforestation. Another concern regarding changes in the atmosphere is that man-made pollutants, principally chlorofluorocarbons, may be depleting the gas ozone in the upper atmosphere. A reduction of ozone would allow greater amounts of harmful ultraviolet radiation to penetrate to the earth's surface.

The temperature of the earth is at a fine balance between the input of radiation from the sun and the absorption of that solar radiation and subsequent reradiation of heat energy from the earth back into space. Life on the planet is dependent on this solar energy and the moderate, constant temperature that results. Changes could possibly occur in the earth's rotation, revolution, or axis tilt. Any such changes would be catastrophic. If any changes in the earth's heat budget occur, however, it is more likely that they will be as a result of changes in the atmosphere brought about by human actions.

## Bibliography

Ahrens, C. Donald. *Meteorology Today.* St. Paul, Minn.: West, 1982. This introductory college-level text on meteorology presents a thorough treatment of weather phenomena and explains the seasons and the effects of solar energy on the atmosphere. Written for students with little background in science or mathematics. Includes many illustrations.

Gabler, Robert E., Robert J. Sager, Sheila M. Brazier, and D. L. Wise. *Essentials of Physical Geography.* 3d ed. New York: Saunders College Publishing, 1987. A general introductory-level text on physical geography. Covers rotation, revolution, solar energy, and the elements of weather and climate. Well illustrated. For the general reader.

Harrison, Lucia Carolyn. *Sun, Earth, Time, and Man.* Chicago: Rand McNally, 1960. This book is considered the classic reference for earth-sun relations. Although dated, it is an excellent source of information and offers a remarkably extensive coverage of earth-sun relations. Most useful to the student who already has a working knowledge of earth-sun relations and wants to investigate further.

Jones, B. W., and Milton Keynes. *The Solar System.* Elmsford, N.Y.: Pergamon Press, 1984. A thorough discussion of the entire solar system from the life cycle of a star to the minor members of the system, including comets and meteoroids. Provides highly detailed information on each of the planets and its satellites. Contains some highly technical data, but they are presented in a lucid manner.

Oberlander, Theodore M., and Robert A. Muller. *Essentials of Physical Geography Today.* 2d ed. New York: Random House, 1987. A general introductory text on physical geography, the book includes explanations of earth-sun relations and the energy balance of the earth, atmosphere, and ocean systems. Well illustrated with maps and diagrams.

Pasachoff, Jay M. *Astronomy Now.* Philadelphia: W. B. Saunders, 1978. An introductory text in astronomy for students with no background in mathematics or physics. Well illustrated, it covers the planets, the solar system, and the galaxies. The portion on the structure and nature of the sun is helpful.

Scott, Ralph C. *Physical Geography.* New York: John Wiley & Sons, 1988. A general introductory-level text on physical geography. Earth-sun relations are presented within an introduction to the study of the earth's weather and climates. Clearly written and well illustrated. Recommended as an initial source.

Strahler, Arthur N., and Alan H. Strahler. *Modern Physical Geography*. 3d ed. New York: John Wiley & Sons, 1987. In this general college-level text on physical geography, earth-sun relations are discussed within the context of the study of weather and climate. Diagrams are well employed to explain the earth's orbit, rotation, revolution, and axis tilt. Easy to read.

Tarbuck, Edward J., and Frederick K. Lutgens. *Earth Science*. 5th ed. Columbus, Ohio: Merrill, 1988. Several chapters in this introductory text deal with the solar system. The nature of solar activity and the motions of the earth are explained. Well illustrated and highly accessible.

*John H. Corbet*

## Cross-References

The Atmosphere's Evolution, 114; The Atmosphere's Structure and Composition, 128; Atmospheric Ozone, 144; Climate, 217; Coal, 232; Earth's Rotation, 576; The Greenhouse Effect, 1004; Heat Sources and Heat Flow, 1065; The Hydrologic Cycle, 1102; Ocean-Atmosphere Interactions, 1779; Paleoclimatology, 1993; Solar Power, 2427; The Origin of the Solar System, 2442.

# EARTH SYSTEM SCIENCE

*Field of study:* Remote sensing

*Scientists have developed a method, called earth system science, that views the planet as a dynamic, unified system of simultaneous, interacting forces. It is hoped that promotion of earth system science can help to stem and even reverse much of the ecological and environmental damage caused by humans.*

### Principal terms

CLIMATE: the sum total of the prevailing long-term weather conditions of an area, determined by such factors as latitude, altitude, and location

DEFORESTATION: a process of destruction of forested areas by removal of trees and other flora

DESERTIFICATION: a process by which deserts are created, expanded, or changed by clearing away peripheral forestry or brush, thus allowing the desert to occupy new spaces

ECOLOGY: the relationship between organisms and their environment

OZONE LAYER: a region of the atmosphere 15-55 kilometers in altitude, which is a concentration of ozone

TECTONICS: the study of the processes forming the major structural features of the earth's crust

## Summary of the Methodology

A new viewpoint of the earth as a set of interacting forces all in motion at the same time has come to replace the traditional series of separate earth science disciplines studied in isolation. This new and promising viewpoint came about as a result of a growing recognition of the interactive nature of earth's forces exerting an influence upon one another, as opposed to the idea that the forces act independently. The result of these developing ideas and viewpoint is an entirely new approach to earth studies. Scientific concepts of a static and quiet earth were replaced by the realization that the planet is a constantly moving and dramatic entity of plate tectonic activity, volcanism, mountain building, earthquakes, severe storms, dynamic oceans, and changing climatic patterns and atmospheric conditions. Scientists view the earth as a unified whole, and instead of concentrating attention on one component at a time, they adopt a "systems approach" that uses total global observation methods together with numerical modeling.

The earth systems science approach was first detailed by an Earth System Science Committee (ESSC) appointed by the Advisory Council of the National Aeronautics and Space Administration (NASA). In 1986, the committee completed a three-year study of research opportunities in earth science and recommended that an integrated, global earth observation and information system be adopted and in full operation by the mid-1990's. The committee's *Overview Report* was released

June 26 of the same year. Requests for the findings of the committee from the National Oceanic and Atmospheric Administration (NOAA) and the National Science Foundation (NSF), along with other federal agencies, have drawn the three top agencies—NASA, NOAA, NSF—into a scientific alliance. The committee's report outlined immediate needs in several wide-reaching areas: scientific understanding of the entire earth as a system of interacting components; the ability to predict both natural and human-induced changes in the earth system; strong, coordinated research and observational programs in NASA, NOAA, and NSF as the core of a major United States effort; long-term measurements, from space and from earth's surface, to describe changes as they occur and as a basis for numerical modeling; modeling, research, and analysis programs to explain the functioning of individual earth system processes and their interactions; a sequence of specialized space research missions of a global approach, including the Upper Atmosphere Research Satellite (UARS), the joint United States/France Ocean Topography Experiment (TOPEX/POSEIDON), and the Geopotential Research Mission (GRM); and an earth-observing system using polar-orbiting platforms planned as part of the U.S. Space Station complex combining NOAA and NASA instrumentation.

The earth system science approach utilizes new technologies in global observations, space science applications, computer innovations, and quantitative modeling. These new tools of advanced technology allow scientists to probe and learn about the interactions responsible for earth evolution and global change. In the quest for practical means to improve the quality of human life, recent advances in technologies for weather prediction, agriculture, and forestry and for navigation and ocean-resource management will accompany a still better understanding of the earth system. Examples of research made possible by new tools are the opportunity to include the effects of global atmospheric motions into models of ocean circulation, the study of volcanic activity as a link between convection in the earth's mantle and worldwide atmospheric properties, and the tracing of the global carbon cycle through the many transformations of carbon biological organisms, atmospheric chemical reactions, and the weathering of earth's solid surface and soils.

Beginning in the 1970's and 1980's, there was a growing realization among scientists that human activities have brought about significant processes of global change that are altering the evolution of the earth at a surprising pace. Widespread concern for the destructive consequences of careless human behavior has prompted several special studies by the sixteen members of the Earth System Science Committee (ESSC), the International Council of Scientific Unions, and the Committee for an International Geosphere-Biosphere Program of the U.S. National Academy of Sciences.

The goal of earth system science is to obtain a scientific understanding of the entire earth system on a global scale by describing how its component parts and their interactions have evolved, how they function, and how they may be expected to continue to evolve on all time scales. This evolution is influenced by human activities—the depletion of the earth's energy and mineral resources and the alteration of atmospheric chemical composition—that sometimes are easily identified. It is the overall long-range consequences of these human actions that are difficult to understand; the changes do not occur fast enough for immediate recognition and, indeed, often take decades to evolve fully. The challenge to earth system science, which provides a definite research focus, is to develop the capability to predict those changes that will occur in the twenty-first century, both naturally and in response to human activity. In meeting this challenge, a vigorous program is being undertaken that includes concepts of global observations, information systems built to process global data, existing numerical models which already are contributing to a detailed understanding of individual earth components and interactions, and the need for interdisciplinary research support and interagency cooperation.

Observations from space, the best vantage point from which to obtain the detailed, global data required to discriminate among worldwide processes operating on both long and short time scales, are essential to the future study of the earth as a system. Rapid variations in atmospheric and ocean properties, global effects of volcanic eruptions, ocean circulations, and motions of the earth's crustal plates are examples of such processes. The Space Science Board of the National Academy of Sciences recommended orbital observation as a major method of global study; the Earth System Science Committee accepted the recommendations and expanded on them. Of particular value are NASA and NOAA satellites already on station in orbit, such as the Laser Geodynamics Satellites, which employ laser ranging to measure motions and deformations of earth's crustal plates. Weather satellites already have supplied a sizable fund of data about the atmosphere and oceans as well as enabled a good start on numerical modeling of weather variations. The committee commented especially on the high value of currently operating programs that permit a coordinated sequence of studies of specific earth system processes, such as the Earth Radiation Budget Experiment (1984), the Laser Geodynamics Satellites (1976 and 1983), the Navy Remote Ocean Sensing System (1985), and the Upper Atmosphere Research Satellite (1982).

In order to implement the full measure of the earth system science concept, an advanced information system is needed to process global data and allow analysis, interpretation, and quantitative modeling. Also required is the implementation of new observing programs such as the ocean color imager, scanning radar altimeter for surface topography, and an atmospheric carbon-monoxide monitor. Thus, a vigorous program of instrument development will have to be prepared for satellite experiments, and ground-level measurements to complement, validate, and interpret global observations from space must be devised. In addition to a vigorous program implementation schedule, the development of new management policies and mechanisms are required to encourage cooperation among agencies around the globe in order to ensure the coordination necessary for a truly worldwide study of the earth. International cooperation is essential to the success of earth system science. A number of major international research programs are already operating, such as the World Climate Research Program, sponsored by the International Council of Scientific Unions, and the World Meteorological Organization. To accomplish these many programs and objectives, the Earth System Science Committee recommends two specific areas in which the three major United States agencies—NASA, NOAA, and NSF—must work closely together. The first is to establish and develop the advanced information system required by earth system science as a cooperative venture, especially to create the necessary management structures, and the second is close cooperation in programs of basic research.

## Applications of the Method

Methods to be used by scientists in the study of earth system science are very new and highly advanced. As the study continues, modifications in these advanced methods will introduce even more sophisticated qualitative and quantitative tools because of the fast pace of technological innovation.

The most significant tool for global observation is the discerning satellite that can precisely measure large areas of the earth at one time. Meteorological satellites to gather data about temperature, weather patterns and forces, and atmospheric changes and ingredients and to monitor variations of climate and storm systems can add an enormous amount of data to the growing fund of global observations. The satellites are placed in geosynchronous orbit at an altitude of 35,000 kilometers so they can continuously monitor the same region of the earth over long periods of time. The satellite orbits at a speed relative to the speed of the earth's rotation so that they remain over the same spot on the earth's surface. Earth observation satellites, working in the infrared band of the spectrum, allow scientists to gather imagery and information about volcanic action, earthquakes, geological formations, mineral resources, and geographic changes to provide still another perspective of the earth. Orbiting the earth from pole to pole many times a day, they are able to make a record of large sections of the earth in a twenty-four-hour period. Earth observation satellites also carry instruments that measure temperatures, record cloud cover, and monitor catastrophic changes. Other satellites measure ocean dynamics such as the temperature of large sections of seas and oceans, wave action, ocean water content, and relationships between water and the land it touches. Special instruments monitor ice conditions and snowfall at sea and watch over changes in polar regions.

Manned spacecraft, carrying astronaut-photographers, are important to provide a platform for getting pictures of discrete regions. The spacecraft also carry radar-imaging devices to measure precise distances and relationships between land features. Continual advances in films and camera optics allow astronauts to gather high-quality pictures and even allow special night photography. The international space station has, as one of its most important objectives, the function of a permanently orbiting platform on which both humans and unattended instruments can work over long periods of time to monitor earth activities and topography. The space station will be able to contribute large amounts of data because it can function both as information gatherer and processor using advanced onboard automated equipment such as specialized computers.

Although much of the earth system science instrumentation will be spaceborne, much of it also will have to be ground-based where measurements and important kinds of data are being gathered on-site. Earth activities such as volcanoes, earthquakes, hurricanes, tornadoes, and thunderstorms, for example, must be measured on the ground to determine their effects on other earth surface processes. Ground data then can be compared and synthesized with data gathered from space to offer a broader view.

One of the most valuable of tools is the computer for the receipt, storage, retrieval, analysis, and supply of large quantities of information. Ground-based and spaceborne computers will be able to work in conjunction with each other for the interaction, comparison, and large-scale analysis of data, which can be networked to any place on earth by means of telephone lines and data-relay satellites. Advanced computers, such as the super computer, aid in processing a truly enormous amount of data from large periods of historic time, thus speeding up the process of analysis. The computers are especially useful in creating theoretical models of various kinds of processes. By feeding weather data from the past hundred years into a computer, for example, scientists can begin to construct long-term models of weather patterns and global changes in climate and rainfall or drought. Soon to be added are innovative artificial intelligence systems that assist in the processing, analysis, and further use of billions of pieces of separate data. A new study method in use is the creation and management of a global information system into which is fed data from countries all over the world; all nations can retrieve data for their own research as well as input data to add to the ongoing process of worldwide data analysis.

## Context

It is imperative that citizens of the twenty-first century understand the forces and processes that are causing global changes because, individually and collectively, they are major contributors to those changes. Human contributions—mostly destructive—include continued clear-cutting of vast forest areas, thus inviting massive deforestation (destruction of forests); removal of protective trees and underbrush from areas adjacent to desert areas, thus encouraging rampant desertification (the spread of desert conditions); and intense pollution of the atmosphere and waterways by carbon monoxide exhaust, massive oil spills, and the use of cosmetic aerosol sprays, thus producing chlorofluorocarbon that attacks and destroys the atmosphere. Over time, these acts have slowly depleted earth's natural resources and violently upset the fragile balance of nature worldwide. When left alone, the earth and its processes follow a natural course of events designed to ensure its own perpetual existence. Human intervention, however, has triggered cataclysmic events that, if not stopped, will cause irreversible damage in the long term and that threaten to bring about the eventual destruction of the planet.

Two of these events—the greenhouse effect and the ozone layer depletion—are already in the beginning stages. The natural balance of atmosphere-ocean-land has been seriously upset. The warming of the planet by trapped solar radiation is raising earth's temperature and is hindering the normal cooling actions of wind, water, and climate. The effect on planets, animals, and humans is being felt already. If continued, the whole process will raise the overall temperature, melt the polar caps, and cause a corresponding rise in ocean levels, which will flood present landmasses. The current destruction of the ozone layer of the atmosphere by chlorofluorocarbons has been carefully studied and documented. If the ozone layer continues to decay, it will fail to block normal amounts of solar radiation, and the temperature rise described as the greenhouse effect will continue to escalate and become a permanent destructive force.

The new methodology of earth system science offers the human species a chance to prevent this disaster, both in the study of earth from a more integrated perspective and in the raising of public awareness of the human practices that are destroying the planet. Nothing less than a sustained worldwide effort is required.

## Bibliography

Earth System Science Committee. *An Integrated Global Earth Observation and Information System to Be in Full Operation by the Mid-1990's*. Boulder, Colo.: University Corporation for Atmospheric Research, 1986. This thirty-page information brief is a statement containing an explanation of the entire concept of earth system science, written by the key people who created the method. A very basic presentation of the subject written in terse and brief language. A highly usable and understandable text on which the reader can rely as one of the starting points for comprehending the entire concept. Copies of the brief may be obtained from the Earth System Sciences Committee, University Corporation for Atmospheric Research, P.O. Box 3000, Boulder, Colorado 80307, or from the Public Affairs offices of the National Aeronautics and Space Administration (NASA), the National Oceanic and Atmospheric Administration (NOAA), and the National Science Foundation (NSF).

Houghton, Richard A., and G. Woodwell. "Global Climatic Change." *Scientific American* 260 (April, 1989): 36-44. Two long-acknowledged experts have teamed up to present yet more disturbing evidence of the rapid global warming trend. Their creation of warming and atmospheric models fit very well with earth system science concepts. Sounding once again the global alarm for major changes in human activities that are accelerating the warming trend, the authors clearly present a picture of the earth's future unless massive and costly preventive programs are undertaken immediately. The text is well written and logically presented, and the graphic illustrations are a perfect complement to the evidence. Appropriate for the high school student and the layperson.

Matthews, Samuel W. "This Changing Earth." *National Geographic* 143 (January, 1973): 1-37. This beautifully illustrated text about the forces which sculpt and change the earth is most likely one of the earliest articles to describe the earth's dynamic processes in a language that the public can readily understand. The subjects of tectonic plate science and continental drift theory are clearly and precisely treated. In addition, the author takes the reader on a historic tour of the development of these modern processes, recalling pioneering scientists and the reception each received as a theorist. Superb diagrams and supportive photography.

National Aeronautics and Space Administration Advisory Council. *Earth System Science Overview.* Washington, D.C.: Government Printing Office, 1986. This exquisite, full-color booklet is the basic document for approaching the subject of earth system science. Created by the Earth System Sciences Committee of the NASA Advisory Council, the fifty-page document details in easy-to-understand text all the intricate natural mechanisms at work on the planet. Far more important, the booklet describes and pictures the entire earth system science concept and outlines in depth how the new tools and methods will be brought together to focus on a global data-gathering and archiving information system through international cooperative efforts. The illustrations are excellent examples of highly professional photography and artwork. Written for the high school student and the layperson.

_____. *Planetary Exploration Through Year 2000.* Washington, D.C.: Government Printing Office, 1983. The immediate value of this comprehensive and detailed full-color booklet created by the Solar System Exploration Committee of the NASA Advisory Council is its use to explain how the earth and its moon fit into the overall solar system. The book shows how continued exploration of the solar system has brought an enormous amount of new data to the field of comparative planetology. The illustrations from NASA files are superb, but the text might prove to be a struggle for the high school student, mainly because of its detail and its heavy focus on technology. Nevertheless, it is still well worth the effort.

National Geographic Society. "Can Man Save This Fragile Earth?" *National Geographic* 174 (December, 1988). This chilling and timely "report" on the health and wealth of planet Earth—commanding a special issue of the magazine—is the result of a symposium sponsored by the National Geographic Society in January, 1988. In 175 pages of thought-provoking text and magnificent illustration, the authors of the nine articles lead the reader through numerous examples of the major destructive forces now at work on our planet, calling for sober assessments of processes and their renewals. Earth system science is described in various perspectives. The reading level is appropriate for the high school student.

"Planet of the Year: Endangered Earth." *Time* 133 (January 2, 1989). This special issue is the result of a major international conference held at Time, Incorporated, in November, 1988, which centered its attention on the plight of the planet. World-renowned experts from many nations, including the Soviet Union, met and discussed the processes that threaten to destroy the earth. Terse text, startling photographs, and urgent recommendations make for a fast-moving narrative of what some scientists regard as "desperation science" in order to stop the already-advancing processes. Text is suitable for junior high school to adult readers.

*Thomas W. Becker*

## Cross-References

Air Pollution, 24; Atmospheric Ozone, 144; Climate, 217; Desertification, 346; Engineering Geophysics, 607; Environmental Health, 615; The Greenhouse Effect, 1004; Groundwater Pollution Remediation, 1035; Hazardous Wastes, 1059; Land Management, 1327; Plate Tectonics, 2079.

# EARTH TIDES

*Type of earth science:* Geophysics
*Field of study:* Geodesy and gravity

*Earth tides are deformations of the crust of the earth as a result of gravitational interaction with the moon and the sun. Knowledge of the effects of these tidal forces is important to earth scientists who search for natural resources.*

### Principal terms

DEFORMATION: the alteration of an object from its normal shape by a force
GRAVIMETER: a device that measures the attraction of gravity
HOMOGENEOUS: having uniform properties throughout
OBLATE SPHEROID: a spherically shaped body that is flattened at the polar regions
OSCILLATE: to fluctuate or to swing back and forth
PENDULUM: a mass suspended in such a way that it can swing freely
PERTURB: to change the path of an orbiting body by a gravitational force
SYNCHRONIZED ROTATION-REVOLUTION: a situation in which the rotation rate of a body is equal to its rate of revolution

## Summary of the Phenomenon

Earth tides are the deformation of the solid portion of the earth by the combined gravitational forces of the moon and the sun. Although other bodies within and beyond the solar system gravitationally attract the earth, the distances are great enough to make their tidal effect upon the earth negligible. Consider the earth-moon system. According to Sir Isaac Newton's law of gravity, every particle of mass in the universe is attracted to every other particle of mass by a force that is directly proportional to the product of the masses and inversely proportional to the square of the distance between them—which means that gravity is always an attractive force, but its magnitude depends to a great extent upon the distance between the two bodies in question. Since gravity is an inverse square law, the following relationship holds true: If the distance between two bodies is doubled, the attraction of gravity becomes one-fourth as great; if the distance between the bodies is tripled, the attraction becomes one-ninth as great, and so on. According to this law, each particle of the moon attracts each particle of the earth. Because these particles are not all equidistant from one another, the force of gravity varies in intensity. Gravitational attraction is greatest between the particles that are closest; therefore the surface of the earth nearest the position of the moon is subjected to more attraction than is the surface of the earth opposite the moon. It is this difference in relative position that causes the tidal force and thus the deformation of the earth.

Albert Michelson measured the earth tides in 1913 by observing water tides in long horizontal pipes. He had assumed that the earth was rigid, but he did not observe the tidal values that the theory indicated he should. The difference could be accounted for when the earth was assigned a rigidity so that it was able to respond to lunar gravitational forces by raising crustal tides to a height of several centimeters.

The ocean tides may be considered as being analogous to the earth tides. Like earth tides, ocean tides are caused by the gravitational forces of both the sun and the moon. Because of its relative closeness, the moon is the greater factor. Its gravitation causes the water in the oceans to bulge outward a distance of one meter or so. There are two water bulges on the surface of the earth: one in the direction of the moon and one in the direction opposite the direction of the moon. This latter bulge forms because of the reduced amount of gravity at that position on the earth's surface. Another way of looking at it might be as follows: The earth is being attracted toward the moon or, in a sense, is falling toward the moon. Therefore, the water on the lunar side is falling toward the moon and is actually ahead of the earth's surface. The water on the opposite side of the earth is also falling toward the moon but cannot quite keep up with the earth's surface and so forms a bulge. Theoretically, as the earth rotates with respect to the moon, the water level rises and falls as these bulges of water are swept around the earth. In reality, the height and timing of tides may vary considerably. In some bays, the tidal water may accumulate to heights of 10 meters and greater. Because there are two tidal bulges, there are two high tides per day.

The sun also exerts a tidal force on the earth, but because of its greater distance, its influence is only about one-half as great as the moon's. Extremely large high tides are generated when the sun, the moon, and the earth lie along a straight line. The tidal forces of the sun and the moon then act in the same direction. These tides are known as spring tides, though they have nothing to do with the season. The nature of the ocean tides provides an immediate observation and a fairly simple observation of the nature of tidal forces.

Tidal forces also have an affect on gravity, as does the shape of the planet. The ancient Greeks taught that the earth is a sphere. The philosopher Plato reasoned that all heavenly bodies are perfect and therefore must be spherical; because the earth was a heavenly body, its shape was thus spherical. In about the year 230 B.C., Eratosthenes calculated the circumference of the earth to be 12,560 kilometers, which is only 112 kilometers less than the current estimate. During the seventeenth century, several measurements were made on the earth's surface. The size on one degree of arc in the Northern Hemisphere proved to be somewhat shorter than a degree of arc farther south. It was concluded from these studies that the earth is flattened toward the poles and thus is not spherical. The shape of the earth is rather an oblate spheroid, as explained by Sir Isaac Newton in his famous work of 1687, *Principia*.

If the earth were a perfect sphere and homogeneous in composition, the gravity measurements at all points on the surface would be identical and the orbits of earth satellites would be perfectly circular or elliptical. Because the earth's gravitational field is uneven, resulting from the fact that the earth is neither perfectly spherical nor homogeneous, the orbits of satellites are somewhat perturbed. The paths of satellites can be observed and plotted with a high degree of precision. The data indicate that the earth is an oblate spheroid, its radius 21 kilometers longer at the equator than at the poles. It behaves as though it were a fluid balanced between gravitational forces, which tend to make it spherical, and centrifugal forces resulting from its rotation, which tend to flatten it.

The acceleration of gravity near the earth's surface is measured in gals, in honor of Galileo. A gal is the amount of force that will accelerate a mass 1 centimeter per second per second, or 1 centimeter per second squared. The total value for the acceleration of gravity is 980 gals, which is equivalent to the more familiar value of 9.8 meters per second squared. It is known that when the moon is directly overhead, at a position known as the zenith, the value for the acceleration of gravity at that point on the earth's surface is slightly less than if the moon were in any other position. This phenomenon is a result of the gravitational influence or tidal force that the moon exerts on the earth. The attraction of the moon's gravity causes a point on the earth's surface to be distended slightly. Values for the amount of distension have been found to be about 0.073 meter. The fact that this point on the earth's surface has been gravitationally pulled away from the center of the earth will result in a slightly reduced value in the acceleration of gravity toward the center of the earth. These values have been found to be in the vicinity of 0.2 milligal. (A milligal is one thousandth of a gal.)

Subtle effects of tidal forces on the earth exist. When the earth and the oceans are subjected to tide-raising forces, energy caused by friction is dissipated. The result of this friction is the reduction in the period of the earth's rotation. In the case of a binary system such as the earth and the moon, the result of tidal forces produces a synchronized state of rotation-revolution. In other words, the rate that the moon rotates on its axis is the same as the rate at which it revolves around the earth in its orbit—which is the reason that the same face of the moon always points toward the earth. This particular phenomenon occurs elsewhere in the solar system; for example, the sun and Mercury, and Pluto and its moon Charon form other such binary systems.

There is a law in physics that states that angular momentum is conserved. If the rotation rates of the earth and the moon are slowing but their masses stay the same, the distance between them must be increasing. Evidence from paleontological studies indicates that at one time, the earth had a faster rotation rate and the moon was much closer than it is today. It is now known that the moon is moving away from the earth 3.2 centimeters per year.

## Methods of Study

At the beginning of the nineteenth century, the concept that the earth was not perfectly rigid but in fact was somewhat deformable began to be accepted. The first studies of the deformation of the earth's crust were conducted in France in the early 1830's. These early studies were accomplished by using containers of mercury and comparing the motion of the liquid metal with the rise and fall of the ocean tides. The horizontal pendulum was the first instrument to record the effect of earth tides with scientific precision. It consisted of a rigid bracket whose base contained three leveling screws. At both the top and the bottom of the bracket (which resembled a C-clamp), two metal wires were attached. These wires were all attached to a metal arm in such a way as to suspend it in position. At the end of the arm was attached a small mass. The slightest vibration caused by changes of the ground would cause the pendulum arm to begin oscillating back and forth. This instrument was but the first of many types and variations of the pendulum.

In the 1900's, the gravimeter came into use in the field of exploration geophysics and was later used to detect the minute changes in gravity brought about by earth tides. Gravimeters are designed to measure the differences in the acceleration of gravity. There are several different types of these instruments, most of which consist of a mass suspended by springs. The greater the force, such as gravity, pulling on the mass, the more the spring stretches. The upward force is a function of the strength of the spring, or the spring constant. When the mass is in balance (not oscillating) the spring constant is equal to the force of gravity. Any change in gravity will then produce a corresponding change in the stretch of the spring. During a period of a maximum earth tide, gravity will be slightly reduced, resulting in a slight upward drift of the mass.

The pendulums and the gravimeter are used to study the vertical deformation of the earth's surface. The linear deformation may be measured by means of a device called an extensometer. The first results from the use of this device were reported in the early 1950's. The extensometer consists of a wire 1.6 millimeters in diameter that is held nearly horizontal between two fixed supports about 20 meters apart. A mass of 350 grams is suspended from the center of the wire by a smaller wire with a diameter of 0.2 millimeter. Variations in the 20-meter distance between the two fixed supports as a result of linear deformations of the earth's surface can cause variations in the tension of the main wire. These variations cause the suspended mass to oscillate vertically. By methods of calibration, the oscillation can be translated into values of linear deformation.

## Context

The knowledge of how earth tides function is necessary for an understanding of the deformable nature of the earth and of the earth's gravitational interaction with the moon and the sun. This knowledge is important to those who explore for the oil, gas, groundwater, and minerals that are necessary for life in the modern world. To the geophysicists who use the technique of gravity surveying, it is necessary to know whether the change in the value of gravity indicated by their instruments is caused by a subsurface geological structure or by the gravity of the moon or the sun. For this reason, gravity surveyors must make what is known as a tide correction, which accounts for the time-varying gravitational attraction of the sun and the moon. The attraction is cyclic because the positions of the sun and moon are constantly changing with regard to a fixed position on the surface of the earth. To those earth scientists who use the technique of searching for magnetic anomalies, or areas where the earth's magnetism is greater or less than expected, the sun's effect on the earth's magnetic field is very important. The sun's tidal force produces wind currents in the earth's ionosphere in the same way that it produces ocean tides. Since these winds in the ionosphere consist of waves of charged particles, there is an associated electric current. With this current comes a fluctuating magnetic field. The geophysicist, therefore, needs to know if the sun's tidal force is causing deviations in the equipment being used.

## Bibliography

Baugher, Joseph F. *The Space-Age Solar System*. New York: John Wiley & Sons, 1988. A well-illustrated, very readable volume on the planets, moons, and other bodies that make up our solar system. Suitable for the layperson.

Howell, Benjamin F. *Introduction to Geophysics*. New York: McGraw-Hill, 1959. A technical volume dealing extensively with various areas in the study of geophysics. Topics such as seismology and seismic waves, gravity, isostasy, tectonics, continental drift, and geomagnetism are covered. The reader should have a working knowledge of differential and integral calculus. Suitable for college students of physics or geophysics.

Melchior, Paul. *The Earth Tides*. Elmsford, N.Y.: Pergamon Press, 1966. A highly detailed, highly technical volume on the discovery and the observation of earth tides. Goes into great detail on the evolution of the instrumentation used for earth tide detection. Suitable for college students of geophysics or engineering.

Robinson, Edwin S., and Cahit Coruh. *Basic Exploration Geophysics*. New York: John Wiley & Sons, 1988. A well-illustrated volume dealing with the science of geophysics both in theory and in applications. Contains well-developed chapters on seismic, gravity, and magnetic exploration techniques. The reader should have a working knowledge of algebra and trigonometry. Suitable for college students of geology, geophysics, or physics.

Spencer, Edgar W. *Dynamics of the Earth*. New York: Thomas Y. Crowell, 1972. An introduction to the principles of physical geology. Covers all aspects of geology, from introductory mineralogy through a study of the agents that shape the planet's surface. Concludes with units on global tectonics and geophysics. These later chapters tend to be somewhat technical, requiring the use of algebra. Suitable for college-level geology students.

Stacy, Frank D. *Physics of the Earth*. New York: John Wiley & Sons, 1969. A technical volume dealing with such topics as earth rotation, gravity, seismology, and internal structure, magnetism, and radioactivity. Advanced mathematics is used throughout. Suitable for college students of physics or geophysics.

Taff, Laurence G. *Celestial Mechanics*. New York: John Wiley & Sons, 1985. A technical volume dealing with Newtonian gravitation, how it manifests itself, and how gravitational bodies interact with one another. Calculus and differential equations must be understood prior to reading. Suitable for college-level students of physics, astrophysics, and mathematics.

Zeilik, Michael, and Elske Smith. *Introductory Astronomy and Astrophysics*. New York: Saunders College Publishing, 1987. A technical volume having to do with such topics as celestial mechanics, interactions of gravitational bodies, the planets, the origin of the solar system and the universe, stars, and cosmology. Some advanced mathematics is used. Suitable for college students of astronomy or astrophysics.

*David W. Maguire*

## Cross-References

Earth-Sun Relations, 399; Earth's Rotation, 576; Earth's Shape, 583; Experimental Rock Deformation, 669; Gravity Anomalies, 997; Ocean Tides, 1832; Stress and Strain, 2490.

# EARTHQUAKE DISTRIBUTION

*Type of earth science:* Geophysics
*Field of study:* Seismology

*For approximately a century, seismologists have been monitoring global earthquake activity. These studies have led to an understanding of earthquake frequency and distribution that contributed dramatically to the confirmation of plate tectonics theory.*

*Principal terms*

BENIOFF ZONE: a narrow zone, defined by earthquake foci, that is tens of kilometers thick, dipping from the surface under the earth's crust

EPICENTER: the point on the earth's surface directly above an earthquake's focus

FOCUS: also known as the hypocenter, the focus is the actual place of rupture inside the earth's crust

P WAVE: the primary or fastest wave traveling away from a seismic event through the rock and consisting of a series of compressions and expansions of the earth material

PLATE BOUNDARY: a region where the earth's crustal plates meet, as a converging (subduction zone), diverging (mid-ocean ridge), transform fault, or collisional interaction

S WAVE: the secondary seismic wave, traveling more slowly than the P waves and consisting of elastic vibrations transverse to the direction of travel; S waves cannot propagate in a liquid medium

SEISMIC BELT: a region of relatively high seismicity, globally distributed; seismic belts mark regions of plate interactions

SEISMIC WAVE: an elastic wave in the earth usually generated by an earthquake source or explosion

SEISMICITY: the occurrence of earthquakes as a function of location and time

SEISMOGRAPH: an instrument used for recording the motions of the earth's surface, caused by seismic waves, as a function of time

SUBDUCTION ZONE: a dipping ocean plate descending into the earth away from an ocean trench

## Summary of the Phenomenon

Although seismic instruments can record them from virtually anywhere on the globe, earthquakes occur primarily along active tectonic regions of the earth's crust where mountain building, folding, and faulting are occurring. More temporal and often less severe earthquakes also accompany volcanic activity. Mapping earthquake epicenters, scientists are able to map the seismicity (earthquake activity as a function of time) of the planet.

Most earthquakes occur along three main belts: the Mid-Atlantic Ridge system; the Alpine Tethys belt, which extends from the Mediterranean Sea through Turkey and Armenia all the way into Asia, where it merges with the third main belt; and the infamous circum-Pacific "Ring of Fire." The least threatening of these is the mid-ocean ridge system such as that found in the Atlantic Ocean, along which new ocean crust is being created. As the sea floor spreads from the volcanic activity occurring at the spreading ridges, earthquakes occur along transform faults that bound the offset ridges. Although population centers are sparse along the mid-ocean ridges, Iceland, the Azores, and other small mid-Atlantic islands are regions of potential quake hazard. Owing to the steady rate of spreading (a few centimeters annually), earthquakes occurring along the ridge offsets tend to be frequent and of relatively low magnitude.

A far more dangerous region of earthquake activity is the Alpine Tethys belt, extending across southern Europe and Asia. A listing of only a few of the major earthquakes along this belt reads like a litany of human suffering and huge losses of property: Persia in 1505; Calabria in southern Italy in 1509, 1783, and 1832; Lisbon in 1755; the Neapolitan in Italy in 1857; numerous quakes in recent decades in Yugoslavia, Romania, Greece, and Turkey; and the tragic 1988 disaster in Soviet Armenia. Volcanic activity also occurs in the region, with notable examples including Mounts Etna and Vesuvius and the island of Thera.

The key to understanding earthquakes lies in the powerful theory of plate tectonics. The earth is far from a geologically "dead" world like its moon. Broken into several large slabs of crust, or lithospheric plates, convection currents caused by the planet's internal heat drive the plates into motion, like a bunch of small rafts crowded onto the surface of a boiling pot of viscous jelly. At the mid-ocean ridges, new sea floor is created by magmatic eruptions—pushing two plates away from each other. These divergent boundaries are characterized by the Mid-Atlantic Ridge, where the North American and European continents (riding on the lithospheric plates) are moving away from each other. Along the Alpine belt, two continents are literally crashing into each other as Africa is pushing into and subducting under the Eurasian plate. The subduction zone is marked by a complex series of transform and thrust faults, which give the region its high seismicity.

Earthquakes, then, are predominantly distributed along plate boundaries. Another converging boundary is found along the Hindu Kush and Himalayan mountain ranges, where the subcontinent of India is crashing into and thrusting under the huge Eurasian plate at the rate of some 5 centimeters per year. The collision has caused the throwing up of the world's highest mountains and is an earthquake-prone region.

Perhaps the most seismically active region of the world lies on the eastern end of the Mediterranean-Himalayan belt. Stretching across Tibet and into China, this colossal zone of high seismicity threatens all who live along its 4,000-kilometer length. More than a dozen earthquakes of Richter magnitude 8.0 or greater have caused well in excess of a million human lives to be lost in this notorious region. An estimated 830,000 casualties in the Shenshi region earthquake of 1556 makes that event what is believed the worst earthquake in historic times. The Kansu earthquake of 1920 led to 200,000 deaths and adds credibility to the claim.

The trans-Asian earthquake belt passes through Burma and Indonesia, ending in the southern Philippines. This transitional region marks the border of the greatest of the earth's seismic belts—the circum-Pacific, or "Ring of Fire." A region of complex plate interactions, the Pacific Rim is no stranger to earthquakes and volcanoes. Perhaps no region characterizes the circum-Pacific belt better than the islands of Japan. In geologic terms, the Japanese islands are an island arc, formed by a subduction zone off the coast of the present landmass. As the sea floor spreads from the ridge systems, it collides with the Asian continental plate. The dense, water-soaked sea floor is subducted at a deep ocean trench. As the oceanic plate descends, the slab grinds and shudders in resistance before finally being swallowed by the mantle. Accounting for 90 percent of the world's earthquakes, trench subduction zones have a seismic fingerprint of ever-deepening quakes that can be very severe shocks.

Sea-floor earthquakes can cause tsunamis (sometimes incorrectly called "tidal waves") along the coastline. A 7.7-magnitude shock hit the Oga Peninsula in 1983 and brought on a tsunami that caused extensive damage. The Fukui earthquake of 1948 and the Great Tokyo earthquake and fire (magnitude 8.2) of 1923, in which 143,000 perished, are stark testimonies to the danger of living near active plate subduction zones. In addition to the trench quakes, the volcanic islands are criss-crossed by numerous faults. Thousands of quakes have been recorded by Japanese historians, dating to well before the birth of Christ.

To the north and east along the circum-Pacific belt, the Aleutian Island arc reaches into the North American continent in Alaska. A complex system of faults and a subduction zone off the coast make Alaska a region of dangerous seismicity. In 1964, one of the most severe earthquakes ever recorded, at 8.6, struck near the port of Valdez and generated a terrifying series of tsunamis that wracked the coast. On Alaska's southern coast is the Fairweather fault, a transform fracture on which a 1958 temblor shook loose 90 million tons of rock, which cascaded into Lituya Bay, raising a wave exceeding 500 meters high. The Fairweather fault is a northern extension of a system of transform faults (so named because the fault is transformed into a ridge or trench at its ends) that includes the most famous of all—the San Andreas fault.

Extending from the Mendocino fracture zone 700 miles south to Mexico, the San Andreas and its attendant system of faults make California earthquake country. A unique type of plate boundary, the San Andreas represents a fracture line along which the oceanic Pacific plate is slowly but inexorably sliding north with respect to the North American continent at a rate of roughly 5 centimeters per year. In places where the fault is displacing smoothly, small tremors regularly shake the California landscape. Yet, in regions where the fault is believed locked, major quakes are impending, placing the large population centers of San Francisco and Los Angeles at risk. On October 17, 1989, one such strong earthquake shook the San Francisco Bay area, causing extensive damage and a number of deaths and injuries. In addition to the San Andreas, the Hayward fault in the north and a multitude of southern California faults further increase the state's seismicity. The Whittier, San Fernando, and Inglewood-Newport faults are among those that threaten Los Angeles.

As seismically active as California is, its seismicity pales by comparison with Latin America. Mexico City's tragic quake of 1985 was a grim reminder of the subduction zone off the coast of western Mexico. Central America is in a particularly precarious position, lying sandwiched between the Cocos, North American, South American, and Caribbean plates, and is thus a zone of active volcanoes and numerous severe deep-trench earthquakes. El Salvador, Guatemala, and Nicaragua are among the nations in greatest earthquake danger. As the Nazca plate bumps into South America's plate, the oceanic plate is subducted and the melting slab has caused the volcanism and massive uplifting of the towering Andes. While the eastern part of South America is seismically quiet, the west coastal regions are known for severe quakes, especially in Peru and Chile.

The circum-Pacific belt continues along the South Pacific through New Zealand. Analogous to the San Andreas, the majestic scenery of New Zealand is regularly shaken by tremors occurring along the Alpine fault. Continuing up through Indonesia, the ring of earthquake and volcanic activity completes its loop.

Other earthquake regions of note include the American Northwest's Cascade volcanic chain, where a series of tremors can indicate pending eruptions. The 1980 explosive eruption of Mount St. Helens in Washington was caused by an earthquake that triggered a landslide, initiating the lateral blast, or nuée ardente.

In California, the San Andreas is not the only region of earthquake activity. An area with an explosive volcanic past in recent geologic times, the Mammoth-Mono Lake region was hit by four magnitude 6.0 temblors in 1980, occurring along the northern perimeter of the Long Valley caldera. South of the possible site of future volcanic and certain seismic events, the Sierra Nevada mountain range is still undergoing periodic spasms of uplift, like the one that caused the Owens Valley quake of 1852.

In the Caribbean, earthquakes and volcanic activity are an ever-present threat along the borders of the Caribbean plate. This seismic belt is actually an extension of the Pacific belt, although it lies on the Atlantic side of the Americas. Examples of major shocks and activity include Port Royale, which plunged 50 feet underwater following a major earthquake in 1692, and Mount Pelée, which destroyed the town of Martinique with a nuée ardente in 1902. Regions of hot spot volcanism are also zones of especially high seismicity. The Hawaiian Islands lie on top of a mantle plume of magma, and the same forces that built the island chain are working on the main island of Hawaii today. A similar region lies beneath the North American continent, the site of Yellowstone National Park in Wyoming, Montana, and Idaho. Both Hawaii and Yellowstone are earthquake-prone regions.

For the most part, continental interiors, especially the Precambrian metamorphic basement and its thin veneer of sedimentary rocks that make up the craton, are regions of low seismicity. Such regions include parts of the United States and Canada in the Great Lakes region, virtually all of South America except for the Pacific coast and Andes belt, and most of Africa. While continental interiors are seismically quiet compared with the active plate margins, there are exceptional regions. Although most United States quakes take place west of the Rockies, the Mississippi Valley has been the site of some of the most severe earthquakes ever, the New Madrid quakes of 1811-1812. New England and South Carolina have also experienced powerful shocks in the past. The western two-thirds of Africa is seismically inactive, but the East African rift valley is a zone of earthquake and volcanic activity where a geologically new plate boundary is rifting the eastern edge of the continent apart. Curiously, the only continent on earth that is seismically quiet is Antarctica.

## Methods of Study

In a sense, the study of where earthquakes occur traces back to the very roots of western and eastern culture roughly four thousand years ago in Mesopotamia and in Asia. The Old Testament and more ancient Middle Eastern documents are filled with accounts of earthquakes toppling cities. The most complete records of seismic activity are, appropriately enough, those of Japan and China. Chinese earthquake records date back thirty centuries, with exhaustive accounts of tragic earthquakes striking the Asian mainland. Japan, which experiences up to one thousand noticeable shocks per year, has been keeping detailed earthquake records on Tokyo's tremors since A.D. 818.

Modern scientific views on earthquake distribution perhaps began in response to the tragic All Saints Day earthquake and tsunamis that wrecked Lisbon in 1755. While a horrified western civilization reeled at the scope of the disaster, which killed many at Lisbon's numerous downtown churches, one of the more insightful minds of the scientific revolution looked at the tragedy more objectively. Immanuel Kant advised that learning about where and why earthquakes occur was a more reasoned approach than blaming the disaster on divine causes.

Some one hundred years after Lisbon's fateful quake, Irishman Robert Mallet published a study of the Neapolitan earthquake of 1857 in which he produced a seismographic map of the world that (except for the mid-ocean ridge systems) is accurate today. Teaching in seismically active Japan, British geology professor John Milne invented the modern seismograph. By the time of the 1906 quake in San Francisco, global seismic observatories were in place and recorded the jolts. Since the distance to an epicenter (the surface site above the actual fracture or focus of the quake) could be determined, a set of three properly placed seismographs, Milne reasoned, could pinpoint the epicenter anywhere on the globe.

Seismic waves generated by an earthquake produce different types of waves. The primary wave, or P wave, is compressional, while the secondary, or shear, waves

(S waves) cause the shaking motions that occur during the most destructive part of the quake. By measuring the ratio of the arrival time of the primary and secondary waves and the size or amplitude of the waves on the seismograph recording, Charles Richter, in 1935, was able to establish a scale for measuring the energy released in a quake, its magnitude. Richter and his colleague at the California Institute of Technology Beno Gutenberg published some of the best maps of worldwide earthquake distribution in 1954.

In the 1950's and 1960's, the United States helped to organize enough of the world's seismic observatories to establish a global monitoring network called the World Wide Standardized Seismograph Network. Data from decades of shocks recorded by the network and oceanographic research vessels led to the revolutionary theory of plate tectonics and its acceptance by the vast majority of earth scientists.

Studying earthquake distribution at the mid-oceanic ridge system and its attendant series of fractures, J. Tuzo Wilson explained the activity in terms of transform faults and helped to confirm the theory of sea-floor spreading. The diverging plate boundary has its antithesis in the converging boundary of the subduction zones. American seismologist Hugo Benioff studied these regions of ever-deepening earthquake foci, and his analysis led to the confirmation of the subduction of oceanic crust at the deep-sea trenches found along the Pacific Rim, named Benioff zones.

Although plate tectonics theory and, specifically, plate boundaries are invoked to explain the vast majority of earthquakes, scientists are still puzzled by earthquakes far from active margins. Examples are the Mississippi Valley region and Charleston, South Carolina, which shook violently in 1886. In these regions, seismologists (well aware of the seismicity of the regions) are alarmed by public perception that the land east of the Rockies is "solid bedrock." The most plausible cause of the Mississippi Valley quake activity is the enormous weight of sediments the great river system has deposited on a weak part of the continental crust. South Carolina is a region riddled with faults, yet it is far from an active plate margin. Seismologists use historical accounts and recent seismic records to predict regions of earthquake hazard. One theory of seismic hazard involves identifying regions where earthquakes have not occurred along active fault regions. Such seismically quiet regions are called "seismic gaps" and represent regions of accumulated strain along which a major rupture may be anticipated.

Using seismicity data, seismologists produce maps that indicate seismic hazard. Not only useful for scientific purposes, such maps help public agencies to create building codes and other earthquake prevention methods appropriate to the earthquake hazard of the region. Studies conducted by the United States Geologic Survey and the National Oceanic and Atmospheric Administration have concluded that the areas of San Francisco and Los Angeles, California; Salt Lake City and Ogden, Utah; Puget Sound, Washington; Hawaii; St. Louis-Memphis, Tennessee; Anchorage and Fairbanks, Alaska; Boston, Massachusetts; Buffalo, New York; and Charleston, South Carolina, are at greatest seismic risk in the United States. Recently, the worldwide network of seismic stations was upgraded with new instruments that record directly onto digital tapes, which enable computers to analyze the seismic waves more swiftly, thus improving observation of the planet's moving plates.

## Context

Approximately once every 30 seconds, a million times a year, the earth's crust shivers. Most of these tremors are only perceptible by sensitive instruments, but more than three thousand are strong enough to be felt by those nearby. Roughly twenty quakes a year are strong enough to do catastrophic damage to populated areas. By tragic coincidence, some of the earth's most active seismic regions are also among its most densely populated. The lands bordering the Mediterranean Sea and Pacific Rim, the mountainous Middle East, India, China, and Japan are all familiar with the havoc of a major shock. In China alone, the death toll exceeds 13 million lives down through the ages. Earthquakes and related phenomena claim up to fifteen thousand lives annually in these regions of dangerous seismicity.

Once regarded in superstitious terror and awe, earthquakes have become a well-understood and accepted, though no less frightening, phenomenon. The study of earthquake distribution has helped to map and explain the earth's lithospheric plates and their interactions, while plate tectonics theory offers a nearly complete explanation of why earthquakes occur where they do.

Knowledge of earthquake distribution is far from an esoteric pursuit. Millions have been killed by seismic activity, with staggering loss of property through the half-tick of geologic time comprising human history. Seismologists still lack the capability of precise prediction of activity, but areas of high seismicity and the ominous seismic gaps warn of quake hazard. In cities such as Tokyo, Los Angeles, San Francisco, and Anchorage, citizens must be prepared for the next big quake, which is as sure to come as the slow but steady movement of the earth's crustal plates.

## Bibliography

Bolt, Bruce A. *Earthquakes: Revised and Updated*. 2d ed. New York: W. H. Freeman, 1987. A revision of the University of California, Berkeley, seismologist's classic, *Earthquakes: A Primer*. Chapter 1 deals with earthquake distribution, and also of special interest are the appendices on world earthquakes and seismicity rates and lists of important earthquakes in the Western Hemisphere. Suitable for the lay reader.

Condie, Kent C., ed. *Plate Tectonics and Crustal Evolution*. 2d ed. Elmsford, N.Y.: Pergamon Press, 1982. An excellent overview of modern plate tectonics theory that synthesizes data from geology, geochemistry, geophysics, and oceanography. Extensive coverage of plate boundary interactions and earthquake distribution. An excellent "Tectonic Map of the World" is enclosed. Nontechnical and suitable for a college-level reader. A useful "Suggestions for Further Reading" is provided at the end of the chapters.

Eiby, G. A. *Earthquakes*. New York: Van Nostrand Reinhold, 1980. Written by an experienced seismologist, this text is filled with charts, maps, and photographs that help demystify the science of seismology. Two chapters address seismic geography of the world. Especially useful for readers interested in the seismicity of New Zealand. A lucid account, suitable for a college-level reader.

Halacy, D. S. *Earthquakes: A Natural History*. Indianapolis: Bobbs-Merrill, 1974. Excellent treatments of historical earthquakes and an extensive discussion of world seismicity patterns. Written for a lay audience, the book is a lively discussion of all aspects of seismology and earthquakes, along with volcanoes and tsunamis.

Lambert, David. *The Field Guide to Geology*. New York: Facts on File, 1988. An excellent reference for the beginning student of geology, it is filled with marvelous diagrams that make the concepts easy to understand. Several sections address earthquake distribution and related topics. Suitable for any level of reader from high school to adult.

Shepard, Francis P. *Geological Oceanography*. New York: Crane, Russak, 1977. Chapter 2 addresses sea-floor spreading and faulting of the oceanic crust, along with trenches and associated earthquake activity. Supplementary reading lists at the end of the chapter, photographs, and diagrams augment the text, which is suitable for a general audience.

Sullivan, Walter. *Continents in Motion*. New York: McGraw-Hill, 1974. Dedicated to Harry Hess and Maurice Ewing, two late pioneers of plate tectonics theory, this book is the classic popular work on moving crustal plates. Lucid explanations of seismic evidence for plate motions and historical vignettes on seismology and earthquakes. A highly readable book.

Verney, Peter. *The Earthquake Handbook*. New York: Paddington Press, 1979. Superb historical accounts of humanity's struggle to understand earthquakes with easy-to-follow discussions of seismology and important sections on earthquake safety and preparedness. Extensive discussion on the causes and distribution of seismic events.

Walker, Bryce. *Earthquake*. Alexandria, Va.: Time-Life Books, 1982. A volume in the Planet Earth series, this book is filled with color photographs and diagrams, with an essay entitled, "Grand Design of a Planet in Flux," addressing plate tectonics' role in earthquake distribution. Contains an index and bibliography and is suitable for all readership levels.

Wilson, J. Tuzo. *Introduction to Continents Adrift and Continents Aground*. San Francisco: W. H. Freeman, 1976. Selected readings from *Scientific American* magazine that are introduced with commentary by Wilson, a leading figure in the history of plate tectonics. Includes discussion of trench earthquakes, transform faults, and collisional boundaries. A classic post-San Fernando earthquake (1971) article by Don L. Anderson on the San Andreas fault will interest students of California's seismicity. Suitable for a general audience.

*David M. Schlom*

## Cross-References

Continental Rift Zones, 275; Earthquake Engineering, 430; Earthquake Hazards, 437; Earthquake Locating, 445; Earthquake Magnitudes and Intensities, 452; Earthquake Prediction, 461; Earthquakes: Elastic Waves, 469; Famous Earthquakes, 476; An Overview of Earthquakes, 484; Plate Tectonics, 2079; The San Andreas Fault, 2243; Seismometers, 2340.

# EARTHQUAKE ENGINEERING

*Type of earth science:* Engineering geology

*Earthquake damage and injury are aggravated by the fact that neither the time nor the location of major tremors can be precisely predicted. Damage to man-made structures may be lessened, however, through the use of proper construction techniques. Earthquake engineering studies the effects of ground movement on buildings, bridges, underground pipes, and dams and determines ways to build future structures or reinforce existing ones so that they can withstand tremors.*

### Principal terms

EPICENTER: the central aboveground location of an earth tremor; that is, the point of the surface directly above the hypocenter

FAILURE: in engineering terms, the fracturing or giving way of an object under stress

FAULT: a fracture or fracture zone in rock, along which the two sides have been displaced vertically or horizontally relative to each other

HYPOCENTER: the central underground location of an earth tremor; also called the focus

NATURAL FREQUENCY: the frequency at which an object or substance will vibrate when struck or shaken

NATURAL PERIOD: the length of time of a single vibration of an object or substance when vibrating at its natural frequency

SHEAR: a stress that forces two contiguous parts of an object in a direction parallel to their plane of contact, as opposed to a stretching, compressing, or twisting force; also called shear stress

UNREINFORCED MASONRY (URM): materials not constructed with reinforced steel (for example, bricks, hollow clay tile, adobe, concrete blocks, and stone)

## Summary of the Methodology

Earthquake engineering attempts to minimize the effects of earthquakes on large structures. Engineers study earthquake motion and its effects on structures, concentrating on the materials and construction techniques used, and recommend design concepts and methods that best permit the structures to withstand the forces.

One might logically expect that the structures nearest an earthquake fault would suffer the most damage from the earthquake. Actually, structural damage seems to bear little direct relation to the faults or to their distance from the structure. It is true that buildings near the fault are subject to rapid horizontal or vertical motion and that if the fault runs immediately beneath a structure (which is more likely in the case of a road or pipe than a building) and displaces more than a few inches, the structure could easily fail. The degree of damage, however, has more to do with the nature of the local soil between the bedrock and the surface. If the soil is noncohesive, such as sand, vibrations may cause it to compact and settle over a wide area. Compaction of the soil raises the pressure of underground water, which then flows upward and saturates the ground. This "liquefaction" of the soil causes it to flow like a fluid so that sand may become quicksand. Surface structures, and even upper layers of soil, may settle unevenly or drop suddenly. Sinkholes and landslides are possible effects.

Ground vibration and most ground motion are caused by seismic waves. These waves are created at the earthquake's focus, where tectonic plates suddenly move along an underground fault. The waves radiate upward to the surface, causing the ground to vibrate. Wave vibrations are measured in terms of frequency—the number of waves that pass a given point per second.

Much earthquake damage depends on what is known as natural frequency. When any object is struck or vibrated by waves, it vibrates at its own frequency, regardless of the frequency of the incoming waves. All solid objects, including buildings, dams, and even the soil and bedrock of an area, have different natural frequencies. If the waves affecting the object happen to be vibrating at the object's frequency, the object's vibrations intensify dramatically—sometimes enough to shake the object apart. For this reason, an earthquake does the most damage when the predominant frequency of the ground corresponds to the natural frequency of the structures.

At one time it was thought that earthquake motion would be greater in soft ground and less in hard ground, but the truth is not that simple. Nineteenth century seismographers discovered that the natural frequency of local ground depends on the ground's particular characteristics and may vary widely from one location to another. The predominant frequency of softer ground is comparatively short, and the maximum velocity and displacement of the ground are greater. In harder ground, the predominant frequency is longer, but the acceleration of the ground is greater. When the ground is of multiple layers of different compositions, the predominant frequency is quite complex.

In order to determine the effect of vibrations on a building, an engineer must do the obvious: shake it. Whereas the effects on a very simple structure such as a pipe or a four-walled shack may be computed theoretically, real-life structures are composed of widely diverse materials. By inducing vibrations in a structure and measuring them with a seismograph, one can easily determine properties such as its natural frequency and its damping (the rate at which vibrations cease when the external force is removed).

The simplest type of test is the free vibration, and the oldest of these is the pull-back test. A cable is attached to the top of the test structure at one end and to the ground or the bottom of an adjacent structure at the other. The cable is pulled taut and suddenly released, causing the structure to vibrate freely. Other tests cause vibrations by striking the structure with falling weights or large pendulums or even by launching small rockets from the structure's top.

Forced-vibration tests subject test structures to an ongoing vibration, thereby giving more complete and accurate measurements of natural frequencies. In the steady-state sinusoidal excitation test, a motor-driven rotating weight is attached to the structure, subjecting it to a constant, unidirectional force of a fixed frequency. The building's movements are recorded, and the motor's speed is then changed to a new frequency. Measurements are taken for a wide range of different frequencies and forces. Surprisingly, the natural frequencies for large multistory buildings are so low that a 150-pound person rocking back and forth will generate measurable inertia in the structure, thereby providing an adequate substitute for relatively complex equipment.

Another useful device is the vibration table: a spring-mounted platform several meters long on each side. Although designed to hold and test model structures, some tables are large enough to hold full-scale structural components—or even small structures themselves. Useful forced vibrations are also provided by underground explosions, high winds, the microtremors that are always present in the ground, and even large earthquakes themselves.

## Applications of the Method

Structures can be designed to withstand some of the stresses put upon them by large ground vibrations. They must be able to resist bending, twisting, compression, tension, and shock. Two approaches are used in earthquake-resistant design. The first is to run dynamic tests to analyze the effects of given ground motions on test structures, determine the stresses on structural elements, and proportion the members and their connections to restrain these loads. This approach may be difficult if no record exists of a strong earthquake on the desired type of ground or if the research is done on simplified, idealized structures. The other approach is to base the designs on the performance of past structures. Unfortunately, new buildings are often built with modern materials and techniques for which no corollary exists in older ones. It follows that earthquake-resistant design is easier to do for simple structures such as roads, shell structures, and one-story buildings than for complex skyscrapers and suspension bridges.

The first concern in examining a structure is its basic configuration. Buildings with an irregular floor plan, such as an "L" or "I" shape, are more likely to twist and warp than are simple rectangles and squares. Warping also tends to occur when doors and windows are nonuniform in size and arrangement. Walls can fail as a result of shear stress, out-of-plane bending, or both. They may also collapse because of the failure of the connections between the walls and the ceiling or floor. In the case of bearing walls, which support the structure, failure may in turn allow the collapse of the roof and upper floors. Nonstructural walls and partitions can be damaged by drift, which occurs when a building's roof or the floor of a given story slides farther in one direction than the floor below it does. This relative displacement between consecutive stories can also damage plastering, veneer, and windowpanes.

Lateral (sideways) crossbracing reduces drift, as do the walls that run parallel to the drift. Another way to avoid drift damage is to let the nonstructural walls "float." In this method, walls are attached only to the floor so that when the building moves laterally, the wall moves with the floor and slides freely against the ceiling. (Alternatively, floating walls may be affixed only to the ceiling.) Windows may be held in frames by nonrigid materials that allow the frames to move and twist without breaking the panes. The stiffness and durability of a wall can be improved by reinforcement. For reinforcement, steel or wooden beams are usually embedded in the wall, but other materials are used as well. If the exterior walls form a rectangular enclosure, they may be prevented from separating at the top corners by a continuous collar, or ring beam.

Frame buildings are those in which the structure is supported by internal beams and columns. These elements provide resistance against lateral forces. Frames can still fail if the columns are forced to bend too far or if the rigid joints fail. Unlike bearing walls, frame-building walls are generally nonstructural; the strength of the frame, however, can be greatly enhanced if the walls are attached to, or built integrally into, the frame. This method is called "infilled-frame" construction. Roofs and upper floors can fail when their supports fail, as mentioned above, or when they are subjected to lateral stress. An effective way to avoid such failure is to reduce the weight of the roof, building it with light materials.

Another danger to walls is an earthquake-induced motion known as pounding, or hammering, which can occur when two adjacent walls vibrate against each other, damaging their common corners. The collision of two walls because of lateral movement or the toppling of either is also called pounding. Columns and other structural elements may also pound each other if they are close enough; in fact, the elements pounding each other may even be on adjacent buildings. If the natural vibrations of the two structures are similar enough, the structures may be tied together and thus forced to vibrate identically so that pounding is prevented. Because such closeness in vibration is rare, the best way to avoid pounding is simply to build the structures too far apart for it to occur.

Shell structures are those with only one or two exterior surfaces, such as hemispheres, flat-roofed cylinders, and dome-topped cylinders. Such shapes are very efficient, for curved walls and roofs possess inherent strength. For this reason, they are sometimes used in low-cost buildings, without reinforced walls. When failure does occur, it is at doors and other openings or near the wall's attachment to the ground or roof, where stress is the greatest.

Much earthquake damage could be prevented if the stresses on a structure as a whole could be reduced. One of the more practical methods of stress reduction uses very rigid, hollow columns in the basement to support the ground floor. Inside these columns are flexible columns that hold the rest of the building. This engineering technique succeeds in reducing stress, but the flexible columns increase the motion of the upper stories. More exotic methods to reduce stress involve separating the foundation columns from the ground by placing them on rollers or rubber pads. Structures with several of these lines of defense are much less likely to collapse;

should a vital section of crossbracing, bearing wall, or partition fail, the building can still withstand an aftershock. Overall, the earthquake resistance of a structure depends on the type of construction, geometry, mass distribution, and stiffness properties. Furthermore, any building can be weakened by improper maintenance or modification.

Buildings using unreinforced masonry (URM) or having URM veneers have a poor history in past earthquakes. Because URM walls are neither reinforced nor structurally tied to the roof and floors, they move excessively during an earthquake and often collapse. Similarly, ground floors with open fronts and little crosswise bracing move and twist excessively, damaging the building. URM chimneys may fall to the ground or through the roof.

Buildings with URM-bearing walls are now forbidden by California building codes, but URM is still common in many less developed areas of the world. There are several low-cost earthquake-resistant alternatives to such construction. Adobe walls may be reinforced with locally available bamboo, asphalt, wire mesh, or split cane. Low-cost buildings should be only one or two stories tall and should have a uniform arrangement of walls, partitions, and openings to obtain a uniform stress distribution. The floor plan should be square or rectangular or, alternatively, have a shell shape such as a dome or cylinder. Roofs and upper floors should be made of lightweight materials—wood, cane, or even plastic, rather than mud or tile— whenever possible, and heavy structural elements should never be attached to non-structural walls.

The Center for Planning and Development Research at the University of California at Berkeley noted certain features of modern wood-frame houses that make them especially susceptible to damage from strong ground motion. In addition to URM walls or foundations, such houses may have insufficient bracing of crawl spaces, unanchored water or gas heaters, and a lack of positive connections between the wooden frame and the underlying foundations. Porches, decks, and other protruding features may be poorly braced. Most of these deficiencies can be corrected.

## Context

The earthquake is arguably the most destructive natural disaster on the planet. No other force has the potential to devastate so large an area in a very short time. Not only can it not be predicted, but there is also even less advance warning for the earthquake than for other types of disaster. A hurricane can be seen coming by radar; a volcano may belch smoke before it erupts. An earthquake simply happens.

Yet the magnitude of the earthquake is not solely responsible for the destruction. Property damage and injury to humans also depend on the type and quality of construction, soil conditions, the nature of the ground motion, and distance from the epicenter. The tremor which struck Anchorage, Alaska, in 1964 measured 8.3 on the Richter scale and killed eleven people; on the other hand, one that hit San Fernando, California, in 1971 measured only 6.6—less than a tenth of the force of the Anchorage quake—and fifty-nine people died. Most of the San Fernando deaths occurred in one building: a hospital that collapsed. It seems likely that the hospital had not been adequately constructed to withstand the stresses to which it was suddenly subjected. The higher damage toll resulted from the soil characteristics in San Fernando and an underground fault that had previously been unmapped.

The only protection earthquake-zone residents have against property damage is that given by the engineers who design and build their buildings, railway structures, dams, harbor facilities, and (especially) nuclear power plants and by the public officials who regulate them. Now that engineers can learn how ground movement affects engineering structures and can design new ones accordingly, many of the earthquake-prone regions have building codes for resistant construction. Laws and programs exist to determine which buildings are unsafe and how they may be made resistant. Unfortunately, not all quake regions have such rules and programs in place, because of apathy, high cost, or other reasons. The high costs of recovery after major quakes, however, certainly provide a compelling rationale for better preparation.

## Bibliography

Center for Planning and Development Research. *An Earthquake Advisor's Handbook for Wood Frame Houses*. Berkeley: University of California, 1982. This slim book was a result of the Earthquake Advisory Service Project at the Center for Planning and Development Research at the University of California, Berkeley. The book is addressed both to the homeowner and to public policy personnel who want to plan an earthquake advisory project. Includes a long, diagrammed how-to section on repairs. Suitable for all readers.

Kanai, Kiyoshi. *Engineering Seismology*. Tokyo: University of Tokyo Press, 1983. This book begins with a discussion of the seismograph and proceeds logically through seismic waves, ground vibrations, and their effects on structures. Concise, but the calculus is difficult in spots. Suitable for college-level students.

Newmark, Nathan M., and Emilio Rosenblueth. *Fundamentals of Earthquake Engineering*. Englewood Cliffs, N.J.: Prentice-Hall, 1971. A highly technical, mostly theoretical graduate textbook and reference manual. Addresses basic dynamics, earthquake behavior, and recommended design concepts. Text is occasionally unclear, even where the language is not especially technical. Some diagrams are given inadequate explanation.

Okamoto, Shunzo. *Introduction to Earthquake Engineering*. New York: Halsted Press, 1973. This textbook has chapters on earthquakes, earthquake-resistant design procedures, and earthquake resistance of roads, tunnels, railways, bridges, and various types of dams. The chapters on seismicity and on historical earthquakes are based on data from Japan, one of the world's most active seismic zones. Written for engineers and college-level students, but the many nontechnical passages are not too difficult to follow.

Reps, William F., and Emil Simiu. *Design, Siting, and Construction of Low-Cost Housing and Community Buildings to Better Withstand Earthquakes and Wind-*

*storms*. Washington, D.C.: U.S. Department of Commerce/National Bureau of Standards, 1974. A report prepared for the U.S. Agency for International Development on the construction of small buildings in earthquake- and windstorm-prone areas of the world. Explains concisely and accessibly the forces put on small buildings, the effects they have, and construction techniques to prevent them. It would be a good primer on earthquake engineering in general were it not for its necessary focus on small, low-cost buildings and ways to build them using inexpensive and locally available materials. Written to a general audience.

Tierney, Kathleen J. *Report of the Coalinga Earthquake of May 2, 1983*. Sacramento, Calif.: Seismic Safety Commission, 1985. This manual focuses on the Coalinga earthquake to show how an earthquake can affect a community physically, financially, and socially and how local and state governments can deal with the after-effects. For all readers.

Wiegel, Robert L., ed. *Earthquake Engineering*. Englewood Cliffs, N.J.: Prentice-Hall, 1969. A large and comprehensive volume on the subject. Based originally on lectures given in a University of California course on engineering. Includes data on earthquake causes, ground motion and effects, mathematical modeling and theory, tests and effects on structures, and design of earthquake-resistant structures. Aimed at students and professionals.

*Shawn V. Wilson*

### Cross-References

Dams and Flood Control, 309; Earthquake Distribution, 421; Earthquake Hazards, 437; Earthquake Locating, 445; Earthquake Magnitudes and Intensities, 452; Earthquake Prediction, 461; Earthquakes: Elastic Waves, 469; Surface Mining Techniques, 1703; Underground Mining Techniques, 1710; Mining Wastes and Reclamation, 1718.

# EARTHQUAKE HAZARDS

*Field of study:* Urban geology and geologic hazards

*Over the past four thousand years, about 13 million persons have died as a result of earthquake activity, and an unknown amount of property damage has occurred as well.*

### Principal terms

CREEP: the very slow downhill movement of soil and rock

EPICENTER: the point on the surface of the earth directly above the focus

FAULT: a fracture or zone of breakage in a rock mass which shows movement or displacement

FOCUS: the point below the surface of the ground where the earthquake originates and its energy is released

INTENSITY: an arbitrary measure of an earthquake's effect on people and buildings, based on the modified Mercalli scale

LANDSLIDE: the rapid downhill movement of soil and rock

LIQUEFACTION: the loss in cohesiveness of water-saturated soil as a result of ground shaking caused by an earthquake

MAGNITUDE: a measure of the amount of energy released by an earthquake, based on the Richter scale

SUBSIDENCE: the sinking of the surface of the land

TSUNAMI: a seismic sea wave created by an undersea earthquake, a violent volcanic eruption, or a landslide at sea

## Summary of the Phenomenon

Earthquakes are the result of the rapid motion and vibrations caused by movement of the ground along a fracture in a rock or along a fault. Movement occurs when rocks are unable to store any more stress, at which time they reach their breaking point, release energy, and create an earthquake. The point of origin of an earthquake below the surface where its energy is released is known as the focus. The focus can be located at either a shallow or a deep depth. The point on the surface of the earth directly above the focus is called the epicenter; it is the spot frequently cited by the news media as the location of the earthquake. Throughout the earth's surface, numerous faults and fault systems exist, but the larger faults are usually confined to specific areas. Earthquakes and faults are not hazardous in themselves, but they can become hazardous when they directly endanger humans and their immediate environment. Each year, the earth is subjected to at least 1 million earthquakes. Only a few, however, are strong enough to cause major structural damage to cities and to kill or injure thousands of persons. The major hazards directly created by an earthquake are ground shaking, ground rupture, and tsunamis. The major indirect hazards are fires, floods, building collapse, disruption of public services, and psychological effects.

Ground shaking occurs as energy released by the earthquake reaches the surface and causes the materials through which it passes to vibrate. The intensity of these vibrations and of the shaking at the surface depends on several factors: the amount of energy released, the depth of the focus, and the type of material through which the energy is moving. The closer the focus is to the surface, the more powerful the earthquake. Also, the denser the material, the more the vibrations will be felt and the stronger will be the resulting ground motion. There are a few documented cases in which very strong ground motion actually caused parked cars to bounce along the road, the surface of the land to move in rippling waves, and trees to become uprooted and snap. Yet, damage to open, uninhabited land is usually minimal. The amount of damage to buildings subjected to strong ground motion is controlled by many complex and interacting factors: the buildings' method of construction, the types of building material used, the depth of the bedrock, the distance from the epicenter, and the duration and intensity of the shaking. Buildings constructed on thin, firm soil and solid bedrock will fare much better than those on thick, soft soil and deep bedrock; however, if the shaking's duration is great, even the most well-constructed building will be destroyed. Such a situation was observed in the earthquake that struck Mexico City in 1985, in which more than one thousand buildings were destroyed and ten thousand persons were killed. This city was built on ancient lake-bed deposits of sand and silt that rapidly lost rigidity as a result of intense shaking, causing tall buildings to collapse vertically, one floor on top of the other. Four other very important elements determine the amount of destruction: the degree of compaction of the soil or bedrock on which the buildings' foundations are resting, the amount of water saturation of this material, its overall chemical composition, and the buildings' physical structure. If construction took place on or within solid bedrock, then the structures would move as a unit and would suffer much less damage. Some buildings may be able to withstand severe shaking for a few seconds, although prolonged shaking will completely destroy them. Ground shaking in the 1964 Alaskan earthquake lasted for about four minutes, causing major damage to the sturdiest of buildings. On the other hand, a particular building may easily withstand the effects of shaking but be destroyed by other factors. In Soviet Armenia during December of 1988, about twenty-five thousand persons were killed because of the effects of multiple aftershocks that shook apart poorly designed structures and buildings that were designed to withstand a lesser degree of ground motion. Moreover, very strong ground motion can knock a building completely off its bedrock foundation, rendering it unusable, or a building may fall prey to other types of ground failure triggered by an earthquake.

Ground failure includes landslides, avalanches, fault scarps, fissuring, subsidence, uplift, creep, sand boils, and liquefaction. Areas such as mountain valleys and regions surrounding an ocean bay can be subjected to these kinds of failure, since they usually consist of recently deposited, fine-grained materials that have not yet been completely compacted or that show variable degrees of groundwater saturation.

Landslides occur when unstable soil and rock move rapidly downslope under the influence of gravity; they usually are started by an earthquake. They commonly occur on steep slopes but can also move down gentle inclines. An avalanche is similar to a landslide but consists of snow and ice mixed with rock and soil. In either case, these masses move with great rapidity and force, sometimes filling, burying, or excavating the land along their path. Some earthquake-induced avalanches have been clocked at velocities of more than 320 kilometers per hour. The Tadzhik Soviet Socialist Republic, in late January of 1988, was hit with an earthquake of a 5.4 magnitude on the Richter scale that shook the ground for almost forty seconds, unleashing a massive landslide that was 8 kilometers wide. It buried the nearby village of Okuli-Bolo with mud to a depth of 15 meters, killing between six hundred and one thousand persons.

Fault scarps are created when a fault intersects the surface of the earth and large chunks of the ground are uplifted or dropped. Within these chunks, deep ground cracks known as fissures appear. Film portrayals of earthquakes notwithstanding, there is no chance that the earth will open, close, and "swallow" anything during an earthquake. Deep ground cracks commonly remain open, since the forces that created them operate only in one direction. Sometimes, however, animals fall into these cracks and appear to have been swallowed. In many places, buildings, roads, and other structures are constructed across an old fault scarp, and they undergo extensive structural damage from vertical or horizontal ground displacement. The largest measured vertical displacement along a fault scarp is 15 meters; the largest horizontal displacement that occurred at one time is 6 meters. The rate of displacement is variable, however, and some faults can show a slow but accumulated horizontal displacement of several kilometers.

The subsidence or depression of the surface of the land may occur when underground fluids such as oil or water are removed or drained by a nearby fault; the land sinks, creating water-filled sag ponds. This process occurs over a long period but does not result in any loss of life. Another slow form of ground failure is earthquake creep, which occurs more or less continuously along a fault. Creep is really an earthquake in slow motion; stored energy is gradually released in the form of very small earthquakes, or microearthquakes, causing the land to move in opposite horizontal directions. It results in the slow bending and breaking of underground pipes and railroad tracks and causes concrete building foundations to crack. The Hayward fault near San Francisco Bay, California, is a prime example.

Under the worst conditions—a low degree of compaction, thick and fine-grained sandy or silty soil, a high degree of water saturation, and intense ground shaking— solid land loses its cohesiveness and strength. It then begins to liquefy and flow by a process known as liquefaction. Tall buildings slowly move as if they were built on shifting sand. An unusual, localized ground failure event related to liquefaction is a sand boil. Rapid ground motion can cause a pressurized mixture of sand and concentrated groundwater to make its way toward the surface and create a small volcano-like mound of sand that spouts sandy water.

A spectacular and extremely hazardous coastal event is the seismic sea wave, or tsunami (sometimes incorrectly called a "tidal wave"). Tsunamis are usually produced by undersea earthquakes; the sea floor undergoes rapid vertical motion along one or more active faults, and energy is transmitted directly from solid rock into the seawater. They can also originate with massive undersea landslides or the violent eruption of an oceanic volcano. The catastrophic eruption of the volcanic island of Krakatoa in 1883 created a series of waves more than 40 meters high that drowned an estimated thirty-six thousand persons who lived along the low-lying coastal areas of Java and Sumatra. The exact cause of all these large waves is not completely understood by geologists and oceanographers. Regardless of their cause, the waves begin to radiate away from their point of origin in a manner similar to when a stone is tossed into a quiet body of water. Generally, tsunamis have a wavelength, or distance between successive wave crests, of greater than 161 kilometers and move at a velocity of more than 966 kilometers per hour; however, these large and fast-moving walls of water are not observable as such in the deep ocean, becoming visible only as they enter shallow water. Here the trough of the wave encounters the sea floor and begins to slow down, allowing the crest to build in size. At this point, water is rapidly sucked out of inland bays and harbors to feed the increasing mass, as it comes roaring into the mainland, drowning people and smashing buildings—in some cases as far inland as 3 kilometers. For example, after tossing trains and fishing boats almost 1 kilometer inland, the seismic sea waves produced from the 1964 Alaskan earthquake traveled south many thousands of kilometers as far as Crescent City, California, where local surfers decided to challenge the now 6-meter-high waves. The east coast of Japan, the Hawaiian Islands, the west coast of the United States, Alaska, Chile, Peru, and most other Pacific coastal regions have suffered damage from these powerful waves. They are rare in the Atlantic Ocean; the last major Atlantic tsunami occurred in 1755, when an offshore earthquake generated a series of waves that hit the coast of Portugal, killing an estimated fourteen thousand persons.

Not as spectacular, but similar to tsunamis, are seiches. Although they also have several origins, they can be produced by an earthquake. Seiches are small, oscillating waves that may travel for several hours, back and fourth within the enclosed basin of a lake or reservoir, sometimes causing flooding and minor structural damage to nearby buildings.

One of the most deadly indirect hazards from an earthquake is fire. Fire has claimed the most number of victims and caused more property damage than all the direct hazards combined. In 1906, the San Francisco earthquake, better known as the San Francisco fire, killed five hundred people, destroyed twenty-five thousand buildings, and burned 12.2 square kilometers of the city. Fires are started by the sparking of downed electrical wires that results in the ignition of ruptured gas lines. They are difficult, if not impossible, to control, since water pressure in hydrants may be low or nonexistent because of the breakage of underground waterpipes. Flooding is another indirect hazard. Although the risk of flooding is usually minimal in a seismically active area, the potential failure of large concrete or earthen dams and reservoirs poses a great threat to nearby life and property. During the 1971 San Fernando earthquake in Southern California, for example, the lower part of the Van Norman earthen dam partially gave way, threatening the eighty thousand people who lived in the surrounding area. If the shaking had continued for another minute, it would have been disastrous for the local community.

The danger of being trapped in a collapsing building during an earthquke is real. No building is "earthquake proof," but steps are being taken to make existing buildings more secure. Most concrete and steel-reinforced buildings built on solid bedrock and most one- or two-story wooden frame houses suffer little or no damage in an earthquake, provided that the ground motion is not too protracted or severe. Generally, older buildings suffer much more damage than newer ones. One of the safest places to be during an earthquake is in a doorway.

## Methods of Study

Although earthquakes cannot be prevented, the dangers that they pose may be either eliminated or reduced. Engineers and city planners want to design buildings that will withstand a certain amount of ground shaking. As structural design improves, the loss of life decreases. Yet, it is very difficult to predict the effect of ground motion on a building design. To design a more flexible building, engineers must perform tests on scale models using simulated or actual samples of the local bedrock and the construction materials. In the state of California, for example, legislation requires the removal of overhanging ledges and the reinforcement of key structural supports in buildings, bridges, and highway overpasses. The installation of numerous cutoff valves on gas, water, and sewage lines can localize and minimize service disruptions, while above-ground pipes, roads, and power lines built across active faults have been designed to anticipate fault motion.

The geologist, however, has the primary responsibility for the gathering of geologic information needed for the accurate assessment of the seismic risk for an area. This information can be obtained by the drafting of a geologic map of the region that includes an accurate tracing of all known faults and fault-derived topographic features, such as scarps and sag ponds, and the identity of the rock types involved. Such a map can help geologists to predict where an earthquake will most likely occur, but it cannot predict the earthquake's intensity, frequency, or time of occurrence without further data. This information may be gained through studies of the long-term movement history of existing faults, the determining of their relative ages, the monitoring of current fault motion, and the detection of previously unknown faults. Once the information is assimilated, an estimate of a possible earthquake's magnitude on the Richter scale, its epicenter, its intensity on the modified Mercalli scale, and the amount of horizontal and vertical ground movement can be made.

If the geologic data indicate that an area may suffer an unacceptable amount of destruction, alternative land-use policies for this area should be adopted. Such policies involve the establishment of a fault hazard easement, whereby construction is restricted to a certain minimum distance from the nearest fault trace or fault zone. Geologic hazard zoning would also identify areas affected by past landslides, floods, and seismic sea waves. In many regions, however, much urban or industrial development already exists in hazardous areas, simply because the danger was not recognized at the time of construction.

Since the recurrence interval between large earthquakes is very long or poorly known, the largest potential hazards exist in areas that have suffered little or no seismic activity. Local governments in areas such as New York City, South Carolina, and Missouri have given little thought to earthquake disaster planning. The New Madrid, Missouri, earthquake of 1811-1812 was felt over a sparsely populated area of 2.6 million square kilometers; large sections of the ground were uplifted, others sank, deep cracks appeared in the ground, and bells were caused to ring in church towers as far away as Boston. It was the most powerful earthquake ever to strike the eastern half of the United States, and it occurred in an area thought to be earthquake-free. If a major earthquake were to strike the East Coast cities today, the property damage and loss of life would be tremendous.

## Context

As the population of the world continues to grow and compete for living space, more and more areas, once considered hazard-free because of their lack of development, are becoming inhabited and may suffer damage from potential movements of the earth. Therefore, research in the area of earthquake control and prediction is growing more important.

Humans' ability to trigger an earthquake was discovered during the early 1970's at the Rocky Mountain Arsenal in Denver, Colorado. There, liquid wastes were disposed by high-pressure injection into wells that were drilled to 3,600 meters below the surface. These liquids reduced the pressure along deep faults, allowing them to slip and causing an increase in the number of minor earthquakes in the area. When the pumping stopped, the number of earthquakes decreased, and when pumping was continued, the tremors began again. A careful study proved that the number of recorded earthquakes was statistically higher than that which would normally be expected. Man-made earthquakes were also created through underground nuclear explosions and the filling of water reservoirs behind major dams. Some geologists believe that these processes may relieve the pressure along faults and prevent a major earthquake from occurring.

The ability to predict an earthquake's time and place is based entirely on the quality of geologic data available for a given area. Geologists look at historic evidence of a fault's movement and at its current activity. The problem lies in the brevity of the record-keeping period. The first seismometer was built around 1889, so the science of seismology is relatively new, and data have been collected on some faults for less than one hundred years. Many more faults have been discovered since that time, and not enough information is available to give a reliable estimate of the seismic activity of a region.

Most earthquakes are preceded by warning signs. Some of these indicators are local ground swelling, an increase in the number and frequency of minor tremors, an increase in the amount of radioactive radon gas in water wells, and unusual animal activity. The problem is that not all earthquakes have these precursors, and they are not always reliable. Moreover, new hazards are created by the prediction of an earthquake. A short-term prediction may cause major traffic jams, panic, riots, and looting. Long-term predictions may cause property values to drop, create a decrease in tourism, and cause the gradual abandonment or economic depression of nearby cities. If the prediction is wrong, the public is unlikely to trust any future predictions, and major lawsuits may arise from injuries or damages resulting from evacuation.

Although formal earthquake predictions had not been made in the United States as of 1989, the U.S. Geological Survey was responsible for estimating the time, place, and severity of an impending American earthquake. Chinese and Japanese geologists, in their countries, had made a few successful predictions, and successful earthquake-related predictions had been made by the United States' National Tsunami Warning Center regarding the arrival of seismic sea waves.

## Bibliography

Cargo, David N., and Bob F. Mallory. *Man and His Geologic Environment.* 2d ed. Reading, Mass.: Addison-Wesley, 1977. Chapter 10 of this college textbook covers earthquakes and volcanoes.

Griggs, Gary B., and John A. Gilchrist. *Geologic Hazards, Resources, and Environmental Planning.* 2d ed. Belmont, Calif.: Wadsworth, 1983. Chapter 2 thoroughly covers geologic hazards related to earthquakes and faulting. Supplemented by an extensive bibliography and many photographs, charts, and maps. Highly recommended.

Howard, Arthur D., and Irwin Remson. *Geology in Environmental Planning.* New York: McGraw-Hill, 1978. Chapter 8, "Earthquakes and the Environment," contains a wide-ranging discussion of earthquakes and their distributions, hazards, prediction, and warning signs. Supplemented with many photographs and line drawings relating to famous earthquakes.

Keller, Edward A. *Environmental Geology.* 5th ed. Columbus, Ohio: Merrill, 1988. Chapter 8 covers earthquakes and related phenomena in a well-illustrated and well-written discussion.

Utgard, R. O., G. D. McKenzie, and D. Foley. *Geology in the Urban Environment.* Minneapolis: Burgess, 1978. Chapter 12, "Seismic Hazards and Land-Use Planning," is a brief outline of earthquake hazards. Chapter 13, "The Status of Earthquake Prediction," presents a quick overview of research in the field. Both chapters are written for the general reader.

*Steven C. Okulewicz*

## Cross-References

# EARTHQUAKE LOCATING

*Type of earth science:* Geophysics
*Field of study:* Seismology

*Earthquake locating requires a network of seismographs. The tremors felt at the earth's surface originate at depth by sudden jerky motions of faults under great pressures. Finding earthquakes requires measuring depths and determining geographic locations of the source zones within the earth where the rocks ruptured.*

*Principal terms*

CORE: the innermost portion of the earth's interior; it measures 2,900 kilometers in diameter

CRUST: the upper 30-60 kilometers of the earth's rocks in which shallow earthquakes occur; it is thickest under continents, thinnest beneath oceans

EPICENTER: the point on the earth's surface directly above the focus of an earthquake

FAULT: a crack in the earth's crust where one side has moved relative to the other

FOCUS: the point beneath the earth's surface where rocks have suddenly fractured along a fault zone, generating a train of seismic waves that travel through the earth and that are experienced at the surface as an earthquake

MANTLE: the portion of the earth's interior between the Moho and the core, from 30-60 kilometers to 2,900 kilometers deep

MOHOROVIČIĆ DISCONTINUITY (MOHO): the lower boundary of the crust, 30-60 kilometers deep on the average; the velocities of P waves and S waves both increase sharply just below the Moho

P WAVE: a type of seismic wave generated at the focus of an earthquake traveling 6-8 kilometers per second, with a push-pull vibratory motion parallel to the direction of propagation; "P" stands for "primary," as P waves are the fastest and first to arrive at a seismic station

S WAVE: a type of seismic wave generated at the focus of an earthquake traveling 3.5-4.8 kilometers per second, with a shear or transverse vibratory motion perpendicular to the direction of propagation; "S" stands for "secondary" because S waves are usually the second to arrive at a seismic station

SEISMOGRAPH: a sensitive instrument that detects vibrations at the earth's surface and records their arrival times, amplitudes, and directions of motion

## Summary of the Methodology

Even though tremors from a single earthquake may be felt for hundreds of kilometers and recorded throughout the world, they always begin at a point or very small region within the earth. Earthquakes are caused when pressures build up to the point that the rocks cannot withstand any more stress, and they snap and move to adjust to the stress. As they rupture, they either form a crack or move along an existing fault, with one side moving with crushing force against the other. This violent internal rubbing creates vibrations that propagate away from the disturbance and ripple across the surface of the earth.

When a violin bow is rubbed against a violin string at a point, the whole string vibrates, and as it vibrates, energy is transmitted to the surrounding air, sending out sonic, or sound, waves. Similarly, when rocks of the earth's interior rapidly rub against one another at a point, all of the neighboring rocks vibrate. As they vibrate, they transmit energy upwards and through the earth. This energy sends out seismic waves felt and measured as tremors of an earthquake throughout a region. Sometimes, if an earthquake is strong enough, seismographs in every corner of the world will measure it.

Locating an earthquake means to find the region within the earth where the rocks ruptured and the vibrations started. For small quakes, the source region is no more than a few meters in size. For very large earthquakes, the source region may be hundreds of meters and even a kilometer or more in dimension. In the case of large quakes, however, the entire area of disturbed fault motion does not move at once. The earthquake still starts at some point in the fault region, then the disturbance moves away from point to point in a chain reaction until the entire stressed region has adjusted. The actual fault motion may occur in one or two seconds for small quakes or extend over a minute or more for the largest quakes.

The point within the earth where the fault began its motion is called the focus, or hypocenter, of the earthquake. The focus is where the rocks break. The geographic location of the point vertically above the focus on the earth's surface is called the epicenter. The epicenter is thus the point on the earth's surface nearest to the focus. It is also the place where the most intense ground motions are usually experienced—but not always. Sometimes, because of the peculiarities of underlying geology, the most violent vibrations experienced above ground are displaced a few kilometers from the epicenter. For this reason, an array of sensitive instruments called seismographs are needed to locate the true epicenter and focus. Surface expressions of an earthquake can be very misleading. The earthquake of September 19, 1985, that devastated Mexico City actually had its epicenter some 400 kilometers away beneath the Pacific Ocean. Because of the geologic peculiarities in that part of the world, Mexico City, at a considerable distance from the source, was more severely shaken than was Acapulco, which was much closer.

Earthquakes are generated from a point or small restricted region within the earth, but they send out waves that can be felt for hundreds of kilometers and recorded by seismographs throughout the entire world. For example, the great New

Madrid, Missouri, earthquakes of 1811-1812 were felt from the Rocky Mountains to the Atlantic seaboard, but their epicenters were in the Mississippi River valley of the midwestern United States.

Among seismologists, "earthquake locating" means finding the focus and epicenter, which requires seismic instrumentation. Finding the regions of strongest shaking and heaviest damage is another kind of investigation in which seismologists also engage, but it does not require seismographs. Earthquakes can be located by well-calibrated seismographs by noting the times that various seismic waves arrive at different stations. By knowing the speeds which P waves, S waves, and other seismic waves travel through the earth and the precise times they arrive at several stations, distances and directions can be calculated and the earthquake epicenter and depth determined. A minimum of three seismic stations scattered around an epicenter are needed to determine a location. At least one station near the epicenter is needed to estimate accurately the depth. For truly reliable and precise measurements within less than 0.1 kilometer, a dozen or more stations are needed at varying distances surrounding the focal region.

All seismic stations are timed to universal time referenced to the zeroth meridian passing through Greenwich, England. This time is broadcast by short-wave radio stations, such as WWV radio in Boulder, Colorado, which broadcasts every second of time, twenty-four hours a day. The time is accurate to within billionths of a second. Seismic stations are equipped with special radios to receive this information and to set their seismographs on a daily basis.

Networks of seismographs can be found throughout the world, including a worldwide net received by radio, satellite, and telephone lines in Golden, Colorado, by the U.S. Geological Survey's National Earthquake Information Service (NEIS). Smaller, more local nets exist around the major faults and seismic zones in the country, including the San Andreas fault system of California; the Puget Sound area of Washington State, the Wasatch fault of Utah; the New Madrid fault of Arkansas, Missouri, and Tennessee; the Charleston, South Carolina, seismic zone; and several seismic areas of New England. Locating earthquakes is a cooperative effort between many seismic stations and scientists throughout the country and the world, including those associated with universities, government facilities, and private corporations. In earthquake seismology, the whole world is the laboratory. Sharing of information—irrespective of state, provincial, or national boundaries—is required to understand, study, and locate earthquakes.

## Applications of the Method

The easiest way to locate an earthquake is when three stations are located in a triangle around its source regions. For example, imagine that an earthquake occurs at exactly 06:00 hours universal time. At the instant the fault rips, two kinds of waves are generated: P waves and S waves. Velocities of P waves in the upper crust of the earth are about 7 kilometers per second, while those of S waves are typically 40 percent less, or 4.2 kilometers per second. When the P wave has traveled

70 kilometers in 20 seconds, the S wave has traveled 42 kilometers. To reach the point the P wave reached in 10 seconds, the S wave will take 16.7 seconds, or 6.7 seconds longer. If a seismic station were at this site, it would record both waves and note that the S wave lost the "race" by 6.7 seconds. Another station 100 kilometers away in another direction would also note the arrival of the P wave and S wave. To travel 100 kilometers, the P wave would take 14.3 seconds, while the S wave would take 23.8 seconds, or 9.5 seconds longer than the P wave. If, in a third direction from the earthquake, another seismic station were situated 160 kilometers away, it would receive both the P and S waves at later times: 06 hours 22.9 seconds and 06 hours 38.1 seconds, respectively. The third seismic station would note a "P minus S" (P−S) arrival time difference of 15.2 seconds. Although the three seismic stations recording the arrivals of P and S waves would not identify where the earthquake had occurred nor the time of its origin, seismologists could calculate the exact time of arrival in universal units to the nearest tenth of a second or better. Even more useful, they would know precisely the difference in arrival times of the P and S waves, which could be read from each station's seismograms.

Each seimographic observatory has sets of empirically determined travel times for P and S waves for various distances from its station. The first station in the example, at 70 kilometers' distance, would refer to the travel time tables and see that for a difference of 6.7 seconds between P and S waves, the event had to be about 70 kilometers away. Seismologists would not know, however, in which direction the waves had come. The staff at the station could draw a circle on a map 70 kilometers in radius, with the location of the station at the center, knowing that somewhere on that circle the earthquake had occurred. By contacting the station located 100 kilometers from the epicenter, the staff at the first station would learn that the seismograph at the second station noted a 9.5-second P−S difference. The staff could then refer to the travel time charts to discover that a 9.5-delay time corresponds to 100 kilometers, thus defining a second circle of that radius, centered on the second station. Similarly, the staff at the first station could contact the third station and obtain another P−S delay time and find that the 15.2-second difference observed there implied a 160-kilometer distance of that station from the earthquake focus.

Plotting the three circles centered on the three station locations with the appropriate radii, the seismologists would find that all three intersect at a single point. That point would be the epicenter. To obtain the depth requires some analysis of the P−S delay times and how closely the three circles intersect precisely at a point. By assuming a depth, calculating the arrival times to the stations, and comparing them to the real arrival times, the seismologist can judge how realistic the assumed depth was. By assuming various depths and repeating the calculations until a close correspondence with real arrival times results, the depth can be said to have been determined. The best way to determine a depth is by having a station very near the epicenter. In this way, the distance from the focus at depth to the station recording at the surface is an approximation of the depth below the epicenter. The most common way to determine depth, however, is by inputting measurements from many stations into a computer and repeating trial calculations until they best resemble the data for a depth determination. Epicenters are also located by the mathematical convergence of data from many stations, even though theoretically only three stations are required.

The P−S delay time technique is the original and most simple way to locate earthquakes. This method does not work in all cases, however; even when it does work, beyond 500 kilometers, the curvature of the earth becomes a contending factor. The simple triangulation method works best for shallow quakes less than one-quarter of the circumference of the world away, or less than 10,000 kilometers.

A shallow earthquake is one that occurs in the crust less than 60 kilometers deep. Most active faults do not extend visibly up through the surface (as does the San Andreas fault in California) but lie buried beneath layers of rock and soil. The deepest earthquakes are 300-700 kilometers deep; those between 300 and 60 kilometers deep are termed "intermediate" by seismologists. Deep earthquakes only occur in certain places, mostly around the perimeter of the Pacific Ocean. For a deep earthquake, even a station at the epicenter would be hundreds of kilometers away, and the seismic energy might take an entire minute to propagate from the focus to the surface.

There are several reasons the P−S delay time triangulation method cannot always work. One reason is that the core of the earth acts like a liquid not a solid. Liquids do not allow S waves to propagate. Hence, beyond a certain distance around the earth, direct S waves cannot be received. The core also bends and diffracts P waves, even though P waves do propagate readily through the core. Because of the inner structure of the earth, receiving P and S waves directly from the focal source zone to a seismic recorder is not possible. Instead of P waves and S waves being the first and second waves to arrive at a station, other kinds of seismic waves—including P and S waves that have been reflected, refracted, and diffracted along complex pathways—will arrive first. When the direct P and S waves are not received by a seismic station, other waves can be used to determined the epicentral distance in an analogous fashion. Hence, seismologists have tables and charts not only for direct P and S wave travel times to their station but also for more than a dozen other ray paths and wave types. By reading all such data from their seismograms and applying multiple travel time calculations, seismologists can determine more precisely depths and epicentral distances.

In the early days of seismology, at the turn of the nineteenth century, earthquake epicenters were found by using large spherical globes, thumb tacks, and pieces of string to strike off intersecting radii. Presently, epicenters and depths are found by sophisticated computer programs that consider the data of numerous stations and numerous phases of the various kinds of seismic waves and their possible wave paths through the earth.

## Context

The science of locating earthquakes, as it has developed over the past 100 years, has been responsible for providing most of what is known about the earth's interior. The Moho, the thickness of the crust, the earth's mantle, the liquid core, and even the inner solid core floating within the fluid outer core—all of these have been deduced from seismograms taken from all over the world. The motions of the earth's crustal plates are also observed by the analysis of seismograms. Locating an earthquake by a seismogram determines much more than just when and where the rocks ruptured. The amount of energy released and the relative directions of motion that occurred on both sides of the fault can also be determined.

The installation by the United States of a worldwide network of seismographs has made it possible over the decades to monitor the underground nuclear experiments of the Soviet Union and other countries. An underground nuclear blast has many of the earmarks of an earthquake and can be located by the same methodologies, but it also has distinctively different seismic characteristics. Studying seismograms of nuclear blasts has helped refine understanding of the earth's inner makeup. Another practical application of earthquake locating is measurement of the tremors associated with volcanic magma moving toward the surface prior to an eruption. Volcanic eruption predictions are based on such data.

## Bibliography

Bolt, Bruce A. *Earthquakes*. New York: W. H. Freeman, 1988. An elementary treatment of earthquakes in general. Could be used by lower-level college students who are nonscience majors.

_____. *Inside the Earth*. New York: W. H. Freeman, 1982. An excellent introduction to seismic waves and how they behave within and define the interior of the earth. College level.

Garland, G. D. *Introduction to Geophysics: Mantle, Core, and Crust*. Philadelphia: W. B. Saunders, 1971. Excellent and thorough treatment of the earth's interior and how its character is deduced from seismic wave behavior as measured by seismographs. Understandable to college science majors.

Richter, Charles F. *Elementary Seismology*. San Francisco: W. H. Freeman, 1958. The author of this classic 768-page text, who was a seismologist for many years at the California Institute of Technology, developed the Richter scale for measuring the intensity of earthquakes. Judging from his book, Dr. Richter must have been an excellent teacher. Even though this source is outdated, its lucid explanations of basic principles make it a worthwhile reference. Contains excellent and detailed chapters on the complexities of earthquake locating, along with examples, charts, diagrams, and travel-time curves. Some sections using differential equations would be for upper-level college students, but most of the book, including the parts on earthquake locating, would be quite readable to any advanced high school student.

Simon, Ruth B. *Earthquake Interpretation*. Golden: Colorado School of Mines, 1968. Basic primer on seismogram interpretation. Aimed at lower-level college science students.

Tarbuck, E. J., and F. K. Lutgens. *Earth Science*. 5th ed. Westerville, Ohio: Charles E. Merrill, 1988. Freshman college text. Covers spectrum of earth sciences with many full-color, excellent illustrations.

Verhoogen, John, et al. *The Earth*. New York: Holt, Rinehart and Winston, 1970. Provides introductory earth science material. Freshman college level.

*David Stewart*

## Cross-References

Continental Crust, 261; Creep, 297; Earthquake Distribution, 421; Earthquake Engineering, 430; Earthquake Hazards, 437; Earthquake Magnitudes and Intensities, 452; Earthquake Prediction, 461; Earthquakes: Elastic Waves, 469; Famous Earthquakes, 476; An Overview of Earthquakes, 484; Normal Faults, 676; Thrust Faults, 683; Transform Faults, 690; Plate Motions, 2071; Plate Tectonics, 2079; Seismic Reflection Profiling, 2333; Seismometers, 2340.

# EARTHQUAKE MAGNITUDES AND INTENSITIES

*Type of earth science:* Geophysics
*Field of study:* Seismology

*The measurement of earthquake intensity (based on observed effects of earthquakes) and magnitude (based on instrument readings) is useful not only for scientists wishing to study and predict earthquakes but also for land-use planning and other aspects of public policy.*

### Principal terms

AMPLITUDE: the displacement of the tracings of the recording pen (or light beam) on a seismogram from its normal position

DEEP-FOCUS EARTHQUAKES: earthquakes whose focus is greater than 300 kilometers below the surface

EPICENTER: the point on the earth's surface directly above the focus of an earthquake

FOCUS: the point within the earth that is the source of the seismic waves generated by an earthquake

HIGH-FREQUENCY SEISMIC WAVES: those earthquake waves that shake the rock through which they travel most rapidly

LOW-FREQUENCY SEISMIC WAVES: those earthquake waves that shake the rock through which they travel most slowly (also called long-period waves)

SEISMOGRAM: an image of earthquake wave vibrations recorded on paper, photographic film, or a video screen

SEISMOGRAPH: the mechanical or mechanical-electrical instrument that detects and records passing earthquake waves

SHALLOW-FOCUS EARTHQUAKES: earthquakes having a focus less than 60 kilometers below the surface

## Summary of the Phenomenon

Magnitude is a numerical rating of the size or strength of an earthquake, based on instrument readings. Intensity is a different kind of numerical rating having to do with the actual effects of an earthquake on people, buildings, and the landscape. Magnitude rating values allow comparison between earthquakes on a worldwide basis, whereas intensity ratings are more useful for comparing relative effects in areas surrounding the epicenter.

Because only human judgment is required for an intensity rating, intensity scales were developed first. Many different scales of earthquake effects have been devised in different countries since Renaissance times. The earliest known scale was developed in Italy and had only four rating values. The earliest widely accepted intensity scale, in use after 1883, was the Rossi-Forel scale, which had ten value ratings. In the United States, a revision of a later European scale, the 1931 modified Mercalli scale, has become the standard. It has twelve possible values, ranging from I, which barely would be felt, to XII, which would be the most violent.

An earthquake of intensity I on the modified Mercalli scale would not be felt except by very few. It might trigger nausea or dizziness if it occurs in the marginal zone of a large earthquake. Level II earthquakes are felt by some persons at rest, especially on upper floors, where building motion may exaggerate ground motion. A level III earthquake is characterized by a brief period of vibration like that of a passing loaded truck. Many do not recognize it as an earthquake. Level IV earthquakes are felt indoors by many, outdoors by few. Buildings may shudder slightly; windows and doors of older homes may rattle, and glassware in cupboards may start clinking. In a level V earthquake, which is widely felt, some people may be awakened. A few may be frightened; some run outside. Windows and glassware may break, and cracks may appear in plaster.

Level VI earthquakes are felt by all; many people are frightened, and many run outside. Some plaster may fall, some brick chimneys may be damaged, and some furniture moves. Objects are often thrown from shelves, and trees shake noticeably. A level VII earthquake frightens all. Its strong shaking may last for many seconds, causing considerable damage to older brick buildings and slight to moderate damage to well-built wood- or steel-frame structures. These quakes are noticed by persons driving vehicles. In a level VIII earthquake, damage to buildings is considerable. Specially designed earthquake-resistant structures can hold up, but many older brick buildings collapse totally. Branches and trunks of trees may break. Damage to most buildings—ranging from collapse to being thrown out of plumb or off the foundation—is caused by level IX earthquakes. Conspicuous ground cracks appear, and buried water and gas pipes break. Level X earthquakes cause most buildings to collapse partially, some totally. Railroad tracks are bent, and buried pipes buckle or break. Landsliding along riverbanks and steep slopes is triggered; obvious ground cracks are widespread. Strong shaking may last for many tens of seconds. After level XI quakes, few structures remain standing. Broad fissures appear in the ground. The earthquake may cause a large tsunami if it occurs near a coastal area. The strong shaking may last a minute or more. Finally, in a level XII earthquake, objects are thrown in the air. Waves are "frozen" in the ground surface. Fewer than a half-dozen earthquakes have been rated at this level of intensity.

Assignment of the lower values on the modified Mercalli scale is possible only if people are present to experience the effects. In the middle and upper values, effects on structures are a primary basis for the assignment of ratings, although earthquakes of greatest intensity may produce long-term geologic effects on the landscape, including ground fissures, fault scarps (clifflike features visible at the earth's surface), landslides, and sandblows (small volcanolike mounds of sediment that erupt from water-saturated ground as a result of severe shaking). Thus, earthquakes that occur in uninhabited areas of the earth cannot be rated unless the shaking was sufficiently strong to produce geologic effects; similarly, rating is impossible for quakes occurring below large areas of the ocean with few or no populated islands, although in some cases, intensity can be estimated if a tsunami is generated.

Because effects on buildings are an important means of differentiating between ratings in the middle and upper part of the scale, the nature of construction becomes an important differentiating criterion. In earthquake-prone California, for example, earthquake-resistant design practices mandated by law have made the average new building less susceptible to damage or destruction than are older buildings. Unless this factor is taken into account, equal-sized earthquakes would be rated lower over time because of less damage as older buildings are replaced.

Despite such problems, the modified Mercalli scale is still quite useful. There are many more people (each of whom is a potential observer of earthquake effects) distributed around the world than there are earthquake-recording instruments. Earthquake intensity ratings begin to be gathered soon after earthquakes large enough to be felt by more than a few people. A government agency (for example, the U.S. Geological Survey) sends questionnaires to people in the area where the earthquake was felt. The forms contain questions related to the specific location and activity of the observer at the time of the earthquake as well as details of what happened before, during, and after the quake. The responses are then rated, using the modified Mercalli scale, and the ratings are plotted on a map. Lines separating the various values, or "isoseismal lines," can then be drawn to show areas having equal intensity. Frequently an irregularly shaped bull's-eye pattern emerges, with the highest rating zone in the middle. This zone of maximum intensity usually contains the earthquake's epicenter.

The size and shape of the pattern of isoseismal lines can be invaluable in land-use planning or zoning of areas that experience frequent earthquake activity. The pattern may give clues about the distribution of land that would make a poor foundation for buildings because of greater susceptibility to seismic shaking. Certain types of sediment overlying bedrock can actually amplify seismic vibrations.

The highest intensity value determined for a specific earthquake is only a rough indicator of the quake's real strength. Quite large shocks can occur at many hundreds of kilometers of depth (deep-focus earthquakes), but because their most damaging vibrations are largely absorbed by rock before arriving at the surface, their maximum intensity ratings are low.

Unlike earthquake intensity determinations, which vary with distance from the epicenter and depend on factors such as the depth of focus and soil depth, the magnitude rating of an earthquake is reported as a single number that is *usually* calculated from an instrumental recording of ground vibrations. ("Usually" is emphasized because an alternative method for magnitude determination has been developed, known as moment magnitude.) Every earthquake large enough to be detected and recorded by seismographs can be assigned a magnitude value. The Richter scale of earthquake magnitude was the first to be used widely. It is named for its originator, Charles F. Richter, professor of seismology at the California Institute of Technology.

When an earthquake occurs, it generates ground vibrations that radiate out to surrounding areas, much as ripples do when a small pebble is dropped into a quiet pond. A seismograph is an instrument designed to detect and record, over time, even very small ground vibrations. It does this by amplifying the motion of the ground on which the seismograph sits when seismic waves pass through it. For some seismographs, the amplified recording (seismogram) is simply a piece of paper wrapped around a cylindrical, clock-driven drum, on which the ground vibrations are recorded as a zigzag line drawn by a recording pen. Larger ground vibrations result in larger zigzags or displacement on the paper. The amount of displacement from the normal or average position is called the amplitude, and it can be measured accurately with a simple fine-scale ruler.

In 1935, Richter first published his method for determining the relative size of the many earthquakes for which he had recordings in southern California. Most of these were small and moderate-sized shallow-focus earthquakes. Eventually, after various modifications, the Richter scale came to be used around the world to measure and compare earthquakes. Richter's original definition of the magnitude of an earthquake is as follows: "The magnitude of any shock is taken as the logarithm of the maximum trace amplitude, expressed in microns, with which the standard short-period [Wood-Anderson] seismometer . . . would register that shock at an epicentral distance of 100 kilometers." Simply stated, the Richter scale magnitude of an earthquake is determined by measuring the greatest displacement from the average of the recording-pen tracing on the seismogram of a standard instrument at a standard distance from the earthquake epicenter (earthquake ground motions weaken as they travel out from the source). The height of the largest amplitude is measured in microns (thousandths of a millimeter). The logarithm of this number (to the base 10) is calculated and becomes the rating number "on the Richter scale." In the example illustrated in the accompanying figure, if an earthquake produced a maximum recording-pen displacement of 1 centimeter, that would be equivalent to 10,000 microns (which is equal to $10^4$ microns). The logarithm of $10^4$ is 4 (the exponent); thus, the earthquake would be rated at 4 on the Richter scale. If the maximum displacement had been $10^5$ microns, it would be rated 5.

Because of the logarithmic nature of the Richter scale, each higher value in whole numbers actually represents a tenfold increase in the amount of ground motion recorded on the seismogram. Compared to an earthquake rated at 4, one rated at 5 involves 10 times more ground-shaking displacement; one rated at 6 would involve 100 times more displacement than 4, and 7 would be 1,000 times more. In other words, the largest earthquakes produce more than 1,000 times more ground motion than those that just begin to damage average American homes.

The figure includes the descriptive terms often used for earthquakes of different sizes (such as "moderate" and "strong"), as well as noting the relative sizes of a few of the largest historical earthquakes. Note that the scale is open-ended, although the largest quake on record had a value of 8.9. Another way to compare earthquakes is to determine the amount of energy they release. The energy released by earthquakes is about 30 times greater for each higher Richter scale value.

For example, an earthquake rated at 6 would be about 900 times (30 × 30) more energetic than one rated at 4.

Methods for magnitude determination have advanced substantially since the original magnitude scale was developed by Richter. His original scale was valid only for shallow-focus earthquakes occurring in the local region of southern California, because it depended on the Wood-Anderson type seismograph. That instrument is "tuned" to pick up the higher-frequency vibrations typical of the small and medium-sized earthquakes of southern California. Later work by Richter and others extended his original scale for use with other instruments tuned to pick up earthquakes that occurred at greater distance (more than 1,000 kilometers from a seismograph station) and had a deeper focus. These magnitude extensions were designed to coincide, as much as possible, with the values of the original scale. The extensional scales, however, use bases that are different from those of the original. One extensional scale, for example, requires a seismograph tuned to pick up only low-frequency vibrations. As a result, magnitude values differ somewhat and are not strictly "on the Richter scale." Technical literature actually limits the use of the term "Richter scale" to magnitude values determined essentially according to the original specifications.

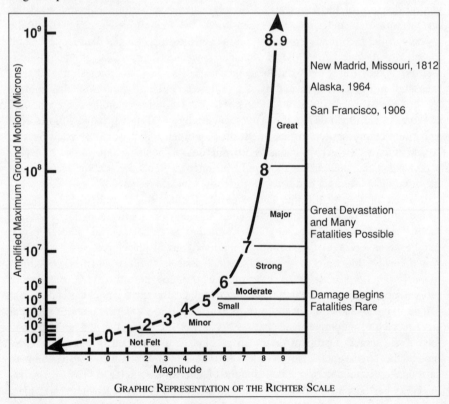

GRAPHIC REPRESENTATION OF THE RICHTER SCALE

For the very largest earthquakes, even the extensional scales become inadequate for ranking accurately the relative strength of earthquakes, because the sensitive instruments are said to become "saturated"—essentially thrown off scale. To solve this problem, a "moment magnitude" scale was developed; it is based not on instrument readings but on data obtained in the field, along the earthquake-generating fault. The average amount of fault offset, the length and width of slippage along the fault, and rock rigidity data are used to calculate the moment magnitude. Because of its greater accuracy, the moment magnitude scale is becoming more commonly used, particularly for medium-sized and larger earthquakes. Although the values of the moment magnitude scale essentially merge with those of the Richter scale for medium-sized earthquakes, at higher values there can be substantial differences. Thus, the largest earthquake rated by moment magnitude is 9.5 (as indicated by the figure).

## Methods of Study

The measurement of intensity and magnitude is important not only for the accurate determination of earthquake size or strength in and of itself but also for earthquake recurrence predictions and for zoning considerations in urban and regional planning. Magnitude studies are also used in the detection of underground nuclear explosions.

A key element to prediction of earthquake recurrence, particularly for the less frequent but larger and more destructive earthquakes, is a detailed record of the relative sizes of earthquakes occurring along a particular fault (or fault segment) through time. The most accurate and consistent indicator of size is the magnitude value. Because instruments needed for magnitude determination have been in existence less than one hundred years, magnitudes of earlier events must be estimated. This can be done using several approaches.

Maximum intensity values correlate with different but known magnitude values in areas where the depth of focus is thought to be consistent through time and where the nature of bedrock absorption of seismic waves is known. For determining maximum intensity values for unrecorded earthquakes of the past, archives and historical documents sometimes yield useful data. For prehistoric earthquakes, newly developed techniques are proving successful in defining the occurrence of large earthquakes and, under the right circumstances, even of their relative sizes. Such old events may be judged by the nature and extent of geologic traces preserved in radiocarbon-datable buried sediments.

Another avenue of study of earthquake recurrence is based on the amount of stored-up energy that is released by earthquakes worldwide in a year. A curve of the energy release can be compared to the occurrences of every possible recurrent earthquake-triggering mechanism—for example, tidal forces. To determine energy released, the moment magnitude must be determined for as many earthquakes as possible, but especially for the largest ones, because they release much more energy overall than do the more numerous smaller ones. One study, for example, revealed a strong correlation between times of higher-than-average earthquake activity (around 1910 and again around 1960) and the extent of "wobbling" of the earth's axis of rotation.

In earthquake-prone areas, seismic risk must be considered in urban and regional planning. The effects of ground shaking at any location are dependent primarily on magnitude, distance from the source of the earthquake waves, and the nature of the bedrock and the type and thickness of materials above it. After historical patterns of earthquake recurrence are determined, particularly their characteristic (or most typical) size, it is possible to make estimates of probable intensity patterns in the vicinity of faults. Detailed maps have been prepared of the areas along the San Andreas fault and for many miles on either side of it, outlining the zones of greatest potential seismic risk. Such maps can be of great value when decisions are being made regarding sites for potential secondary earthquake hazards such as nuclear power plants, fuel storage depots, and dams.

Additionally, seismic detection and characterization of distant underground nuclear explosions is of considerable political importance. One method of attempting to discriminate between a nuclear explosion and a natural seismic event is by analysis of its magnitude as recorded by several types of seismographs, each "tuned" to pick up different frequencies of ground vibrations. Ratios between such magnitude values appear to be quite useful for this purpose.

## Context

Nearly every time a news broadcast makes reference to a damaging earthquake somewhere in the world, a number on the Richter scale is mentioned to give the listener some idea of the relative size of the event. If the earthquake has happened in a remote part of the globe and has not caused significant damage, it becomes merely another of the many facts that are soon forgotten. If the earthquake has happened where one's relative or a friend lives, however, that number on the Richter scale becomes extremely important because it is one of the first available indicators of possible severity. It can be determined within minutes after earthquake waves have been detected at seismological observatories, whereas direct communication from and damage assessment at the site of the earthquake may be very slow in coming. Exactly what does a value of 7.3, for example, mean to those who were near the epicenter? How does that figure compare to the value associated with damage to homes? (That number is about 5 on the Richter scale.)

Many of the world's large cities are located close to active earthquake-generating faults. What effect will a major earthquake in such a city have on the economy of that area, and how in turn will its misfortune affect the rest of the world? What would happen if the flow of goods between the United States and Japan were suddenly disrupted for a long period because of an 8.5-magnitude earthquake near Tokyo or Los Angeles? The initial answers to these and many other questions may someday hinge on that critical number on the Richter scale.

Aspects of earthquake intensity are less likely to be mentioned in the media except, perhaps, when covering local aspects of seismic risk along a certain fault or the risk of earthquakes in various areas of the United States. Maps identifying zones of potential seismic hazard are likely to become more common as their need becomes more apparent. The lack of such knowledge and of the will to act on it could be costly in terms of lives and property.

One of the most instructive illustrations of seismic intensity patterns is a map comparison of the 1906 San Francisco earthquake and a similar-sized earthquake in southern Missouri. The seismic wave absorptive properties of the bedrock of the western margin of North America is much greater than that of the central and eastern states. As a result, except in California, little damage is expected to occur from earthquakes in the United States—even from major ones. A great earthquake in the New Madrid fault zone of southern Missouri, however, is likely to have a wide zone of maximum intensity, resulting in severe damage in cities hundreds of miles from the epicenter.

## Bibliography

Bolt, Bruce A. *Earthquakes*. New York: W. H. Freeman, 1988. An authoritative introduction to most aspects of earthquakes, including magnitude and intensity. Includes lists of important earthquakes, a glossary, a bibliography of titles suitable for the general reader, and an interesting "earthquake quiz" with answers. Suitable for high school or college-level readers.

Eiby, G. A. *Earthquakes*. Auckland, New Zealand: Heineman, 1980. A relatively technical discussion of earthquakes and seismology. Suitable for college-level readers.

Gere, James M., and Haresh C. Shah. *Terra Non Firma: Understanding and Preparing for Earthquakes*. New York: W. H. Freeman, 1984. Similar in many respects to Bolt's book, described above. Includes a table relating maximum intensity values of the modified Mercalli scale to Richter scale magnitude values (page 87) and a table relating the duration of strong motion to Richter scale values (page 173). Suitable for high school or college-level readers.

Nance, John, and Howard Cady. *On Shaky Ground*. New York: William Morrow, 1988. One of the best-written and easiest to understand accounts of the actual effects of some of the most significant earthquakes of various magnitudes. Based on interviews with survivors as well as with top researchers in seismology. Strongly recommended.

Richter, C. F. *Elementary Seismology*. San Francisco: W. H. Freeman, 1958. An older but still very useful textbook source of earthquake information. Suitable for college-level readers.

Walker, Bryce. *Earthquake*. Alexandria, Va.: Time-Life Books, 1982. A well-written popular account of earthquakes; includes many good illustrations. Suitable for high school-level readers.

*Valentine J. Ansfield*

**Cross-References**

# EARTHQUAKE PREDICTION

*Field of study:* Urban geology and geologic hazards

*Predicting the location and timing of earthquakes is an active area of research in many countries throughout the world. Although significant progress has been made in understanding the causes and consequences of earthquakes, scientists are still unable to predict with sufficient accuracy the occurrence of major temblors.*

> *Principal terms*
> CRUST: the outermost layer of the earth, which consists of materials that are relatively light
> ELASTIC REBOUND THEORY: the theory that states that rocks across a fault remain attached while accumulating energy and deforming; the energy is released in a sudden slip, which produces an earthquake
> FAULTING: the process of fracturing the earth such that rocks on opposite sides of the fracture move relative to each other; faults are the structures produced during the process
> LITHOSPHERE: the earth's rigid outer layer, which is composed of the crust and uppermost mantle
> SEISMICITY: the temporal and spatial distribution of earthquakes
> SEISMOLOGY: the study of earthquakes and their causes
> STRESS: a force acting in a specified direction over a given area

## Summary of the Phenomenon

Chinese scientists pioneered the study of earthquakes hundreds of years ago. Since that time, predicting the location and time of major earthquakes has been an important part of seismology. Earthquakes occur, with varying frequency, in diffuse belts in nearly every region of the globe. The distribution of earthquakes is explained easily by the modern theory of plate tectonics, which holds that the surface of the earth is composed of a mosaic of interlocking rigid plates that move relative to one another at speeds up to 12 centimeters per year. Motions along the boundaries of the plates produce earthquakes; if the plates are not able to accommodate the motions easily, then large earthquakes may accompany the relative motion between the plates. The widespread occurrence of earthquakes makes them important to everyone, and for people living near plate boundaries, earthquakes play an even more potentially destructive role in shaping the environment.

Many countries are actively involved in earthquake prediction research. Since the early 1960's, effort has been particularly high in Japan, the People's Republic of China, the Soviet Union, and the United States. The overall goal of these research efforts is to attain the same level of reliability in earthquake prediction as in weather prediction. Although the majority of effort has been focused on predicting the exact time and place of a major earthquake, an equally important, though often overlooked, aspect of earthquake prediction is an assessment of the severity of ground shaking for a specific site. This information is crucial for public policy discussions on the location of dams, hospitals, schools, and nuclear reactors, all of which may be at significant risk during a major earthquake.

Earthquakes are generated when some portion of the earth's rigid outer layer, called the lithosphere, ruptures catastrophically along a sharp discontinuity or fault. This creates significant ground motion near the source of the rupture. Earthquakes occur most commonly at the three types of boundaries of lithospheric plates, which are known as convergent or destructive, divergent or constructive, and transcurrent. The largest number of earthquakes are at divergent plate boundaries located along mountain ridges in the ocean basins. Because these earthquakes are small and far from population centers on the continents, little effort is expended to predict ruptures along divergent plate boundaries. In contrast, earthquakes at convergent or transcurrent plate boundaries, although fewer in number, are larger. Most convergent and transcurrent boundaries coincide with continental margins along which the majority of the global population lives. For this reason, earthquake prediction research focuses on convergent and transcurrent plate boundaries such as those in Japan and California.

Slip on fault planes of large earthquakes is on the order of 10-20 meters, and the forces responsible for faulting are simply the result of the relative motions of the plates at the plate boundaries. Rocks near a region of an impending earthquake may accumulate motion and change volume and shape for hundreds of years prior to causing a rupture. When the lithosphere does finally break, energy stored by the rocks is released suddenly as seismic waves that travel through and around the surface of the earth. These waves generate the intense vibrations associated with an earthquake. For great earthquakes, the rupture may extend for as much as 1,000 kilometers, and it may propagate at speeds in excess of 10,000 kilometers per hour.

Seismologists categorize earthquakes by several different features, but the two most important for earthquake prediction are an earthquake's location and its magnitude or size. The location is described by an epicenter, which is the projection of the earthquake's focus within the lithosphere onto the earth's surface. The magnitude is a number from 1 to 10 on a scale devised by Charles Richter that describes the relative changes in ground motion recorded on a seismometer. The so-called Richter scale is logarithmic; an increase from a value of 1 to 2 corresponds to a tenfold increase in ground motion and to an approximately thirtyfold increase in the amount of energy released during the rupture. The Richter scale is based on a "standard seismometer" placed at a "standard distance" from the epicenter of the earthquake. The traditional Richter scale magnitudes are denoted by "M" to distinguish them from other more recent magnitude scales. Richter originally devised his magnitude scale to be most appropriate for describing moderate local earthquakes in California. Unfortunately, despite its widespread use, the scale is not a good measure of the energy released from very small or very large earthquakes.

Seismologists have learned much about the rupture process that causes earthquakes by studying the ground motion close to and far away from the source. The development of modern seismological instruments and procedures in the early twentieth century led seismologists to the discovery that different rupture mechanisms are at work in different plate tectonic settings. Early attempts at earthquake prediction used analysis of the frequency of major earthquakes in specific regions of the globe to determine whether any significant pattern was apparent. This approach proved to be fruitless. With the acceptance of elastic rebound theory to describe the rupture mechanism for earthquakes, seismologists shifted their attention away from statistical analysis of earthquake occurrences toward developing methods to understand the "trigger" of major earthquakes. Most seismologists agree that the energy necessary to produce a major earthquake is accumulated slowly relative to the time it takes for a rupture to occur. If no trigger were involved in the rupture process, prediction of earthquakes would be extremely difficult, if not impossible. Modern seismologists interested in earthquake prediction primarily rely on developing methods to understand any precursory phenomena that would enable them to predict at least several days or weeks in advance the location of large (M greater than or equal to 6.0) to great (M greater than 8.0) earthquakes. Of course, if an impending earthquake is far removed—for example, more than 1,000 kilometers—from any population center, the need to alert the public is minimal.

Over the years, investigators have suggested a variety of potential triggers to earthquakes. These include rapidly changing or severe weather conditions; variations in the gravitational forces among the moon, sun, earth, and other planets in the solar sytem; and volcanic activity. Scientists have searched historical seismicity records, including extensive catalogs for California, for relationships between the suggested triggers and the occurrence of earthquakes, without much success. For example, every 179 years, the planets of the solar system align. Some researchers suggested that this alignment would increase the gravitational forces acting upon the earth and thereby trigger an increase in seismicity. The last such planetary alignment was in 1982, and no significant increase in earth seismicity occurred.

Because the research on earthquake triggers has been largely unsuccessful, seismologists have turned their attention away from potential triggers of major earthquakes and toward the role of changing physical properties prior to an earthquake. Some promising properties that are currently being studied include shifts in ground elevation near the site of an impending earthquake; variations in the velocity of certain types of seismic waves as they traverse regions that may produce a major quake; increased escape of radon, helium, and other gases from vents and cracks in the earth's surface prior to the earthquake; changes in the electrical conductivity of rocks near the region of impending rupture; and fluctuations in pore fluid pressure in the rocks near major fault zones. In addition, seismologists also have focused on recognizing certain premonitory swarms of smaller quakes, called foreshocks, that may foreshadow a major earthquake. Another technique is assessing the time between major earthquakes in a specific region. If an area that is expected to produce earthquakes is seismically quiet—that is, a gap exists in its seismic activity—then the area may be more likely to experience an earthquake in the near future. This is referred to as "seismic gap" theory. Finally, strange animal behavior has been linked to periods of several days to several hours prior to an earthquake. Some researchers have claimed that cats and dogs tend to run away from home or exhibit unusual behavior, such as seeking out special hiding places, before the onset of an earthquake. Individual reports of odd animal behavior are substantiated by the increase in advertisements for lost pets in local newspapers during the days before a major earthquake. Scientists have suggested that some animals are sensitive to minute changes in their environment, which allows them to "sense" an earthquake prior to onset of severe ground shaking. Research in this area is actively pursued in China and Italy. Most workers, however, are interested in developing instruments that would be able to measure the same effects that disturb animals. Although many of these effects are known to occur prior to a major earthquake, scientists still must develop highly sensitive devices that will alert them in enough time to evacuate or prepare the region near an impending earthquake.

Despite the numerous uncertainties that enter into forecasting an earthquake, some have been successfully predicted. The most spectacular was the Haicheng earthquake of northeast China in February, 1975. Five hours before the earthquake, warnings were issued and several million people from towns in the vicinity of the predicted epicenter were evacuated. Devastation was widespread, but loss of human life was minimal. Scientists who later visited the area estimated that hundreds of thousands of lives were saved. Unfortunately, the Chinese were only able to predict that a great earthquake was to strike the T'ang-shan region within five years. In August, 1976, a very strong earthquake struck this area without warning, leaving 700,000 people dead.

## Methods of Study

Several methods are used by seismologists to study earthquake prediction. The techniques include analysis of seismograms to identify either foreshock or aftershock patterns that signal an impending large earthquake, examination of active fault zones in the field to determine the frequency of great earthquakes over the last tens of thousands of years, and investigation of deep boreholes to characterize the orientations and magnitudes of stresses associated with active faults. In addition, elaborate arrays of sophisticated instruments are frequently deployed near active faults to collect geophysical data that may shed light on earthquakes.

The energy carried by seismic waves is recorded on seismometers or seismographs, which are instruments that monitor ground motion. Seismometers are composed of a mass attached to a pendulum. During an earthquake, the mass remains still, and the amount that the earth moves around it is measured. Ground motion is recorded on a chart as a series of sharp peaks and valleys that deviate from the background value, measured during times of no earthquake activity. The arrival of the waves at different times at different places allows seismologists to calculate the epicenter of an earthquake. The height or amplitude relative to the background noise of the first peak in a long series of peaks associated with a particular earthquake is an estimate of the magnitude of that earthquake.

Since the early twentieth century, seismometers have recorded hundreds of thousands of earthquakes per year worldwide. Seismologists have carefully cataloged many seismograms, the actual paper records of ground motion from a particular location, so that they may be easily compared. Examining these records in detail has allowed seismologists to deduce certain characteristics of major earthquakes. They have noted, for example, that most large earthquakes are followed by a series of smaller earthquakes in the same region. These smaller earthquakes are called aftershocks, and they allow seismologists to constrain the orientation and dimensions of the rupture or fault plane that produced the main earthquake. With the development of modern seismometers and digital recording networks in the 1970's and 1980's, seismologists began to recognize certain precursory seismicity patterns in addition to aftershock sequences. These precursory phenomena are referred to as foreshock sequences and, as yet, are poorly understood. Seismologists hope that with enough data on the overall seismicity of an area, they will be able to note deviations from normal patterns that would signal the onset of a major earthquake.

Information about prehistoric seismic activity must be obtained by examining ancient fault zones exposed at the surface of the earth. Large motions between two rock masses produce characteristic features that may be identified in the field. Geologists are now examining the recent rock record near the San Andreas fault in California. Careful mapping of areas that have been excavated across the fault zone has yielded evidence for large earthquakes prior to historical and seismological records. The now well established technique of carbon 14 dating was applied to organic material trapped in the fault zone to determine the approximate age, location, and intensity of several ancient earthquakes. The data, although sparse, seem to suggest that great earthquakes occur every fifty to three hundred years. In addition, there is some indication that great earthquakes may occur closely spaced in time with significant periods of quiescence between them. This type of analysis is similar to the seismic gap theory, where catalogs of seismograms are examined to determine what known faults or regions that have been active previously are currently inactive and perhaps are ready for renewed activity.

Another method used by scientists to understand precursory phenomena associated with earthquakes is drilling deep boreholes into the earth's crust near major fault zones. One such hole is in Fort Cajon, California. At this site, researchers are examining changes in pore fluid pressure and electrical conductivity in the bore hole. In addition, instruments measure the orientation of fractures in the borehole's walls. These fractures are related to the forces acting on the rocks deep in the crust, and some researchers are attempting to relate these manifestations of stress to earthquake fault orientation. Geophysicists hope that the newest techniques will measure these stresses in real time, so they will be able to compare these data to those obtained from studies of seismicity. Understanding the behavior of a major fault zone at depth may prove useful in predicting earthquakes in the future.

Many countries are carrying out elaborate experiments in areas of repeated seismic activity. One example is in central California on the San Andreas fault near the town of Parkfield. There, geophysicists have arrayed a variety of instruments including seismometers, tiltmeters, gravimeters, and laser surveying equipment to measure ground motion, elevation changes, gravity variations, and minute amounts of slip on the fault. Based on seismic records, scientists have discovered that earthquakes with magnitudes of approximately 5.0 M occur with predictable frequency. The experiments are designed to learn as much as possible about the changes that occur in the region prior to, during, and after an earthquake of moderate size. Scientists hope that these data will allow them to know what features to monitor to predict much larger earthquakes in other areas.

## Context

Earthquake prediction remains critical to modern society because most of the world's population lives along convergent plate boundaries and, thus, within the destructive reach of a great earthquake. The purpose of earthquake prediction, then, is to prepare a society for any earthquakes with magnitudes capable of disturbing normal life. This may include warning and evacuation of the local population or assessing the risks of severe ground motion on current or future structures. In addition to strong ground motion, earthquakes may be responsible for hazards such as tsunamis, avalanches, and fires. In both the great San Francisco earthquake of 1906 and the Tokyo earthquake of 1923, many of the fatalities attributed to the earthquakes were actually the result of the subsequent fires that consumed the cities. Another danger of earthquakes is soil liquefaction, which occurs when the seismic waves cause the soil to lose rigidity and slide away. When this happens, the soil can no longer support structures. Although the structures may be strong enough to withstand the shaking associated with an earthquake, their foundations may be undermined, causing the building to topple.

Perhaps the most promising aspect of earthquake prediction is the development of stringent building codes. After each major earthquake in southern California, for example, municipal, county, and state statutes are changed to reflect new data concerning the behavior of building materials during strong ground motion. Engineers now know that unreinforced masonry buildings are likely to be destroyed in even a moderate earthquake. Because the seismic risk is high in Japan and California, these areas now have the most stringent building codes in the world. That these codes can prevent much unnecessary loss of property and human life unfortunately can be demonstrated by a comparison of the 1971 San Fernando and 1988 Armenian earthquakes. Both of the earthquakes were of similar magnitude—slightly greater than 6.0 M—yet the San Fernando earthquake resulted in about fifty deaths, most of which were in one wing of an old hospital building, while tens of thousands perished in the Armenian earthquake because of the collapse of poorly constructed masonry buildings.

Humans will never be able to prevent earthquakes and their potentially devastating effects. Understanding how, why, when, and where earthquakes occur, therefore, is extremely important to society. Earthquake prediction, like weather prediction, is one way that society seeks to minimize harmful effects of these complex natural phenomena.

## Bibliography

Berlin, G. Lennis. *Earthquakes and the Urban Environment*. Vols. 2 and 3. Boca Raton, Fla.: CRC Press, 1980. These books are two volumes of a three-part series written by a geographer who is primarily concerned with effective land-use planning in seismically active areas. Volume 3 concentrates on strategies to minimize the effects of great earthquakes, such as disaster planning and improved building codes. Many of the social aspects of earthquakes in an urban environment are presented, including human response and insurance. Volume 2 addresses earthquake prediction and building codes. Both volumes contain an extensive reference list of more than 1,400 articles and books. These volumes can be quite technical and are recommended for college-level readers.

Bolt, Bruce A. *Earthquakes: A Primer*. San Francisco: W. H. Freeman, 1988. As the title suggests, an excellent introductory text on earthquakes. Earthquake prediction is discussed extensively in one chapter. The illustrations and photographs of the effects of earthquakes add considerably to the text. Anyone interested in earthquakes will find this an invaluable source.

Eiby, G. A. *Earthquakes*. New York: Van Nostrand Reinhold, 1980. A reference aimed at beginning college-level students. Well illustrated and addresses all topics relevant to earthquakes and seismology. Earthquake prediction and the effect of large earthquakes on man-made structures are discussed in two separate chapters.

Iacopi, Robert. *Earthquake Country*. 3d rev. ed. Menlo Park, Calif.: Lane Books, 1971. Part of the Sunset Book series, this source is directed toward the lay reader. Discusses California geology in relation to seismic risk in a straightforward and nontechnical way. Contains many photographs of the effects of earthquakes on both man-made structures and the natural landscape. Also has a foreword by Charles F. Richter, the inventor of the famous Richter scale.

Mogi, Kiyoo. *Earthquake Prediction*. San Diego, Calif.: Academic Press, 1985. A comprehensive and highly technical text that discusses most aspects of earthquake prediction. The majority of prediction experiments that are described are from Japan. The reader is expected to have a considerable background in earth science and mathematics. The text is suitable for senior college-level students.

National Academy of Sciences. *Earthquake Prediction and Public Policy*. Washington, D.C.: Government Printing Office, 1975. This book was prepared by a National Research Council panel on the public policy implications of earthquake prediction. The panel was composed of outstanding scientists and engineers involved in all fields of earthquake research, in addition to sociologists and other public figures. They specifically evaluate seismic risk in certain regions of the

United States and propose action to prepare these regions for significant earthquakes. Guidelines for earthquake prediction research are discussed. This text is suitable for anyone.

Press, Frank, and Raymond Siever. *The Earth*. 4th ed. New York: W. H. Freeman, 1986. One of the finest illustrated introductory texts on geology. The book has chapters focusing on plate tectonics, seismology, and earthquakes. A map of the major plates is on the inside back cover. The glossary is huge and indispensable. Senior high school and college-level students should find this text suitable for general background information.

Rikitake, Tsuneji. *Earthquake Forecasting and Warning*. Norwell, Mass.: Kluwer Academic Publishers, 1982. Focuses on advances in earthquake prediction in Japan, California, the Soviet Union, and the People's Republic of China. The major programs for earthquake study in each of these regions are discussed. Several case studies in Japan are presented in detail. The reader is required to have an excellent understanding of geophysics. Suitable for senior college-level students.

Uyeda, Seiya. *The New View of the Earth*. Translated by Masako Ohnuki. San Francisco: W. H. Freeman, 1978. The historical development of the theory of plate tectonics is presented, in addition to an excellent explanation of the theory itself. The text is well illustrated and is nontechnical. Designed primarily for the nonscientist.

*Glen S. Mattioli*
*Pamela Jansma*

## Cross-References

Earthquake Distribution, 421; Earthquake Engineering, 430; Earthquake Hazards, 437; Earthquake Locating, 445; Earthquake Magnitudes and Intensities, 452; Famous Earthquakes, 476; An Overview of Earthquakes, 484; Normal Faults, 676; Thrust Faults, 683; Transform Faults, 690; Land-Use Planning, 1335; Plate Tectonics, 2079; The San Andreas Fault, 2243; Soil Liquefaction, 2402.

# EARTHQUAKES: ELASTIC WAVES

*Type of earth science:* Geophysics
*Field of study:* Seismology

*The vibrations of the earth, felt as earthquakes, are elastic waves in soil and solid rock. These waves are similar to sound waves, which travel through the air, and sonic waves, which travel through water.*

*Principal terms*

BODY WAVE: a seismic wave that propagates interior to a body; there are two kinds, P waves and S waves, that travel through the earth, reflecting and refracting off of the several layered boundaries within the earth

ELASTIC MATERIAL: a substance that, when compressed, bent, stretched, or deformed in any way, undergoes a degree of deformation that is proportional to the applied force and returns back to its original shape as soon as the force is removed

HOMOGENEOUS: having the same properties at every point; if elastic waves propagate in exactly the same way at every point, they are homogeneous

IDEAL SOLID: a theoretical solid that is isotropic, is homogeneous, and responds elastically under applied forces, stresses, compressions, tensions, or shears

ISOTROPIC: having properties the same in all directions; if elastic waves propagate at the same velocity in all directions, they are isotropic

REFLECTION: when an elastic wave strikes a boundary between two substances or between two rock layers of different seismic velocities, part of the incident ray bounces back (reflects)

REFRACTION: when an elastic wave passes through a boundary between two rock layers of different seismic velocities, the rays passing through are bent (refracted) in another direction

SURFACE WAVE: a seismic wave that propagates parallel to a free surface and whose amplitudes disappear at depth; there are two kinds, Rayleigh waves and Love waves, that travel at the surface around the earth

## Summary of the Phenomenon

Elastic waves are experienced frequently every day: Everything heard is an elastic wave in the air; every vibration felt, in the ground as a truck passes or in the floor from vibrations in a building, is from elastic waves in solid matter. Although the experience of elastic wave energy is familiar, the exact nature of this phenomenon is not something visible to the eye or easily described in a visual way. Ripples resulting from dropping an object in a still body of water move in ever-increasing circles away from the splash; such waves are not elastic; rather, they are gravity waves. Yet, elastic waves are analogous to this example in that they originate from a disturbance and propagate outward and away in concentric circles or spheres.

An elastic wave moves in an elastic medium, which can be a solid, liquid, or gas. A substance is said to respond elastically if when it is compressed, stretched, bent, or submitted to shear forces it deforms in proportion to the applied force and then immediately returns to its original unstressed state when the force is removed. A good illustration of this property is a spring scale. A 1-kilogram weight placed on the scale will cause the spring inside the scale to be stretched (deformed) into a longer length, such as dropping 1 centimeter. A 2-kilogram weight on the scale would cause it to move down 2 centimeters. Hence, the displacement of the spring is proportional to the force applied. When the weights are removed from the scale, it immediately returns to zero, its original unstressed length and shape. This is elastic behavior. If the spring of the scale stretched 1 centimeter for 1 kilogram and then stretched more or less than a centimeter for the second kilogram, it would not be elastic because it would not be a proportional response. Also, if the spring did not return to zero after the weight was removed but retained some permanent deformation, it would not be elastic.

In the case of wave propagation in the earth, consider the effect of striking the ground with a sledgehammer. When struck, the ground would be suddenly compressed, which would be transmitted to the neighboring soil and rock around and beneath the strike. Except in the immediate vicinity of the blow, where permanent deformation (nonelastic) may occur, the response of the neighboring soil and rock would be elastic. It would be temporarily compressed by the force of the blow and then immediately relax back into the former condition. A compression wave would irradiate spherically away from the blow, traveling across the surface (like the ripples on a pond) and down into the earth. In the passing of an elastic wave, the medium passing the wave is restored to its original unstressed state as if no wave had ever come through at all.

Elastic waves travel at certain velocities depending on the density and elastic stiffness or compressibility of the medium. If a substance is soft, elastic waves move more slowly; if it is very stiff, elastic waves move fast. In air, sound waves move at approximately 300 meters per second; in water, sonic waves move at roughly 1,200 meters per second; in rock, compressional waves move at a rate of from 3,000 to more than 10,000 meters per second, depending on the rock's hardness and how deeply it is buried.

If within a medium through which elastic waves can move the velocity is the same everywhere, that medium is called "homogeneous." If, in addition, at any given point in that medium the velocities are the same in all directions, the substance is termed "isotropic." In most rocks of the earth, which occur in layers, the deeper below the surface, the higher the velocity becomes. The increasing weight of the overburden acting on rocks found deeper in the earth causes their density and stiffness to change, and, generally, in the vertical direction the velocity of a seismic wave is different from its velocity in horizontal directions. Thus, many rocks of the earth are not isotropic; neither are they homogeneous. By analyzing seismograms from earthquakes, quarry blasts, and underground nuclear explosions, the inhomogeneities and anisotropies of the earth have been described to give a picture of what the earth's interior is like.

There are two basic kinds of elastic wave: P waves, or compressional waves, and S waves, or shear waves. P waves are sometimes called "push-pull" waves because they consist of a series of pushes (compressions) and pulls (rarefactions), where the motion of a particle of matter as the wave passes by is parallel to the direction the wave passed. S waves are sometimes called "shake" or "shear" waves, because they consist of shearing or shaking motions where the movement of a particle of matter as the wave passes by is transverse, or perpendicular, to the direction the wave passed. A "Slinky" toy spring, held in two hands, can provide an illustration of sending waves back and forth. The alternate stretched and compressed parts of the spring move from one end to the other. If a long rope is tied to a post and the end is shaken up and down, a wave will move from the shaken end to the post, but the motion of the particles of the rope are up and down, transverse to the wave motion. P waves can move in all substances, solid, liquid, or gas. S waves can move only in solids. Compressional and shear waves are the only types that can propagate anywhere interior to a solid, like the rocks of the earth. These are called "body waves." Earthquakes generate both compressional and shear waves at the source where the fault moves.

There are two other important kinds of elastic waves, but these travel only parallel to free surfaces, like the surface of the earth, and have amplitudes that decay with depth. They are called "surface waves." The two kinds are "Rayleigh waves" and "Love waves," each named after the scientist who discovered and described it.

When a Rayleigh wave passes by on the surface of the earth, a particle of soil or rock is first moved forward, then up, then backward, and then down to its starting point in an elliptical path. For Rayleigh waves, when the displaced particle is at the top of its elliptical motion, it is moving in the opposite direction of the Rayleigh wave front. This is called an "elliptic retrograde" motion. When a Love wave passes by on the surface of the earth, a particle of soil or rock is moved from side to side perpendicular to the direction of the wave front. Love waves are horizontally polarized shear waves traveling parallel with the surface.

With regard to velocity, compressional waves are the fastest; next are shear waves, which move at roughly six-tenths the speed of the compressional wave; slowest are the surface waves, which move at approximately nine-tenths the speed of shear waves.

One final aspect needs to be described in talking about elastic waves, and this is the form of the wave. Regardless of the type of wave (P, S, Rayleigh, or Love), they all consist of trains of disturbances that move through the earth. A wave that has only one vibration is a pulse. In elastic waves, even ones that sound like sharp pops or explosions, there is a train of several cycles of vibration—sometimes a few seconds in duration and sometimes for many minutes or even hours. (Rayleigh and Love waves can be recorded for an hour or more on seismographs when generated by a very strong earthquake.)

The form of a wave is described by its frequency and its amplitude, as well as by its particle motion. Frequency is merely the number of times per second that the vibrations occur as the wave passes. Earthquake waves have frequencies of from several cycles per second down to several seconds per cycle. In addition to the time between peaks of an elastic wave's passage, there is also a distance that can be measured between peaks. This is called the "wavelength." For waves in the earth, the wavelengths can vary from a few meters (for high-frequency P and S waves) to a kilometer or more (for low-frequency surface waves). Hence, in an earthquake one part of a railroad track can be under compression, being sheared to the left, while a few hundred meters away another part is under tension, being sheared to the right, all at the same instant.

## Methods of Study

Elastic waves in the earth are measured and recorded by various kinds of seismographs. Some measure vertical motions only, some horizontal; some measure compressional waves only, such as those that move through water. To describe the particle motion of a train of passing waves requires a set of three seismographs: one for vertical motion and two for horizontal—one for east-west motion and one for north-south.

Seismic stations permanently installed to monitor earthquakes are built in a variety of ways, depending on what is to be measured. A given seismic sensor can only detect a given band of frequencies; outside that band it is insensitive. Since earthquakes generate a wide range of frequencies from high to ultralow, some stations measure high frequencies (also called "short periods") while others measure low frequencies (called "long periods"). Moreover, seismic sensors respond only to a given range of amplitudes. Hence, some earthquake observatories have extremely sensitive instruments that detect and magnify even the tiniest vibrations 100,000 times or more. Other stations also have so-called strong motion instruments that do not record at all, unless a real jolt passes through. This diversity in equipment is necessary, because when strong high-amplitude seismic waves hit a high-magnification instrument, the readings go off the scale and cannot be deciphered. On the other end, strong-motion equipment is insensitive to smaller tremors.

Because the interaction of seismic waves with the details (inhomogeneities) within the earth's interior enables what is there to be described, buried out of sight, artificially generated seismic waves are sometimes used to find oil and other things of interest belowground. Virtually all the oil discovered in the mid-twentieth century has been found by means of "reflection seismic profiling." This method, used by oil companies the world over, usually entails the use of an explosive to send elastic waves into the ground. Then, by an array of seismic sensors called geophones, deployed to catch the reflections at the land surface, geophysicists can deduce the structures of the subsurface. Some seismic profiling methods employ only P waves, while some have been successful with artificial S-wave sources.

When P and S waves hit a boundary between two rock layers, they each split into four parts. A P wave, for example, will reflect back both a P and an S wave and will also transmit a portion of its energy through the boundary into the next layer down that also splits into a P wave and an S wave. The wave bouncing back is the "reflected" portion of the incident wave, while the part that passes through is the "refracted" portion. An incident S wave similarly splits into four parts, a reflected P and S and a refracted P and S.

Even though a source of elastic waves may be simple, generating only one kind of wave, as soon as boundaries between differing layers are encountered, other kinds of waves result, reflecting and refracting in many directions. Those that eventually find themselves back at the surface can be recorded. When P and S waves arrive at the surface, it is their complex interaction at the surface that produces the Rayleigh and Love waves. With regard to earthquake-generated waves, not only do waves reflect from the source back to the surface off the boundaries of crust, mantle, and core, but some waves can pass completely through the earth and be recorded on the other side. During an exceptionally strong earthquake, waves can refract through to the other side and then return again through the core and mantle to be recorded again on the original side. Surface waves generated by large earthquakes have also been known to circumnavigate the globe, sometimes circling several times before their amplitudes become too small to detect. In very large earthquakes (those of 8.6 or more on the Richter scale), these waves have been measured to complete as many as ten or more passages around the world, taking approximately 3 hours for each trip.

A wave train of a single type can change from one type to another repeatedly along its ray path. This is of great interest to seismologists. For example, a P wave may start from where it is generated at an earthquake fault and travel down until it hits the Mohorovičić, or Moho, discontinuity, the boundary between the earth's upper crust and mantle below. There it can refract through, turning into an S wave, bending its direction of travel slightly, and taking on a new velocity. As it propagates farther and farther downward, it speeds up until it hits the boundary of the outer core, where it must either change again or reflect back toward the surface. If it passes through the boundary, it must transform back into a P wave because the outer core of the earth acts like a plastic liquid and will not permit the passage of S waves. Continuing on past the center of the earth, it would strike the boundary between core and mantle on the other side and, again, it could change back into an S wave. As it traveled up toward the other side of the earth, it would gradually slow in speed until it hit the Moho on the other side. There it could turn, again, into a

P wave and move through the crust until it emerged at the ground surface. There it would be reflected back toward the earth's interior or, perhaps, follow a curved ray path that would skip back to the surface at another location.

During this long and varied path, the ray would travel at P-wave velocities when in a compressional phase and at S-wave velocities (roughly 40 percent slower) when in a shear phase.

## Context

It is evident that elastic wave propagation within a solid medium like the layered earth is very complex. Waves bound between various boundaries, skipping around the curved earth's surface, transforming from P to S phases within and from body to surface waves at the land's surface. It is easy to understand, then, why the study of elastic waves in the earth requires analysis of many recordings (seismograms) from many points all over the earth's surface and taken with a variety of instruments— some measuring high frequencies, some low, some responding only to strong vibrations, some with high "gain" (or sensitivity) to measure the small and the weak.

Understanding elastic wave propagation within the earth not only has been the means by which seismologists have been able to define the inner structure of the earth but also has enabled the discovery of almost all of the oil deposits found since the mid-twentieth century. Other practical applications include the monitoring of underground nuclear testing to verify that countries are living up to their treaties. Also, because submarine earthquakes are the cause of seismic sea waves, and because the seismic waves passing through the earth travel several times faster than the seismic sea waves (or tsunamis) do through water, these destructive waves from the sea can be predicted, sometimes hours before they strike a coastline, thus saving many lives.

## Bibliography

Aki, Keiiti, and Paul G. Richards. *Quantitative Seismology: Theory and Methods*. 2 vols. San Francisco: W. H. Freeman, 1980. This is an advanced text on elastic waves and earthquake seismology. A modern version of Ewing, Jardetzky, and Press (cited below) and the treatise by Love (also cited below), it is written at the graduate university level.

Bolt, Bruce A. *Inside the Earth*. San Francisco: W. H. Freeman, 1982. This book is an elementary but thorough treatment of seismic waves in the earth, useful to lower-level college or advanced high school students.

Bullen, K. E., and Bruce A. Bolt. *Introduction to Theory of Seismology*. 4th ed. Cambridge, England: Cambridge University Press, 1985. A thorough treatment of elastic wave theory, it is readable at the undergraduate science-major level.

Ewing, W. Maurice, Wenceslas S. Jardetzky, and Frank Press. *Elastic Waves in Layered Media*. New York: McGraw-Hill, 1957. This is a definitive text on elastic waves in layered media as they occur within the earth. Mathematical, it is written for graduate-school-level or advanced physics students.

Love, A. E. H. *A Treatise on the Mathematical Theory of Elasticity.* Mineola, N.Y.: Dover, 1944. First published in 1884 in Cambridge, England, this comprehensive work remains important. The Love waves of earthquake seismology were first described and discovered by the author. Best suited for graduate students.

Richter, Charles F. *Elementary Seismology.* San Francisco: W. H. Freeman, 1958. This is a classic work by the seismologist who devised the Richter scale. While dated in some subject areas, it is very readable and thorough. The chapter on elastic waves and their propagation through the earth is excellent.

*David Stewart*

## Cross-References

Earthquake Distribution, 421; Earthquake Engineering, 430; Earthquake Hazards, 437; Earthquake Locating, 445; Earthquake Magnitudes and Intensities, 452; Earthquake Prediction, 461; Famous Earthquakes, 476; An Overview of Earthquakes, 484; Seismic Reflection Profiling, 2333; Seismometers, 2340.

# FAMOUS EARTHQUAKES

*Type of earth science:* Geophysics
*Field of study:* Seismology

*Most of the casualties from great earthquakes occur from building collapse, fire, landslides, and tsunamis. Modern concepts of plate tectonics can account for the location of most great earthquakes, and sound planning can do much to minimize the dangers from them.*

### Principal terms

AFTERSHOCKS: earthquakes that follow a major earthquake and have nearly the same focus; they are caused by residual stresses not released by the main shock

EPICENTER: the point on the surface of the earth directly above the focus of an earthquake

FAULT: a fracture within the earth along which opposing masses of rock slip to produce earthquakes

FOCUS: the area or point within the earth where an earthquake originates

INTENSITY: the strength of shaking that an earthquake causes at a given point; intensity is generally strongest near the epicenter of an earthquake

MAGNITUDE: a measure of ground motion and energy release in an earthquake; an increase of one magnitude means roughly a thirtyfold increase in energy release

PLATE TECTONICS: the crust of the earth consists of a number of moving plates; most earthquakes occur at plate boundaries where moving plates are in contact

SEISMOGRAPH: an instrument for recording motion of the ground in an earthquake; most seismographs are pendulums that remain static as the ground moves

TSUNAMI: a large sea wave caused by coastal earthquakes, probably generated by submarine landslides; not all coastal earthquakes result in tsunamis

## Summary of the Phenomenon

Two measures are used for describing the strength of earthquakes: intensity and magnitude. Intensity, generally rated on the twelve-point modified Mercalli scale, is the degree of shaking noted at a given point. Intensity depends on the distance to the focus, the local geology, and the observer. Customarily expressed in Roman numerals, intensity ranges from I (felt by only a few observers) to XII (total destruction; ground motion powerful enough to throw objects into the air). Magnitude, usually expressed in terms of the Richter scale, is a measure of ground motion as measured on seismographs and is related to the total energy of an earthquake. The scale is defined so that an increase of one magnitude corresponds to a tenfold increase in ground oscillation, or approximately a thirtyfold increase in energy release. Earthquakes of magnitude 3 are often unnoticed; those of magnitude 5 produce widespread minor damage; those of magnitude 7 are considered major; and those above 8 are considered great. The greatest magnitude ever recorded is 8.9. Contrary to popular misconception, there is no upper or lower limit to the Richter scale; it appears, however, that the crust cannot store enough elastic energy to generate earthquakes of magnitudes greater than 9.

Clear relationships exist between plate tectonics and the occurrence of great earthquakes. The magnitude of an earthquake generally corresponds to the area of fault surface where slippage occurs. The larger the slippage area, the greater the energy required to overcome friction. Because the ocean basins have a thin crust (about 5 kilometers thick), great earthquakes are rare in the ocean basins. Most great earthquakes are associated with continental crust, which has an average thickness of 40 kilometers.

The greatest earthquakes (magnitude 8.5 and higher) occur where plates converge, such as in Japan or on the west coast of South America. In these regions, one plate dips beneath the other at a shallow angle, resulting in a very large area of fault surface. Rifts, where continental crust is pulled apart, and transcurrent faults, where one block of continental crust slides horizontally past another, also have produced earthquakes above magnitude 8. The most famous transcurrent fault is the San Andreas fault of California. A few great earthquakes have also occurred well within plates. Some are reasonably well understood: Most of the earthquakes of China and central Asia are a response to the collision of India with Asia. Others, such as the Charleston and New Madrid earthquakes in the United States, are poorly understood.

Little is known of great earthquakes of the distant past. The casualty figures reported for ancient earthquakes are often unreliable. Nevertheless, it can usually be assumed that earthquakes that devastated large areas also inflicted great casualties. Even for modern earthquakes, destruction is often so great that casualty figures can only be estimates; different sources frequently list casualty figures differing by many thousands.

Perhaps the earliest great earthquake to have major historical impact struck the Minoan civilization on Crete about 1450 B.C. During this earthquake, it appears that all the major palace complexes on Crete were destroyed. This earthquake possibly was related to the catastrophic eruption of Thera (Santorini), a volcano in the Aegean Sea approximately 120 kilometers north of Crete. The exact order of events is still uncertain.

The first earthquake to be well described destroyed the Greek city of Sparta in 464 B.C., killing a reported 20,000 people. In A.D. 62, the city of Pompeii in Italy was severely damaged by an earthquake. Pompeii is famous for being buried by an eruption of Vesuvius seventeen years later. An earthquake on July 21, 365, devastated Alexandria, Egypt, killing 50,000 and destroying the Pharos, or lighthouse—one of the Seven Wonders of the World.

The greatest killer earthquake in history struck Shaanxi in north-central China on January 24, 1556. In this region of China, many traditional dwellings were dug into hillsides of loess (wind-deposited silt). Collapse of these cave homes and landslides triggered by the earthquake reportedly killed 830,000. The area of devastation was so large that the death toll was certainly in the hundreds of thousands.

The catalog of famous modern earthquakes begins with the Lisbon earthquake of November 1, 1755. The city of Lisbon, Portugal, was demolished by three shocks between 9:30 and 10:00 A.M., with additional major aftershocks at 11:00 A.M. and 1:00 P.M. Approximately 70,000 people were killed by building collapse, fire, and a tsunami. Considerable damage also occurred in nearby Morocco. The Lisbon earthquake is sometimes listed as one of the greatest earthquakes of all times, producing widespread destruction as far away as Algeria and even being felt in the West Indies. In reality, the earthquakes in Algeria and the West Indies were separate events unrelated to the Lisbon earthquake. The earthquake produced effects far beyond the region where the shock was actually felt. Lake oscillations (seiches) were noted all over Western Europe, clocks stopped, and church bells rang. Many of these phenomena were noted and recorded carefully; observations showed that a wavelike disturbance had traveled outward from Lisbon. The Lisbon earthquake was thus the first earthquake to be studied systematically by modern scientific methods.

By coincidence, one of the strongest earthquakes ever to strike New England occurred off eastern Massachusetts on November 18, 1755. This event, which occurred just before news of the Lisbon shock reached America, heightened American consciousness of the Lisbon disaster. The first great earthquakes to be recorded in the United States were those that struck the New Madrid, Missouri, area on December 16, 1811, January 23, 1812, and February 7, 1812. These events are among the few recorded earthquakes of intensity XII, and they took place in a region not generally considered earthquake-prone. Surface effects in the epicentral area were profound. The Mississippi River was churned into turmoil, and large tracts of unstable ground were affected by surface cracks and subsidence. The shocks were felt as far away as New Orleans and caused church bells to ring in Boston. Because of the sparse population in the New Madrid area at that time, only one death was reported. The New Madrid earthquakes, despite the vast area over which they were felt, were not of extremely large magnitude: They probably had a magnitude between 7.5 and 8. In the central United States, flat-lying and uniform rock layers transmit seismic waves with high efficiency, so that an earthquake at New Madrid is felt over a much larger area than an equally powerful earthquake in a geologically complex region such as California.

On January 9, 1857, a major earthquake (probably magnitude 8) struck southern California. At least 60 kilometers of the San Andreas fault ruptured near Fort Tejon, north of Los Angeles. A strong earthquake (possibly magnitude 7) struck

Charleston, South Carolina, on August 31, 1886. The earthquake was felt over most of the east coast of the United States and killed approximately 110 people. This earthquake was the first in the United States to receive wide scientific attention.

For many Americans, the word "earthquake" is synonymous with the San Francisco earthquake of April 18, 1906. The earthquake, with a magnitude of 8.3, was officially reported to have killed about 700, but later estimates have placed the death toll as high as 2,500. In October, 1989, an earthquake of magnitude 7.1 would again leave the city with fatalities. The 1906 earthquake triggered fires that could not be fought because of ruptured water mains. As a result, a large area of the city was burned. From a scientific standpoint, the earthquake is important because it revealed the extent of the San Andreas fault. North of San Francisco, fence lines and roads were offset as much as 6 meters by the fault. The fault ruptured for at least 280 kilometers, possibly as much as 400.

On September 1, 1923, an earthquake of magnitude 8.3 destroyed much of Tokyo and Yokohama, Japan. This earthquake is notable for the devastating fire that followed it. The earthquake struck when thousands of open cooking fires were in use all over Tokyo. Traditional Japanese construction, which relies extensively on wood and bamboo, is very resistant to collapse in earthquakes but is also very combustible. The earthquake set thousands of fires that coalesced into a firestorm— a self-sustaining whirlwind in which updrafts above the fire draw air in from the outside and keep the fire supplied with oxygen. About 140,000 people died. Forty thousand of those who died had taken refuge in an open square and suffocated from lack of air.

A little-known earthquake (magnitude 7.9) in southeastern Alaska on July 9, 1958, is remarkable for creating the highest wave ever recorded. The earthquake triggered an avalanche into one arm of Lituya Bay, sending the water 530 meters over a ridge on the other side of the bay. Anchorage, Alaska, was damaged by a magnitude-8.3 earthquake on Good Friday, March 27, 1964. Much of the damage to Anchorage was the result of liquefaction of an unstable layer of clay a few meters below the surface. When the seismic shaking liquefied the clay, the ground above broke up, tilted, or collapsed. A tsunami, reaching up to 30 meters in height, devastated the nearby coast. Of the 131 people killed in Alaska, 122 were killed by the tsunami. The tsunami swept down the coast of North America, causing little damage in most places. At Crescent City, California, however, the bottom topography of the harbor focused the wave, which swept into the center of town, killing twelve people. Surveys of the epicentral region showed that almost 300,000 square kilometers of crust had been measurably deformed. Some points on the coast moved seaward by 20 meters; shorelines were uplifted by 15 meters in places. These motions are among the greatest ever documented for any earthquake.

A magnitude-7.7 earthquake in Peru on May 31, 1970, killed about 70,000 people, including the victims of one of the worst landslide disasters in history. The earthquake triggered a rock and ice avalanche from the summit of 6,768-meter Huascaran, the highest peak in Peru. A portion of the landslide rode over a 250-meter ridge and buried the town of Yungay, killing approximately 20,000 people. This earthquake was the worst earthquake disaster in the Southern Hemisphere.

The greatest earthquake disaster of the twentieth century in terms of loss of life—and the second greatest in history—took place on July 28, 1976, when a magnitude-8.2 earthquake struck Tangshan in northeastern China, an urban area with about 10 million people. According to the most widely accepted estimate, 600,000 people were killed.

The worst earthquake to strike North America killed 20,000 people in Mexico City on September 19, 1985. The epicenter of the magnitude-8 earthquake was actually on the Pacific coast, some 400 kilometers from Mexico City, yet damage on the coast was light. Buildings on the coast were generally modern, well built, and with foundations on bedrock. Mexico City, in contrast, is built on an ancient lake bed. Unconsolidated sediment shakes badly in earthquakes, accounting for the great damage in Mexico City. Many modern steel-frame buildings were undamaged, while poor-grade masonry suffered badly.

On December 7, 1988, an earthquake measuring magnitude 8 killed an estimated 80,000 people in Soviet Armenia. This event was notable for its political impact, because it happened at a time when the Soviet Union appeared to be moving toward greater political openness. For the first time in many years, the Soviet Union accepted foreign relief efforts after a natural disaster and permitted foreign news coverage at a disaster scene.

## Methods of Study

Great earthquakes present special problems and opportunities for geologists. Because of their great energy release, earthquakes are detected clearly by instruments all over the planet; these records frequently reveal details of earth's structure that cannot be detected on the records of smaller earthquakes. The infrequency and unpredictability of great earthquakes, however, mean that instruments and observers are rarely close by when the event occurs, and instruments that are close by are often destroyed.

Ground motion during great earthquakes can be measured by special seismographs called strong-motion seismographs. Strong-motion studies require that instruments be set up in locations that might experience major earthquakes. These instruments are left in place, possibly for years. After remaining dormant for a long time, the instruments must work properly when the earthquake occurs. The need to place and periodically tend instruments that may never record an event makes strong-motion studies expensive.

It is possible to simulate the effects of earthquakes on buildings. During the planning stage, models of the proposed building can be tested on a vibrating table or through computer modeling. Existing buildings can be shaken artificially. The apparatus for testing buildings consists of a set of large, rotating, off-center weights. Sensors at critical points in the building can detect motion without subjecting the building to destructive vibrations. Corrective measures might include reinforcing weak portions of the structure or redesigning connecting wings so that they can vibrate independently.

Short-term earthquake prediction on the lines of severe weather warning is probably not achievable in the near future. Geologists are pursuing a variety of studies aimed at assessing the long-term likelihood of great earthquakes. One obvious and low-cost approach is simply to compile all historical records of earthquakes. China and the Middle East, areas with the longest and best written records, show variations in intensity and location of earthquakes on a time scale of centuries. The short historical record of the United States is insufficient for long-term seismic studies.

One way to extend the record of great earthquakes is to look for geological changes created by ancient events. In Japan, uplifted shorelines have been identified with specific historical earthquakes. At Pallett Creek, north of Los Angeles, trenches across the San Andreas fault have revealed evidence of earthquakes over the last 2,000 years. Each earthquake ruptured sediment layers below the then-existing ground surface. Radiocarbon dating (using radioactive carbon in the sediment as a geologic clock) establishes the age of each fault break. The average interval of great earthquakes in this area is approximately 140 years, but actual intervals have ranged from seventy-five to three hundred years.

## Context

Most of the casualties from great earthquakes result from a few basic causes. Building collapse is a major cause of loss of life. Wood-frame buildings, which are flexible, and steel-frame buildings, which are very strong, are the safest kinds of buildings during earthquakes. Nonreinforced masonry and adobe (mud brick) are the most dangerous; unfortunately, these construction styles are very common in underdeveloped nations. Fire is another major threat in urban areas. Earthquakes overturn stoves and furnaces, rupture gas lines, and create electrical short circuits. At the same time, ruptured water mains and streets blocked with rubble impede fire-fighting efforts. Earthquake-induced landslides are a hazard in mountainous areas and have caused tremendous loss of life.

Tsunamis are a threat in coastal areas. Believed to be generated by submarine landslides, tsunamis are waves of low height and long length that travel at up to 600 kilometers per hour. Because of their breadth and low height, they are entirely unnoticed by ships at sea, but can cause great damage when they reach shore, sometimes thousands of kilometers away. Whether a tsunami causes damage depends greatly on its direction of travel, local tide and weather conditions, and particularly on the bottom topography near shore. Tsunami warnings are routinely issued after large earthquakes.

There are a few misconceptions about great earthquakes. After a newsworthy earthquake, people often wonder if earthquakes are becoming unusually frequent. The reverse has been true in the twentieth century: There are about two earthquakes per year of magnitude 8 on the average, in contrast to an annual average of eight during the years 1896-1907. One apparent pattern is real, however: Great killer earthquakes are becoming more common. The reason is demographic rather than geologic. Many seismically active regions are in underdeveloped nations where populations, especially in cities, are growing explosively and where construction standards are often poor. The population at risk from earthquakes is steadily increasing.

There are a few geologic misconceptions about earthquakes. Earthquakes frequently cause ground subsidence in areas underlain by poorly consolidated materials, often causing cracks to open on the surface; but stories of fissures opening and engulfing people, buildings, or even entire villages are unfounded. Most of these stories are probably inspired by landslides. Earthquakes and volcanoes tend to occur in the same geologic settings, and there are some recorded cases of major earthquakes associated with the eruption of a nearby volcano. As a general rule, though, earthquakes do not trigger volcanic activity. Also, the earthquakes that accompany volcanic eruptions are generally not very large.

## Bibliography

Anderson, D. L. "The San Andreas Fault." *Scientific American* 224 (February, 1971): 52. A description of the most famous North American fault, particularly good for its block diagrams showing the complex southern portion of the fault system. *Scientific American* is written for nonspecialists at a college reading level.

Boore, D. M. "The Motion of the Ground in Earthquakes." *Scientific American* 237 (December, 1977): 68. A summary of how earthquakes occur, the types of motions they cause, and their effects on structures.

Coffman, Jerry L., Carl A. Von Hake, and C. W. Stover. *Earthquake History of the United States*. U.S. Department of Commerce Publication 41-1. Washington, D.C.: National Oceanic and Atmospheric Administration and U.S. Geological Survey, 1982. The most detailed general reference on earthquakes in the United States. Contains lists of events by geographic area, descriptions of all widely felt earthquakes, maps of earthquake epicenters, and detailed references. Written at a nontechnical level. A must for any student of earthquakes.

Molnar, P., and P. Tapponier. "The Collision Between India and Eurasia." *Scientific American* 236 (April, 1977): 30. The collision between India and Eurasia causes faulting and great earthquakes over all of China and central Asia. Simple mechanical models duplicate the behavior of the crust remarkably well.

Nash, J. R. *Darkest Hours*. Chicago: Nelson-Hall, 1976. A nontechnical encyclopedia of disasters. Descriptions of events are generally accurate, but some errors in geological terminology were noted. Has extensive reference lists for each type of disaster, mostly popular books and periodicals. Individual articles lack references, and specific events can be hard to find. For example, the article on the great 1923 Tokyo earthquake is titled "Japan."

Richter, C. F. *Elementary Seismology*. San Francisco: W. H. Freeman, 1958. A college-level text. Predates the general acceptance of plate tectonics by geologists, so many of its geological speculations are dated. Still valuable for its discussions of the history of seismology and the Richter scale, the effects of earthquakes, and descriptions of great earthquakes. There are lists of great earthquakes, with references for most of them.

Wesson, R. L., and R. E. Wallace. "Predicting the Next Great Earthquake in California." *Scientific American* 252 (February, 1985): 35. A summary of the major active faults in California, their history, and an assessment of the likelihood of activity in the near future. The most likely location for the next great earthquake is the southern San Andreas fault or one of its branches in the Los Angeles basin.

*Steven I. Dutch*

## Cross-References

# AN OVERVIEW OF EARTHQUAKES

*Type of earth science:* Geophysics
*Field of study:* Seismology

*An earthquake is the sudden movement of the ground caused by the rapid release of energy that has accumulated along fault zones in the earth's crust. The earth's fundamental structure and composition are revealed by earthquakes through the study of waves that are both reflected and refracted from the interior of the earth.*

*Principal terms*

CRUST: the uppermost 5-40 kilometers of the earth

DEFORMATION: a change in the shape of a rock

ELASTIC REBOUND: the process whereby rocks snap back to their original shape after they have been broken along a fault as a result of an applied stress

LITHOSPHERE: the solid part of the upper mantle and the crust where earthquakes occur

MANTLE: the thick layer under the crust that contains convection currents that move the crustal plates

STRAIN: the percent deformation resulting from a given stress

STRESS: a force per unit area

## Summary of the Phenomenon

Earthquakes are sudden vibrational movements of the earth's crust and are caused by a rapid release of energy within the earth. They are of critical importance to humans, first, because they reveal much about the interior of the earth and, second, because they are potentially one of the most destructive naturally occurring forces found on earth.

The outermost skin of the earth, called the crust, is in constant motion as a result of large convection cells within the upper mantle that circulate heat from the interior of the earth toward the surface. The crust of the earth is about 5 kilometers thick in the oceanic basins and about 40 kilometers thick in the continental masses, while the upper mantle is about 700 kilometers thick. Because the crust is relatively thin compared to the upper mantle, the crust is broken up into several plates that float along the top of each convection cell in the upper mantle. Most earthquakes occur along the boundaries separating the individual plates and are represented by faults that may be thousands of kilometers long and tens of kilometers deep. Although the vast majority of earthquakes occur along these plate boundaries, some also occur within the plate interior. The rocks on either side of the fault fit tightly together and produce great resistance to movement. As the blocks of rock attempt to move against one another, the resistance of movement causes stress, which is a force per unit area, to build up along the fault. As the stress continues to build, the rocks in the immediate vicinity slowly deform, or bend until the strength of the rock is exceeded at some point along the fault. Suddenly, the rocks break violently and return to their undeformed state, much as a rubber band snaps to its original shape when it breaks. This rapid release of stress is called elastic rebound. The point at which the stress is released is called the focus of an earthquake, and that point at the earth's surface directly above the focus is called the epicenter.

The release of energy associated with elastic rebound manifests itself as waves propagating away from the focus. When these waves of energy reach the surface of the earth, the land will oscillate, causing an earthquake. These waves move through the earth in two ways. P (primary) waves move in a back-and-forth motion in which the motion of the rock is in the same direction as the direction of energy propagation. This type of wave motion is analogous to placing a spring in a tube and pushing on one end of the spring. The motion of the spring in the tube is in the same direction as is the motion of the energy. These waves are called primary because they move through the earth faster than do other waves—up to about 25 kilometers per second. Thus, P waves are the first waves to be received at a seismic recording station. Because the individual atoms in a rock move back and forth along the direction of energy movement, P waves can move through solids and liquids and, for this reason, do not tell geologists much about the state (solid or liquid) of a given rock at depth. In contrast to P waves, for S waves, the rock motion is perpendicular to the direction of energy propagation. Guitar strings vibrate in a similar manner: Each part of the guitar string moves back and forth while the energy moves along the string to the ends. S waves are the second waves to be received at a seismic recording station and derive their name from this fact. Unlike P waves, S waves cannot move through liquids but can move through solids. Thus, when a P wave is received by a seismic station but is not followed by an S wave, seismologists know that a liquid layer is between the focus of the earthquake and the receiving seismic station. Both S and P waves are bent, or refracted, as they move in the earth's interior. This refraction occurs as the result of the increase in density of rocks at greater depths. Furthermore, both types of waves are reflected off sharp boundaries, representing a change in rock type located within the earth. Thus, by using these properties of S and P waves, geologists have mapped the interior of the earth and know whether a given region is solid or liquid.

Although S and P waves represent the way seismic energy moves through the earth, once this energy reaches the earth's surface, much of it is converted to another type of wave. L (Love) waves move in the same manner as do S waves, but they are restricted to surface propagation of energy. L waves have a longer wavelength and are usually restricted to within a few kilometers of the epicenter of an earthquake. These waves cause more damage to structures than do P and S waves because the longer wavelength causes larger vibrations of the earth's surface.

The amount of energy released by an earthquake is of vital importance to humans. Many active fault zones, such as the famous San Andreas fault in California, produce earthquakes on an almost daily basis, although most of these earthquakes are not felt and cause no damage to man-made structures. These minor earthquakes indicate that the stress that is accumulating along some portion of a fault is continuously being released. It is only when the stresses accumulate without continual release that large devastating earthquakes occur. The intensity of an earthquake is dependent not only on the energy released by the earthquake but also on the nature of rocks or sediments at the earth's surface. Softer sediments such as the thick muds that underlie Mexico City will vibrate with a greater magnitude than will the very rigid rocks, such as granites, found in other parts of the world. Thus, the great earthquake that devastated Mexico City in 1985 was in part the result of the nature of the sediments upon which the city is built.

For a given locality, earthquakes occur in cycles. Stress accumulates over a period of time until the forces exceed the strength of the rocks, causing an increase in minor earthquake activity. Shortly thereafter, several foreshocks, or small earthquakes, occur immediately before a large earthquake. When a large earthquake occurs, it is usually followed by many aftershocks, which may also be rather intense. These aftershocks occur as the surrounding rocks along the fault plane readjust to the release of stress by the major earthquake. The cycle then repeats itself with a renewed increase in stress along the fault. Although seismologists can usually tell what part of the seismic cycle a region is experiencing, it is difficult to predict the duration of each of these cycles; thus, it is impossible to predict precisely when an earthquake will occur.

## Methods of Study

Seismographs are the primary instruments used to study earthquakes. All seismographs consist of five fundamental elements: a support structure, a pivot, an inertial mass, a recording device, and a clock. The support structure for a seismograph is always solidly attached to the ground in such a fashion that it will oscillate with the earth during an earthquake. A pivot, consisting of a bar attached to the support structure via a low-friction hinge, separates a large mass from the rest of the seismograph. This pivot allows the inertial mass to remain stationary during an earthquake while the rest of the instrument moves with the ground. The recording device consists of a pen attached to the inertial mass and a roll of paper that is attached to the support structure. Finally, the clock records the exact time on the paper so that the time of arrival of each wave type is noted. When an earthquake wave arrives at a seismic station, the support structure moves with the ground. The inertial mass and the pen, however, remain stationary. As the paper is unrolled, usually by a very accurate motor, the wave is recorded on the paper by the stationary pen. Modern seismographs, however complex in design, always contain these basic elements. The clock, which each minute places a small tick mark on the recording, is calibrated on a daily basis by a technician using international time signals from atomic clocks. The recording pen often consists of an electromagnet that converts movement of the inertial mass relative to the support structure to an electrical current that drives a light pen. The light pen emits a narrow beam of light onto long strips of photographic film that are developed at a later date.

Seismologists have adopted two widely used scales, which are called the Richter and Mercalli scales, to measure the energy released by an earthquake. The Richter magnitude scale is based on the amplitude of seismic waves that are recorded at seismic stations. Because seismic stations are rarely located at the epicenter of earthquakes, the amplitude of the seismic wave must be corrected for the amount of energy lost over the distance that the wave traveled. Thus, the Richter magnitude reported by any seismic station for a given earthquake will be approximately the same. Richter magnitudes are open-ended, meaning that any amount of seismic energy can be calculated. The weakest earthquakes have Richter magnitudes less than 3.0 and release energy less than $10^{14}$ ergs. These earthquakes are not usually felt but are recorded by seismic stations. Earthquakes between magnitudes 4.0 and 5.5 are felt but usually cause no damage to structures; they release energy between $10^{15}$ and $10^{16}$ ergs. Earthquakes that have magnitudes between 5.5 and 7.0 cause slight to considerable damage to buildings and release energy between $10^{18}$ and $10^{24}$ ergs. Earthquakes that are greater than 7.5 on the Richter scale generate energy up to $10^{25}$ ergs—as much as a small nuclear bomb. The Mercalli intensity scale is not based on the energy released by an earthquake but rather on the amount of shaking that is felt on the ground; it rates earthquakes from Roman numerals I to XII. Unlike the Richter scale, the Mercalli scale provides descriptions of sensations felt by observers and of the amount of damage that results from an earthquake. Thus, an earthquake of Mercalli intensity I is felt only by a very few persons, while an earthquake of intensity XII causes total destruction of virtually all buildings.

Both the Mercalli and Richter scales have advantages and disadvantages. The Mercalli scale provides the public with a more descriptive understanding of the intensity of an earthquake than does the Richter scale. The damage caused by an earthquake is a function not only of the energy released by such an event but also of the nature of the sediments or rocks upon which the buildings in the vicinity are constructed. The Richter scale is best used to study specifically the amount of energy release by an earthquake. Finally, the Richter scale, which is purely quantitative, does not rely on subjective observations such as those required by the Mercalli scale.

The exact location of an earthquake epicenter can be deduced from three seismographic stations using triangulation techniques. Because the P and S waves travel at different velocities in the earth, seismologists can determine the distance from the station to the epicenter. They calculate the difference in time between the first arrival of the P and S waves, respectively, at the station. They then divide this time difference by the difference in wave velocities to obtain the distance to the epicenter. The earthquake must have occurred along a circle whose radius is the distance so calculated and whose center is the seismographic station; any three stations that record the event can be used to draw three such circles, which will intersect at a single point. This point is the epicenter.

## Context

Earthquakes are one of the most important processes that occur within the earth because they have such a profound effect on how and where people should develop cities. Geologists understand how and where earthquakes occur yet, despite their best efforts, they still cannot accurately determine when an earthquake will happen. They are merely able to predict that a large earthquake will occur in a particular region "in the near future." Very great earthquakes of magnitude 8 or greater, such as the San Francisco earthquake of 1906, occur about every five to ten years throughout the world. Industrialized societies, such as Japan, the United States, and many European countries, have developed buildings that are capable of withstanding devastating seismic catastrophes, but other countries are not as fortunate. Furthermore, some great earthquakes occur in regions that are not considered seismically active. The great Charleston, South Carolina, earthquake of 1886 or the Tangshan, China, earthquake of 1976 are examples of seismic events that could not have been easily predicted using modern technology. In such regions, buildings are not designed to withstand devastating earthquakes. Finally, many regions of the world do not experience earthquakes on a daily basis and, thus, their governments lack the motivation to plan adequately for such potential catastrophic events.

## Bibliography

Bolt, Bruce A. *Earthquakes: A Primer*. San Francisco: W. H. Freeman, 1988. This book is an excellent introduction to earthquakes and is written at a level that most laypersons can understand.

Hodgson, John H. *Earthquakes and Earth Structure*. Englewood Cliffs, N.J.: Prentice-Hall, 1964. This source provides the reader with an understanding of how earthquakes are used to determine the structure and composition of the interior of the earth.

McKenzie, D. P. "The Earth's Mantle." *Scientific American* 249 (September, 1983): 66-78. This article, written at the college undergraduate level, is a very complete description of current scientific understanding of the interior of the earth.

Nichols, D. R., and J. M. Buchanan-Banks. *Seismic Hazards and Land-Use Planning*. U.S. Geological Survey Circular 690. Washington, D.C.: Government Printing Office, 1974. The effect of earthquakes on man-made structures is discussed in this short bulletin. Written explicitly for the layperson by the United States government, it provides additional sources of information for land-use planning.

Press, Frank. "Earthquake Prediction." *Scientific American* 232 (May, 1975): 14-23. Press's article details geologists' current understanding of earthquake prediction. Also provides a discussion of the methods by which earthquakes can be predicted. Written at the college undergraduate level.

Press, Frank, and R. Siever. *Earth*. 4th ed. San Francisco: W. H. Freeman, 1985. This text includes one of the most complete descriptions of the causes of earthquakes, their measurement, where they occur, how they can be predicted, and how they affect humans. Places earthquakes into the scope of the science of geology. An excellent bibliography, index, and a short geologic dictionary. Written for the freshman college student.

United States Department of the Interior. *Earthquake Information Bulletin.* Washington, D.C.: Government Printing Office. This bimonthly bulletin provides the reader with a concise understanding of where earthquakes occur in the United States and which regions are likely to be affected in the future. Also lists other sources of information on earthquakes. For general and specialized readers.

*A. Kem Fronabarger*

## Cross-References

# EARTH'S AGE

*Type of earth science:* Geochemistry
*Field of study:* Geochronology

*Determining the age of the earth is one of the great achievements of science. Until the eighteenth century, all geological phenomena were believed to have been produced by historical catastrophes such as great floods and earthquakes. The new geology showed that the earth was billions of years old, rather than thousands as many had previously believed, and that the earth had the form it did because of slow uniform processes rather than catastrophes.*

*Principal terms*

CATASTROPHISM: the theory that the large-scale features of the earth were created suddenly by catastrophes in the past; the opposite of uniformitarianism

GEOCHRONOLOGY: the study of the time scale of the earth; it attempts to develop methods that allow the scientist to reconstruct the past by dating events such as the formation of rocks

ISOTOPE: atoms with the same number of protons in the nucleus but with differing numbers of neutrons; a particular element will generally have several different isotopes occurring naturally

RADIOACTIVITY: the process by which an unstable atomic nucleus spontaneously emits a particle (or particles) and changes into another atom

SEDIMENTARY: rocks that are formed by a layering process that is generally easily visible in a cross section of the rock

UNIFORMITARIANISM: the theory that processes currently operating in nature have always been operating; it suggests that the large-scale features of the earth were developed very slowly over vast periods of time

## Summary of the Phenomenon

In the middle of the seventeenth century, Joseph Barber Lightfoot of the prestigious University of Cambridge in England penned the following words: "Heaven and earth, center and circumference, were made in the same instant of time, and clouds full of water, and man was created by the Trinity on the 26th of October 4004 B.C. at 9 o'clock in the morning." At the time that Lightofoot wrote those words, this statement expressed the most informed opinion on the age of the earth—namely, that it could be calculated by adding up the ages of the people recorded in the Old Testament and assuming that Adam and Eve were created at about the same time as was the earth. This was the method that most scientists—including Nicolaus Copernicus, Johannes Kepler, and Sir Isaac Newton—used to date the earth, and much effort was expended analyzing the first few books of the Old Testament "scientifically."

A little over a century later, a Scottish geologist named James Hutton suggested that there was a better way to determine the past history of the earth than by poring over biblical genealogies. Hutton believed that processes currently operating in nature could be extrapolated back in time to shed light on the historical development of the earth. This idea—that historical processes are essentially the same as present processes—is called uniformitarianism. In 1785, he presented his new views on geology in a paper entitled "Theory of the Earth: Or, An Investigation of the Laws Observable in the Composition, Dissolution, and Restoration of Land upon the Globe." Uniformitarianism became the foundation of the newly developing science of historical geology. Charles Lyell, who was born in the year of Hutton's death, extended these new ideas and laid the foundation for what was to become a powerful new science. The major argument was over the age of the earth. Was it really billions of years old, as suggested by new discoveries and theories, or was it only a few thousand years old, as everyone had previously believed? The materials from which the earth is constructed are certainly very old. Many of the atoms in the earth date from the beginning of the universe, 15 to 20 billion years ago. The establishment of criteria by which the age of anything will be determined is guided by the need for that age to be a meaningful physical quantity. The conventional definition of age for a person (number of years since birth) is meaningful; the number of years since the origin of the atoms in a person's body would not be meaningful, because it is not relevant to that particular person's duration of existence as that person. A meaningful definition for the age of the earth can thus be formulated as follows: The age of the earth is the time since its composite materials acquired an organization that could be identified with the present earth.

Current theories of the formation of the earth suggest that the atoms of the earth and all the other members of the solar system formed a cloud of interstellar material that existed in a corner of the Milky Way galaxy several billion years ago. Under the influence of gravity, this cloud of material began to condense in those regions where the concentration of material was sufficiently higher than average. This nebular cloud, as it is called, gave birth to the earth, the sun, and the planets. As the material from which the earth was forming condensed, a number of events occurred: The density increased to the point where the mutual repulsion of the particles balanced the gravity from the newly formed "planet"; the planet became hotter as friction from the now-dense material became a significant source of energy; and energy given off by materials inside the planet was unable to escape into space and was absorbed, further increasing the temperature. The early earth was therefore very hot and existed in a molten state for many years.

There is thus no unique age for the earth. Rather, there is a time period that can realistically be described as the "birth" of the earth. This time period was millions of years long, and any dates given for the age of the earth must necessarily reflect this ambiguity. Fortunately, the age of the earth is measured in billions of years, so the uncertainties surrounding the exact time of its birth do not significantly affect measurements of its age.

Since the initial formation of the earth, many processes have been taking place: Unstable (radioactive) materials have been decaying into other elements; the initial rotation rate has been declining as friction from the tides and the moon has worked to slow the rotation of the earth; mountains have been rising under the influence of global tectonics, and rivers have been formed from the ceaseless activities of erosion; and evolution has been transforming the planet, changing sterile compounds into organic, and barren wasteland into ecological congestion as the phenomenon of life has manifested itself over the face of the globe. As these various physical processes traverse the earth, they leave footprints as evidence of their passing. When these footprints are studied, the history of the earth can be reconstructed. In some cases, this reconstruction can lead all the way back to the origin of the earth, thus providing an answer to the question "How old is the earth?"

## Methods of Study

Current estimates put the age of the earth at about 4.6 billion years. This figure is firmly supported by a number of measurements—some very direct and straightforward and some rather subtle. Life itself can be used as a clock. For example, trees add distinguishable layers of growth at a rate of one a year; these are the familiar "rings" that can be counted on a stump of wood. Counting these rings provides a very accurate clock for determining the age of the tree. Giant sequoias in California are regularly dated at about three thousand years old, and the bristlecone pine has been dated at almost five thousand years. Samples of sedimentary rock, which form yearly layers called varves, can extend back as far as twenty thousand years. Unfortunately, all these annual processes that provide a direct year-by-year chronicle of earth history provide no useful data beyond a few tens of thousands of years.

There are other, less direct, uniformitarian processes, however, that perform somewhat better in this regard. Measurements of erosion, the salinity of the ocean, the strength and direction of the earth's magnetic field, and the internal heat of the earth can all yield values for the "age" of the earth, measured in millions rather than thousands of years. The validity of each of these indirect measurements requires a strict uniformitarian character for the nature of the process; this assumption, however, is not legitimate for most of these processes, which explains why the ages determined from their application are so discordant and unreliable.

The most consistent geological chronometer is based on radioactive decay, an atomic/nuclear phenomenon. All atoms consist of a densely packed nucleus housing a number of protons, which have a positive charge, and neutrons, which have no charge. Because the protons are all positively charged, they repel one another; an atomic nucleus would immediately explode if it were not for a different nuclear force, called the strong force, that holds them together. Every nucleus exists in a state of dynamic tension as the electrical force tries to blow it apart and the strong nuclear force tries to hold it together. Certain nuclei are frequently unstable; that is, they have a tendency to disintegrate spontaneously into other, more stable, nuclei. This disintegration is initiated by yet another nuclear force, the weak force.

Usually the protons in the nucleus of an atom are paired with a particular number of neutrons in such a way that the nucleus will be stable. For the first few elements on the periodic table, the neutron/proton ratio is equal to one, but for larger atoms, the ratio increases as the neutrons start to outnumber the protons. For almost all the elements, there are certain nuclear combinations of protons and neutrons that are stable. By definition, members of the same atomic species have the same number of protons in the nucleus and thus the same atomic number. Atoms with differing numbers of neutrons are called isotopes of that element. Carbon, for example, normally has twelve particles in the nucleus—six protons and six neutrons—and is therefore designated carbon 12. A common isotope, however, has two extra neutrons and is designated carbon 14.

The detailed structure of a particular nucleus determines its long-term stability. Most of the nuclear configurations found in nature, such as hydrogen and helium, are stable indefinitely, or at least for a time that is much longer than the age of the universe (about 20 billion years). Unstable nuclei, on the other hand, are stable for only a finite period of time, which can be either very short (a fraction of a second) or very long (billions of years), depending on the composition of the particular nucleus.

The period of stability for an unstable nucleus is known as its half-life. A half-life is defined to be the time period during which one-half of the nuclei of a given sample will spontaneously decay into another nuclear species. The half-life of carbon 14, for example, is about 5,730 years. This means that in 5,730 years, one-half of an original carbon 14 nucleus, called the parent, will spontaneously decay into another element, nitrogen 14, called the "daughter" element. Over time, the parent element will gradually transform into the daughter. The ratio of daughter to parent can be used to determine how long the parent has been decaying and thus how old the material containing the parent is. It is important to note that the assumption of uniformitarianism for radioactive decay rates is considered very reasonable. Unlike the other processes mentioned above, there seems to be very few mechanisms in nature that can disturb the constancy of the radioactive "clock."

A number of radioactive materials are found in nature, all with differing half-lives. Each can be used to find the ages consistent with their half-lives; that is, a material with a long half-life, such as uranium 238 (whose half-life is almost 5 billion years), can be used to date objects that are billions of years old, and carbon 14 can be used to date objects that are thousands of years old.

Radioactive dating has been applied to many rocks found on the earth. The oldest rocks believed to have formed on the earth are from a volcano in western Greenland and have been dated at about 3.8 billion years, using uranium 238. It is difficult to find very ancient rocks on the surface of the earth, because most of the earth's surface has been rebuilt many times since the earth was born. There are probably older rocks in the deep interior of the earth.

The currently accepted age for the earth, 4.6 billion years, was obtained by dating meteorites that fall to earth from space. These meteorites are believed to have been formed at the same time as was the earth and to have existed in the vacuum of space until they were captured by the gravity from the earth. Similar dates have been obtained from the rocks brought back from the moon, which is believed to have formed at about the same time as the earth.

While many questions remain about the details of the formation of the earth, two facts seem clear: First, the earth owes its origin to the same processes that brought the solar system into existence; second, those processes can be dated with a high degree of confidence at between 4 and 5 billion years ago.

## Context

The problem of the age of the earth is part of a much larger scientific question, which exists at the interface between the very practical study of the earth and its various properties and the more esoteric question of the origin and evolution of the universe as a whole. On the practical side, knowledge of the earth's various and occasionally delicate properties is important for the future of the human race. By knowing how long the earth has been in existence, scientists are better able to understand the processes that have shaped the surface of the earth into the form that it has today. Predicting earthquakes, hunting for oil, monitoring the spread of the sea floor—all these practical questions require knowledge of large-scale planetary processes, the same kind of knowledge that illuminates the question of the age of the earth. Furthermore, knowing that the earth is billions of years old and can easily survive for billions more should encourage human societies to take better care of the planet.

From a more esoteric or speculative point of view, the age of the earth is important because it speaks to the most fundamental questions that are asked about the place of human beings in the universe. How old is this planet? How was it formed? In the century or so since geological science overthrew the seventeenth century notion of a much younger earth, people have struggled with finding a new place in the universe. The argument that began centuries ago is still heard in courtrooms across the United States as "creation science" once again argues that the earth is thousands, not billions, of years old. Legal battles rage over the issue of whether high schools across the country should teach geochronology that is based on religious dogma rather than on scientific research. Research is still being done on this very important scientific question and no doubt will continue into the foreseeable future as the human mind strives to learn more about the earth. The growing awareness of how dependent humans are on the continued health of the earth is a powerful incentive to learn more about their planetary home.

## Bibliography

Haber, Frances C. *The Age of the World: Moses to Darwin.* Baltimore: Johns Hopkins University Press, 1959. Reprint. Westport, Conn.: Greenwood Press,

1978. This interesting book does not focus on current estimates of the age of the earth but rather on the historical controversy that emerged when nonbiblical values for the age of the earth began to be accepted. Provides insight into the conflict between science and dogma.

Hurley, Patrick M. *How Old Is the Earth?* Garden City, N.Y.: Doubleday, 1959. One of the few full-length books on geochronology for the layperson. Even though published thirty years ago, it is still valid, as most of the material relevant to the age of the earth has not changed appreciably since its publication.

Ozima, Minoru. *The Earth: Its Birth and Growth*. Cambridge, England: Cambridge University Press, 1981. A translation of a Japanese book that was written by a scientist whose specialty is geochronology. Written at an introductory level.

Stearn, Colin W., et al. *Geological Evolution of North America*. New York: John Wiley & Sons, 1979. Several excellent chapters discussing the age of the earth. Contains an excellent chapter on geological time and the various ways it can be measured.

Stokes, William Lee. *Essentials of Earth History: An Introduction to Historical Geology*. 4th ed. Englewood Cliffs, N.J.: Prentice-Hall, 1982. A standard introductory text on historical geology. All the various methods for determining the age of the earth are discussed in the first few chapters.

Stokes, William Lee, et al. *Introduction to Geology: Physical and Historical*. Englewood Cliffs, N.J.: Prentice-Hall, 1978. Textbook similar to Stokes's other book in terms of its discussion of geochronology.

Thackray, John. *The Age of the Earth*. New York: Cambridge University Press, 1989. A very short publication, about forty pages long, published by a British geological museum. Contains more pictures than text, but the pictures, most in color, are helpful and make this an interesting source.

*Karl Giberson*

## Cross-References

The Evolution of the Earth's Composition, 496; Earth's Oldest Rocks, 561; Earth's Origin, 569; Geochronology: Fission Track Dating, 826; Geochronology: K-Ar and Ar-Ar Dating, 833; Geochronology: Radiocarbon Dating, 840; Geochronology: Rb-Sr Dating, 848; Geochronology: Sm-Nd Dating, 855; Geochronology: U-Th-Pb Dating, 862; Nucleosynthesis, 1764; Radioactive Decay, 2136; Radioactive Minerals, 2143; Elemental Distribution in the Solar System, 2434; The Origin of the Solar System, 2442; Uniformitarianism, 2571.

# THE EVOLUTION OF EARTH'S COMPOSITION

*Type of earth science:* Geochemistry

*Understanding the processes that have evolved the earth can help to unify various earth and biological sciences. The theories about earth's evolution are speculative, and much of the earth's earliest history is unknown. Using meteorites and some of the oldest-known crustal rocks, geochemists are trying to unravel the mysteries of the early earth's composition.*

### Principal terms

ACCRETION: the process by which small bodies called planetesimals are attracted by mutual gravitation to form larger bodies called protoplanets

ARCHEAN EON: the older of a two-part division of the Precambrian, also known as the Archeozoic

CHONDRITES: stony meteorites that contain rounded silicate inclusion grains called chondrules; they are believed to have formed by crystallization of liquid silicate droplets and volatiles

DIFFERENTIATION: the process by which a planet is divided into zones as heavy elements (metals) sink to the core, while lighter elements collect near the surface

ISOTOPE: atoms of an element that have the same number of protons in the nucleus, the same atomic number, and the same chemical properties but that have different atomic masses because they have different numbers of neutrons in the nucleus

MAFIC and ULTRAMAFIC: rock-forming magmas that are high in dense, refractory elements such as iron and magnesium; oceanic basalts are examples of mafic rocks

REFRACTORY (SIDEROPHILE) ELEMENTS: elements least likely to be driven off by heating; the last elements to be melted as a rock is heated to form magma

VOLATILE ELEMENTS: elements most likely to be driven off by heating; those that are first to melt or be driven off as gas in a heated rock

ZIRCONS: mineral inclusions found in granitic rocks, zircons are often the only evidence left of early crustal rocks

## Summary of the Phenomenon

About 4.5 billion years ago, scientists believe, a massive star exploded in a supernova event that shined as brightly as a whole galaxy of stars. Shock waves from the celestial fireworks overtook a cloud of gas and dust a few light-years away and triggered its contraction, simultaneously seeding the nebula with heavy elements (those heavier than iron on the periodic table). The solar nebula's collapse led to the formation of the sun (which swept up most of the matter), and the planets formed by the accretion of small bodies called planetesimals. As the planetesimals grew into protoplanets, their gravitational fields increased, so they continued to sweep up material not garnered by the protosun. The innermost planets, Mercury, Venus, Earth, and Mars, contained the dense metals and rocks, while the outer planets were mostly made of gases and volatile ices. During the protoearth's initial accretion process, small, cold bodies collided to form a large mass of homogeneously heterogeneous composition. By the process of differentiation, the heavier metallic elements, such as iron and nickel, migrated to the core of the early earth, while the lighter elements migrated to the outer portions of the contracting planet.

Meteorites offer clues to the composition of the earth. Extraterrestrial pieces of an asteroid or planetesimal, meteorites are remnants of the earliest period of planetary formation and come in three basic types. Stony meteorites comprise the most abundant group and are composed of silica-associated, or lithophile, elements such as those found in the earth's crustal materials. Stony-iron meteorites are composed of roughly equal parts of rock (typically olivine) suspended in a matrix of iron. Iron meteorites are composed of siderophile elements, iron being the major constituent, along with (perhaps) 10-20 percent nickel. Iron meteorites are of particular interest to scientists attempting to model the composition of the earth's core. The mean density of the earth is about 5.5 grams per cubic centimeter. The mean density of crustal rocks, however, is only about 2.7 grams per cubic centimeter (water is conveniently 1 gram per cubic centimeter), which indicates a core density of ten to twelve times that of water. The only known objects approaching these densities are the iron meteorites.

After the initial accretion of the planetesimal materials and just prior to differentiation of the lithophile and siderophile elements, the earth's thermal history began through the process of radioactive decay. During this early thermal period, short-lived radioactive nuclides (atoms of a specific isotope, distinguished by their atomic and mass numbers) produced heating seven times greater than that of today's molten core. Most of the heating was attributable to the decay of potassium 40 as well as of the short half-lived elements such as aluminum 26. After about 100,000 years, the planet separated into the iron-nickel core and magnesium-iron-silicate lower mantle. Over a longer time scale (probably more than 10 million years), the high-volatility compounds, such as lead, mercury, thallium, and bismuth, along with the noble gases, water in hydrated silicates, and carbon-based organic compounds, all condensed. This volatile-rich material migrated to the surface, where it was melted into magmas in a continuous period of crustal reprocessing that lasted for about 1 billion years.

The earth's original inventory of gases appears to have been lost, based on the relative present abundances of the rare gases (helium, neon, argon, krypton, xenon, and radon) compared to the present silicon content of the earth. Later periods of volcanic outgassing and perhaps impacts with volatile-rich cosmic objects such as carbonaceous chondritic meteorites and comets may also have played a role in the evolution of the atmosphere and oceans. Separated into three main layers—the crust, mantle, and core—the earth is an active body, its internal heat far from exhausted. The complexity of the chemical composition increases as one examines each successive outward layer. This generalized model gives a starting point with which to examine the complex nature of earth materials. Earth's wide range of pressure and temperature regimes helps explain why there are more than two thousand distinct minerals and numerous different combinations of minerals in rock types.

The core is actually composed of two basic parts: the solid inner core, with a density equal to twelve times that of water and a radius of 1,300 kilometers, and a molten outer core, 2,200 kilometers thick, with a density of about 10 grams per cubic centimeter. This model consists of an essentially iron-nickel inner core at high pressure and a metallic outer core that also contains iron sulfide and light elements such as silicon, carbon, and oxygen. As a whole, the core unit comprises about 32 percent of the earth's mass. Comprising the outer 68 percent of the earth's bulk, the mantle makes the crust, atmosphere, and oceans insignificant by comparison. The mantle is rich in dense, or mafic, rocks such as olivine and pyroxene (which comes in two basic types, calcium-rich or calcium-poor), with olivine the dominant mineral.

Basic earth materials are derived via reaction series from mafic magmas melting and settling out in the mantle's upper regions. As the temperatures drop in the melt zone, a discontinuous series (a set of discrete reactions) occurs. Magnetite, an oxide of iron and titanium, is the first to settle out, with the highest melting point at about 1,400 degrees Celsius. Olivine, a mineral whose silicate structure is a simple tetrahedron, is the next to solidify out of the melt, with a density of 3.2-4.4, followed by the single chain structure pyroxene, with a density of 3.2-3.6. As temperatures in the magma drop to near 1,000 degrees Celsius, the amphibole group forms with a lesser density, 2.9-3.2. As the cooling progresses, the structures increase in complexity with the micas—biotite and muscovite, which form in planar sheets. Next in the cooling sequence would be orthoclase, or potassium feldspar, and plagioclase, or calcium feldspar, and, finally, quartz, which are all distinguished by their characteristic three-dimensional diamond shapes and varying colors. The calcic through sodic plagioclase to muscovite, biotite, and quartz occurs in a smooth, or continuous, transition rather than the stepwise, or discontinuous, reactions that characterize the formation of olivine through biotite.

An estimate of the crustal elemental composition of the earth indicates that only a handful of elements (oxygen, silicon, aluminum, iron, magnesium, calcium, sodium, and titanium) make up more than 99 percent of the earth's crust. The simple oxide quartz is the most common of the silicate minerals, which account for 95 percent of the crust. With these facts in mind, one can start to hypothesize about how the continents evolved. About 700 million years after the initial formation of the earth through accretion and differentiation, the first rocks of the Archean eon formed. They are composed of olivine, pyroxene, and anorthite (calcium-rich plagioclase feldspar), which settled out of the basaltic magma. The lighter plagioclase would rise to the surface to form a hardened crust of anorthosite, the same material that comprises the moon's ancient highlands, which are about 3.8 billion years old.

The anorthosite formed a thick sheet that was fractured into pieces and subjected to further heating through radioactive decay, leading to an essentially granitic rock layer 10-15 kilometers thick. Extensive volcanic activity and high surface temperatures gradually diminished until the hydrosphere (water cycle) was established. The earth's crust is divided into two main types: the dense, or mafic, oceanic crust and the lighter, or sialic (silica-aluminum), continental crust. Archean rocks (up to 3.5 billion years old) found in the stable interiors of the continents contain massive anorthosite inclusions and may be viewed as the nuclei of the continents.

About the time of the formation of the continental nuclei, or cratons (relatively stable portions of crust), the oldest-known sedimentary rocks accumulated as the rock cycle began, eroding the parent igneous rocks into secondary types of rock. This occurrence may coincide with the beginning of plate tectonics, as the lithosphere (rock crust) of the earth broke into plates and began its hallmark active motion. Life is thought to have arisen at about the same time, with primitive blue-green algae found in strata 2.8 billion years old. With the oceans growing in volume and salinity and the development of oxygen-releasing blue-green algae, earth's geochemistry became more complex. Chemically precipitated rocks of calcium carbonate, commonly known as limestones, are an example of the evolving rock cycle.

Life forms shaped the earth's chemical composition. By the end of Precambrian time, oxygen levels had reached 1 percent of its present value. Multicelled animals in the oceans scrubbed the carbon dioxide from the atmosphere and locked it up in the carbonate rocks, forming biochemically precipitated limestones. By the late Paleozoic era, coal formations grew as a result of the first land forests being periodically inundated by ocean transgressions.

## Methods of Study

Perhaps no other earth science is as speculative as that of early earth history and the geochemical evolution of the earth. Varying models for crustal development are advanced and overturned annually. Despite the problems of extrapolating back to a time before there were solid rocks, the established models are based on some solid lines of evidence as well as on conjecture. In 1873, American geologist James D. Dana made one of the initial advances in the study of the earth's internal chemical composition when he suggested that analogies could be drawn from the study of meteorites. Believed to be pieces of differentiated bodies that were later disintegrated into smaller pieces, meteorites come in differing types that are analogous to the earth's interior. Because meteorite types approximate elemental distribution in the earth, they are valuable samples for laboratory examination by scientists. Geochemists studying meteorites have derived radiometric dates of 4.6 billion years— corresponding to the initial time of accretion and differentiation of the planets.

Geophysicists use seismic waves to study the earth's interior. Changes in velocity and deflections of the waves passing through the earth have revealed a differentiated earth with a very dense core, less dense mantle, and a light crust "floating" on top. The well-established theory of plate tectonics has shown that the crust is broken into pieces, or plates, that are moving, driven by convection currents in the upper mantle. Some of the major challenges confronting earth scientists are the questions about how the earth's crust formed and about when plate movement began.

During the 1960's, interest in Archean crustal evolution was aroused by the discovery of Archean era magnesium-oxygen-rich lavas similar to those found in the early Precambrian. Called komatiites, these rocks date back to 3.7 billion years ago and represent ultramafic lavas that form at 1,100 degrees Celsius. Komatiites are generally found around greenstone belts, an agglomeration of Archean basaltic, andesitic, and rhyolitic volcanics, along with their weathering and erosion derived sediments. One hundred million years older than any previously known rocks, the finds led to further exploration of Archean formations by field geologists in West Greenland-Labrador, Zimbabwe, Transvaal-Swaziland, Ontario-Quebec, southern India, Western Australia, and, more recently, China and Brazil.

Important work by field geologists in these regions launched a new era in Precambrian geology. The primary targets for study are the greenstone belts and granitic-gneiss associations. An important twentieth century find included detrital zircon, discovered in Australia. An age of 4.2 billion years for the zircons was determined using precise ion microprobe analysis. The zircon find is significant because it places an approximate birth date for the continental crust, as zircon is a mineral constituent of granite (recall that oceanic crust is composed of mafic and ultramafic rocks while continental crust is granitic).

The drive to study Archean rocks was further fueled by the United States' Apollo missions to the moon, which returned rocks of slightly older age from the lunar surface. At the same time, geochemists were able to refine their study of these ancient rocks with more sophisticated methods to determine ratios of isotopes in the samples. Instruments common in the geochemical lab today are X-ray diffraction and gamma-ray spectrometers, which probe the nuclei of atoms to determine the spectral fingerprint of elements and their various isotopes. Isotopic ratios in rocks are of particular interest to geochemists because they provide clues as to chemical cycles in nature, such as the sulfur, chemical, nitrogen, and oxygen cycles. The equilibria of these cycles, as indicated by the isotopic ratios, offer insights into volcanic, oceanic, biological, and atmospheric cycles and conditions in the past.

It is generally accepted by most earth scientists that crustal formation and heat flow were substantially greater in Archean times. The question is whether this crust was broken into moving lithospheric plates as it has been for the past 900 million years. The question of plate motion during this early period has generated debate among scientists and has led to two general theories of early crustal evolution. If plate tectonics was occurring 4 billion years ago, one would expect to find formations of arc deposits and complexes similar to the Franciscan formation in California's coast range. Oölite and arc deposits are terranes that accumulate near zones of subduction, where dense mafic rocks are recycled into the mantle. Such formations have not been found to date—geologic evidence arguing against rapid plate motion.

If crustal rock production was great and yet plate tectonics minimal, what process shaped the early earth? An answer may have emerged from one of the earth's sister planets. Shrouded in clouds, Venus did not give up the mysteries of its geology until the radar maps generated by Soviet and American spacecraft. Like Mars, with its giant volcanoes in the Tharsis region, Venus appears to have great shield volcanoes and continentlike regions the size of Africa and Australia. Hot-spot volcanism, in which plumes of magma rising from the planetary interior erupt to form shield volcanoes at the surface, may indeed be the key to understanding incipient plate tectonics on the early earth. The question of whether hot-spot magmatism and some form of plate movement is occurring on Venus would be answered by the NASA Magellan mission, planned to arrive at the planet in the 1990's.

## Context

Perhaps no other area of scientific study is as intriguing and controversial as that of the origin and evolution of the earth. Geochemists have been at the forefront of the quest for understanding the earth's present geology in terms of its past. Before the 1960's, little was known of the earth's history during early Precambrian times. This lack is significant when one realizes that the Precambrian comprises about 87 percent of the geologic time scale.

It is likely that new techniques used to analyze rocks and minerals in the laboratory will lead to a better understanding of the formation of the earth's crustal materials and the evolution of moving crustal plates. Precise dating of zircons from ancient rocks, isotope analysis, and high-resolution seismic data will help scientists to comprehend the relationships between the granite-greenstones and gneiss terranes (crustal blocks) that typify Archean formations.

Studying materials on other solar system bodies will also lead to a better understanding of the early earth and its evolution. The U.S. NASA Mars Observer will carry a gamma-ray spectrometer designed to study the surface composition of Mars' crust and its distribution of elements. The question of whether the earth's early history was dominated by hot-spot volcanism (the case on Mars with its huge volcanoes) will receive valuable evidence from this and future studies of asteroids, meteorites, the moon, Mars, and Venus.

## Bibliography

Burchfiel, B. Clark, et al. *Physical Geology.* Westerville, Ohio: Charles E. Merrill, 1982. An excellent and comprehensive textbook covering all aspects of geology suitable for the lay reader or liberal studies college student. Of special interest are chapter 2 on mineralogy, chapter 7 on the earth's interior, chapter 9 on crustal materials and mountain building, and chapter 10 on the origin and differentiation of the earth and early geologic time.

Fyfe, W. S. *Geochemistry*. Oxford, England: Clarendon Press, 1974. Part of the Oxford Chemistry series, this work was written for lower-division college chemistry students. Although in some respects dated, it is nevertheless a brief (about one-hundred-page) and excellent introduction to the science of geochemistry. Of special interest is chapter 9, "Evolution of the Earth." The book has a bibliography, glossary, and index.

Gregor, C. Bryan, et al. *Chemical Cycles in the Evolution of the Earth*. New York: John Wiley & Sons, 1988. A systems approach to geochemistry, this book is suitable for the serious college student. Although filled with graphs, tables, and chemical equations, sections are very readable for the layperson. Discussions of mineralogical, oceanic, atmospheric, and other important chemical cycles are extensive and the work is well referenced.

Kroner, A., G. N. Hanson, and A. M. Goodwin, eds. *Archaean Geochemistry: The Origin and Evolution of the Archaean Continental Crust*. Berlin: Springer-Verlag, 1984. A collection of reports by the world's leading geochemists studying the geochemistry of the world's oldest rocks. Although many of the articles are technical in nature, the abstracts, introductions, and summaries are accessible to a college-level reader interested in the work of top international scientists.

Levin, Harold L. *The Earth Through Time*. 3d ed. Philadelphia: Saunders College, 1988. An excellent and very readable text dealing with historical geology. Filled with illustrations, photographs, and figures, this book is suitable for the layperson. Chapters on planetary beginnings, origin and evolution of the early earth, and plate tectonics are of special interest. Contains an excellent glossary and index.

McCall, Gerald J. H., ed. *The Archean: Search for the Beginning*. Stroudsburg, Pa.: Dowden, Hutchinson and Ross, 1977. A superb collection of thirty-eight papers by outstanding geologists, arranged under topical headings. The papers are at times technical, but the editor provides an introduction and integrating commentary that helps bridge the gap for the nontechnical reader. Contains a subject index.

Ponnamperuma, Cyril, ed. *Chemical Evolution of the Early Precambrian*. New York: Academic Press, 1977. A collection of papers from the second colloquium of the Laboratory of Chemical Evolution of the University of Maryland, held in 1975. Written by experts in the field, the papers are still, for the most part, accessible to the nontechnical reader. The volume contains a subject index.

Salop, Lazarus J. *Geological Evolution of the Earth During the Precambrian*. Berlin: Springer-Verlag, 1983. A top Soviet geologist conducts an exhaustive survey of Precambrian geology. Suitable for a college-level reader with a serious interest in the subject. Contains numerous graphs and tables, with extensive references.

Tarling, D. H. *Ecolution of the Earth's Crust*. New York: Academic Press, 1978. Written for the undergraduate-level college reader with some background in geology, this volume is an excellent collection of nontechnical, well-written essays covering the origin and evolution of the earth's crust and plate tectonics. Contains references and an index.

Wedepohl, Karl H. *Geochemistry.* New York: Holt, Rinehart and Winston, 1971. An accessible and brief introduction to geochemistry fundamentals. Contains an excellent chapter on meteorites and cosmic abundances of the elements. Suitable for the nontechnical reader, with index and references. A good starting point for those unfamiliar with mineral formation.

Wetherill, George W., A. L. Albee, and F. G. Stehli, eds. *Annual Review of Earth and Planetary Sciences.* Vol. 13. Palo Alto, Calif.: Annual Reviews, 1985. Three articles of interest to the earth history student are "Evolution of the Archean Crust," by Alfred Kroner, and "Oxidation States of the Mantle: Past, Present, and Future" and "The Magma Ocean Concept and Lunar Evolution," by Richard Arculus. Kroner's article is particularly readable for the college-level audience, with an excellent overview of the historical views on Precambrian geology. References at the end of each article.

*David M. Schlom*

## Cross-References

The Archean Eon, 92; The Atmosphere's Evolution, 114; Earth's Age, 490; Earth's Core, 504; Earth's Core-Mantle Boundary, 511; Earth's Crust, 518; Earth's Differentiation, 525; Earth's Mantle, 555; Earth's Oldest Rocks, 561; Earth's Origin, 569; Earth's Structure, 589; Igneous Rocks: Ultramafic, 1207; The Origin of Magmas, 1428; Meteorites: Nickel-Irons, 1652.

# EARTH'S CORE

*Type of earth science:* Geophysics
*Field of study:* Seismology

*The core is the earth's densest, hottest region and its fundamental source of internal heat. The thermal energy released by the core's continuous cooling stirs the overlying mantle into slow, convective motions that eventually reach the surface to move continents, build mountains, and produce earthquakes.*

### Principal terms

CONVECTION: the process in liquids and gases by which hot, less dense materials rise upward to be replaced by cold, sinking fluids

CORE: the spherical, mostly liquid mass located 2,900 kilometers below the earth's surface; the central, solid part is known as the inner core

MAGNETIC FIELD: a force field, generated in the core, that pervades the earth and resembles that of a bar magnet

P WAVES: seismic waves transmitted by alternating pulses of compression and expansion; they pass through solids, liquids, and gases

S WAVES: seismic waves transmitted by an alternating series of sideways movements in a solid; they cannot be transmitted through liquids or gases

SEISMIC WAVES: elastic oscillatory disturbances spreading outward from an earthquake or man-made explosion; they provide the most important data about the earth's interior

## Summary of the Phenomenon

The earth's core extends from a depth of 2,900 kilometers to the center of the earth, 6,371 kilometers below the surface. The core is largely liquid, although toward the center, it becomes solid. The liquid part is known as the outer core; the solid part, the inner core. Ambient pressures inside the core range from 1 million to nearly 4 million atmospheres, and temperatures probably reach more than 5,000 degrees Celsius at the earth's center.

Being almost twice as dense as the rest of the planet, the core contains one-third of the earth's mass but occupies a mere one-seventh of its volume. Surrounding the core is the mantle. The boundary between the solid mantle and the underlying liquid core is the core-mantle boundary (CMB), a surface that demarcates the most fundamental compositional discontinuity in the earth's interior. Below it, the core is mostly made of iron-nickel oxides. Above it, and all the way to the surface, the mantle is made of silicates (rock-forming minerals). The solid inner core contains 1.7 percent of the earth's mass, and its composition may simply be a frozen version of the liquid core. The boundary between the liquid and the solid cores is known as the inner core boundary (ICB); it appears sharp to seismic waves, which easily reflect off it.

The core has lower wave-transmission velocities and higher densities than the mantle, a consequence of its being of a different chemical composition. The core is probably composed of 80 to 90 percent (by weight) iron or iron-nickel alloy and 20 to 10 percent sulfur, silicon, and oxygen; it therefore must be a good electrical and thermal conductor. The mantle, in contrast, is composed mainly of crystalline silicates of magnesium and iron and is therefore a poor conductor of electricity and a good thermal insulator.

This sharp contrast in physical properties is a major end product of the way in which the earth evolved thermally, gravitationally, and chemically. It is difficult, however, to tell whether the earth's core formed first and the earth was accreted from the infall of meteorites and other gravitationally bound materials or, alternatively, the core differentiated out of an already formed protoearth, in which silicates and iron were separated after a cataclysmic "iron catastrophe." This event may have occurred when iron, slowly heated by radioactivity, suddenly melted and sank by gravity toward the earth's center, forming the core. Unfortunately, the two scenarios are equally likely, and both give the same end result; moreover, there probably are other scenarios. Calculations show, however, that iron sinking to the core must have released great amounts of energy that would have eventually heated and melted the entire earth. Cooling of the outer parts proceeded rapidly, by convection, but as the silicate mantle solidified, it created a thermal barrier for the iron-rich core, which, not being able to cool down as readily, remained molten. The inner core began then to form at the earth's center, where the pressure was greatest and solidification was (barely) possible.

The most tangible consequence of the existence of a fluid, electrically conducting core is the presence of a magnetic field in the earth that has existed for at least 3.5 billion years with a strength not very different from what it has today. The process that generates and maintains the geomagnetic field is attributable to a self-exciting dynamo mechanism—that is, an electromagnetic induction process that transforms the motions of the conducting fluid into electric currents, which in turn induce a magnetic field that strengthens the existing field. (For the system to get started, at least a small magnetic field must be present to initiate the generation of electric currents.) The increased magnetic field in turn induces stronger currents, which further strengthen the field, and so on. As the magnetic field increases beyond a certain high value, it begins to affect the fluid flow; there is a mechanical force, known as the Lorentz force, that is induced in a conductor as it moves across a magnetic field. The stronger the magnetic field, the stronger the Lorentz force becomes and the more it will tend to modify the motion of the fluid so as to oppose the growth of the magnetic field. The result is a self-regulating mechanism which, over time, will attain a steady state.

A dynamo mechanism is needed to explain the geomagnetic field, because there can be no permanently magnetized substances inside the earth. Magnetic substances lose their magnetism as their temperature increases above the so-called Curie temperature (around 500 degrees Celsius for most magnetic substances), and most of the mantle below the depth of 30 kilometers and all the core is at temperatures well above the Curie point. The basic problem, then, is to find a source of energy that can maintain the steady regime of flow in the core against decay by somehow maintaining the fluid currents that induce the field. A favored view is that the necessary energy to maintain the flow is provided by the growth of the inner core as it is fed by the liquid core. According to some researchers, this process would provide enough gravitational energy to stir the core throughout. Thermally and compositionally driven flows can also be invoked as possible models of core fluid dynamics, but there is still no evidence that decides the question.

A most extraordinary feature of the core-generated magnetic field is that, at least over the past few hundred million years, it has reversed its polarity with irregular frequency. For example, it is known that at times the field has reversed as frequently as three times every million years, but in other cases, more than 20 million years went by without a noticeable reversal. A reversed geomagnetic field means simply that the magnetic needle of a compass would point in the opposite direction as it does today. (For convenience, the present orientation of the needle is considered normal.) The important point is that the rocks that form (for example, lavas that cool below the Curie point as they become solid rock) during either a reverse or a normal period acquire and preserve that magnetism. Unlike the swinging compass needle, a rock keeps the magnetic field direction that existed at the time of its formation forever frozen in its iron-bearing minerals. Therefore, rocks formed throughout geologic time have recorded the alternating rhythms of normal and reverse earth magnetism. This sequence of magnetic reversals contains the clue to the core's nature.

Geophysicists are anxious to learn whether the core is vigorously convecting as a consequence of the inner core's growth. If that were the case, the core would be delivering a great amount of heat to the mantle, whose low thermal conductivity would create a barrier to the upcoming heat. As a result, the local temperature gradient at the base of the mantle would probably be very high, so that a layer 100 kilometers thick, say, at the base of the mantle, would be gravitationally unstable. From this layer, thermal inhomogeneities would rise through the mantle in the form of plumes of buoyant, hot, lower-mantle material. Several such plumes might reach the upper mantle or set the entire mantle into convection. These convection currents would be responsible for the motion of the tectonic plates on the earth's surface and, consequently, for the uplifting of mountain ranges, the formation of oceanic basins, and the occurrence of volcanic eruptions and earthquakes. Continental drift and plate tectonics, the most visible effects of the internal cooling of the earth, would thus be linked to the growth of the inner core and to earth's earliest history. This view of the earth is very speculative, but it is favored by many geoscientists, who recognize its beauty and simplicity.

## Methods of Study

Knowledge of the structure, physical properties, and composition of the core is entirely based on indirect evidence gathered mostly from analyses of seismic waves, the study of the earth's gravitational and magnetic fields, and laboratory experiments on the behavior of rocks and minerals at high pressures and temperatures. The first evidence for the existence of the core was presented in a paper suggestively entitled "The Constitution of the Interior of the Earth, As Revealed by Earthquakes," published in 1906 by Richard D. Oldham, of the geological survey of India. Thirty years later, Inge Lehmann, from the Copenhagen seismological observatory, presented seismic evidence for the existence of the inner core. In the past few decades, with the advent of high-speed computers and technological advances in seismometry, seismologists have developed increasingly sensitive instrumentation to record seismic waves worldwide and sophisticated mathematical theories that allow them to construct models of the core that explain the observed data.

Seismic waves provide the most important data about the core. Earthquakes or large explosions generate elastic waves that propagate throughout the earth. These seismic waves may penetrate deep in the earth and, after being reflected or transmitted through major discontinuities such as the CMB and ICB, travel back to the surface to be recorded at the seismic stations of the global network. The most direct information that seismic or elastic waves carry is their travel time. Knowing the time it takes for elastic waves to traverse some region of the earth's interior allows the calculation of their velocity of propagation in that region. The velocity of seismic waves strongly depends on the density and rigidity, or stiffness, of the material through which they propagate, so estimates of the mechanical properties of the earth can in principle be derived from seismic travel time analyses. Seismic waves that propagate through the deep interior of the earth are of two types: compressional waves (also called P waves) and shear waves (also called S waves). Compressional waves produce volume changes in the elastic medium; shear waves produce shape distortion without volume change. If the medium has some rigidity, both P and S waves can be transmitted. If the medium has no rigidity, it offers no resistance to a change in shape; no elastic connection exists that can communicate shearing motions from a point in the medium to its neighbors, so S waves cannot propagate, although P waves can.

After many years of careful observations, it has been determined that S waves are not transmitted through the outer core. Therefore, the outer core material has no rigidity, but behaves as a fluid would. Similar observations suggest that the inner core is solid; the actual rigidity of the inner core is very difficult to estimate, however, since shear waves inside the inner core are isolated from the mantle by the outer core and can only travel through it as P waves converted from S waves at the ICB. Nevertheless, when the whole earth is set into vibration by a very large earthquake, the average rigidity of the inner core can be estimated by comparing the observed frequencies of oscillation with those theoretically computed for models of the earth that include a solid inner core. Model studies have indicated that the inner core is indeed solid, because a totally liquid core model does not satisfy the observations.

The average velocity of P waves in the earth is about 10 kilometers per second, whereas the average P-wave velocity in the rocks accessible to measurement at the earth's surface is 4 to 5 kilometers per second. The S-wave velocity is nearly half that of P waves in solids and zero in perfect fluids.

The velocity of P waves drops abruptly from 13.7 kilometers per second at the base of the mantle to 8.06 kilometers per second across the CMB, at the top of the core. From this point down, the velocity steadily increases to 10.35 kilometers per second at the ICB, where it jumps discontinuously to 11.03 kilometers per second at the top of the inner core. From there to the center of the earth, the velocity of P waves increases slowly to reach 11.3 kilometers per second. The S-wave velocity increases from zero at the ICB to around 3.6 kilometers per second at the earth's center. The core's density abruptly increases from 5,500 kilograms per cubic meter at the base of the mantle to nearly 10,000 kilograms per cubic meter just underneath the CMB. From there, the density increases slowly to nearly 13,100 kilograms per cubic meter at the earth's center. In comparison, the density of mercury at room temperature and ambient pressure is 13,600 kilograms per cubic meter.

That the core is mostly iron is consistent with iron's being cosmically more abundant than other heavy elements and with the high electrical conductivity the core needs to have in order to generate the earth's magnetic field. The fluidity of the outer core has been demonstrated by measurements not only of seismic wave transmission but also of the oscillation period of gravitational waves in the core excited by the lunisolar tides. The existence of a sustained, steady magnetic field is also consistent with a fluid outer core.

Seismic data can probe the inner core only partially from the earth's surface, unless the source of the seismic waves and the receivers are located antipodally to each other. Such an arrangement would allow scientists to measure seismic waves that had penetrated the center of the earth. It would be possible to construct a global experiment to investigate the inner core by deploying an array of highly sensitive seismic sensors antipodal to either a seismically active region or an underground nuclear explosion testing ground. Despite the wealth of unique data that would be obtained from such an experiment, it would be a very expensive endeavor, and not devoid of risk.

New views of the earth's interior are produced, sometimes unexpectedly, by the analyses of data collected by satellite missions. Data from orbiting satellites that measure tiny variations of the earth's gravitational field, combined with computer-aided seismic tomography of the earth's interior, have revealed large-density anomalies at the base of the mantle and a large relief of more than 2 kilometers on the CMB. Seismic tomography uses earthquake-generated waves that penetrate the mantle in a multitude of directions to map the three-dimensional structure of its deep interior, just as computerized medical tomography uses multiple X-ray images to create a three-dimensional view of internal organs of the body. Essential to the success of these studies, however, is the installation of dense networks of seismic sensors all over the surface of the earth; this installation, however, is another very expensive procedure.

## Context

It is almost certain that whether or not geophysicists discover the actual cause of the geomagnetic field will not affect the everyday life of the people of the world.

Any study of the earth's physical environment is likely to provide insight into the nature and future of the planet and, consequently, the future of mankind. If geophysicists come to understand how the earth's core works, they will be able to predict the geomagnetic field's activity for years to come. Thus, they will be able to predict an upcoming reversal. According to the best estimates, a reversal does not occur suddenly but takes about ten thousand years. That means that during a reversal, there is a time of very small or even zero field intensity. Under such conditions, the magnetic shielding that prevents the highly energetic solar wind particles from reaching the earth's surface will disappear, leaving the earth directly exposed to lethal radiations.

The inner core has not yet been sufficiently explored with seismic waves. One reason is that it is the remotest region of the earth and therefore the most difficult to reach; another is that it is hidden beneath the "seismic noise" created by the crust, mantle, and outer core. The inner core, however, holds the key to the understanding of the earth's early history and its subsequent development as a planet.

## Bibliography

Bolt, Bruce A. *Inside the Earth: Evidence from Earthquakes*. San Francisco: W. H. Freeman, 1982. An elementary treatment of what is known about the earth's interior, mostly through the study of seismic waves, the author's major field of research. The book contains abundant diagrams that illustrate accurately important results of the investigation of the core and mantle. For readers with some knowledge of mathematics, the book includes brief derivations of important formulas, separated by "boxes" from the main text. It is well written and includes anecdotal descriptions of great scientific discoveries along with personal views of the history and development of seismology. Illustrated.

Clark, Sydney P. *Structure of the Earth*. Englewood Cliffs, N.J.: Prentice-Hall, 1971. Although slightly out of date, this short review of the earth's structure and composition is an excellent first reading to gain a global perspective on geology and geophysics. Illustrations are abundant and very clear. The text is simply written, yet the author manages to convey complex concepts about tectonics, wave propagation, and ray theory with ease. The chapter dedicated to seismology is the best and most carefully written section of the book.

Hamblin, W. Kenneth. *The Earth's Dynamic Systems: A Textbook in Physical Geology*. New York: Macmillan, 1989. This geology textbook offers an integrated view of the earth's interior not common in books of this type. The illustrations, diagrams, and charts are superb. Includes a glossary and laboratory guide. Suitable for high school readers.

Jacobs, J. A. *The Earth's Core*. 2d ed. New York: Academic Press, 1987. This is a highly technical text, but it is perhaps the best reference for a detailed description of the most accepted core models. The tables—which give the numerical values of the density, temperature, rigidity, and wave velocity distributions within the earth—are of interest to anyone wanting a quantitative description of the core. A long list of research articles is included.

Jeanloz, Raymond. "The Earth's Core." *Scientific American* 249 (September, 1983): 56-65. The best elementary treatment of the structure and composition of the core. Jeanloz is a leading expert in the field. In this article, the origin, evolution, and present state and composition of the core are discussed in detail. The language is precise but not too specialized. The entire issue is dedicated to the earth and earth dynamics, so it should be of great interest to some readers.

Press, Frank, and Raymond Siever. *Earth*. 3d ed. San Francisco: W. H. Freeman, 1985. The most geophysical and probably the best written of all elementary geology textbooks. It includes an intriguing description of the evolution of the earth, the iron catastrophe, and the formation of the atmosphere. Well illustrated. Includes a glossary.

*J. A. Rial*

## Cross-References

# EARTH'S CORE-MANTLE BOUNDARY

*Type of earth science:* Geophysics
*Field of study:* Seismology

*The core-mantle boundary is a pronounced discontinuity separating the outer core from the mantle of the earth. It is a chemical and mineralogical as well as a thermal boundary. The topography of the core-mantle boundary is believed to be controlled by the dynamic processes in the mantle and the outer core.*

### Principal terms

CORE-DIFFRACTED PHASES: those elastic waves incident at the outer core at a grazing angle that are diffracted and arrive within the shadow zones for direct waves

CORE-REFLECTED PHASES: elastic waves that are reflected from the core-mantle boundary

CORE-TRANSMITTED PHASES: elastic waves that travel through the earth's core

CRUST: the thin, surface layer of the earth, with an average thickness of 34 kilometers; it consits of low-density, silicate rocks

EPICENTER: the region at the earth's surface directly above the focus, or hypocenter, of an earthquake

FOCUS: the region within the earth from which earthquake waves emanate; also called hypocenter

LONGITUDINAL (P) WAVES: elastic waves in a medium where particle displacements are parallel to the direction of wave propagation

MANTLE: a zone, located at depths of approximately 34-2,885 kilometers, consisting of silicate minerals

OUTER CORE: a zone, located at depths of approximately 2,885-5,144 kilometers, that is in a liquid state and consists of iron sulfides and iron oxides

SHEAR (S) WAVES: elastic waves in a solid medium where displacements are perpendicular to the direction of wave propagation

## Summary of the Phenomenon

The core-mantle boundary (CMB) is a prominent discontinuity within the earth. The mantle above the boundary is largely solid, of relatively low temperature, and primarily composed of magnesium and iron silicates. The outer core below the boundary is liquid, of higher temperature, and composed of dense materials such as iron oxides and iron sulfide alloys. This boundary separates two dynamic systems: one operating in the mantle as hot spots and convection cells, the other—in the outer core—consisting of convection currents and eddies of the core fluid. The motions of the core fluid appear to be responsible for the earth's magnetic field. The approximate depth of the CMB is 2,885 kilometers.

Detailed studies of the seismic velocities in the earth led K. E. Bullen to divide the interior of the earth into seven concentric, spherical zones termed A through G. For an earthquake occurring in the crust or the upper mantle, the downgoing waves pass through the different zones of the earth before they emerge at the surface. To study the CMB, the effects of these zones on seismic propagation need to be considered. It has been found that the earth is laterally heterogeneous, particularly the crust (zone A), the low-velocity zone of the upper mantle (B), and the lower-most part of the mantle (D"). The D" zone, known as the core-mantle transition zone, is approximately 200-300 kilometers thick and is located just above the CMB. A suggestion was made that the D" zone was thinly layered, which resulted in variations in the reflected amplitude of waves from the CMB. However, accurate analysis of the short-period seismic waves recorded by seismological arrays indicated that such is not the case. Studies utilizing inversions of seismic waveforms and travel times indicate large-scale variations (more than 1,000 kilometers) in the velocities in the D" zone. The P-wave velocity varies as much as 1.5 percent, which is three to four times more than in the middle part of the mantle. The longitudinal (P) waves appear to travel faster in the portions of this zone that are located below North America, China, the eastern part of the Indian Ocean, and off the Pacific coast of Chile. Lower P-wave velocities are observed below the southern part of Africa, the New Hebrides Islands, the South Pacific Ocean, and the Argentine Basin.

Similar large-scale variations have also been observed for shear (S) waves. The D" zone under the American continents, Asia, the northern Indian and Pacific oceans, and Antarctica are characterized by higher S-wave velocities. Lower S-wave velocities are observed underneath the Central and South Pacific Ocean, the Atlantic Ocean, the major parts of Africa, and the southern part of the Indian Ocean. These long wavelength velocity variations in the D" zone appear to continue upward in the mantle. Thus, the thermally induced convection currents and hot spots in the mantle appear to be related to large-scale, lateral velocity variations in the D" zone. The lateral heterogeneity of the D" zone is also evident in the short-scale (less than 100-kilometer) and the intermediate-scale (100-1,000-kilometer) lengths, determined primarily through studies of scattered core phases and waveform modeling techniques.

Improvements in instrumentation have enabled scientists to simulate in the laboratory the physical and chemical conditions of the lower mantle and the outermost core. It appears that the lower mantle is primarily composed of magnesium-iron silicates present in the perovskite structure. Although some amount of aluminum-calcium silicates and magnesium-iron oxides may also be present, their relative abundance is not known. Measurement of the melting point of silicate perovskite led scientists to estimate the temperature of the D" zone in the range of 2,600-3,100 Kelvins. Similar studies of outer core materials, which are primarily iron sulfides and iron oxides, indicate that the temperature of the outermost core is at least 3,800 Kelvins. Thus, the temperature increases by about 700 Kelvins in the D" zone, resulting in partial melting of some minerals and thereby making the zone soft with anomalous characteristics.

Seismologists studying the core-mantle boundary (CMB) by means of reflected waves from the core have long been frustrated by the strong scatter of the reflected amplitudes. A major part of this scatter is believed to be the result of undulations of the core-mantle boundary. The lateral extent of these undulations is of the order of thousands of kilometers. The elevation of the boundary may change as much as 5-8 kilometers above or below its normal depth. Topographic highs of the CMB have been observed beneath the Indian Ocean, the Pacific Ocean, and the Atlantic Ocean (particularly in the North Atlantic). The CMB is depressed below the Tonga-Karmadec area, the China-Japan region, Central Africa, and off the west coast of South America. Because most of these areas are associated with the subduction of oceanic plates, the CMB structure is believed to be caused by the dynamic processes in the mantle, which may again be related to the convection processes in the outer core. Subduction of a crustal plate is caused by the downwelling convective flow in the mantle. When the convective flow reaches the core boundary, it depresses the CMB into the hot, liquid core. Core fluids may partially invade the "topographic low" of the CMB, altering the chemical composition of the D″ zone. Similarly, beneath an upwelling zone of mantle flow, liquid core material may be "sucked" up into the mantle, creating a topographic high of the CMB. The "lows" of the CMB, being subjected to the higher temperatures of the outer core, may melt and recrystallize at the topographic "highs" of the CMB. Thus, the overall effect is to smooth the CMB, which is continually disturbed by the convective circulations in the mantle. With heat dissipation in the mantle, the outer core slowly cools and the core materials crystallize and underplate the mantle. Thus, the outer core slowly shrinks with time, and the CMB gets deeper.

Although near the earth's surface the temperature increases quickly with depth, the rate of increase slows below 200 kilometers depth. The core-mantle boundary not only is a compositional boundary but also appears to be a thermal boundary, where the temperature increases by at least 700 Kelvins. Thermal coupling between the mantle and the outer core, however, may change laterally, resulting in a variable heat flow across the boundary. Although no consensus has been reached among scientists, it is possible that the mantle dynamics are at least partially responsible for controlling the heat flow.

The earth behaves like a large magnet. The magnetic field of the earth—that is, the geomagnetic field—undergoes a slow change known as the secular variation. The origin of the geomagnetic field appears to be related to motions of the outer core fluid. Studies suggest that the deep mantle and the outer core play a significant role in shaping the secular variations. Upwellings in the outer core material are associated with the hot and seismically slow regions of the D″ zone; downwellings are associated with the cold and higher-velocity portions of D″. Cold regions in the mantle transmit greater amounts of heat from the outer core, thereby setting up mantle circulations. The topography of the CMB is controlled by the circulations in the mantle as well as in the outer core. The topographic relief of the CMB may also set up a lateral temperature gradient which may be responsible for the secular variation of the magnetic field.

## Methods of Study

Various subdisciplines of geophysics are being utilized to determine the nature and the structure of the core-mantle boundary (CMB). They include, among others, seismology, geodesy, and geodynamics, high-temperature and high-pressure mineral physics, geothermometry, and geomagnetism. Seismology has been the most important among all these subdisciplines and has contributed most of the information about the earth's interior.

Seismology deals with earthquakes and the propagation of earthquake waves through the earth. Whenever an earthquake occurs, different types of waves are generated. Surface waves travel along the earth's surface, and longitudinal (P) waves and shear (S) waves travel through the interior of the earth. It is often helpful to visualize P and S waves in the form of rays originating from an earthquake focus, or hypocenter, and radiating in all directions through the earth. Because of the increased rigidity and incompressibility of rocks downward, the velocities of these waves increase with depth. As a result, the downgoing seismic rays (except for vertical or near-vertical rays) are curved back to the surface. Thus, the seismographic stations that are farther away from the epicenter record direct seismic rays, which penetrate through the deeper layers in the mantle.

The outer core has no rigidity, as it is liquid. Consequently, the velocities of seismic waves decrease abruptly as they cross the CMB. P waves decrease from 13.5 to 8.5 kilometers per second and are steeply refracted in the outer core. S waves do not propagate through the outer core. As a result, shadow zones are produced for both direct P and S waves recorded at the ground surface beyond 12,000 kilometers from the epicenter. The presence of liquid outer core was discovered through the existence of the shadow zones and the absence of core-transmitted shear waves.

Seismic rays emerging at steep angles from the hypocenter encounter the CMB. Part of the incident energy is reflected back from the boundary, and the rest is refracted through the outer core. A P wave can be reflected back as a P and as an S wave, called PcP and PcS waves (or phases) respectively. Similarly, an S wave reflected back from the CMB as a P or an S wave is called ScP or ScS. These core-reflected phases have been important in the study of the nature, shape, and depth of the CMB. Because S waves cannot transmit through liquid, the refracted energy in the outer core propagates in the form of P waves. These waves are designated as a K phase. Thus, PKP is a phase that travels from the hypocenter in the mantle as a P wave, propagates as a P (that is, K) in the outer core, and reemerges in the mantle as a P wave. Similarly, SKS and other combinations, such as PKS and SKP, are often observed in the seismic records. A joint study of the core-reflected phases (for example, PcP) and the core phases (for example, PKP) is often important in resolving the depths and topography of the CMB. Seismic rays incident at a large angle on the CMB are diffracted. Study of these diffracted waves provides important information on the D″ zone above the CMB. Using the waveform modeling techniques, scientists are determining the thickness and fine structures of the D″ zone.

Another important tool is seismic tomography. It utilizes the same principle used in CAT-scan X rays of humans. In a CAT scan, the X-ray source and the camera are rotated around the body and a large number of images are produced. A computer processes these images and forms a three-dimensional image of the internal organs of the subject. The seismological data collected worldwide can similarly be processed to form a three-dimensional image of the earth's interior. Seismic tomography is providing valuable information on the CMB as well as the earth's mantle.

A large earthquake sets the earth vibrating like a bell. If the earth were perfectly spherical with uniform layering, it would produce a pure tone, vibrating at a preferred frequency. Departures from the spherical shape of the earth, as well as depth-related discontinuities, produce additional tones involving distortions of the earth. Thus, recordings of these various modes of the earth's vibrations, known as free oscillations, can furnish information about the shape of the CMB.

Satellite measurements of the earth's gravity field and the geodetic observations of the geoid can also provide us with information on the CMB. Theoretical models of the earth's interior, particularly the mantle, the D″ zone, and the CMB, can be constructed to match observed geoidal undulations and the gravity anomalies. It appears that a 2-3-kilometer change in elevation of the CMB can explain 90 percent of the observed large-scale gravity anomalies. Astronomic observations of the earth's wobble also furnish additional constraints on the shape of the CMB. The earth has an equatorial bulge caused by its rotation. The moon pulls at the bulge and attempts to align it along the orbital plane of the moon, generating a wobble, or a nutational motion, of the earth's axis. (This motion is similar to the wobble of a spinning top or a gyroscope.) Deformation of the CMB, which is not formed by rotation, produces certain irregularities in the nutational motion. Studies of these irregularities indicate that the undulations of the CMB are less than 1 kilometer in height.

Major developments in instrumentation have made it possible to simulate in the laboratory the temperature and pressure conditions of the deep mantle. Scientists can now study how the crystal structures of minerals change with increased temperature and pressure. Measurements on the electrical properties of rocks under high pressure, and possible alloying of iron by sulfur and oxygen that may occur in the outer core, are also being studied. These investigations are important for complete understanding of the mineral compositions, structure, temperature, and pressure environment of the earth's deep interior.

## Context

The study of the core-mantle boundary (CMB) is important from several perspectives. The CMB is believed to be associated with deep mantle plumes, the mantle convection currents that drive the lithospheric plates, and may be responsible for secular variations of the geomagnetic field. As the most pronounced discontinuity within the earth, the undulations at the CMB may also cause regional gravity anomalies and can affect the transmission of seismic waves. The transmission effects of seismic waves crossing the CMB should be determined in order to study the geometry and the physical and chemical parameters of materials at the boundary as well as the outer and inner core of the earth. Furthermore, because core-reflected phases travel along vertical or near vertical paths in the mantle, they are often utilized to study heterogeneity and the seismic behavior in the mantle. Knowledge of the nature of the CMB is necessary to determine these mantle characteristics.

Scientists from various geophysical subdisciplines have made a concerted effort to investigate the structure and nature of the CMB and the deep interior of the earth. A committee on Studies of the Earth's Deep Interior (SEDI), under the auspices of the International Union of Geodesy and Geophysics (IUGG) and the American Geophysical Union (AGU), was formed to stimulate exchange of scientific information about the earth's interior. The first meeting of SEDI was held in Spain in 1988; starting with the fall of 1987, special sessions on the earth's deep interior have been held at most of the AGU meetings. The Twenty-fifth General Assembly of the International Association of Seismology and Physics of the Earth's Interior (IASPEI) also held a symposium on this subject at its meeting in Istanbul, Turkey, in August, 1989.

## Bibliography

Bolt, Bruce A. *Earthquakes*. New York: W. H. Freeman, 1988. This volume presents information on the earth's interior obtained from seismological studies. Suitable for high school and college levels.

_____. *Inside the Earth*. San Francisco: W. H. Freeman, 1982. A good introduction to seismology for the nonscientist, this well-illustrated, concise book summarizes the seismological methods and the results.

Eiby, G. A. *About Earthquakes*. New York: Harper & Row, 1957. Lucidly written, this book provides the historical perspective of seismological discoveries. Suitable for high school and undergraduate students.

Hodgson, J. H. *Earthquakes and Earth Structures*. Englewood Cliffs, N.J.: Prentice-Hall, 1964. This volume summarizes the important seismological observations prior to 1960. Suitable for high school and undergraduate students.

Kerr, Richard A. "Continents of the Core-Mantle Boundary." *Science* 233 (August 1, 1986): 523-524. This short, well-written article provides some of the results of current research about the core-mantle boundary. Appropriate for readers at any level.

Lay, T. "Structure of the Core-Mantle Transition Zone: A Chemical and Thermal Boundary." *EOS: Transactions of the American Geophysical Union* 70, no. 4 (1989): 44-59. This is an important review article on the transition zone at the core-mantle boundary. Suitable for university-level audience with some background in the geosciences.

_____. "Structure of the Earth: Mantle and Core." *Reviews of Geophysics* 25 (June, 1987): 1161-1167. This important review article summarizes major works on the mantle and the core. Appropriate for university-level readers.

Young, C. J., and T. Lay. "The Core-Mantle Boundary." *Annual Review of Earth Planetary Sciences* 15 (1987): 25. A summary of recent research in the core-mantle boundary. The treatment is at a university level.

*D. K. Chowdhury*

## Cross-References

Earthquakes: Elastic Waves, 469; An Overview of Earthquakes, 484; Earth's Core, 504; Earth's Mantle, 555; Earth's Shape, 583; Earth's Structure, 589; Geothermometry and Geobarometry, 922; Gravity Anomalies, 997; The Lithosphere, 1380; Lithospheric Plates, 1387.

# EARTH'S CRUST

*Type of earth science:* Geophysics
*Field of study:* Seismology

*Humankind's existence and modern society depend upon the crust of the earth. The dynamic changes involved in the creation and destruction of crustal rock also liberate gases and water that form oceans and the atmosphere, cause earthquakes, and create mineral deposits essential to society.*

### Principal terms

ANDESITE: a volcanic igneous rock type intermediate in composition and density between granite and basalt

BASALT: a dark-colored igneous rock rich in iron and magnesium and composed primarily of the mineral compounds calcium feldspar (anorthite) and pyroxene

DENSITY: the mass per unit of volume (grams per cubic centimeter) of a solid, liquid, or gas

GRANITE: a silica-rich igneous rock light in color, composed primarily of the mineral compounds quartz and potassium- and sodium-rich feldspars

ISOSTASY: the concept that suggests that the crust of the earth is in or is trying to achieve flotational equilibrium by buoyantly floating on denser mantle rocks beneath

P WAVE: the fastest elastic wave generated by an earthquake or artificial energy source; basically an acoustic or shock wave that compresses and stretches solid material in its path

PLATE TECTONICS: the theory that the crust and upper mantle of the earth are divided into a number of moving plates about 100 kilometers thick that meet at trench sites and separate at oceanic ridges

REFLECTION: the bounce of wave energy off a boundary that marks a change in density of material

REFRACTION: the change in direction of a wave path upon crossing a boundary resulting from a change in density and thus seismic velocity of the materials

SNELL'S LAW: a statement of the fact that refraction of seismic waves across a boundary will occur such that the ratio of the two velocities of the material on either side of the boundary is equal to the size of the two angles on either side of the boundary formed by the ray path and a line perpendicular to the boundary

## Summary of the Phenomenon

The crust of the earth is the outermost layer of rock material of the earth.

It is distinct from the region of rocks lying beneath it, called the mantle, in that the rock materials that comprise the crust are of a different composition and a lower density. Density may be described as the weight per unit of volume of solid materials. Therefore, if a cubic centimeter of granite, which makes up much of the crust of the earth of continents such as North America, could be weighed, it would total 2.7 grams. Deeper crustal rocks under continents have higher densities, some approaching the 3.3 grams per cubic centimeter characteristic of upper mantle rocks. A sample of crustal rock underlying the ocean basins would reveal that it is a rock type known as basalt, with a density of about 2.9 grams per cubic centimeter.

Compared with the rocks of the mantle, the rocks of the earth's crust are quite varied. The rocks of the crust can be classified as belonging to one of three broad groups: igneous, sedimentary, and metamorphic. Both granite and basalt are igneous rocks. Such rocks are formed by cooling and crystallization from a high-temperature state called magma or lava. Other igneous rock types of the earth's crust that are intermediate in rock composition and density between granite and basalt include andesite and granodiorite. Igneous rocks may form by melting of other igneous and metamorphic rocks in the crust or upper mantle, or by melting of sedimentary rocks.

Metamorphic rocks are formed from other rocks that have been subjected to pressures and temperatures high enough to cause the rock to respond by change in the crystalline structure of the rock materials. These temperatures are not high enough to melt the rock. Such changes often occur in the deep parts of the crust, where heat is trapped and great pressure occurs from the weight of the overlying rock. As a consequence of this high pressure, densities of metamorphic rocks of the lower crust average about 2.9 grams per cubic centimeter.

Sedimentary rocks of the earth's crust are formed by chemical change and physical breakdown into fragments of other rocks exposed to the atmosphere and water of the earth's surface. The density of sedimentary rocks is generally less than that of igneous rocks, ranging from about 2.2 to as high as 2.7 grams per cubic centimeter.

The boundary between the rocks of the crust and the mantle is known as the Mohorovičić discontinuity, or simply Moho. The nature of this boundary varies from place to place. Under parts of the crust that have recently been stretched or compressed by mountain-building forces, such as under the great desert basins of the western United States, the Moho is a very sharp, distinct boundary. Elsewhere, in the interior of continents that have not been deformed for long time periods, the Moho appears to be an area of gradual density change with increasing depth rather than a distinct boundary. The position of the Moho, and thus the thickness of the crust, varies widely. The crust is thickest under the continents, reaching a maximum of 70 kilometers beneath young mountain chains such as the Himalaya. Under the ocean basins, the crustal thickness varies from 5 to 15 kilometers.

Thickness of the crust is directly related to its formation and evolution through geologic time. Only within the last twenty-five years have geoscientists understood this relationship. The crustal rocks of the earth are constantly being created, deformed, and destroyed by a process known as plate tectonics. Plate tectonics is a theory that suggests that the crust and upper mantle of the earth are divided into a number of separate rock layers that resemble giant plates. These plates are in motion, driven by heat from the earth's interior. Where the heat reaches the surface along boundaries between plates on the ocean floor, new rocks are formed by rising lava, creating new ocean basin crust. Because new crust is being created, crust must be consumed or destroyed elsewhere so that the earth's volume will remain constant. The sites where crust is consumed also lie on the ocean floor. Topographically, such sites are deep trenches where the crust bends down into the mantle to be heated and remelted. Such a process of recycling ocean-basin crust means, first of all, that ocean-basin crust is never geologically very old. The oldest sea-floor crust in the western Pacific is 175 million years old as compared to about 4.5 billion years for the age of the earth. Second, it suggests that since ocean-basin crust goes through a geologically short life and uncomplicated history, it has a rather uniform thickness of about 5 to 15 kilometers, unchanged between the time it is born and the time it is destroyed.

Continental crust has a much longer life and a more complicated history, reflected in a highy variable crustal thickness. It is initially created at the sites where oceanic crust is consumed, also known as subduction zones. As the crust and upper mantle, or lithospheric plate, is bent back down into the earth, it is heated up. Eventually, melting of part of this rock material occurs, creating volcanoes near trench sites. Such volcanoes have lavas rich in elements such as calcium, potassium, and sodium. When these lavas cool to form rock, the rock type that results is an andesite, named for volcanic rocks abundant in the Andes of South America. These continental volcanic rocks are less dense than basalts and, once created, remain on the top of a lithospheric plate, where they are carried along by the motion of the sea floor and underlying lithospheric plate as it moves away from the ocean ridge boundaries. Eventually, the sea-floor motion may cause pieces of this continental crust to collide and weld together, forming larger pieces of continental crust. Thus, continents grow with time by two processes: volcanism above subduction zones and collision. The process of collision causes rocks to pile up like a throw rug pushed against a wall, creating high mountains that also extend downward with roots that increase crustal thickness. Continents thus grow along their edges where young mountain belts, called orogenic belts, are found, such as the Andes and the mountain systems of the western United States. The crust is relatively thick under young mountain belts, piling upward and sinking downward simultaneously to form a thick wedge of rock. In this sense, it is much like a buoyant iceberg, with the majority of its mass below the water or, in this case, below sea level. The buoyancy of the lighter continental rocks above the denser mantle rocks is known as the principle of isostasy, or flotational equilibrium. Just as the iceberg must reach a flotational level by displacing a volume of water equal to its mass, so must the continental crustal rocks displace a volume of denser mantle rocks to reach their buoyancy level. Thus,

under higher mountainous terrain thicker crust is found, whereas at lower elevations, such as under the ocean basin, the thinnest crust is found.

Toward the center of continental landmasses are core areas of older rocks known
as cratons. The age of rocks found in the cratons range from about 500 million to
an extreme of 3.8 billion years. The cratons of the world compose about one-half of
the area of the continental crust and have been free of deformation and mountain-
building forces for long periods of time. Consequently, their surfaces tend to be
relatively flat as a result of surface processes such as weathering and stream-cutting
acting on the exposed rocks over a geologically long period of time. The thickness
of the continental crust in cratonic areas is variable, which is a reflection of their
long and complex histories. These areas were at one time thickened because of
mountain-building activity, but long and varying periods of stability have caused
them to lose some crustal thickness as well. Figures for central Canada and the
United States show a range of from 30 to 50 kilometers for thickness of the craton.

## Methods of Study

Elastic waves are created by both earthquakes and artificial sources and may be
used to study the crust of the earth. This branch of earth science is called seismology. When energy is released in rock by a source, the rock is set in motion with an
up-and-down or back-and-forth wavelike motion. These waves force the rock to
respond like a rubber band, stretching and compressing it without permanently
deforming it. Such a response is called elastic. This response can be used as a key to
studying the physical properties of the rocks because of a wave generated by a
seismic relationship between velocity and rock properties. The fastest elastic wave
is the primary, or P, wave. This wave is basically an acoustic wave or sound wave
traveling in rock, compressing and stretching rock materials in its path. Therefore,
the density, rigidity, and compressibility of a material determine wave velocity. A
simple example would be to compare the velocity of an acoustic wave in air, called
the speed of sound, to that in rock. The result is that in air near sea level, an
acoustic wave travels at about 0.3 kilometer per second, whereas in rocks near the
earth's surface, the same kind of wave travels at about 5 kilometers per second. Air
is much less dense than rock and has no rigidity (no permanent shape).

Rocks of the lower crust beneath the continents have P-wave velocities of between 6.8 and 7.0 kilometers per second. It can be shown in the laboratory that
metamorphic rocks known as granulites, when placed under the pressures and
temperatures of the lower crustal depths, have velocities in this range. Other rocks
under the same pressures and temperatures (600 to 900 degrees Celsius, 5,000 to
10,000 atmospheres) may have similar velocities. Samples of lower crustal rocks
known as xenoliths, however, exist at the surface, having been brought up by
volcanic activity. These samples also suggest that granulite is a good choice.

Rocks of the upper crust in continental areas have P-wave velocities of around
6.2 kilometers per second. Here, rocks at the surface of a granite to granodiorite
composition suggest the appropriate choice of rock. When such rocks are velocity-

tested in the laboratory under the appropriate range of pressures and temperatures, there is a good match between rock type and velocity.

The composition of the oceanic crust is well known. Here, basalts yield a velocity of around 6.7 kilometers per second, reflecting the rather uniform composition of the geologically simpler oceanic crust. Finally, part of the continental crust is mantled by sedimentary rocks. This material has among the lowest velocities, ranging from less than 2 kilometers per second up to an extreme of about 6 kilometers per second and reflecting a wide range of compositions as well as the presence of open space and fluids contained therein.

The thickness of continental crust has been determined by the study of seismic waves that bounce off (reflect) or bend (refract) when they cross the Moho. The density contrast and resulting change in velocity of seismic waves when they cross the Moho from crust to mantle cause the wave path to change angle or bend. The same phenomenon occurs when light crosses from air to liquid in a glass. This can be shown by placing a straight straw in the liquid and gazing along its length. The straw will appear bent even though it is actually the light wave that has bent.

Waves that leave the source at one critical angle will cross the boundary and travel along beneath it, radiating energy back to the surface at the same angle. This is the critically refracted ray path, and the sine of the critical angle can be predicted from Snell's law of refraction to be the ratio of the crust and mantle velocities. The geometry of this wave path is determined by two factors, the ratio of the crust and mantle velocities, and the thickness of the crust. The thicker the crust, the longer the travel time of the wave for a particular pair of velocities. Using critically refracted P waves, thicknesses have been estimated for much of the crust.

It has been possible in many areas to check the crustal thickness determined by critically refracted waves by using information from reflected waves. This has been applied with particular success to the study of earth's crust in continental areas. The technique is similar to that of depth sounding in ships, in which an acoustic wave is sent down from a ship, bounces off the bottom, and returns. The depth is proportional to the time of travel of the wave, also called the two-way time. The depth can be found by multiplying water velocity by travel time. The same basic procedure has been used under the continents with artificial acoustic wave sources such as explosives and vibrator trucks.

## Context

An understanding of the geometry, evolution, and composition of the earth's crust increases humankind's knowledge of the nature of the world. It is easy to show that humankind's very existence, as well as the material wealth of modern societies, is totally dependent on the crust of the earth. The crustal state is one of dynamic evolution, with rock materials being created, deformed, and destroyed at plate tectonic boundaries. The process that makes creation and destruction of rocks possible is that of crystallization and melting of the mineral compounds that compose rock, a process known as volcanism. Volcanic activity over the billions of years of the earth's existence has, by the expulsion of gases trapped in lavas that reach the surface, provided the water vapor and other gases necessary to form the oceans and atmosphere, which are necessary to support life.

An understanding of volcanoes, of the how, why, and where they occur, requires an understanding of the earth's crust and of crustal dynamics. Certainly, this can be important as viewed from the perspective of Mount St. Helens and other volcanoes of the northwestern United States. Mount St. Helens is a volcano formed by remelting of part of the oceanic crust that is slowly being taken back into the interior of the earth. As this process of subduction and remelting of the oceanic crust will continue into the future for millions of years, so will eruptions continue to occur at Mount St. Helens, as well as at other volcanoes of the Cascade Mountains. Thus, an understanding of the crust of the earth shows that the disastrous May 18, 1980, eruption of Mount St. Helens was not a onetime event.

The dynamic evolution of the earth's crust is also accompanied by the movement of large plates of the crust and upper mantle, up to 100 kilometers thick, against one another. The San Andreas fault of California is one place where two of these plates of crustal material rub against each other. The forces created by this motion are released as energy in large earthquakes, posing a threat to life and property. Eventually, knowledge of how crustal rocks change and respond to these forces before an impending earthquake may allow their prediction.

Exploration for important economic minerals is guided by knowledge about the evolution and composition of the crust. The creation of valuable metal deposits, such as gold and copper, during volcanic activity at ocean ridge sites where new oceanic crustal rocks are also being created is occurring in the Red Sea between Africa and Asia. Consequently, exploration efforts for such metallic ores can be directed toward identifying ancient ridge site deposits. The formation of continental sedimentary rocks in the Gulf of Mexico is trapping organic materials that will be turned into oil and natural gas. Looking for similar types of sedimentary rocks in the appropriate crustal environment would be worthwhile for explorers in the petroleum and natural gas industries.

## Bibliography

Bally, A. W. *Seismic Expression of Structural Styles*. Tulsa, Okla.: American Association of Petroleum Geologists, 1983. An excellent visual treatment of the structure and layering of primarily the upper crust throughout the world. Sections into the crust of offshore Scotland and northwest Germany show the Moho. Suitable for a broad audience from general readers to scientific specialists.

Bott, M. H. P. *The Interior of the Earth*. New York: Elsevier, 1982. This book was intended for undergraduate and graduate students of geology and geophysics as well as for other scientists interested in the topic. The plate tectonic framework of the outer part of the earth is strongly emphasized.

Brown, G. C., and A. E. Mussett. *The Inaccessible Earth*. London: Allen & Unwin, 1981. A good general introduction geared toward the undergraduate college student. The primary topics are the internal state and composition of the earth. Included is background material on seismology and three chapters discussing the earth's crust.

Phillips, O. M. *The Heart of the Earth*. San Francisco: Freeman, Copper, 1968. An excellent and well-written book intended for a general college and noncollege audience with no background in geophysics. The book has an excellent chapter on seismology and the way in which earthquake waves are used to determine physical properties from velocity and to infer crustal structure by refracted waves.

Smith, David G., ed. *The Cambridge Encyclopedia of Earth Sciences*. Cambridge, England: Cambridge University Press, 1981. This general reference provides an excellent overview of the earth sciences. Chapter 10 is an extensive discussion of the earth's crust, including useful illustrations and diagrams. Contains a glossary, an index, and recommendations for further reading.

Taylor, Stuart R., and Scott M. McLennan. *The Continental Crust: Its Composition and Evolution*. Boston: Blackwell Scientific, 1985. A text aimed at undergraduate and graduate geology and geophysics students as well as general earth scientists. It is clearly written and up-to-date and has excellent, well-rounded scientific references.

*David S. Brumbaugh*

## Cross-References

Continental Crust, 261; Continental Growth, 268; Continental Structures, 290; Earthquake Distribution, 421; Earthquakes: Elastic Waves, 469; The Evolution of Earth's Composition, 496; Earth's Structure, 589; Igneous Rocks: Andesitic, 1146; Igneous Rocks: Basaltic, 1158; Igneous Rocks: Granitic, 1180; Isostasy, 1269; Lithospheric Plates, 1387; Mountain Belts, 1725; Plate Margins, 2063; Plate Motions, 2071; Plate Tectonics, 2079.

# MAGILL'S
# SURVEY
# OF
# SCIENCE

# ALPHABETICAL LIST

## EARTH SCIENCE

# CATEGORY LIST